Introductory Algebra

Custom Edition for Moraine Valley Community College

Taken from:
Beginning & Intermediate Algebra, Fifth Edition
by Elayn Martin-Gay

Cover Art: Courtesy of Photodisc/Getty Images.

Taken from:

Beginning & Intermediate Algebra, Fifth Edition
by Elayn Martin-Gay
Copyright © 2013, 2009, 2005, 2001, 1996 by Pearson Education, Inc.
Published by Pearson
Upper Saddle River, New Jersey 07458

This special edition published in cooperation with Pearson Learning Solutions.

All trademarks, service marks, registered trademarks, and registered service marks are the property of their respective owners and are used herein for identification purposes only.

Pearson Learning Solutions, 501 Boylston Street, Suite 900, Boston, MA 02116
A Pearson Education Company
www.pearsoned.com

Printed in the United States of America

1 2 3 4 5 6 7 8 9 10 V311 17 16 15 14 13 12

000200010271300274

RH

ISBN 10: 1-256-69544-0
ISBN 13: 978-1-256-69544-8

This book is dedicated to students everywhere—and we should all be students. After all, is there anyone among us who really knows too much? Take that hint and continue to learn something new every day of your life.

Best of wishes from a fellow student: Elayn Martin-Gay

Contents

APPENDICES

Student Resources

These resources, located in the back of the text, give you a variety of tools conveniently located in one place to help you succeed in math.

Study Skills Builders

Attitude and Study Tips:

1. Have You Decided to Complete This Course Successfully?
2. Tips for Studying for an Exam
3. What to Do the Day of an Exam
4. Are You Satisfied with Your Performance on a Particular Quiz or Exam?
5. How Are You Doing?
6. Are You Preparing for Your Final Exam?

Organizing Your Work:

7. Learning New Terms
8. Are You Organized?
9. Organizing a Notebook
10. How Are Your Homework Assignments Going?

MyMathLab and MathXL:

11. Tips for Turning in Your Homework on Time
12. Tips for Doing Your Homework Online
13. Organizing Your Work
14. Getting Help with Your Homework Assignments
15. Tips for Preparing for an Exam
16. How Well Do You Know the Resources Available to You in MyMathLab?

Additional Help Inside and Outside Your Textbook:

17. How Well Do You Know Your Textbook?
18. Are You Familiar with Your Textbook Supplements?
19. Are You Getting All the Mathematics Help That You Need?

The Bigger Picture–Study Guide Outline

Practice Final Exam

Answers to Selected Exercises

A New Tool to Help You Succeed

Introducing Martin-Gay's New Student Organizer

The new **Student Organizer** guides you through three important parts of studying effectively—note-taking, practice, and homework.

It is designed to help you organize your learning materials and develop the study habits you need to be successful. The Student Organizer includes:

- How to prepare for class
- Space to take class notes
- Step-by-step worked examples
- Your Turn exercises (modeled after the examples)
- Answers to the Your Turn exercises as well as worked-out solutions via references to the Martin-Gay text and videos
- Helpful hints and directions for completing homework assignments

A flexible design allows instructors to assign any or all parts of the Student Organizer.

The Student Organizer is available in a loose-leaf, notebook-ready format. It is also available for download in MyMathLab.

For more information, please go to

www.pearsonhighered.com/martingay

www.mypearsonstore.com
   (search Martin-Gay, Beginning & Intermediate Algebra, Fifth Edition)
your Martin-Gay MyMathLab® course

Martin-Gay Video Resources to Help You Succeed

Interactive DVD Lecture Series

Active Learning at Your Pace

Designed for use on your computer or DVD player, these interactive videos include a 15–20 minute lecture for every section in the text as well as Concept Checks, Study Skills Builders, and a Practice Final Exam.

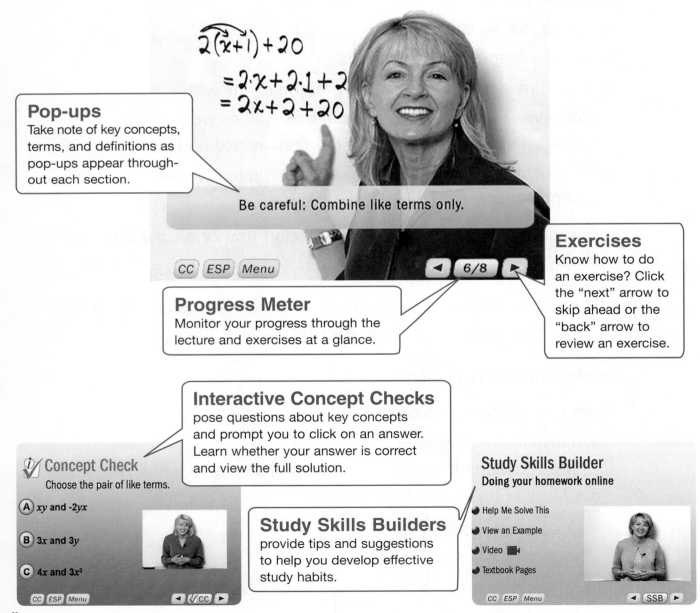

Pop-ups
Take note of key concepts, terms, and definitions as pop-ups appear throughout each section.

$$2(x+1) + 20$$
$$= 2 \cdot x + 2 \cdot 1 + 2$$
$$= 2x + 2 + 20$$

Be careful: Combine like terms only.

CC ESP Menu   ◀ 6/8 ▶

Exercises
Know how to do an exercise? Click the "next" arrow to skip ahead or the "back" arrow to review an exercise.

Progress Meter
Monitor your progress through the lecture and exercises at a glance.

Interactive Concept Checks
pose questions about key concepts and prompt you to click on an answer. Learn whether your answer is correct and view the full solution.

✓ Concept Check
Choose the pair of like terms.

(A) xy and $-2yx$

(B) $3x$ and $3y$

(C) $4x$ and $3x^2$

CC ESP Menu   ◀ ✓ CC ▶

Study Skills Builders
provide tips and suggestions to help you develop effective study habits.

Study Skills Builder
Doing your homework online

● Help Me Solve This
● View an Example
● Video 🎥
● Textbook Pages

CC ESP Menu   ◀ SSB ▶

Chapter Test Prep Videos

Step-by-step solutions on video for all chapter test exercises from the text. Available via:

- Interactive DVD Lecture Series
- MyMathLab®
- You Tube™

Here we will simplify by combining like terms.

Rew Pause Play   Volume

English and Spanish Subtitles Available

AlgebraPrep Apps for the iPhone™ and iPod Touch®

Your 24/7 Algebra Tutor–Anytime, Anywhere!

Choose to take a Practice Test or a MiniTest (designed to take 10 minutes or less).

Practice Test exercises provide answer feedback to help you study and self-correct.

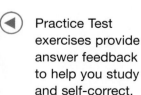

Step-by-step video solutions give you the guidance of an expert tutor whenever you need help.

Preface

Beginning & Intermediate Algebra, **Fifth Edition,** was written to provide a solid foundation in algebra for students who might not have previous experience in algebra. Specific care was taken to make sure students have the most up-to-date, relevant text preparation for their next mathematics course or for nonmathematical courses that require an understanding of algebraic fundamentals. I have tried to achieve this by writing a user-friendly text that is keyed to objectives and contains many worked-out examples. As suggested by AMATYC and the NCTM Standards (plus Addenda), real-life and real-data applications, data interpretation, conceptual understanding, problem solving, writing, cooperative learning, appropriate use of technology, mental mathematics, number sense, estimation, critical thinking, and geometric concepts are emphasized and integrated throughout the book.

The many factors that contributed to the success of the previous editions have been retained. In preparing the Fifth Edition, I considered comments and suggestions of colleagues, students, and many users of the prior edition throughout the country.

What's New in the Fifth Edition?

- **The Martin-Gay Program** has been revised and enhanced with a new design in the text and MyMathLab to actively encourage students to use the text, video program, and Student Organizer as an integrated learning system.

- **The Student Organizer** is designed by me to help students develop the study habits they need to be successful. This Organizer guides students through the three main components of studying effectively—note-taking, practice, and homework—and helps them develop the habits that will enable them to succeed in future courses. The Student Organizer can be packaged with the text in loose-leaf, notebook-ready format and is also available for download in MyMathLab.

- **New Vocabulary, Readiness & Video Check** questions have been added prior to every section exercise set. These exercises quickly check a student's understanding of new vocabulary words. The **readiness** exercises center on a student's understanding of a concept that is necessary in order to continue to the exercise set. **New video check questions for the Martin-Gay Interactive Lecture videos** are now included in every section for each learning objective. **These exercises are all available for assignment in MyMathLab** and are a great way to assess whether students have viewed and understood the key concepts presented in the videos.

- **The Interactive DVD Lecture Series,** featuring your text author (Elayn Martin-Gay), provides students with active learning at their own pace. The videos offer the following resources and more:

    A complete lecture for each section of the text highlights key examples and exercises from the text. New "pop-ups" reinforce key terms, definitions, and concepts.

    An interface with menu navigation features allows students to quickly find and focus on the examples and exercises they need to review.

    Interactive Concept Check exercises measure students' understanding of key concepts and common trouble spots.

    The Interactive DVD Lecture Series also includes the following resources for test prep:

    The Practice Final Exam helps students prepare for an end-of-course final. Students can watch full video solutions to each exercise.

The Chapter Test Prep Videos help students during their most teachable moment–when they are preparing for a test. This innovation provides step-by-step solutions for the Chapter Test exercises found at the end of each chapter in the text. The videos are captioned in English and Spanish. For the Fifth Edition, the chapter test prep videos are also available on YouTube™.

- **The Martin-Gay MyMathLab course** has been updated and revised to provide more exercise coverage, including assignable video check questions, and an expanded video program. There are section lecture videos for every section, students can also access at the specific objective level, and there are an increased number of watch clips at the exercise level to help students while doing homework in MathXL. Suggested homework assignments have been premade for assignment at the instructor's discretion.

- **New MyMathLab Ready to Go courses** (access code required) provide students with all the same great MyMathLab features that you're used to, but make it easier for instructors to get started. Each course includes preas-signed homework and quizzes to make creating your course even simpler. Ask your Pearson representative about the details for this particular course or to see a copy of this course.

- **A new section** (12.4) devoted specifically to exponential growth and decay and applications has been added. This section includes the definition and examples of half-life.

- **The new Student Resources** section, located in the back of the text, gives students a variety of tools that are conveniently located in one place to help them achieve success in mathematics.

  — **Study Skills Builders** give students tips and suggestions on successful study habits and help them take responsibility for their learning. Assignable exercises check students' progress in improving their skills.

  — The **Bigger Picture—Study Guide Outline** covers key concepts of the course—simplifying expressions and solving equations and inequalities— to help students transition from thinking section-by-section to thinking about how the material they are learning fits into mathematics as a whole. This outline provides a model for students on how to organize and develop their own study guide.

  — The **Practice Final Exam** helps students prepare for the end-of-the-course exam. Students can also watch the step-by-step solutions to all the Practice Final Exam exercises on the new Interactive DVD Lecture Series and in MyMathLab.

  — The **Answers to Selected Exercises** section allows students to check their answers for all Practice exercises; odd-numbered Vocabulary, Readiness & Video Check exercises; odd-numbered section exercises; odd-numbered Chapter Review and Cumulative Review exercises; and all Integrated Review and Chapter Test exercises.

- **New guided application exercises** appear in many sections throughout the text, beginning with Section 2.4. These applications prompt students on how to set up the application and get started with the solution process. These guided exercises will help students prepare to solve application exercises on their own.

- **Enhanced emphasis on Study Skills** helps students develop good study habits and makes it more convenient for instructors to incorporate or assign study skills in their courses. The following changes have been made in the Fifth Edition:

  Section 1.1, Tips for Success in Mathematics, has been updated to include helpful hints for doing homework online in MyMathLab. Exercises pertaining to doing homework online in MyMathLab are now included in the exercise set for 1.1.

The Study Skills Builders, formerly located at the end of select exercise sets, are now included in the new **Student Resources** section at the back of the book and are organized by topic for ease of assignment. This section now also includes new Study Skills Builders on doing homework online in MyMathLab.

- All exercise sets have been reviewed and updated to ensure that even- and odd-numbered exercises are paired.

Key Pedagogical Features

The following key features have been retained and/or updated for the Fifth Edition of the text:

Problem-Solving Process This is formally introduced in Chapter 2 with a four-step process that is integrated throughout the text. The four steps are **Understand, Translate, Solve,** and **Interpret.** The repeated use of these steps in a variety of examples shows their wide applicability. Reinforcing the steps can increase students' comfort level and confidence in tackling problems.

Exercise Sets Revised and Updated The exercise sets have been carefully examined and extensively revised. Special focus was placed on making sure that even- and odd-numbered exercises are paired.

Examples Detailed, step-by-step examples were added, deleted, replaced, or updated as needed. Many of these reflect real life. Additional instructional support is provided in the annotated examples.

Practice Exercises Throughout the text, each worked-out example has a parallel Practice Exercise. These invite students to be actively involved in the learning process. Students should try each Practice Exercise after finishing the corresponding example. Learning by doing will help students grasp ideas before moving on to other concepts. Answers to the Practice Exercises are provided in the back of the text.

Helpful Hints Helpful Hints contain practical advice on applying mathematical concepts. Strategically placed where students are most likely to need immediate reinforcement, Helpful Hints help students avoid common trouble areas and mistakes.

Concept Checks This feature allows students to gauge their grasp of an idea as it is being presented in the text. Concept Checks stress conceptual understanding at the point-of-use and help suppress misconceived notions before they start. Answers appear at the bottom of the page. Exercises related to Concept Checks are included in the exercise sets.

Mixed Practice Exercises Found in the section exercise sets, each requires students to determine the problem type and strategy needed to solve it just as they would need to do on a test.

Integrated Reviews A unique, mid-chapter exercise set that helps students assimilate new skills and concepts that they have learned separately over several sections. These reviews provide yet another opportunity for students to work with "mixed" exercises as they master the topics.

Vocabulary Check Provides an opportunity for students to become more familiar with the use of mathematical terms as they strengthen their verbal skills. These appear at the end of each chapter before the Chapter Highlights. Vocabulary, Readiness & Video Check exercises also provide vocabulary practice at the section level.

Chapter Highlights   Found at the end of every chapter, these contain key definitions and concepts with examples to help students understand and retain what they have learned and help them organize their notes and study for tests.

Chapter Review   The end of every chapter contains a comprehensive review of topics introduced in the chapter. The Chapter Review offers exercises keyed to every section in the chapter, as well as Mixed Review exercises that are not keyed to sections.

Chapter Test and Chapter Test Prep Video   The Chapter Test is structured to include those problems that involve common student errors. The **Chapter Test Prep Videos** give students instant access to a step-by-step video solution of each exercise in the Chapter Test.

Cumulative Review   Follows every chapter in the text (except Chapter 1). Each odd-numbered exercise contained in the Cumulative Review is an earlier worked example in the text that is referenced in the back of the book along with the answer.

Writing Exercises   ↘ These exercises occur in almost every exercise set and require students to provide a written response to explain concepts or justify their thinking.

Applications   Real-world and real-data applications have been thoroughly updated and many new applications are included. These exercises occur in almost every exercise set and show the relevance of mathematics and help students gradually, and continuously, develop their problem-solving skills.

Review and Preview Exercises   These exercises occur in each exercise set (except in Chapter 1) and are keyed to earlier sections. They review concepts learned earlier in the text that will be needed in the next section or chapter.

Exercise Set Resource Icons   Located at the opening of each exercise set, these icons remind students of the resources available for extra practice and support:

See Student Resources descriptions on page xviii for details on the individual resources available.

Exercise Icons   These icons facilitate the assignment of specialized exercises and let students know what resources can support them.

- ▶ Video icon: exercise worked on the Interactive DVD Lecture Series and in MyMathLab.
- △ Triangle icon: identifies exercises involving geometric concepts.
- ↘ Pencil icon: indicates a written response is needed.
- ▦ Calculator icon: optional exercises intended to be solved using a scientific or graphing calculator.

Optional: Graphing Calculator Exploration Boxes and Calculator Exercises   The optional Graphing Calculator Explorations provide keystrokes and exercises at appropriate points to give an opportunity for students to become familiar with these tools. Section exercises that are best completed by using a calculator are identified by ▦ for ease of assignment.

Student and Instructor Resources

STUDENT RESOURCES

Student Organizer

Guides students through the 3 main components of studying effectively–note-taking, practice, and homework.

The organizer includes before-class preparation exercises, note-taking pages in a 2-column format for use in class, and examples paired with exercises for practice for each section. It is 3-hole-punched. Also available in MyMathLab.

Student Solutions Manual

Provides complete worked-out solutions to

- the odd-numbered section exercises; all Practice Exercises; all exercises in the Integrated Reviews, Chapter Reviews, Chapter Tests, and Cumulative Reviews

Interactive DVD Lecture Series

Provides students with active learning at their pace. The videos offer:

- A complete lecture for each text section. The interface allows easy navigation to examples and exercises students need to review.
- Interactive Concept Check exercises
- Study Skills Builders
- Practice Final Exam
- Chapter Test Prep Videos

Chapter Test Prep Videos

- Step-by-step solutions to every exercise in each Chapter Practice Test.
- Available in MyMathLab® and on YouTube, and in the Interactive DVD Lecture Series.

INSTRUCTOR RESOURCES

Annotated Instructor's Edition

Contains all the content found in the student edition, plus the following:

- Answers to exercises on the same text page
- Answers to graphing exercises and all video exercises
- Teaching Tips throughout the text placed at key points.
- Classroom Examples in the margin paired to each example in the text.

Instructor's Resource Manual with Tests and Mini-Lectures

- Mini-lectures for each text section
- Additional Practice worksheets for each section
- Several forms of test per chapter–free response and multiple choice
- Group activities
- Video key to the example number in the video questions and section exercises worked in the videos
- Answers to all items

Instructor's Solutions Manual
TestGen® (Available for download from the IRC)

Online Resources
MyMathLab® (access code required)

MathXL® (access code required)

Acknowledgments

There are many people who helped me develop this text, and I will attempt to thank some of them here. Cindy Trimble and Carrie Green were *invaluable* for contributing to the overall accuracy of the text. Dawn Nuttall, Courtney Slade, and JoAnne Thomasson were *invaluable* for their many suggestions and contributions during the development and writing of this Fifth Edition. Debbie Meyer and Amanda Zagnoli of Integra-Chicago provided guidance throughout the production process.

A very special thank you goes to my editor, Mary Beckwith, for being there 24/7/365, as my students say. Last, my thanks to the staff at Pearson for all their support: Patty Bergin, Heather Scott, Michelle Renda, Chris Hoag, and Greg Tobin.

I would like to thank the following reviewers for their input and suggestions:

Sandi Athanassiou, *University of Missouri–Columbia*
Michelle Beerman, *Pasco-Hernandez Community College*
Monika Bender, *Central Texas College*
Bob Hervey, *Hillsborough Community College*
Michael Maltenfort, *Truman College*
Jorge Romero, *Hillsborough Community College*
Joseph Wakim, *Brevard Community College*
Flo Wilson, *Central Texas College*
Marie Caruso and students, *Middlesex Community College*

I would also like to thank the following dedicated group of instructors who participated in our focus groups, Martin-Gay Summits, and our design review for the series. Their feedback and insights have helped to strengthen this edition of the text. These instructors include:

Billie Anderson, *Tyler Junior College*
Joey Anderson, *Central Piedmont Community College*
Cedric Atkins, *Mott Community College*
Teri Barnes, *McLennan Community College*
Andrea Barnett, *Tri-County Technical College*
Lois Beardon, *Schoolcraft College*
Michelle Beerman, *Pasco-Hernandez Community College*
Laurel Berry, *Bryant & Stratton College*
John Beyers, *University of Maryland*
Jennifer Brahier, *Pensacola Junior College*
Bob Brown, *Community College of Baltimore County–Essex*
Lisa Brown, *Community College of Baltimore County–Essex*
NeKeith Brown, *Richland College*
Sue Brown, *Guilford Technical Community College*
Gail Burkett, *Palm Beach State College*
Cheryl Cantwell, *Seminole Community College*
Janie Chapman, *Spartanburg Community College*
Jackie Cohen, *Augusta State College*
Julie Dewan, *Mohawk Valley Community College*
Janice Ervin, *Central Piedmont Community College*
Karen Estes, *St. Petersburg College*
Richard Fielding, *Southwestern College*
Sonia Ford, *Midland College*
Julie Francavilla, *State College of Florida*
Cindy Gaddis, *Tyler Junior College*
Nita Graham, *St. Louis Community College*
Pauline Hall, *Iowa State College*
Elizabeth Hamman, *Cypress College*
Kathy Hoffmaster, *Thomas Nelson Community College*
Pat Hussey, *Triton College*
Dorothy Johnson, *Lorain County Community College*
Sonya Johnson, *Central Piedmont Community College*

Irene Jones, *Fullerton College*
Paul Jones, *University of Cincinnati*
Mike Kirby, *Tidewater Community College*
Kathy Kopelousos, *Lewis and Clark Community College*
Nancy Lange, *Inver Hills Community College*
Judy Langer, *Westchester Community College*
Lisa Lindloff, *McLennan Community College*
Sandy Lofstock, *St. Petersburg College*
Kathy Lovelle, *Westchester Community College*
Jamie Malek, *Florida State College*
Jean McArthur, *Joliet Junior College*
Kevin McCandless, *Evergreen Valley College*
Daniel Miller, *Niagara County Community College*
Marcia Molle, *Metropolitan Community College*
Carol Murphy, *San Diego Miramar College*
Charlotte Newsom, *Tidewater Community College*
Greg Nguyen, *Fullerton College*
Eric Ollila, *Jackson Community College*
Linda Padilla, *Joliet Junior College*
Rena Petrello, *Moorpark College*
Davidson Pierre, *State College of Florida*
Marilyn Platt, *Gaston College*
Susan Poss, *Spartanburg Community College*
Natalie Rivera, *Estrella Mountain Community College*
Judy Roane, *Pearl River Community College*
Claudinna Rowley, *Montgomery Community College, Rockville*
Ena Salter, *State College of Florida*
Carole Shapero, *Oakton Community College*
Janet Sibol, *Hillsborough Community College*
Anne Smallen, *Mohawk Valley Community College*
Mike Stack, *South Suburban College*
Barbara Stoner, *Reading Area Community College*
Jennifer Strehler, *Oakton Community College*
Ellen Stutes, *Louisiana State University Eunice*
Tanomo Taguchi, *Fullerton College*
Sam Tinsley, *Richland College*
Linda Tucker, *Rose State College*
MaryAnn Tuerk, *Elgin Community College*
Gwen Turbeville, *J. Sargeant Reynolds Community College*
Walter Wang, *Baruch College*
Leigh Ann Wheeler, *Greenville Technical Community College*
Jenny Wilson, *Tyler Junior College*
Valerie Wright, *Central Piedmont Community College*

A special thank you to those students who participated in our design review: Katherine Browne, Mike Bulfin, Nancy Canipe, Ashley Carpenter, Jeff Chojnachi, Roxanne Davis, Mike Dieter, Amy Dombrowski, Kay Herring, Todd Jaycox, Kaleena Levan, Matt Montgomery, Tony Plese, Abigail Polkinghorn, Harley Price, Eli Robinson, Avery Rosen, Robyn Schott, Cynthia Thomas, and Sherry Ward.

Elayn Martin-Gay

About the Author

Elayn Martin-Gay has taught mathematics at the University of New Orleans for more than 25 years. Her numerous teaching awards include the local University Alumni Association's Award for Excellence in Teaching, and Outstanding Developmental Educator at University of New Orleans, presented by the Louisiana Association of Developmental Educators.

Prior to writing textbooks, Elayn Martin-Gay developed an acclaimed series of lecture videos to support developmental mathematics students in their quest for success. These highly successful videos originally served as the foundation material for her texts. Today, the videos are specific to each book in the Martin-Gay series. The author has also created Chapter Test Prep Videos to help students during their most "teachable moment"—as they prepare for a test—along with Instructor-to-Instructor videos that provide teaching tips, hints, and suggestions for each developmental mathematics course, including basic mathematics, prealgebra, beginning algebra, and intermediate algebra. Her most recent innovations are the AlgebraPrep Apps for the iPhone and iPod Touch. These Apps embrace the different learning styles, schedules, and paces of students and provide them with quality math tutoring.

Elayn is the author of 12 published textbooks as well as interactive multimedia mathematics, all specializing in developmental mathematics courses. She has participated as an author across the broadest range of educational materials: textbooks, videos, tutorial software, and courseware. This provides the opportunity of various combinations for an integrated teaching and learning package that offers great consistency for the student.

Applications Index

CHAPTER 1 Review of Real Numbers

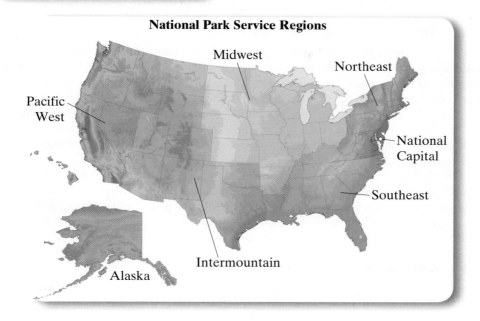

National Park Service Regions

Midwest

Northeast

Pacific West

National Capital

Southeast

Intermountain

Alaska

The National Park Service (NPS) is a federal agency that manages all national parks and many other historic monuments and properties. The NPS has 21,989 employees and had a total of 281 million recreational visitors in 2010 alone. The map above shows the different geographic regions of the NPS, and the bar graph below shows the number of recreational visits per year shown.

In Section 1.2, Exercises 71 through 76, we shall study this bar graph further.

In this chapter, we review the basic symbols and words—the language—of arithmetic and introduce using variables in place of numbers. This is our starting place in the study of algebra.

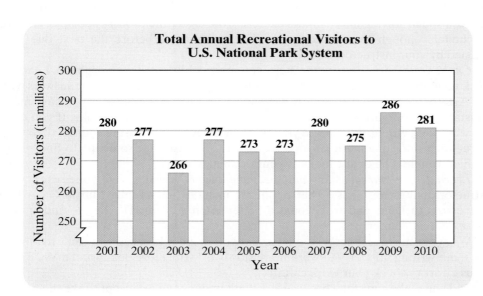

Total Annual Recreational Visitors to U.S. National Park System

Number of Visitors (in millions)

Year	2001	2002	2003	2004	2005	2006	2007	2008	2009	2010
	280	277	266	277	273	273	280	275	286	281

1.1 Tips for Success in Mathematics

OBJECTIVES

1 Get Ready for This Course.

2 Understand Some General Tips for Success.

3 Understand How to Use This Text.

4 Get Help as Soon as You Need It.

5 Learn How to Prepare for and Take an Exam.

6 Develop Good Time Management.

> **Helpful Hint**
> **MyMathLab®** and **MathXL®** If you are doing your homework online, you can work and rework those exercises that you struggle with until you master them. Try working through all the assigned exercises twice before the due date.

> **Helpful Hint**
> **MyMathLab®** and **MathXL®** If you are completing your homework online, it's important to work each exercise on paper before submitting the answer. That way, you can check your work and follow your steps to find and correct any mistakes.

Before reading this section, remember that your instructor is your best source of information. Please see your instructor for any additional help or information.

OBJECTIVE
1 Getting Ready for This Course

Now that you have decided to take this course, remember that a *positive attitude* will make all the difference in the world. Your belief that you can succeed is just as important as your commitment to this course. Make sure you are ready for this course by having the time and positive attitude that it takes to succeed.

Next, make sure that you have scheduled your math course at a time that will give you the best chance for success. For example, if you are also working, you may want to check with your employer to make sure that your work hours will not conflict with your course schedule.

On the day of your first class period, double-check your schedule and allow yourself extra time to arrive on time in case of traffic problems or difficulty locating your classroom. Make sure that you bring at least your textbook, paper, and a writing instrument. Are you required to have a lab manual, graph paper, calculator, or some other supplies besides this text? If so, also bring this material with you.

OBJECTIVE
2 General Tips for Success

Following are some general tips that will increase your chance for success in a mathematics class. Many of these tips will also help you in other courses you may be taking.

Exchange names and phone numbers or email addresses with at least one other person in class. This contact person can be a great help if you miss an assignment or want to discuss math concepts or exercises that you find difficult.

Choose to attend all class periods. If possible, sit near the front of the classroom. This way, you will see and hear the presentation better. It may also be easier for you to participate in classroom activities.

Do your homework. You've probably heard the phrase "practice makes perfect" in relation to music and sports. It also applies to mathematics. You will find that the more time you spend solving mathematics exercises, the easier the process becomes. Be sure to schedule enough time to complete your assignments before the next due date assigned by your instructor.

Check your work. Review the steps you made while working a problem. Learn to check your answers in the original problems. You may also compare your answers with the "Answers to Selected Exercises" section in the back of the book. If you have made a mistake, try to figure out what went wrong. Then correct your mistake. If you can't find what went wrong, don't erase your work or throw it away. Bring your work to your instructor, a tutor in a math lab, or a classmate. It is easier for someone to find where you had trouble if he or she looks at your original work.

Learn from your mistakes and be patient with yourself. Everyone, even your instructor, makes mistakes. (That definitely includes me—Elayn Martin-Gay.) Use your errors to learn and to become a better math student. The key is finding and understanding your errors.

Was your mistake a careless one, or did you make it because you can't read your own math writing? If so, try to work more slowly or write more neatly and make a conscious effort to check your work carefully.

Did you make a mistake because you don't understand a concept? Take the time to review the concept or ask questions to understand it better.

Did you skip too many steps? Skipping steps or trying to do too many steps mentally may lead to preventable mistakes.

Know how to get help if you need it. It's all right to ask for help. In fact, it's a good idea to ask for help whenever there is something that you don't understand. Make sure you know when your instructor has office hours and how to find his or her office. Find out whether math tutoring services are available on your campus. Check on the hours, location, and requirements of the tutoring service.

Organize your class materials, including homework assignments, graded quizzes and tests, and notes from your class or lab. All of these items will make valuable references throughout your course and when studying for upcoming tests and the final exam. Make sure that you can locate these materials when you need them.

Read your textbook before class. Reading a mathematics textbook is unlike reading a novel or a newspaper. Your pace will be much slower. It is helpful to have paper and a pencil with you when you read. Try to work out examples on your own as you encounter them in your text. You should also write down any questions that you want to ask in class. When you read a mathematics textbook, sometimes some of the information in a section will be unclear. But after you hear a lecture or watch a lecture video on that section, you will understand it much more easily than if you had not read your text beforehand.

Don't be afraid to ask questions. You are not the only person in class with questions. Other students are normally grateful that someone has spoken up.

Turn in assignments on time. This way, you can be sure that you will not lose points for being late. Show every step of a problem and be neat and organized. Also be sure that you understand which problems are assigned for homework. If allowed, you can always double-check the assignment with another student in your class.

OBJECTIVE

3   Using This Text ▶

Many helpful resources are available to you. It is important to become familiar with and use these resources. They should increase your chances for success in this course.

- *Practice Exercises*. Each example in every section has a parallel Practice exercise. As you read a section, try each Practice exercise after you've finished the corresponding example. This learn-by-doing approach will help you grasp ideas before you move on to other concepts. Answers are at the back of the text.
- *Chapter Test Prep Videos*. These videos provide solutions to all of the Chapter Test exercises worked out by the author. This supplement is very helpful before a test or exam.
- *Interactive DVD Lecture Series*. Exercises marked with a ▶ are fully worked out by the author on the DVDs. The lecture series provides approximately 20 minutes of instruction per section.
- *Symbols at the Beginning of an Exercise Set*. If you need help with a particular section, the symbols listed at the beginning of each exercise set will remind you of the numerous supplements available.
- *Objectives*. The main section of exercises in each exercise set is referenced by an objective, such as 1 or 2, and by an example(s). There is also often a section of exercises entitled "Mixed Practice," which is referenced by two or more objectives or sections. These are mixed exercises written to prepare you for your next exam. Use all of this referencing if you have trouble completing an assignment from the exercise set.
- *Icons (Symbols)*. Make sure that you understand the meaning of the icons that are beside many exercises. ▶ tells you that the corresponding exercise may be viewed on the video segment that corresponds to that section. ✎ tells you that this exercise is a writing exercise in which you should answer in complete sentences. △ tells you that the exercise involves geometry.
- *Integrated Reviews*. Found in the middle of each chapter, these reviews offer you a chance to practice—in one place—the many concepts that you have learned separately over several sections.
- *End-of-Chapter Opportunities*. There are many opportunities at the end of each chapter to help you understand the concepts of the chapter.

   Vocabulary Checks contain key vocabulary terms introduced in the chapter.

   Chapter Highlights contain chapter summaries and examples.

   Chapter Reviews contain review problems. The first part is organized section by section and the second part contains a set of mixed exercises.

▶ **Helpful Hint**

MyMathLab® and **MathXL®** When assignments are turned in online, keep a hard copy of your complete written work. You will need to refer to your written work to be able to ask questions and to study for tests later.

▶ **Helpful Hint**

MyMathLab® and **MathXL®** Be aware of assignments and due dates set by your instructor. Don't wait until the last minute to submit work online. Allow 6–8 hours before the deadline in case you have technology trouble.

▶ **Helpful Hint**

MyMathLab® In MyMathLab, you have access to the following video resources:

- Lecture Videos for each section
- Chapter Test Prep Videos

Use these videos provided by the author to prepare for class, review, and study for tests.

Chapter Tests are sample tests to help you prepare for an exam. The Chapter Test Prep Videos, found in this text, contain all the Chapter Test exercises worked by the author.

Cumulative Reviews consist of material from the beginning of the book to the end of that particular chapter.

- *Student Resources in Your Textbook.* You will find a **Student Resources** section at the back of this textbook. It contains the following to help you study and prepare for tests:

Study Skill Builders contain study skills advice. To increase your chance for success in the course, read these study tips and answer the questions.

Bigger Picture—Study Guide Outline provides you with a study guide outline of the course, with examples.

Practice Final provides you with a Practice Final Exam to help you prepare for a final. The video solutions to each question are provided in the Interactive DVD Lecture Series and within MyMathLab®.

- *Resources to Check Your Work.* The **Answers to Selected Exercises** section provides answers to all odd-numbered section exercises and all integrated review and chapter test exercises.

OBJECTIVE

4 Getting Help

If you have trouble completing assignments or understanding the mathematics, get help as soon as you need it! This tip is presented as an objective on its own because it is so important. In mathematics, usually the material presented in one section builds on your understanding of the previous section. This means that if you don't understand the concepts covered during a class period, there is a good chance that you will not understand the concepts covered during the next class period. If this happens to you, get help as soon as you can.

Where can you get help? Many suggestions have been made in this section on where to get help, and now it is up to you to get it. Try your instructor, a tutoring center, or a math lab, or you may want to form a study group with fellow classmates. If you do decide to see your instructor or go to a tutoring center, make sure that you have a neat notebook and are ready with your questions.

OBJECTIVE

5 Preparing for and Taking an Exam

Make sure that you allow yourself plenty of time to prepare for a test. If you think that you are a little "math anxious," it may be that you are not preparing for a test in a way that will ensure success. The way that you prepare for a test in mathematics is important. To prepare for a test:

1. Review your previous homework assignments.

2. Review any notes from class and section-level quizzes you have taken. (If this is a final exam, also review chapter tests you have taken.)

3. Review concepts and definitions by reading the Chapter Highlights at the end of each chapter.

4. Practice working out exercises by completing the Chapter Review found at the end of each chapter. (If this is a final exam, go through a Cumulative Review. There is one at the end of each chapter except Chapter 1. Choose the review found at the end of the latest chapter that you have covered in your course.) *Don't stop here!*

5. It is important to place yourself in conditions similar to test conditions to find out how you will perform. In other words, as soon as you feel that you know the material, get a few blank sheets of paper and take a sample test. A Chapter Test is available at the end of each chapter, or you can work selected problems from the Chapter

Review. Your instructor may also provide you with a review sheet. During this sample test, do not use your notes or your textbook. Then check your sample test. If you are not satisfied with the results, study the areas that you are weak in and try again.

6. On the day of the test, allow yourself plenty of time to arrive where you will be taking your exam.

When taking your test:

1. Read the directions on the test carefully.

2. Read each problem carefully as you take the test. Make sure that you answer the question asked.

3. Watch your time and pace yourself so that you can attempt each problem on your test.

4. If you have time, check your work and answers.

5. Do not turn your test in early. If you have extra time, spend it double-checking your work.

OBJECTIVE

6   Managing Your Time

As a college student, you know the demands that classes, homework, work, and family place on your time. Some days, you probably wonder how you'll ever get everything done. One key to managing your time is developing a schedule. Here are some hints for making a schedule:

1. Make a list of all your weekly commitments for the term. Include classes, work, regular meetings, extracurricular activities, etc. You may also find it helpful to list such things as laundry, regular workouts, grocery shopping, etc.

2. Next, estimate the time needed for each item on the list. Also make a note of how often you will need to do each item. Don't forget to include time estimates for the reading, studying, and homework you do outside of your classes. You may want to ask your instructor for help estimating the time needed.

3. In the exercise set that follows, you are asked to block out a typical week on the schedule grid given. Start with items with fixed time slots like classes and work.

4. Next, include the items on your list with flexible time slots. Think carefully about how best to schedule items such as study time.

5. Don't fill up every time slot on the schedule. Remember that you need to allow time for eating, sleeping, and relaxing! You should also allow a little extra time in case some items take longer than planned.

6. If you find that your weekly schedule is too full for you to handle, you may need to make some changes in your workload, classload, or other areas of your life. You may want to talk to your advisor, manager or supervisor at work, or someone in your college's academic counseling center for help with such decisions.

1.1 Exercise Set   MyMathLab®

1. What is your instructor's name?

2. What are your instructor's office location and office hours?

3. What is the best way to contact your instructor?

4. Do you have the name and contact information of at least one other student in class?

5. Will your instructor allow you to use a calculator in this class?

6. Why is it important that you write step-by-step solutions to homework exercises and keep a hard copy of all work submitted?

7. Is a tutoring service available on campus? If so, what are its hours? What services are available?

8. Have you attempted this course before? If so, write down ways that you might improve your chances of success during this second attempt.

9. List some steps that you can take if you begin having trouble understanding the material or completing an assignment. If you are completing your homework in MyMathLab® and MathXL®, list the resources you can use for help.

10. How many hours of studying does your instructor advise for each hour of instruction?

11. What does the ＼ icon in this text mean?

12. What does the ● icon in this text mean?

13. What does the △ icon in this text mean?

14. What are Practice exercises?

15. When might be the best time to work a Practice exercise?

16. Where are the answers to Practice exercises?

17. What answers are contained in this text and where are they?

18. What and where are the study skills builders?

19. What and where are Integrated Reviews?

20. How many times is it suggested that you work through the homework exercises in MathXL® before the submission deadline?

21. How far in advance of the assigned due date is it suggested that homework be submitted online? Why?

22. Chapter Highlights are found at the end of each chapter. Find the Chapter 1 Highlights and explain how you might use it and how it might be helpful.

23. Chapter Reviews are found at the end of each chapter. Find the Chapter 1 Review and explain how you might use it and how it might be useful.

24. Chapter Tests are at the end of each chapter. Find the Chapter 1 Test and explain how you might use it and how it might be helpful when preparing for an exam on Chapter 1. Include how the Chapter Test Prep Videos may help. If you are working in MyMathLab® and MathXL®, how can you use previous homework assignments to study?

25. Read or reread objective 6 and fill out the schedule grid below.

	Monday	Tuesday	Wednesday	Thursday	Friday	Saturday	Sunday
1:00 a.m.							
2:00 a.m.							
3:00 a.m.							
4:00 a.m.							
5:00 a.m.							
6:00 a.m.							
7:00 a.m.							
8:00 a.m.							
9:00 a.m.							
10:00 a.m.							
11:00 a.m.							
Noon							
1:00 p.m.							
2:00 p.m.							
3:00 p.m.							
4:00 p.m.							
5:00 p.m.							
6:00 p.m.							
7:00 p.m.							
8:00 p.m.							
9:00 p.m.							
10:00 p.m.							
11:00 p.m.							
Midnight							

1.2 Symbols and Sets of Numbers

OBJECTIVES

1 Use a Number Line to Order Numbers.

2 Translate Sentences into Mathematical Statements.

3 Identify Natural Numbers, Whole Numbers, Integers, Rational Numbers, Irrational Numbers, and Real Numbers.

4 Find the Absolute Value of a Real Number.

OBJECTIVE
1 Using a Number Line to Order Numbers

We begin with a review of the set of natural numbers and the set of whole numbers and how we use symbols to compare these numbers. A **set** is a collection of objects, each of which is called a **member** or **element** of the set. A pair of brace symbols { } encloses the list of elements and is translated as "the set of" or "the set containing."

Natural Numbers

The set of **natural numbers** is $\{1, 2, 3, 4, 5, 6, \ldots\}$.

Whole Numbers

The set of **whole numbers** is $\{0, 1, 2, 3, 4, \ldots\}$.

The three dots (an ellipsis) means that the list continues in the same manner indefinitely.

These numbers can be pictured on a **number line.** We will use number lines often to help us visualize distance and relationships between numbers.

A number line

To draw a number line, first draw a line. Choose a point on the line and label it 0. To the right of 0, label any other point 1. Being careful to use the same distance as from 0 to 1, mark off equally spaced distances. Label these points 2, 3, 4, 5, and so on. Since the whole numbers continue indefinitely, it is not possible to show every whole number on this number line. The arrow at the right end of the line indicates that the pattern continues indefinitely.

Picturing whole numbers on a number line helps us see the order of the numbers. Symbols can be used to describe concisely in writing the order that we see.

The **equal symbol** $=$ means "is equal to."

The symbol $\neq$ means "is not equal to."

These symbols may be used to form a **mathematical statement.** The statement might be true or it might be false. The two statements below are both true.

$2 = 2$ states that "two is equal to two."

$2 \neq 6$ states that "two is not equal to six."

If two numbers are not equal, one number is larger than the other.
The symbol $>$ means "is greater than."
The symbol $<$ means "is less than." For example,

$3 < 5$

$2 > 0$ or $0 < 2$

$3 < 5$ states that "three is less than five."

$2 > 0$ states that "two is greater than zero."

On a number line, we see that a number **to the right of** another number is **larger.** Similarly, a number **to the left of** another number is smaller. For example, 3 is to the left of 5 on a number line, which means that 3 is less than 5, or $3 < 5$. Similarly, 2 is to the right of 0 on a number line, which means 2 is greater than 0, or $2 > 0$. Since 0 is to the left of 2, we can also say that 0 is less than 2, or $0 < 2$.

The symbols $\neq$, $<$, and $>$ are called **inequality symbols.**

▶ Helpful Hint

Notice that $2 > 0$ has exactly the same meaning as $0 < 2$. Switching the order of the numbers and reversing the direction of the inequality symbol does not change the meaning of the statement.

$3 < 5$ has the same meaning as $5 > 3$.

Also notice that, when the statement is true, the inequality arrow points to the smaller number.

EXAMPLE 1 Insert <, >, or = in the space between each pair of numbers to make each statement true

a. 2   3   **b.** 7   4   **c.** 72   27

Solution

a. 2 < 3 since 2 is to the left of 3 on the number line.

b. 7 > 4 since 7 is to the right of 4 on the number line.

c. 72 > 27 since 72 is to the right of 27 on the number line.   □

PRACTICE

1   Insert <, >, or = in the space between each pair of numbers to make each statement true.

a. 5   8   **b.** 6   4   **c.** 16   82

Two other symbols are used to compare numbers.
The symbol ≤ means "is less than or equal to."
The symbol ≥ means "is greater than or equal to." For example,

$$7 \le 10 \text{ states that "seven is less than or equal to ten."}$$

This statement is true since 7 < 10 is true. If either 7 < 10 or 7 = 10 is true, then 7 ≤ 10 is true.

$$3 \ge 3 \text{ states that "three is greater than or equal to three."}$$

This statement is true since 3 = 3 is true. If either 3 > 3 or 3 = 3 is true, then 3 ≥ 3 is true.

The statement 6 ≥ 10 is false since neither 6 > 10 nor 6 = 10 is true. The symbols ≤ and ≥ are also called **inequality symbols.**

EXAMPLE 2 Tell whether each statement is true or false.

a. 8 ≥ 8   **b.** 8 ≤ 8   **c.** 23 ≤ 0   **d.** 23 ≥ 0

Solution

a. True. Since 8 = 8 is true, then 8 ≥ 8 is true.

b. True. Since 8 = 8 is true, then 8 ≤ 8 is true.

c. False. Since neither 23 < 0 nor 23 = 0 is true, then 23 ≤ 0 is false.

d. True. Since 23 > 0 is true, then 23 ≥ 0 is true.   □

PRACTICE

2   Tell whether each statement is true or false.

a. 9 ≥ 3   **b.** 3 ≥ 8   **c.** 25 ≤ 25   **d.** 4 ≤ 14

OBJECTIVE

2 Translating Sentences

Now, let's use the symbols discussed to translate sentences into mathematical statements.

EXAMPLE 3 Translate each sentence into a mathematical statement.

a. Nine is less than or equal to eleven.

b. Eight is greater than one.

c. Three is not equal to four.

Solution

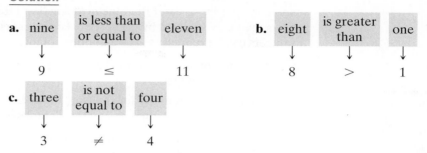

a. nine | is less than or equal to | eleven

9 ≤ 11

b. eight | is greater than | one

8 > 1

c. three | is not equal to | four

3 ≠ 4

3   Translate each sentence into a mathematical statement.

a. Three is less than eight.

b. Fifteen is greater than or equal to nine.

c. Six is not equal to seven.

OBJECTIVE

3   Identifying Common Sets of Numbers

Whole numbers are not sufficient to describe many situations in the real world. For example, quantities less than zero must sometimes be represented, such as temperatures less than 0 degrees.

Numbers Less Than Zero on a Number Line

Zero

$-5\ -4\ -3\ -2\ -1\ \ 0\ \ 1\ \ 2\ \ 3\ \ 4\ \ 5$

Numbers less than 0 are to the left of 0 and are labeled $-1, -2, -3$, and so on. A $-$ sign, such as the one in -1, tells us that the number is to the left of 0 on a number line. In words, -1 is read "negative one." A $+$ sign or no sign tells us that a number lies to the right of 0 on the number line. For example, 3 and $+3$ both mean positive three.

The numbers we have pictured are called the set of **integers.** Integers to the left of 0 are called **negative integers;** integers to the right of 0 are called **positive integers.** The integer **0 is neither positive nor negative.**

negative integers ┊ positive integers

$-5\ -4\ -3\ -2\ -1\ \ 0\ \ 1\ \ 2\ \ 3\ \ 4\ \ 5$

Integers

The set of **integers** is $\{ \ldots, -3, -2, -1, 0, 1, 2, 3, \ldots \}$.

The ellipses (three dots) to the left and to the right indicate that the positive integers and the negative integers continue indefinitely.

EXAMPLE 4   Use an integer to express the number in the following. "Pole of Inaccessibility, Antarctica, is the coldest location in the world, with an average annual temperature of 72 degrees below zero." (*Source: The Guinness Book of Records*)

Solution   The integer -72 represents 72 degrees below zero.

4   Use an integer to express the number in the following. The elevation of Laguna Salada in Mexico is 10 meters below sea level. (*Source: The World Almanac*)

A problem with integers in real-life settings arises when quantities are smaller than some integer but greater than the next smallest integer. On a number line, these quantities may be visualized by points between integers. Some of these quantities between integers can be represented as a quotient of integers. For example,

The point on a number line halfway between 0 and 1 can be represented by $\frac{1}{2}$, a quotient of integers.

The point on a number line halfway between 0 and -1 can be represented by $-\frac{1}{2}$. Other quotients of integers and their graphs are shown to the left.

These numbers, each of which can be represented as a quotient of integers, are examples of **rational numbers.** It's not possible to list the set of rational numbers using the notation that we have been using. For this reason, we will use a different notation.

> ### Rational Numbers
> $$\left\{ \frac{a}{b} \,\middle|\, a \text{ and } b \text{ are integers and } b \neq 0 \right\}$$

We read this set as "the set of all numbers $\frac{a}{b}$ such that a and b are integers and b **is not equal to 0.**" Notice that every integer is also a rational number since each integer can be expressed as a quotient of integers. For example, the integer 5 is also a rational number since $5 = \frac{5}{1}$.

The number line also contains points that cannot be expressed as quotients of integers. These numbers are called **irrational numbers** because they cannot be represented by rational numbers. For example, $\sqrt{2}$ and π are irrational numbers.

> ### Irrational Numbers
> The set of **irrational numbers** is
>
> {Nonrational numbers that correspond to points on the number line}.
>
> That is, an irrational number is a number that cannot be expressed as a quotient of integers.

Both rational numbers and irrational numbers can be written as decimal numbers. The decimal equivalent of a rational number will either terminate or repeat in a pattern. For example, upon dividing we find that

$$\text{Rational Numbers} \begin{cases} \dfrac{3}{4} = 0.75 \ (\text{decimal number terminates or ends}) \\[2mm] \dfrac{2}{3} = 0.66666\ldots \ (\text{decimal number repeats in a pattern}) \end{cases}$$

The decimal representation of an irrational number will neither terminate nor repeat. For example, the decimal representations of irrational numbers $\sqrt{2}$ and π are

$$\text{Irrational Numbers} \begin{cases} \sqrt{2} = 1.414213562\ldots \ (\text{decimal number does not terminate or repeat in a pattern}) \\[2mm] \pi = 3.141592653\ldots \ (\text{decimal number does not terminate or repeat in a pattern}) \end{cases}$$

(For further review of decimals, see the Appendix.)

Combining the rational numbers with the irrational numbers gives the set of **real numbers.** One and only one point on a number line corresponds to each real number.

> ### Real Numbers
> The set of **real numbers** is
>
> {All numbers that correspond to points on the number line}

▶ Helpful Hint

From our previous definitions, we have that

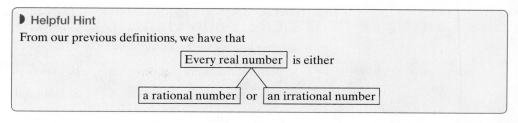

On the following number line, we see that real numbers can be positive, negative, or 0. Numbers to the left of 0 are called **negative numbers;** numbers to the right of 0 are called **positive numbers.** Positive and negative numbers are also called **signed numbers.**

Several different sets of numbers have been discussed in this section. The following diagram shows the relationships among these sets of real numbers.

Common Sets of Numbers

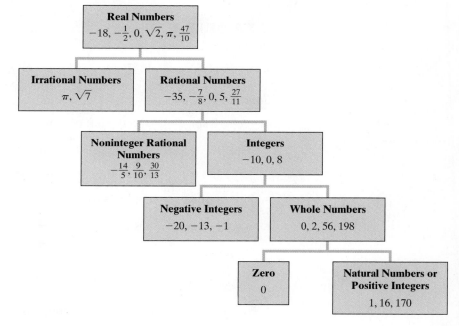

EXAMPLE 5   Given the set $\left\{-2, 0, \frac{1}{4}, -1.5, 112, -3, 11, \sqrt{2}\right\}$, list the numbers in this set that belong to the set of:

a. Natural numbers   b. Whole numbers

c. Integers   d. Rational numbers

e. Irrational numbers   f. Real numbers

Solution

a. The natural numbers are 11 and 112.

b. The whole numbers are 0, 11, and 112.

c. The integers are $-3, -2, 0, 11,$ and 112.

d. Recall that integers are rational numbers also. The rational numbers are $-3, -2,$ $-1.5, 0, \frac{1}{4}, 11,$ and 112.

e. The irrational number is $\sqrt{2}$.

f. The real numbers are all numbers in the given set.   □

PRACTICE
5 Given the set $\left\{25, \dfrac{7}{3}, -15, \dfrac{-3}{4}, \sqrt{5}, -3.7, 8.8, -99\right\}$, list the numbers in this set that belong to the set of:

a. Natural numbers   **b.** Whole numbers

c. Integers   **d.** Rational numbers

e. Irrational numbers   **f.** Real numbers

We now extend the meaning and use of inequality symbols such as $<$ and $>$ to all real numbers.

Order Property for Real Numbers

For any two real numbers a and b, a is less than b if a is to the left of b on a number line.

$a < b$ or also $b > a$

EXAMPLE 6 Insert $<, >$, or $=$ in the appropriate space to make each statement true.

a. $-1 \quad 0$ **b.** $7 \quad \dfrac{14}{2}$ **c.** $-5 \quad -6$

Solution

a. $-1 < 0$ since -1 is to the left of 0 on a number line.

$-1 < 0$

b. $7 = \dfrac{14}{2}$ since $\dfrac{14}{2}$ simplifies to 7.

c. $-5 > -6$ since -5 is to the right of -6 on the number line.

$-5 > -6$

PRACTICE
6 Insert $<, >$, or $=$ in the appropriate space to make each statement true.

a. $0 \quad 3$ **b.** $15 \quad -5$ **c.** $3 \quad \dfrac{12}{4}$

OBJECTIVE
4 Finding the Absolute Value of a Real Number ▶

A number line also helps us visualize the distance between numbers. The distance between a real number a and 0 is given a special name called the **absolute value** of a. "The absolute value of a" is written in symbols as $|a|$.

Absolute Value

The absolute value of a real number a, denoted by $|a|$, is the distance between a and 0 on a number line.

For example, $|3| = 3$ and $|-3| = 3$ since both 3 and -3 are a distance of 3 units from 0 on a number line.

> ▶ Helpful Hint
> Since $|a|$ is a distance, $|a|$ is always either positive or 0, never negative. That is, **for any real number a, $|a| \geq 0$.**

EXAMPLE 7 Find the absolute value of each number.

a. $|4|$ **b.** $|-5|$ **c.** $|0|$ **d.** $\left|-\dfrac{1}{2}\right|$ **e.** $|5.6|$

Solution

a. $|4| = 4$ since 4 is 4 units from 0 on a number line.

b. $|-5| = 5$ since -5 is 5 units from 0 on a number line.

c. $|0| = 0$ since 0 is 0 units from 0 on a number line.

d. $\left|-\dfrac{1}{2}\right| = \dfrac{1}{2}$ since $-\dfrac{1}{2}$ is $\dfrac{1}{2}$ unit from 0 on a number line.

e. $|5.6| = 5.6$ since 5.6 is 5.6 units from 0 on a number line.

PRACTICE
7 Find the absolute value of each number.

a. $|-8|$ **b.** $|9|$ **c.** $|-2.5|$ **d.** $\left|\dfrac{5}{11}\right|$ **e.** $|\sqrt{3}|$

EXAMPLE 8 Insert $<$, $>$, or $=$ in the appropriate space to make each statement true.

a. $|0|$ __ 2 **b.** $|-5|$ __ 5 **c.** $|-3|$ __ $|-2|$ **d.** $|5|$ __ $|6|$ **e.** $|-7|$ __ $|6|$

Solution

a. $|0| < 2$ since $|0| = 0$ and $0 < 2$. **b.** $|-5| = 5$ since $5 = 5$.

c. $|-3| > |-2|$ since $3 > 2$. **d.** $|5| < |6|$ since $5 < 6$.

e. $|-7| > |6|$ since $7 > 6$.

PRACTICE
8 Insert $<$, $>$, or $=$ in the appropriate space to make each statement true.

a. $|8|$ __ $|-8|$ **b.** $|-3|$ __ 0 **c.** $|-7|$ __ $|-11|$ **d.** $|3|$ __ $|2|$ **e.** $|0|$ __ $|-4|$

Vocabulary, Readiness & Video Check

Use the choices below to fill in each blank.

real   natural   whole   irrational
$|b|$ inequality   integers   rational

1. The _____ numbers are $\{0, 1, 2, 3, 4, \ldots\}$.

2. The _____ numbers are $\{1, 2, 3, 4, 5, \ldots\}$.

3. The symbols $\neq$, $\leq$, and $>$ are called _____ symbols.

4. The _____ are $\{\ldots, -3, -2, -1, 0, 1, 2, 3, \ldots\}$.

5. The _____ numbers are {all numbers that correspond to points on the number line}.

6. The _____ numbers are $\left\{\dfrac{a}{b} \,\middle|\, a \text{ and } b \text{ are integers}, b \neq 0\right\}$.

7. The _____ numbers are {nonrational numbers that correspond to points on the number line}.

8. The distance between a number b and 0 on a number line is _____.

Martin-Gay Interactive Videos

See Video 1.2

Watch the section lecture video and answer the following questions.

OBJECTIVE
1

9. In Example 2, why is the symbol < inserted between the two numbers?

OBJECTIVE
2

10. Write the sentence given in Example 4 and translate it to a mathematical statement, using symbols.

OBJECTIVE
3

11. Which sets of numbers does the number in ▣ Example 6 belong to? Why is this number not an irrational number?

OBJECTIVE
4

12. Complete this statement based on the lecture given before ▣ Example 8. The _____ of a real number *a*, denoted by $|a|$, is the distance between *a* and 0 on a number line.

1.2 Exercise Set

MyMathLab®

Insert <, >, *or* = *in the appropriate space to make the statement true. See Example 1.*

1. 7   3

2. 9   15

3. 6.26   6.26

4. 2.13   1.13

5. 0   7

6. 20   0

7. −2   2

8. −4   −6

9. The freezing point of water is 32° Fahrenheit. The boiling point of water is 212° Fahrenheit. Write an inequality statement using < or > comparing the numbers 32 and 212.

10. The freezing point of water is 0° Celsius. The boiling point of water is 100° Celsius. Write an inequality statement using < or > comparing the numbers 0 and 100.

△ **11.** An angle measuring 30° is shown and an angle measuring 45° is shown. Use the inequality symbol ≤ or ≥ to write a statement comparing the numbers 30 and 45.

30°   45°

△ **12.** The sum of the measures of the angles of a triangle is 180°. The sum of the measures of the angles of a parallelogram is 360°. Use the inequality symbol ≤ or ≥ to write a statement comparing the numbers 360 and 180.

Sum is 360°

Sum is 180°

Are the following statements true or false? See Examples 2 and 6.

13. 11 ≤ 11

14. 4 ≥ 7

15. 10 > 11

16. 17 > 16

17. 3 + 8 ≥ 3(8)

18. 8·8 ≤ 8·7

19. 9 > 0

20. 4 < 7

21. −6 > −2

22. 0 < −15

TRANSLATING

Write each sentence as a mathematical statement. See Example 3.

23. Eight is less than twelve.

24. Fifteen is greater than five.

25. Five is greater than or equal to four.

26. Negative ten is less than or equal to thirty-seven.

27. Fifteen is not equal to negative two.

28. Negative seven is not equal to seven.

Use integers to represent the values in each statement. See Example 4.

29. The highest elevation in California is Mt. Whitney, with an altitude of 14,494 feet. The lowest elevation in California is Death Valley, with an altitude of 282 feet below sea level. (*Source:* U.S. Geological Survey)

30. Driskill Mountain, in Louisiana, has an altitude of 535 feet. New Orleans, Louisiana, lies 8 feet below sea level. (*Source:* U.S. Geological Survey)

31. The number of graduate students at the University of Texas at Austin is 28,000 fewer than the number of undergraduate students. (*Source:* University of Texas at Austin)

32. The number of students admitted to the class of 2011 at UCLA was 38,792 fewer students than the number that had applied. (*Source:* UCLA)

33. Aaron Miller deposited $350 in his savings account. He later withdrew $126.

34. Aris Peña was deep-sea diving. During her dive, she ascended 30 feet and later descended 50 feet.

Tell which set or sets each number belongs to: natural numbers, whole numbers, integers, rational numbers, irrational numbers, and real numbers. See Example 5.

35. 0

36. $\frac{1}{4}$

37. −2

38. $-\frac{1}{2}$

39. 6

▶ **41.** $\dfrac{2}{3}$

43. $-\sqrt{5}$

40. 5

42. $\sqrt{3}$

44. $-1\dfrac{5}{9}$

Tell whether each statement is true or false.

45. Every rational number is also an integer.

46. Every negative number is also a rational number.

47. Every natural number is positive.

48. Every rational number is also a real number.

49. 0 is a real number.

50. Every real number is also a rational number.

51. Every whole number is an integer.

52. $\dfrac{1}{2}$ is an integer.

53. A number can be both rational and irrational.

54. Every whole number is positive.

Insert $<$, $>$, or $=$ in the appropriate space to make a true statement. See Examples 6 through 8.

55. $-10 \quad -100$

57. $32 \quad 5.2$

59. $\dfrac{18}{3} \quad \dfrac{24}{3}$

61. $-51 \quad -50$

▶ **63.** $|-5| \quad -4$

65. $|-1| \quad |1|$

67. $|-2| \quad |-3|$

▶ **69.** $|0| \quad |-8|$

56. $-200 \quad -20$

58. $7.1 \quad -7$

60. $\dfrac{8}{2} \quad \dfrac{12}{3}$

62. $|-20| \quad -200$

64. $0 \quad |0|$

66. $\left|\dfrac{2}{5}\right| \quad \left|-\dfrac{2}{5}\right|$

68. $-500 \quad |-50|$

70. $|-12| \quad \dfrac{24}{2}$

CONCEPT EXTENSIONS

The graph below is called a bar graph. This particular graph shows the annual numbers of recreational visitors to U.S. National Parks. Each bar represents a different year, and the height of the bar represents the number of visitors (in millions) in that year.

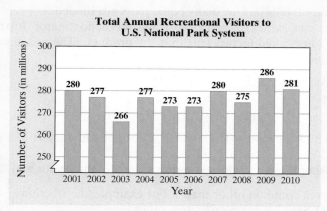

Total Annual Recreational Visitors to U.S. National Park System

(*Note:* The ⌇ symbol means that some numbers are missing. Along the vertical data line, notice the numbers between 0 and 250 are missing or not shown.)

71. In which year(s) was the number of visitors the greatest?

72. What was the greatest number of visitors shown?

73. In what year(s) was the number of visitors greater than 280 million?

74. In what year(s) was the number of visitors less than 270 million?

75. Write an inequality statement comparing the number of annual visitors in 2001 and 2010.

76. Do you notice any trends shown by this bar graph?

The bar graph shows cranberry production from the top five cranberry-producing states.

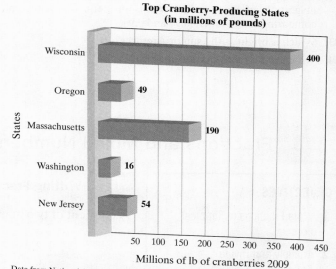

Top Cranberry-Producing States (in millions of pounds)

Data from National Agricultural Statistics Service

77. Write an inequality comparing the 2009 cranberry production in Oregon with the 2009 cranberry production in Washington.

78. Write an inequality comparing the 2009 cranberry production in Massachusetts with the 2009 cranberry production in Wisconsin.

79. Determine the difference between the 2009 cranberry production in Washington and the 2009 cranberry production in New Jersey.

80. According to the bar graph, which two states had almost equal 2009 cranberry crops?

The apparent magnitude of a star is the measure of its brightness as seen by someone on Earth. The smaller the apparent magnitude, the brighter the star. Use the apparent magnitudes in the table on page 16 to answer Exercises 81 through 86.

81. The apparent magnitude of the sun is -26.7. The apparent magnitude of the star Arcturus is -0.04. Write an inequality statement comparing the numbers -0.04 and -26.7.

Star	Apparent Magnitude	Star	Apparent Magnitude
Arcturus	−0.04	Spica	0.98
Sirius	−1.46	Rigel	0.12
Vega	0.03	Regulus	1.35
Antares	0.96	Canopus	−0.72
Sun	−26.7	Hadar	0.61

(Data from *Norton's Star Atlas and Reference Handbook*, 20th Edition, edited by Ian Ridpath. © 2004 Pearson Education, Inc.)

82. The apparent magnitude of Antares is 0.96. The apparent magnitude of Spica is 0.98. Write an inequality statement comparing the numbers 0.96 and 0.98.

83. Which is brighter, the sun or Arcturus?

84. Which is dimmer, Antares or Spica?

85. Which star listed is the brightest?

86. Which star listed is the dimmest?

Rewrite the following inequalities so that the inequality symbol points in the opposite direction and the resulting statement has the same meaning as the given one.

87. $25 \geq 20$

88. $-13 \leq 13$

89. $0 < 6$

90. $5 > 3$

91. $-10 > -12$

92. $-4 < -2$

93. In your own words, explain how to find the absolute value of a number.

94. Give an example of a real-life situation that can be described with integers but not with whole numbers.

1.3 Fractions and Mixed Numbers

OBJECTIVES

1 Write Fractions in Simplest Form.

2 Multiply and Divide Fractions.

3 Add and Subtract Fractions.

4 Perform Operations on Mixed Numbers.

OBJECTIVE

1 Writing Fractions in Simplest Form

A quotient of two numbers such as $\frac{2}{9}$ is called a **fraction.** The parts of a fraction are:

Fraction bar $\rightarrow \frac{2}{9}$ $\leftarrow$ Numerator
$\leftarrow$ Denominator

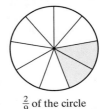

$\frac{2}{9}$ of the circle is shaded.

A fraction may be used to refer to part of a whole. For example, $\frac{2}{9}$ of the circle above is shaded. The denominator 9 tells us how many equal parts the whole circle is divided into, and the numerator 2 tells us how many equal parts are shaded.

To simplify fractions, we can factor the numerator and the denominator. In the statement $3 \cdot 5 = 15$, 3 and 5 are called **factors** and 15 is the **product.** (The raised dot symbol indicates multiplication.)

$$3 \quad \cdot \quad 5 \quad = \quad 15$$
$$\uparrow \qquad \uparrow \qquad\qquad \uparrow$$
$$\text{factor} \quad \text{factor} \quad\quad \text{product}$$

To **factor** 15 means to write it as a product. The number 15 can be factored as $3 \cdot 5$ or as $1 \cdot 15$.

A fraction is said to be **simplified** or in **lowest terms** when the numerator and the denominator have no factors in common other than 1. For example, the fraction $\frac{5}{11}$ is in lowest terms since 5 and 11 have no common factors other than 1.

To help us simplify fractions, we write the numerator and the denominator as a product of **prime numbers.**

Prime Number and Composite Number

A **prime number** is a natural number, other than 1, whose only factors are 1 and itself. The first few prime numbers are

$$2, 3, 5, 7, 11, 13, 17, 19, 23, 29, \text{ and so on.}$$

A natural number, other than 1, that is not a prime number is called a **composite number.**

▶ **Helpful Hint**
The natural number 1 is neither prime nor composite.

Every composite number can be written as a product of prime numbers. We call this product of prime numbers the **prime factorization** of the composite number.

EXAMPLE 1   Write each of the following numbers as a product of primes.

a. 40   **b.** 63

Solution

a. First, write 40 as the product of any two whole numbers other than 1.

$$40 = 4 \cdot 10$$

Next, factor each of these numbers. Continue this process until all of the factors are prime numbers.

$$40 = 4 \quad \cdot \quad 10$$
$$= 2 \cdot 2 \cdot 2 \cdot 5$$

All the factors are now prime numbers. Then 40 written as a product of primes is

$$40 = 2 \cdot 2 \cdot 2 \cdot 5$$

b. $63 = 9 \quad \cdot \quad 7$
$$= 3 \cdot 3 \cdot 7$$

PRACTICE
1   Write each of the following numbers as a product of primes.

a. 36   **b.** 200

To use prime factors to write a fraction in lowest terms (or simplified form), apply the fundamental principle of fractions.

Fundamental Principle of Fractions

If $\dfrac{a}{b}$ is a fraction and c is a nonzero real number, then

$$\frac{a \cdot c}{b \cdot c} = \frac{a}{b}$$

To understand why this is true, we use the fact that since c is not zero, $\dfrac{c}{c} = 1$.

$$\frac{a \cdot c}{b \cdot c} = \frac{a}{b} \cdot \frac{c}{c} = \frac{a}{b} \cdot 1 = \frac{a}{b}$$

We will call this process dividing out the common factor of c.

EXAMPLE 2   Simplify each fraction (write it in lowest terms).

a. $\dfrac{42}{49}$ **b.** $\dfrac{11}{27}$ **c.** $\dfrac{88}{20}$

Solution

a. Write the numerator and the denominator as products of primes; then apply the fundamental principle to the common factor 7.

$$\frac{42}{49} = \frac{2 \cdot 3 \cdot 7}{7 \cdot 7} = \frac{2 \cdot 3}{7} \cdot \frac{7}{7} = \frac{2 \cdot 3}{7} = \frac{6}{7}$$

b. $\dfrac{11}{27} = \dfrac{11}{3 \cdot 3 \cdot 3}$

There are no common factors other than 1, so $\dfrac{11}{27}$ is already in simplest form.

c. $\dfrac{88}{20} = \dfrac{2 \cdot 2 \cdot 2 \cdot 11}{2 \cdot 2 \cdot 5} = \dfrac{2}{2} \cdot \dfrac{2}{2} \cdot \dfrac{2 \cdot 11}{5} = \dfrac{22}{5}$

PRACTICE

2 Write each fraction in lowest terms.

a. $\dfrac{63}{72}$ **b.** $\dfrac{64}{12}$ **c.** $\dfrac{7}{25}$

✓CONCEPT CHECK

Explain the error in the following steps.

a. $\dfrac{15}{55} = \dfrac{1\cancel{5}}{5\cancel{5}} = \dfrac{1}{5}$ **b.** $\dfrac{6}{7} = \dfrac{\cancel{5} + 1}{\cancel{5} + 2} = \dfrac{1}{2}$

OBJECTIVE

2 Multiplying and Dividing Fractions

To multiply two fractions, multiply numerator times numerator to obtain the numerator of the product; multiply denominator times denominator to obtain the denominator of the product.

> **Multiplying Fractions**
>
> $$\frac{a}{b} \cdot \frac{c}{d} = \frac{a \cdot c}{b \cdot d} \qquad \text{if } b \neq 0 \text{ and } d \neq 0$$

EXAMPLE 3 Multiply $\dfrac{2}{15}$ and $\dfrac{5}{13}$. Simplify the product if possible.

Solution $\dfrac{2}{15} \cdot \dfrac{5}{13} = \dfrac{2 \cdot 5}{15 \cdot 13}$ Multiply numerators.
  Multiply denominators.

Next, simplify the product by dividing the numerator and the denominator by any common factors.

$$= \frac{2 \cdot \overset{1}{\cancel{5}}}{3 \cdot \underset{1}{\cancel{5}} \cdot 13}$$

$$= \frac{2}{39}$$

PRACTICE

3 Multiply $\dfrac{3}{8}$ and $\dfrac{7}{9}$. Simplify the product if possible.

Answers to Concept Check:
answers may vary

Before dividing fractions, we first define **reciprocals.** Two fractions are reciprocals of each other if their product is 1.

For example:

The reciprocal of $\dfrac{2}{3}$ is $\dfrac{3}{2}$ because $\dfrac{2}{3} \cdot \dfrac{3}{2} = \dfrac{6}{6} = 1$.

The reciprocal of 5 is $\dfrac{1}{5}$ because $5 \cdot \dfrac{1}{5} = \dfrac{5}{1} \cdot \dfrac{1}{5} = \dfrac{5}{5} = 1$.

To divide fractions, multiply the first fraction by the reciprocal of the second fraction.

> **Dividing Fractions**
>
> $$\frac{a}{b} \div \frac{c}{d} = \frac{a}{b} \cdot \frac{d}{c}, \qquad \text{if } b \neq 0, d \neq 0, \text{ and } c \neq 0$$

EXAMPLE 4   Divide. Simplify all quotients if possible.

a. $\dfrac{4}{5} \div \dfrac{5}{16}$ **b.** $\dfrac{7}{10} \div 14$ **c.** $\dfrac{3}{8} \div \dfrac{3}{10}$

Solution

a. $\dfrac{4}{5} \div \dfrac{5}{16} = \dfrac{4}{5} \cdot \dfrac{16}{5} = \dfrac{\overbrace{4 \cdot 16}}{5 \cdot 5} = \dfrac{64}{25}$ — The numerator and denominator have no common factors.

b. $\dfrac{7}{10} \div 14 = \dfrac{7}{10} \div \dfrac{14}{1} = \dfrac{7}{10} \cdot \dfrac{1}{14} = \dfrac{\cancel{7}^{1} \cdot 1}{2 \cdot 5 \cdot 2 \cdot \cancel{7}_{1}} = \dfrac{1}{20}$

c. $\dfrac{3}{8} \div \dfrac{3}{10} = \dfrac{3}{8} \cdot \dfrac{10}{3} = \dfrac{\cancel{3}^{1} \cdot \cancel{2}^{1} \cdot 5}{\cancel{2}_{1} \cdot 2 \cdot 2 \cdot \cancel{3}_{1}} = \dfrac{5}{4}$

PRACTICE
4   Divide. Simplify all quotients if possible.

a. $\dfrac{3}{4} \div \dfrac{4}{9}$ **b.** $\dfrac{5}{12} \div 15$ **c.** $\dfrac{7}{6} \div \dfrac{7}{15}$

OBJECTIVE
3   **Adding and Subtracting Fractions**

To add or subtract fractions with the same denominator, combine numerators and place the sum or difference over the common denominator.

> **Adding and Subtracting Fractions with the Same Denominator**
>
> $$\frac{a}{b} + \frac{c}{b} = \frac{a + c}{b}, \qquad \text{if } b \neq 0$$
>
> $$\frac{a}{b} - \frac{c}{b} = \frac{a - c}{b}, \qquad \text{if } b \neq 0$$

EXAMPLE 5   Add or subtract as indicated. Simplify each result if possible.

a. $\dfrac{2}{7} + \dfrac{4}{7}$ **b.** $\dfrac{3}{10} + \dfrac{2}{10}$ **c.** $\dfrac{9}{7} - \dfrac{2}{7}$ **d.** $\dfrac{5}{3} - \dfrac{1}{3}$

Solution

a. $\dfrac{2}{7} + \dfrac{4}{7} = \dfrac{2 + 4}{7} = \dfrac{6}{7}$ **b.** $\dfrac{3}{10} + \dfrac{2}{10} = \dfrac{3 + 2}{10} = \dfrac{5}{10} = \dfrac{\cancel{5}^{1}}{2 \cdot \cancel{5}_{1}} = \dfrac{1}{2}$

c. $\dfrac{9}{7} - \dfrac{2}{7} = \dfrac{9 - 2}{7} = \dfrac{7}{7} = 1$ **d.** $\dfrac{5}{3} - \dfrac{1}{3} = \dfrac{5 - 1}{3} = \dfrac{4}{3}$

PRACTICE
5 Add or subtract as indicated. Simplify each result if possible.

a. $\dfrac{8}{5} - \dfrac{3}{5}$ **b.** $\dfrac{8}{5} - \dfrac{2}{5}$ **c.** $\dfrac{3}{5} + \dfrac{1}{5}$ **d.** $\dfrac{5}{12} + \dfrac{1}{12}$

To add or subtract fractions without the same denominator, first write the fractions as equivalent fractions with a common denominator. **Equivalent fractions** are fractions that represent the same quantity. For example,

$$\frac{3}{4} \text{ and } \frac{12}{16} \text{ are equivalent fractions}$$

Whole

$$\frac{3}{4} = \frac{12}{16}$$

since they represent the same portion of a whole, as the diagram shows. Count the larger squares, and the shaded portion is $\dfrac{3}{4}$. Count the smaller squares, and the shaded portion is $\dfrac{12}{16}$. Thus, $\dfrac{3}{4} = \dfrac{12}{16}$.

We can write equivalent fractions by multiplying a given fraction by 1, as shown in the next example. Multiplying a fraction by 1 does not change the value of the fraction.

EXAMPLE 6 Write $\dfrac{2}{5}$ as an equivalent fraction with a denominator of 20.

Solution Since $5 \cdot 4 = 20$, multiply the fraction by $\dfrac{4}{4}$. Multiplying by $\dfrac{4}{4} = 1$ does not change the value of the fraction.

Multiply by $\dfrac{4}{4}$ or 1.

$$\frac{2}{5} = \frac{2}{5} \cdot \frac{4}{4} = \frac{2 \cdot 4}{5 \cdot 4} = \frac{8}{20}$$

Thus, $\dfrac{2}{5} = \dfrac{8}{20}$.

PRACTICE
6 Write $\dfrac{2}{3}$ as an equivalent fraction with a denominator of 21.

To add or subtract with different denominators, we first write the fractions as **equivalent fractions** with the same denominator. We use the smallest or **least common denominator,** or **LCD.** (The LCD is the same as the least common multiple of the denominators.)

EXAMPLE 7 Add or subtract as indicated. Write each answer in simplest form.

a. $\dfrac{2}{5} + \dfrac{1}{4}$ **b.** $\dfrac{19}{6} - \dfrac{23}{12}$ **c.** $\dfrac{1}{2} + \dfrac{17}{22} - \dfrac{2}{11}$

Solution

a. Fractions must have a common denominator before they can be added or subtracted. Since 20 is the smallest number that both 5 and 4 divide into evenly, 20 is the **least common denominator** (LCD). Write both fractions as equivalent fractions with denominators of 20. Since

$$\frac{2}{5} \cdot \frac{4}{4} = \frac{2 \cdot 4}{5 \cdot 4} = \frac{8}{20} \quad \text{and} \quad \frac{1}{4} \cdot \frac{5}{5} = \frac{1 \cdot 5}{4 \cdot 5} = \frac{5}{20}$$

then

$$\frac{2}{5} + \frac{1}{4} = \frac{8}{20} + \frac{5}{20} = \frac{13}{20}$$

b. The LCD is 12. We write both fractions as equivalent fractions with denominators of 12.

$$\frac{19}{6} - \frac{23}{12} = \frac{38}{12} - \frac{23}{12}$$

$$= \frac{15}{12} = \frac{\overset{1}{\cancel{3}} \cdot 5}{2 \cdot 2 \cdot \underset{1}{\cancel{3}}} = \frac{5}{4}$$

c. The LCD for denominators 2, 22, and 11 is 22. First, write each fraction as an equivalent fraction with a denominator of 22. Then add or subtract from left to right.

$$\frac{1}{2} = \frac{1}{2} \cdot \frac{11}{11} = \frac{11}{22}, \qquad \frac{17}{22} = \frac{17}{22}, \qquad \text{and} \qquad \frac{2}{11} = \frac{2}{11} \cdot \frac{2}{2} = \frac{4}{22}$$

Then

$$\frac{1}{2} + \frac{17}{22} - \frac{2}{11} = \frac{11}{22} + \frac{17}{22} - \frac{4}{22} = \frac{24}{22} = \frac{12}{11}$$

PRACTICE
7   Add or subtract as indicated. Write answers in simplest form.

a. $\frac{5}{11} + \frac{1}{7}$ **b.** $\frac{5}{21} - \frac{1}{6}$ **c.** $\frac{1}{3} + \frac{29}{30} - \frac{4}{5}$

OBJECTIVE
4   Performing Operations on Mixed Numbers ▶

To multiply or divide mixed numbers, first write each mixed number as an improper fraction. To recall how this is done, let's write $3\frac{1}{5}$ as an improper fraction.

$$3\frac{1}{5} = 3 + \frac{1}{5} = \frac{15}{5} + \frac{1}{5} = \frac{16}{5}$$

Because of the steps above, notice that we can use a shortcut process for writing a mixed number as an improper fraction.

$$3\frac{1}{5} = \frac{5 \cdot 3 + 1}{5} = \frac{16}{5}$$

EXAMPLE 8   Divide: $2\frac{1}{8} \div 1\frac{2}{3}$

Solution   First write each mixed number as an improper fraction.

$$2\frac{1}{8} = \frac{8 \cdot 2 + 1}{8} = \frac{17}{8}; \qquad 1\frac{2}{3} = \frac{3 \cdot 1 + 2}{3} = \frac{5}{3}$$

Now divide as usual.

$$2\frac{1}{8} \div 1\frac{2}{3} = \frac{17}{8} \div \frac{5}{3} = \frac{17}{8} \cdot \frac{3}{5} = \frac{51}{40}$$

The fraction $\frac{51}{40}$ is improper. To write it as an equivalent mixed number, remember that the fraction bar means division and divide.

$$\begin{array}{r} 1\frac{11}{40} \\ 40\overline{)51} \\ -40 \\ \hline 11 \end{array}$$

Thus, the quotient is $\frac{51}{40}$ or $1\frac{11}{40}$.

PRACTICE
8   Multiply: $5\frac{1}{6} \cdot 4\frac{2}{5}$

As a general rule, if the original exercise contains mixed numbers, write the result as a mixed number if possible.

When adding or subtracting mixed numbers, you might want to use the following method.

EXAMPLE 9 Subtract: $50\dfrac{1}{6} - 38\dfrac{1}{3}$

Solution

$$50\dfrac{1}{6} = \quad 50\dfrac{1}{6} = \quad 49\dfrac{7}{6} \qquad 50\dfrac{1}{6} = 49 + 1 + \dfrac{1}{6} = 49\dfrac{7}{6}$$

$$-38\dfrac{1}{3} = -38\dfrac{2}{6} = -38\dfrac{2}{6}$$
$$\overline{} \quad \overline{} \quad 11\dfrac{5}{6}$$

PRACTICE
9 Subtract: $76\dfrac{1}{12} - 35\dfrac{1}{4}$

Vocabulary, Readiness & Video Check

Use the choices below to fill in each blank. Some choices may be used more than once.

| simplified | reciprocals | equivalent | denominator |
| product | factors | fraction | numerator |

1. A quotient of two numbers, such as $\dfrac{5}{8}$, is called a(n) _____.

2. In the fraction $\dfrac{3}{11}$, the number 3 is called the _____ and the number 11 is called the _____.

3. To factor a number means to write it as a(n) _____.

4. A fraction is said to be _____ when the numerator and the denominator have no common factors other than 1.

5. In $7 \cdot 3 = 21$, the numbers 7 and 3 are called _____ and the number 21 is called the _____.

6. The fractions $\dfrac{2}{9}$ and $\dfrac{9}{2}$ are called _____.

7. Fractions that represent the same quantity are called _____ fractions.

Martin-Gay Interactive Videos

See Video 1.3

Watch the section lecture video and answer the following questions.

OBJECTIVE 1
8. What is the common factor in the numerator and denominator of ⊞ Example 1? What principle is used to simplify this fraction?

OBJECTIVE 2
9. During the solving of ⊞ Example 3, what two things change in the first step?

OBJECTIVE 3
10. What is the first step needed in order to subtract the fractions in ⊞ Example 6 and why?

OBJECTIVE 4
11. For ⊞ Example 7, why is the sum not left as $4\dfrac{7}{6}$?

1.3 Exercise Set MyMathLab®

Represent the shaded part of each geometric figure by a fraction.

1.

2.

3.

4.

△ **39.** $\frac{4}{9}$ foot, $\frac{7}{8}$ foot

△ **40.** $\frac{3}{11}$ meter, $\frac{2}{5}$ meter

Write each number as a product of primes. See Example 1.

5. 33 **6.** 60 **7.** 98
8. 27 **9.** 20 **10.** 56
11. 75 **12.** 32 **13.** 45
14. 24

Write the fraction in lowest terms. See Example 2.

15. $\frac{2}{4}$ **16.** $\frac{3}{6}$ **17.** $\frac{10}{15}$
18. $\frac{15}{20}$ **19.** $\frac{3}{7}$ **20.** $\frac{5}{9}$
21. $\frac{18}{30}$ **22.** $\frac{42}{45}$ **23.** $\frac{120}{244}$
24. $\frac{360}{700}$

Multiply or divide as indicated. Simplify the answer if possible. See Examples 3 and 4.

25. $\frac{1}{2}\cdot\frac{3}{4}$ **26.** $\frac{7}{11}\cdot\frac{3}{5}$ **27.** $\frac{2}{3}\cdot\frac{3}{4}$
28. $\frac{7}{8}\cdot\frac{3}{21}$ **29.** $\frac{1}{2}\div\frac{7}{12}$ **30.** $\frac{7}{12}\div\frac{1}{2}$
31. $\frac{3}{4}\div\frac{1}{20}$ **32.** $\frac{3}{5}\div\frac{9}{10}$ **33.** $\frac{7}{10}\cdot\frac{5}{21}$
34. $\frac{3}{35}\cdot\frac{10}{63}$ **35.** $\frac{25}{9}\cdot\frac{1}{3}$ **36.** $\frac{1}{4}\cdot\frac{19}{6}$

The area of a plane figure is a measure of the amount of surface of the figure. Find the area of each figure below. (The area of a rectangle is the product of its length and width. The area of a triangle is $\frac{1}{2}$ the product of its base and height.)

△ **37.** $\frac{3}{5}$ mile, $\frac{11}{12}$ mile

△ **38.** $\frac{1}{2}$ meter, $\frac{5}{4}$ meters

Add or subtract as indicated. Write the answer in lowest terms. See Example 5.

41. $\frac{4}{5}-\frac{1}{5}$ **42.** $\frac{6}{7}-\frac{1}{7}$
43. $\frac{4}{5}+\frac{1}{5}$ **44.** $\frac{6}{7}+\frac{1}{7}$
45. $\frac{17}{21}-\frac{10}{21}$ **46.** $\frac{18}{35}-\frac{11}{35}$
47. $\frac{23}{105}+\frac{4}{105}$ **48.** $\frac{13}{132}+\frac{35}{132}$

Write each fraction as an equivalent fraction with the given denominator. See Example 6.

49. $\frac{7}{10}$ with a denominator of 30
50. $\frac{2}{3}$ with a denominator of 9
51. $\frac{2}{9}$ with a denominator of 18
52. $\frac{8}{7}$ with a denominator of 56
53. $\frac{4}{5}$ with a denominator of 20
54. $\frac{4}{5}$ with a denominator of 25

Add or subtract as indicated. Write the answer in simplest form. See Example 7.

55. $\frac{2}{3}+\frac{3}{7}$ **56.** $\frac{3}{4}+\frac{1}{6}$
57. $\frac{4}{15}-\frac{1}{12}$ **58.** $\frac{11}{12}-\frac{1}{16}$
59. $\frac{5}{22}-\frac{5}{33}$ **60.** $\frac{7}{10}-\frac{8}{15}$
61. $\frac{12}{5}-1$ **62.** $2-\frac{3}{8}$

Each circle in Exercises 63–68 represents a whole, or 1. Use subtraction to determine the unknown part of the circle.

63. $\frac{3}{10}$, $\frac{5}{10}$, ?

64. $\frac{3}{11}$, $\frac{2}{11}$, ?

65.

66.

67.

68.

Perform the indicated operations. See Examples 8 and 9.

69. $5\frac{1}{9} \cdot 3\frac{2}{3}$

70. $2\frac{3}{4} \cdot 1\frac{7}{8}$

71. $8\frac{3}{5} \div 2\frac{9}{10}$

72. $1\frac{7}{8} \div 3\frac{8}{9}$

73. $17\frac{2}{5} + 30\frac{2}{3}$

74. $26\frac{11}{20} + 40\frac{7}{10}$

75. $8\frac{11}{12} - 1\frac{5}{6}$

76. $4\frac{7}{8} - 2\frac{3}{16}$

MIXED PRACTICE

Perform the following operations. Write answers in simplest form.

77. $\frac{10}{21} + \frac{5}{21}$

78. $\frac{11}{35} + \frac{3}{35}$

79. $\frac{10}{3} - \frac{5}{21}$

80. $\frac{11}{7} - \frac{3}{35}$

81. $\frac{2}{3} \cdot \frac{3}{5}$

82. $\frac{3}{4} \cdot \frac{7}{12}$

83. $\frac{2}{3} \div \frac{3}{5}$

84. $\frac{3}{4} \div \frac{7}{12}$

85. $5 + \frac{2}{3}$

86. $7 + \frac{1}{10}$

87. $7\frac{2}{5} \div \frac{1}{5}$

88. $9\frac{5}{6} \div \frac{1}{6}$

89. $\frac{1}{2} - \frac{14}{33}$

90. $\frac{7}{15} - \frac{7}{25}$

91. $\frac{23}{105} - \frac{2}{105}$

92. $\frac{57}{132} - \frac{13}{132}$

93. $1\frac{1}{2} + 3\frac{2}{3}$

94. $2\frac{3}{5} + 4\frac{7}{10}$

95. $\frac{2}{3} - \frac{5}{9} + \frac{5}{6}$

96. $\frac{8}{11} - \frac{1}{4} + \frac{1}{2}$

The perimeter of a plane figure is the total distance around the figure. Find the perimeter of each figure in Exercises 97 and 98.

△ **97.**

△ **98.**

99. In your own words, explain how to add two fractions with different denominators.

100. In your own words, explain how to multiply two fractions.

The following trail chart is given to visitors at the Lakeview Forest Preserve.

Trail Name	Distance (miles)
Robin Path	$3\frac{1}{2}$
Red Falls	$5\frac{1}{2}$
Green Way	$2\frac{1}{8}$
Autumn Walk	$1\frac{3}{4}$

101. How much longer is Red Falls Trail than Green Way Trail?

102. Find the total distance traveled by someone who hiked along all four trails.

CONCEPT EXTENSIONS

The graph shown is called a circle graph or a pie chart. Use the graph to answer Exercises 103 through 106.

Fraction of U.S. Screens by Theater Type

Single screens
1/25

Miniplexes
(2–7 screens)
21/100

Megaplexes
(16 or more screens)
29/100

Multiplexes
(8–15 screens)
23/50

Data from Motion Picture Association of America

103. What fraction of U.S. movie screens are in miniplexes?

104. What fraction of U.S. movie screens are in single-screen theaters or multiplexes?

105. What theater type has the greatest fraction of screens?

106. What fraction of U.S. movie screens are in megaplexes or miniplexes?

For Exercises 107 through 110, determine whether the work is correct or incorrect. If incorrect, find the error and correct. See the Concept Check in this section.

107. $\dfrac{12}{24} = \dfrac{2+4+6}{2+4+6+12} = \dfrac{1}{12}$

108. $\dfrac{30}{60} = \dfrac{2\cdot3\cdot5}{2\cdot2\cdot3\cdot5} = \dfrac{1}{2}$

109. $\dfrac{2}{7} + \dfrac{9}{7} = \dfrac{11}{14}$

110. $\dfrac{16}{28} = \dfrac{2\cdot5+6\cdot1}{2\cdot5+6\cdot3} = \dfrac{1}{3}$

1.4 Exponents, Order of Operations, Variable Expressions, and Equations

OBJECTIVES

1 Define and Use Exponents and the Order of Operations.

2 Evaluate Algebraic Expressions, Given Replacement Values for Variables.

3 Determine Whether a Number Is a Solution of a Given Equation.

4 Translate Phrases into Expressions and Sentences into Statements.

OBJECTIVE

1   Using Exponents and the Order of Operations

Frequently in algebra, products occur that contain repeated multiplication of the same factor. For example, the volume of a cube whose sides each measure 2 centimeters is $(2\cdot2\cdot2)$ cubic centimeters. We may use **exponential notation** to write such products in a more compact form. For example,

$$2\cdot2\cdot2 \quad \text{may be written as} \quad 2^3.$$

The 2 in 2^3 is called the **base**; it is the repeated factor. The 3 in 2^3 is called the **exponent** and is the number of times the base is used as a factor. The expression 2^3 is called an **exponential expression.**

base $\rightarrow 2^3 = 2\cdot2\cdot2 = 8$ $\leftarrow$ exponent

2 is a factor 3 times

2 cm

Volume is $(2\cdot2\cdot2)$ cubic centimeters.

EXAMPLE 1   Evaluate the following:

a. 3^2 [read as "3 squared" or as "3 to the second power"]
b. 5^3 [read as "5 cubed" or as "5 to the third power"]
c. 2^4 [read as "2 to the fourth power"]
d. 7^1 **e.** $\left(\dfrac{3}{7}\right)^2$

Solution

a. $3^2 = 3\cdot3 = 9$ **b.** $5^3 = 5\cdot5\cdot5 = 125$
c. $2^4 = 2\cdot2\cdot2\cdot2 = 16$ **d.** $7^1 = 7$
e. $\left(\dfrac{3}{7}\right)^2 = \left(\dfrac{3}{7}\right)\left(\dfrac{3}{7}\right) = \dfrac{9}{49}$

1   Evaluate:

a. 1^3 **b.** 5^2 **c.** $\left(\dfrac{1}{10}\right)^2$ **d.** 9^1 **e.** $\left(\dfrac{2}{5}\right)^3$

▶ **Helpful Hint**

$2^3 \neq 2 \cdot 3$ since 2^3 indicates repeated **multiplication** of the same factor.

$$2^3 = 2 \cdot 2 \cdot 2 = 8, \text{ whereas } 2 \cdot 3 = 6.$$

Using symbols for mathematical operations is a great convenience. However, the more operation symbols present in an expression, the more careful we must be when performing the indicated operation. For example, in the expression $2 + 3 \cdot 7$, do we add first or multiply first? To eliminate confusion, **grouping symbols** are used. Examples of grouping symbols are parentheses ( ), brackets [ ], braces { }, and the fraction bar. If we wish $2 + 3 \cdot 7$ to be simplified by adding first, we enclose $2 + 3$ in parentheses.

$$(2 + 3) \cdot 7 = 5 \cdot 7 = 35$$

If we wish to multiply first, $3 \cdot 7$ may be enclosed in parentheses.

$$2 + (3 \cdot 7) = 2 + 21 = 23$$

To eliminate confusion when no grouping symbols are present, use the following agreed-upon order of operations.

Order of Operations

Simplify expressions using the order below. If grouping symbols such as parentheses are present, simplify expressions within those first, starting with the innermost set. If fraction bars are present, simplify the numerator and the denominator separately.

1. Evaluate exponential expressions.
2. Perform multiplications or divisions in order from left to right.
3. Perform additions or subtractions in order from left to right.

Now simplify $2 + 3 \cdot 7$. There are no grouping symbols and no exponents, so we multiply and then add.

$$2 + 3 \cdot 7 = 2 + 21 \quad \text{Multiply.}$$
$$= 23 \quad \text{Add.}$$

EXAMPLE 2   Simplify each expression.

a. $6 \div 3 + 5^2$ **b.** $20 \div 5 \cdot 4$ **c.** $\dfrac{2(12 + 3)}{|-15|}$ **d.** $3 \cdot 4^2$ **e.** $\dfrac{3}{2} \cdot \dfrac{1}{2} - \dfrac{1}{2}$

Solution

a. Evaluate 5^2 first.

$$6 \div 3 + 5^2 = 6 \div 3 + 25$$

Next divide, then add.

$$= 2 + 25 \quad \text{Divide.}$$
$$= 27 \quad \text{Add.}$$

b. $20 \div 5 \cdot 4 = 4 \cdot 4$
$$= 16$$

▶ **Helpful Hint**

Remember to multiply or divide in order from left to right.

c. First, simplify the numerator and the denominator separately.

$$\frac{2(12+3)}{|-15|} = \frac{2(15)}{15} \quad \text{Simplify numerator and denominator separately.}$$

$$= \frac{30}{15}$$

$$= 2 \qquad \text{Simplify.}$$

d. In this example, only the 4 is squared. The factor of 3 is not part of the base because no grouping symbol includes it as part of the base.

$$3 \cdot 4^2 = 3 \cdot 16 \quad \text{Evaluate the exponential expression.}$$
$$= 48 \qquad \text{Multiply.}$$

e. The order of operations applies to operations with fractions in exactly the same way as it applies to operations with whole numbers.

$$\frac{3}{2} \cdot \frac{1}{2} - \frac{1}{2} = \frac{3}{4} - \frac{1}{2} \quad \text{Multiply.}$$

$$= \frac{3}{4} - \frac{2}{4} \quad \text{The least common denominator is 4.}$$

$$= \frac{1}{4} \qquad \text{Subtract.}$$

PRACTICE
2   Simplify each expression

a. $6 + 3 \cdot 9$ **b.** $4^3 \div 8 + 3$ **c.** $\left(\frac{2}{3}\right)^2 \cdot |-8|$

d. $\dfrac{9(14-6)}{|-2|}$ **e.** $\dfrac{7}{4} \cdot \dfrac{1}{4} - \dfrac{1}{4}$

> ▶ **Helpful Hint**
>
> Be careful when evaluating an exponential expression. In $3 \cdot 4^2$, the exponent 2 applies only to the base 4. In $(3 \cdot 4)^2$, we multiply first because of parentheses, so the exponent 2 applies to the product $3 \cdot 4$.
>
> $$3 \cdot 4^2 = 3 \cdot 16 = 48 \qquad (3 \cdot 4)^2 = (12)^2 = 144$$

Expressions that include many grouping symbols can be confusing. When simplifying these expressions, keep in mind that grouping symbols separate the expression into distinct parts. Each is then simplified separately.

EXAMPLE 3   Simplify $\dfrac{3 + |4 - 3| + 2^2}{6 - 3}$.

Solution   The fraction bar serves as a grouping symbol and separates the numerator and denominator. Simplify each separately. Also, the absolute value bars here serve as a grouping symbol. We begin in the numerator by simplifying within the absolute value bars.

$$\frac{3 + |4 - 3| + 2^2}{6 - 3} = \frac{3 + |1| + 2^2}{6 - 3} \quad \text{Simplify the expression inside the absolute value bars.}$$

$$= \frac{3 + 1 + 2^2}{3} \quad \text{Find the absolute value and simplify the denominator.}$$

$$= \frac{3 + 1 + 4}{3} \quad \text{Evaluate the exponential expression.}$$

$$= \frac{8}{3} \quad \text{Simplify the numerator.}$$

PRACTICE
3   Simplify $\dfrac{6^2 - 5}{3 + |6 - 5| \cdot 8}$.

EXAMPLE 4 Simplify $3[4 + 2(10 - 1)]$.

Solution Notice that both parentheses and brackets are used as grouping symbols. Start with the innermost set of grouping symbols.

> **Helpful Hint**
> Be sure to follow order of operations and resist the temptation to incorrectly add 4 and 2 first.

$$3[4 + 2(10 - 1)] = 3[4 + 2(9)] \quad \text{Simplify the expression in parentheses.}$$
$$= 3[4 + 18] \quad \text{Multiply.}$$
$$= 3[22] \quad \text{Add.}$$
$$= 66 \quad \text{Multiply.}$$

PRACTICE
4 Simplify $4[25 - 3(5 + 3)]$.

EXAMPLE 5 Simplify $\dfrac{8 + 2 \cdot 3}{2^2 - 1}$.

Solution

$$\frac{8 + 2 \cdot 3}{2^2 - 1} = \frac{8 + 6}{4 - 1} = \frac{14}{3}$$

PRACTICE
5 Simplify $\dfrac{36 \div 9 + 5}{5^2 - 3}$.

OBJECTIVE
2 Evaluating Algebraic Expressions

In algebra, we use symbols, usually letters such as x, y, or z, to represent unknown numbers. A symbol that is used to represent a number is called a **variable.** An **algebraic expression** is a collection of numbers, variables, operation symbols, and grouping symbols. For example,

$$2x, \quad -3, \quad 2x + 10, \quad 5(p^2 + 1), \quad \text{and} \quad \frac{3y^2 - 6y + 1}{5}$$

are algebraic expressions.

Expression	Meaning
$2x$	$2 \cdot x$
$5(p^2 + 1)$	$5 \cdot (p^2 + 1)$
$3y^2$	$3 \cdot y^2$
xy	$x \cdot y$

If we give a specific value to a variable, we can **evaluate an algebraic expression.** To evaluate an algebraic expression means to find its numerical value once we know the values of the variables.

Algebraic expressions are often used in problem solving. For example, the expression

$$16t^2$$

gives the distance in feet (neglecting air resistance) that an object will fall in t seconds.

EXAMPLE 6   Evaluate each expression if $x = 3$ and $y = 2$.

a. $2x - y$ **b.** $\dfrac{3x}{2y}$ **c.** $\dfrac{x}{y} + \dfrac{y}{2}$ **d.** $x^2 - y^2$

Solution

a. Replace x with 3 and y with 2.

$$\begin{aligned} 2x - y &= 2(3) - 2 \quad \text{Let } x = 3 \text{ and } y = 2. \\ &= 6 - 2 \qquad\quad \text{Multiply.} \\ &= 4 \qquad\qquad \text{Subtract.} \end{aligned}$$

b. $\dfrac{3x}{2y} = \dfrac{3 \cdot 3}{2 \cdot 2} = \dfrac{9}{4}$ Let $x = 3$ and $y = 2$.

c. Replace x with 3 and y with 2. Then simplify.

$$\frac{x}{y} + \frac{y}{2} = \frac{3}{2} + \frac{2}{2} = \frac{5}{2}$$

d. Replace x with 3 and y with 2.

$$x^2 - y^2 = 3^2 - 2^2 = 9 - 4 = 5$$ □

PRACTICE

6   Evaluate each expression if $x = 2$ and $y = 5$.

a. $2x + y$ **b.** $\dfrac{4x}{3y}$ **c.** $\dfrac{3}{x} + \dfrac{x}{y}$ **d.** $x^3 + y^2$

OBJECTIVE

3   Determining Whether a Number Is a Solution of an Equation

Many times, a problem-solving situation is modeled by an equation. An **equation** is a mathematical statement that two expressions have equal value. The equal symbol "=" is used to equate the two expressions. For example,

$$3 + 2 = 5, \quad 7x = 35, \quad \frac{2(x - 1)}{3} = 0, \text{ and } I = PRT \text{ are all equations.}$$

> ▶ Helpful Hint
> An equation contains the equal symbol "=". An algebraic expression does not.

✓**CONCEPT CHECK**

Which of the following are equations? Which are expressions?

a. $5x = 8$ **b.** $5x - 8$ **c.** $12y + 3x$ **d.** $12y = 3x$

When an equation contains a variable, deciding which values of the variable make an equation a true statement is called **solving** an equation for the variable. A **solution** of an equation is a value for the variable that makes the equation true. For example, 3 is a solution of the equation $x + 4 = 7$ because if x is replaced with 3, the statement is true.

$$x + 4 = 7$$
$$\downarrow$$
$$3 + 4 = 7 \quad \text{Replace } x \text{ with 3.}$$
$$7 = 7 \quad \text{True}$$

Similarly, 1 is not a solution of the equation $x + 4 = 7$ because $1 + 4 = 7$ is **not** a true statement.

EXAMPLE 7 Decide whether 2 is a solution of $3x + 10 = 8x$.

Solution Replace x with 2 and see if a true statement results.

$$3x + 10 = 8x \qquad \text{Original equation}$$
$$3(2) + 10 \overset{?}{=} 8(2) \qquad \text{Replace } x \text{ with 2.}$$
$$6 + 10 \overset{?}{=} 16 \qquad \text{Simplify each side.}$$
$$16 = 16 \qquad \text{True}$$

Since we arrived at a true statement after replacing x with 2 and simplifying both sides of the equation, 2 is a solution of the equation. □

PRACTICE
7 Decide whether 4 is a solution of $9x - 6 = 7x$.

OBJECTIVE
4 Translating Phrases to Expressions and Sentences to Statements

Now that we know how to represent an unknown number by a variable, let's practice translating phrases into algebraic expressions and sentences into statements. Oftentimes, solving problems requires the ability to translate word phrases and sentences into symbols. Below is a list of some key words and phrases to help us translate.

> ▶ Helpful Hint
> Order matters when subtracting and dividing, so be especially careful with these translations.

Addition $(+)$	*Subtraction* $(-)$	*Multiplication* $(\cdot)$	*Division* $(\div)$	*Equality* $(=)$
Sum	Difference of	Product	Quotient	Equals
Plus	Minus	Times	Divide	Gives
Added to	Subtracted from	Multiply	Into	Is/was/should be
More than	Less than	Twice	Ratio	Yields
Increased by	Decreased by	Of	Divided by	Amounts to
Total	Less			Represents/ Is the same as

EXAMPLE 8 Write an algebraic expression that represents each phrase. Let the variable x represent the unknown number.

a. The sum of a number and 3
b. The product of 3 and a number
c. Twice a number
d. 10 decreased by a number
e. 5 times a number, increased by 7

Solution

a. $x + 3$ since "sum" means to add
b. $3 \cdot x$ and $3x$ are both ways to denote the product of 3 and x
c. $2 \cdot x$ or $2x$
d. $10 - x$ because "decreased by" means to subtract
e. $\underbrace{5x}_{5 \text{ times a number}} + 7$ □

PRACTICE
8 Write an algebraic expression that represents each phase. Let the variable x represent the unknown number.

a. Six times a number
b. A number decreased by 8
c. The product of a number and 9
d. Two times a number, plus 3
e. The sum of 7 and a number

▶ Helpful Hint

Make sure you understand the difference when translating phrases containing "decreased by," "subtracted from," and "less than."

Phrase	*Translation*
A number decreased by 10	$x - 10$
A number subtracted from 10	$10 - x$
10 less than a number	$x - 10$
A number less 10	$x - 10$

} Notice the order.

Now let's practice translating sentences into equations.

EXAMPLE 9   Write each sentence as an equation or inequality. Let x represent the unknown number.

a. The quotient of 15 and a number is 4.

b. Three subtracted from 12 is a number.

c. Four times a number, added to 17, is not equal to 21.

d. Triple a number is less than 48.

Solution

a. In words: the quotient of 15 and a number   is   4

Translate: $\dfrac{15}{x}$ $=$ 4

b. In words: three subtracted **from** 12   is   a number

Translate: $12 - 3$ $=$ x

Care must be taken when the operation is subtraction. The expression $3 - 12$ would be incorrect. Notice that $3 - 12 \neq 12 - 3$.

c. In words: four times a number   added to   17   is not equal to   21

Translate: $4x$ $+$ 17 $\neq$ 21

d. In words: triple a number   is less than   48

Translate: $3x$ $<$ 48   □

PRACTICE

9   Write each sentence as an equation or inequality. Let x represent the unknown number.

a. A number increased by 7 is equal to 13.

b. Two less than a number is 11.

c. Double a number, added to 9, is not equal to 25.

d. Five times 11 is greater than or equal to an unknown number.

Graphing Calculator Explorations

Exponents

To evaluate exponential expressions on a scientific calculator, find the key marked $\boxed{y^x}$ or $\boxed{\wedge}$. To evaluate, for example, 3^5, press the following keys: $\boxed{3}\,\boxed{y^x}\,\boxed{5}\,\boxed{=}$ or $\boxed{3}\,\boxed{\wedge}\,\boxed{5}\,\boxed{=}$.

↕ or

$\boxed{\text{ENTER}}$

The display should read $\boxed{243}$ or $\boxed{\begin{array}{l}3\wedge5\\ 243\end{array}}$

Order of Operations

Some calculators follow the order of operations, and others do not. To see whether your calculator has the order of operations built in, use your calculator to find $2 + 3 \cdot 4$. To do this, press the following sequence of keys:

$\boxed{2}\,\boxed{+}\,\boxed{3}\,\boxed{\times}\,\boxed{4}\,\boxed{=}$.

↕ or

$\boxed{\text{ENTER}}$

The correct answer is 14 because the order of operations is to multiply before we add. If the calculator displays $\boxed{14}$, then it has the order of operations built in.

Even if the order of operations is built in, parentheses must sometimes be inserted. For example, to simplify $\dfrac{5}{12 - 7}$, press the keys

$\boxed{5}\,\boxed{\div}\,\boxed{(}\,\boxed{1}\,\boxed{2}\,\boxed{-}\,\boxed{7}\,\boxed{)}\,\boxed{=}$.

↕ or

$\boxed{\text{ENTER}}$

The display should read $\boxed{1}$ or $\boxed{\begin{array}{l}5/(12 - 7)\\ 1\end{array}}$

Use a calculator to evaluate each expression.

1. 5^4 **2.** 7^4

3. 9^5 **4.** 8^6

5. $2(20 - 5)$ **6.** $3(14 - 7) + 21$

7. $24(862 - 455) + 89$ **8.** $99 + (401 + 962)$

9. $\dfrac{4623 + 129}{36 - 34}$ **10.** $\dfrac{956 - 452}{89 - 86}$

Vocabulary, Readiness & Video Check

Use the choices below to fill in each blank.

equation   variable   base   grouping

expression   solution   solving   exponent

1. In the expression 5^2, the 5 is called the _____ and the 2 is called the _____.

2. The symbols $(\ )$, $[\ ]$, and $\{\ \}$ are examples of _____ symbols.

3. A symbol that is used to represent a number is called a(n) _____.

4. A collection of numbers, variables, operation symbols, and grouping symbols is called a(n) _____.

5. A mathematical statement that two expressions are equal is called a(n) _____.

6. A value for the variable that makes an equation a true statement is called a(n) _____.

7. Deciding what values of a variable make an equation a true statement is called _____ the equation.

Martin-Gay Interactive Videos

See Video 1.4

Watch the section lecture video and answer the following questions.

OBJECTIVE
1

8. In Example 3 and the lecture before, what is the main point made about the order of operations?

OBJECTIVE
2

9. What happens with the replacement value for z in Example 6 and why?

OBJECTIVE
3

10. Is the value 0 a solution of the equation given in Example 9? How is this determined?

OBJECTIVE
4

11. Earlier in this video the point was made that equations have =, while expressions do not. In the lecture before Example 10, translating from English to math is discussed and another difference between expressions and equations is explained. What is it?

1.4 Exercise Set   MyMathLab®

Evaluate. See Example 1.

1. 3^5

2. 2^5

3. 3^3

4. 4^4

5. 1^5

6. 1^8

7. 5^1

8. 8^1

9. 7^2

10. 9^2

11. $\left(\dfrac{2}{3}\right)^4$

12. $\left(\dfrac{6}{11}\right)^2$

13. $\left(\dfrac{1}{5}\right)^3$

14. $\left(\dfrac{1}{2}\right)^5$

15. $(1.2)^2$

16. $(1.5)^2$

17. $(0.04)^3$

18. $(0.03)^3$

MIXED PRACTICE

Simplify each expression. See Examples 2 through 5.

19. $5 + 6 \cdot 2$

20. $8 + 5 \cdot 3$

21. $4 \cdot 8 - 6 \cdot 2$

22. $12 \cdot 5 - 3 \cdot 6$

23. $2(8 - 3)$

24. $5(6 - 2)$

25. $2 + (5 - 2) + 4^2$

26. $6 - 2 \cdot 2 + 2^5$

27. $5 \cdot 3^2$

28. $2 \cdot 5^2$

29. $\dfrac{1}{4} \cdot \dfrac{2}{3} - \dfrac{1}{6}$

30. $\dfrac{3}{4} \cdot \dfrac{1}{2} + \dfrac{2}{3}$

31. $2[5 + 2(8 - 3)]$

32. $3[4 + 3(6 - 4)]$

33. $\dfrac{19 - 3 \cdot 5}{6 - 4}$

34. $\dfrac{4 \cdot 3 + 2}{4 + 3 \cdot 2}$

35. $\dfrac{|6 - 2| + 3}{8 + 2 \cdot 5}$

36. $\dfrac{15 - |3 - 1|}{12 - 3 \cdot 2}$

37. $\dfrac{3 + 3(5 + 3)}{3^2 + 1}$

38. $\dfrac{3 + 6(8 - 5)}{4^2 + 2}$

39. $\dfrac{6 + |8 - 2| + 3^2}{18 - 3}$

40. $\dfrac{16 + |13 - 5| + 4^2}{17 - 5}$

41. $2 + 3[10(4 \cdot 5 - 16) - 30]$

42. $3 + 4[8(5 \cdot 5 - 20) - 41]$

43. $\left(\dfrac{2}{3}\right)^3 + \dfrac{1}{9} + \dfrac{1}{3} \cdot \dfrac{4}{3}$

44. $\left(\dfrac{3}{8}\right)^2 + \dfrac{1}{4} + \dfrac{1}{8} \cdot \dfrac{3}{2}$

For Exercises 45 and 46, match each expression in the first column with its value in the second column.

45.
a. $(6 + 2) \cdot (5 + 3)$	19
b. $(6 + 2) \cdot 5 + 3$	22
c. $6 + 2 \cdot 5 + 3$	64
d. $6 + 2 \cdot (5 + 3)$	43

46.
a. $(1 + 4) \cdot 6 - 3$	15
b. $1 + 4 \cdot (6 - 3)$	13
c. $1 + 4 \cdot 6 - 3$	27
d. $(1 + 4) \cdot (6 - 3)$	22

*Evaluate each expression when $x = 1$, $y = 3$, and $z = 5$.
See Example 6.*

47. $3y$

48. $4x$

49. $\dfrac{z}{5x}$

50. $\dfrac{y}{2z}$

51. $3x - 2$

52. $6y - 8$

▶ **53.** $|2x + 3y|$

54. $|5z - 2y|$

55. $xy + z$

56. $yz - x$

57. $5y^2$

58. $2z^2$

*Evaluate each expression if $x = 12$, $y = 8$, and $z = 4$.
See Example 6.*

59. $\dfrac{x}{z} + 3y$

60. $\dfrac{y}{z} + 8x$

61. $x^2 - 3y + x$

62. $y^2 - 3x + y$

▶ **63.** $\dfrac{x^2 + z}{y^2 + 2z}$

64. $\dfrac{y^2 + x}{x^2 + 3y}$

Neglecting air resistance, the expression $16t^2$ gives the distance in feet an object will fall in t seconds.

65. Complete the chart below. To evaluate $16t^2$, remember to first find t^2, then multiply by 16.

Time t (in seconds)	Distance $16t^2$ (in feet)
1	
2	
3	
4	

66. Does an object fall the same distance *during* each second? Why or why not? (See Exercise 65.)

Decide whether the given number is a solution of the given equation. See Example 7.

67. Is 5 a solution of $3x + 30 = 9x$?

68. Is 6 a solution of $2x + 7 = 3x$?

69. Is 0 a solution of $2x + 6 = 5x - 1$?

70. Is 2 a solution of $4x + 2 = x + 8$?

71. Is 8 a solution of $2x - 5 = 5$?

▶ **72.** Is 6 a solution of $3x - 10 = 8$?

73. Is 2 a solution of $x + 6 = x + 6$?

74. Is 10 a solution of $x + 6 = x + 6$?

▶ **75.** Is 0 a solution of $x = 5x + 15$?

76. Is 1 a solution of $4 = 1 - x$?

TRANSLATING

Write each phrase as an algebraic expression. Let x represent the unknown number. See Example 8.

77. Fifteen more than a number

78. A number increased by 9

79. Five subtracted from a number

80. Five decreased by a number

81. The ratio of a number and 4

82. The quotient of a number and 9

▶ **83.** Three times a number, increased by 22

84. Twice a number, decreased by 72

TRANSLATING

Write each sentence as an equation or inequality. Use x to represent any unknown number. See Example 9.

▶ **85.** One increased by two equals the quotient of nine and three.

86. Four subtracted from eight is equal to two squared.

▶ **87.** Three is not equal to four divided by two.

88. The difference of sixteen and four is greater than ten.

89. The sum of 5 and a number is 20.

90. Seven subtracted from a number is 0.

91. The product of 7.6 and a number is 17.

92. 9.1 times a number equals 4.

93. Thirteen minus three times a number is 13.

94. Eight added to twice a number is 42.

CONCEPT EXTENSIONS

Fill in each blank with one of the following:
add   subtract   multiply   divide

95. To simplify the expression $1 + 3 \cdot 6$, first _____.

96. To simplify the expression $(1 + 3) \cdot 6$, first _____.

97. To simplify the expression $(20 - 4) \cdot 2$, first _____.

98. To simplify the expression $20 - 4 \div 2$, first _____.

99. Are parentheses necessary in the expression $2 + (3 \cdot 5)$? Explain your answer.

100. Are parentheses necessary in the expression $(2 + 3) \cdot 5$? Explain your answer.

△ *Recall that perimeter measures the distance around a plane figure and area measures the amount of surface of a plane figure. The expression $2l + 2w$ gives the perimeter of the rectangle below (measured in units), and the expression lw gives its area (measured in square units). Complete the chart below for the given lengths and widths. Be sure to include units.*

	Length: l	Width: w	Perimeter of Rectangle: $2l + 2w$	Area of Rectangle: lw
101.	4 in.	3 in.		
102.	6 in.	1 in.		
103.	5.3 in.	1.7 in.		
104.	4.6 in.	2.4 in.		

105. Study the perimeters and areas found in the chart on the previous page. Do you notice any trends?

106. In your own words, explain the difference between an expression and an equation.

107. Insert one set of parentheses so that the following expression simplifies to 32.

$$20 - 4 \cdot 4 \div 2$$

108. Insert one set of parentheses so that the following expression simplifies to 28.

$$2 \cdot 5 + 3^2$$

Determine whether each is an expression or an equation. See the Concept Check in this section.

109. **a.** $5x + 6$
b. $2a = 7$
c. $3a + 2 = 9$
d. $4x + 3y - 8z$
e. $5^2 - 2(6 - 2)$

110. **a.** $3x^2 - 26$
b. $3x^2 - 26 = 1$
c. $2x - 5 = 7x - 5$
d. $9y + x - 8$
e. $3^2 - 4(5 - 3)$

111. Why is 4^3 usually read as "four cubed"? (*Hint:* What is the volume of the **cube** below?)

4 cm

112. Why is 8^2 usually read as "eight squared"? (*Hint:* What is the area of the **square** below?)

8 inches

113. Write any expression, using 3 or more numbers, that simplifies to -11.

114. Write any expression, using 4 or more numbers, that simplifies to 7.

115. The area of a figure is the total enclosed surface of the figure. Area is measured in square units. The expression lw represents the area of a rectangle when l is its length and w is its width. Find the area of the following rectangular-shaped lot.

100 feet

120 feet

116. A trapezoid is a four-sided figure with exactly one pair of parallel sides. The expression $\frac{1}{2}h(B + b)$ represents its area, when B and b are the lengths of the two parallel sides and h is the height between these sides. Find the area if $B = 15$ inches, $b = 7$ inches, and $h = 5$ inches.

7 inches

5 inches

15 inches

117. The expression $\dfrac{d}{t}$ represents the average speed in miles per hour if a distance of d miles is traveled in t hours. Find the speed to the nearest whole number if the distance between Dallas, Texas, and Kaw City, Oklahoma, is 432 miles, and it takes Peter Callac 8.5 hours to drive the distance.

118. The expression $\dfrac{I}{PT}$ represents the rate of interest being charged if a loan of P dollars for T years required I dollars in interest to be paid. Find the interest rate if a $650 loan for 3 years to buy a used IBM personal computer requires $126.75 in interest to be paid.

1.5   Adding Real Numbers

OBJECTIVES

1 Add Real Numbers.

2 Solve Applications That Involve Addition of Real Numbers.

3 Find the Opposite of a Number.

OBJECTIVE
1   Adding Real Numbers

Real numbers can be added, subtracted, multiplied, divided, and raised to powers, just as whole numbers can. We use a number line to help picture the addition of real numbers. We begin by adding numbers with the same sign.

EXAMPLE 1   Add: $3 + 2$

Solution   Recall that 3 and 2 are called **addends.** We start at 0 on a number line and draw an arrow representing the addend 3. This arrow is three units long and points to the right since 3 is positive. From the tip of this arrow, we draw another arrow, representing the addend 2. The number below the tip of this arrow is the sum, 5.

$$3 + 2 = 5$$ □

PRACTICE

1 Add using a number line: $2 + 4$.

EXAMPLE 2 Add: $-1 + (-2)$

Solution Here, -1 and -2 are addends. We start at 0 on a number line and draw an arrow representing -1. This arrow is one unit long and points to the left since -1 is negative. From the tip of this arrow, we draw another arrow, representing -2. The number below the tip of this arrow is the sum, -3.

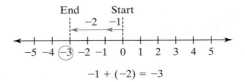

$$-1 + (-2) = -3$$ □

PRACTICE

2 Add using a number line: $-2 + (-3)$.

Thinking of signed numbers as money earned or lost might help make addition more meaningful. Earnings can be thought of as positive numbers. If \$1 is earned and later another \$3 is earned, the total amount earned is \$4. In other words, $1 + 3 = 4$.

On the other hand, losses can be thought of as negative numbers. If \$1 is lost and later another \$3 is lost, a total of \$4 is lost. In other words,

$$(-1) + (-3) = -4.$$

Using a number line each time we add two numbers can be time consuming. Instead, we can notice patterns in the previous examples and write rules for adding signed numbers. When adding two numbers with the same sign, notice that the sign of the sum is the same as the sign of the addends.

> **Adding Two Numbers with the Same Sign**
> Add their absolute values. Use their common sign as the sign of the sum.

EXAMPLE 3 Add.

a. $-3 + (-7)$ **b.** $-1 + (-20)$ **c.** $-2 + (-10)$

Solution Notice that each time, we are adding numbers with the same sign.

a. $-3 + (-7) = -10$ ⟵ Add their absolute values: $3 + 7 = 10$.
⟵ Use their common sign.

b. $-1 + (-20) = -21$ ⟵ Add their absolute values: $1 + 20 = 21$.
⟵ Common sign.

c. $-2 + (-10) = -12$ ⟵ Add their absolute values.
⟵ Common sign. □

PRACTICE

3 Add. **a.** $-5 + (-8)$ **b.** $-31 + (-1)$

Adding numbers whose signs are not the same can also be pictured on a number line.

EXAMPLE 4   Add: $-4 + 6$

Solution

$$-4 + 6 = 2$$

☐

PRACTICE
4   Add using a number line: $-3 + 8$.

Using temperature as an example, if the thermometer registers 4 degrees below 0 degrees and then rises 6 degrees, the new temperature is 2 degrees above 0 degrees. Thus, it is reasonable that $-4 + 6 = 2$.

Once again, we can observe a pattern: when adding two numbers with different signs, the sign of the sum is the same as the sign of the addend whose absolute value is larger.

Adding Two Numbers with Different Signs

Subtract the smaller absolute value from the larger absolute value. Use the sign of the number whose absolute value is larger as the sign of the sum.

EXAMPLE 5   Add.

a. $3 + (-7)$ **b.** $-2 + 10$ **c.** $0.2 + (-0.5)$

Solution   Notice that each time, we are adding numbers with different signs.

a. $3 + (-7) = -4$ ⟵ Subtract their absolute values: $7 - 3 = 4$.
                The negative number, -7, has the larger absolute value so the sum is negative.

b. $-2 + 10 = 8$ ⟵ Subtract their absolute values: $10 - 2 = 8$.
                The positive number, 10, has the larger absolute value so the sum is positive.

c. $0.2 + (-0.5) = -0.3$ ⟵ Subtract their absolute values: $0.5 - 0.2 = 0.3$.
                The negative number, -0.5, has the larger absolute value so the sum is negative.

☐

PRACTICE
5   Add.

a. $15 + (-18)$ **b.** $-19 + 20$ **c.** $-0.6 + 0.4$

In general, we have the following:

Adding Real Numbers

To add two real numbers

1. with the *same sign*, add their absolute values. Use their common sign as the sign of the answer.

2. with *different signs*, subtract their absolute values. Give the answer the same sign as the number with the larger absolute value.

EXAMPLE 6 Add.

a. $-8 + (-11)$ **b.** $-5 + 35$ **c.** $0.6 + (-1.1)$

d. $-\dfrac{7}{10} + \left(-\dfrac{1}{10}\right)$ **e.** $11.4 + (-4.7)$ **f.** $-\dfrac{3}{8} + \dfrac{2}{5}$

Solution

a. $-8 + (-11) = -19$ Same sign. Add absolute values and use the common sign.

b. $-5 + 35 = 30$ Different signs. Subtract absolute values and use the sign of the number with the larger absolute value.

c. $0.6 + (-1.1) = -0.5$ Different signs.

d. $-\dfrac{7}{10} + \left(-\dfrac{1}{10}\right) = -\dfrac{8}{10} = -\dfrac{4}{5}$ Same sign.

e. $11.4 + (-4.7) = 6.7$

f. $-\dfrac{3}{8} + \dfrac{2}{5} = -\dfrac{15}{40} + \dfrac{16}{40} = \dfrac{1}{40}$ □

> ▶ **Helpful Hint**
> Don't forget that a common denominator is needed when adding or subtracting fractions. The common denominator here is 40.

PRACTICE
6   Add.

a. $-\dfrac{3}{5} + \left(-\dfrac{2}{5}\right)$ **b.** $3 + (-9)$

c. $2.2 + (-1.7)$ **d.** $-\dfrac{2}{7} + \dfrac{3}{10}$

EXAMPLE 7 Add.

a. $3 + (-7) + (-8)$ **b.** $[7 + (-10)] + [-2 + |-4|]$

Solution

a. Perform the additions from left to right.

$$3 + (-7) + (-8) = -4 + (-8) \quad \text{Adding numbers with different signs.}$$
$$= -12 \quad \text{Adding numbers with like signs.}$$

b. Simplify inside brackets first.

> ▶ **Helpful Hint**
> Don't forget that brackets are grouping symbols. We simplify within them first.

$$[7 + (-10)] + [-2 + |-4|] = [-3] + [-2 + 4]$$
$$= [-3] + [2]$$
$$= -1 \quad \text{Add.} \quad □$$

PRACTICE
7   Add.

a. $8 + (-5) + (-9)$ **b.** $[-8 + 5] + [-5 + |-2|]$

✓**CONCEPT CHECK**
What is wrong with the following calculation?
$5 + (\cancel{-22}) = 17$

OBJECTIVE
2   Solving Applications by Adding Real Numbers

Positive and negative numbers are often used in everyday life. Stock market returns show gains and losses as positive and negative numbers. Temperatures in cold climates often dip into the negative range, commonly referred to as "below zero" temperatures. Bank statements report deposits and withdrawals as positive and negative numbers.

EXAMPLE 8   **Calculating Temperature**

In Philadelphia, Pennsylvania, the record extreme high temperature is 104°F. Decrease this temperature by 111 degrees, and the result is the record extreme low temperature. Find this temperature. (*Source:* National Climatic Data Center)

Solution:

In words:

| extreme low temperature | = | extreme high temperature | + | decrease of 111° |

Translate:

| extreme low temperature | = | 104 | + | (−111) |

$$= -7$$

The record extreme low temperature in Philadelphia, Pennsylvania, is −7°F.   ☐

PRACTICE

8   If the temperature was −7° Fahrenheit at 6 a.m., and it rose 4 degrees by 7 a.m. and then rose another 7 degrees in the hour from 7 a.m. to 8 a.m., what was the temperature at 8 a.m.?

OBJECTIVE

3   **Finding the Opposite of a Number**

To help us subtract real numbers in the next section, we first review the concept of opposites. The graphs of 4 and −4 are shown on a number line below.

```
      4 units      4 units
  |<---------->|<---------->|
<--+--●--+--+--+--+--+--+--+--●--+-->
  -5 -4 -3 -2 -1  0  1  2  3  4  5
```

Notice that 4 and −4 lie on opposite sides of 0, and each is 4 units away from 0.

This relationship between −4 and +4 is an important one. Such numbers are known as **opposites** or **additive inverses** of each other.

Opposites or Additive Inverses

Two numbers that are the same distance from 0 but lie on opposite sides of 0 are called **opposites** or **additive inverses** of each other.

EXAMPLE 9   Find the opposite or additive inverse of each number.

a. 5   **b.** −6   **c.** $\dfrac{1}{2}$ **d.** −4.5

Solution

a. The opposite of 5 is −5. Notice that 5 and −5 are on opposite sides of 0 when plotted on a number line and are equal distances away.

b. The opposite of −6 is 6.

c. The opposite of $\dfrac{1}{2}$ is $-\dfrac{1}{2}$.

d. The opposite of −4.5 is 4.5.   ☐

PRACTICE

9   Find the opposite or additive inverse of each number.

a. $-\dfrac{5}{9}$ **b.** 8   **c.** 6.2   **d.** −3

We use the symbol "−" to represent the phrase "the opposite of" or "the additive inverse of." In general, if a is a number, we write the opposite or additive inverse of a as $-a$. We know that the opposite of -3 is 3. Notice that this translates as

the opposite of -3 is 3

$$-\quad\quad (-3)\quad =\quad 3$$

This is true in general.

If a is a number, then $-(-a) = a$.

EXAMPLE 10 Simplify each expression.

a. $-(-10)$ **b.** $-\left(-\dfrac{1}{2}\right)$ **c.** $-(-2x)$ **d.** $-|-6|$

Solution

a. $-(-10) = 10$ **b.** $-\left(-\dfrac{1}{2}\right) = \dfrac{1}{2}$ **c.** $-(-2x) = 2x$

d. Since $|-6| = 6$, then $-|-6| = -6$.

PRACTICE
10 Simplify each expression.

a. $-|-15|$ **b.** $-\left(-\dfrac{3}{5}\right)$ **c.** $-(-5y)$ **d.** $-(-8)$

Let's discover another characteristic about opposites. Notice that the sum of a number and its opposite is 0.

$$10 + (-10) = 0$$
$$-3 + 3 = 0$$
$$\frac{1}{2} + \left(-\frac{1}{2}\right) = 0$$

In general, we can write the following:

The sum of a number a and its opposite $-a$ is 0.
$$a + (-a) = 0$$

This is why opposites are also called additive inverses. Notice that this also means that the opposite of 0 is then 0 since $0 + 0 = 0$.

Vocabulary, Readiness & Video Check

Use the choices below to fill in each blank.

a positive number n opposites
a negative number 0 $-n$

1. Two numbers that are the same distance from 0 but lie on opposite sides of 0 are called _____.
2. If n is a number, then $n + (-n) =$ _____.
3. If n is a number, then $-(-n) =$ _____.
4. The sum of two negative numbers is always _____.

Martin-Gay Interactive Videos

See Video 1.5

Watch the section lecture video and answer the following questions.

OBJECTIVE 1
5. Complete this statement based on the lecture given before ▣ Example 1. To add two numbers with the same sign, add their _____ and use their common sign as the sign of the sum.

OBJECTIVE 1
6. What is the sign of the sum in ▣ Example 6 and why?

OBJECTIVE 2
7. What is the real life application of negative numbers used in ▣ Example 9? The answer to ▣ Example 9 is −6. What does this number mean in the context of the problem?

OBJECTIVE 3
8. ▣ Example 12 illustrates the idea that if *a* is a real number, the opposite of −*a* is *a*. ▣ Example 13 looks similar to ▣ Example 12, but it's actually quite different. Explain the difference.

1.5 Exercise Set

MyMathLab®

MIXED PRACTICE

Add. See Examples 1 through 7.

1. 6 + 3
2. 9 + (−12)
3. −6 + (−8)
4. −6 + (−14)
5. 8 + (−7)
6. 6 + (−4)
7. −14 + 2
8. −10 + 5
9. −2 + (−3)
10. −7 + (−4)
11. −9 + (−3)
12. 7 + (−5)
13. −7 + 3
14. −5 + 9
15. 10 + (−3)
16. 8 + (−6)
17. 5 + (−7)
18. 3 + (−6)
19. −16 + 16
20. 23 + (−23)
21. 27 + (−46)
22. 53 + (−37)
23. −18 + 49
24. −26 + 14
25. −33 + (−14)
26. −18 + (−26)
27. 6.3 + (−8.4)
28. 9.2 + (−11.4)
29. $|-8| + (-16)$
30. $|-6| + (-61)$
31. 117 + (−79)
32. 144 + (−88)
33. −9.6 + (−3.5)
34. −6.7 + (−7.6)
35. $-\dfrac{3}{8} + \dfrac{5}{8}$
36. $-\dfrac{5}{12} + \dfrac{7}{12}$
37. $-\dfrac{7}{16} + \dfrac{1}{4}$
38. $-\dfrac{5}{9} + \dfrac{1}{3}$
39. $-\dfrac{7}{10} + \left(-\dfrac{3}{5}\right)$
40. $-\dfrac{5}{6} + \left(-\dfrac{2}{3}\right)$
41. −15 + 9 + (−2)
42. −9 + 15 + (−5)
43. −21 + (−16) + (−22)
44. −18 + (−6) + (−40)
45. −23 + 16 + (−2)
46. −14 + (−3) + 11
47. $|5 + (-10)|$
48. $|7 + (-17)|$
49. 6 + (−4) + 9
50. 8 + (−2) + 7
51. [−17 + (−4)] + [−12 + 15]
52. [−2 + (−7)] + [−11 + 22]
53. $|9 + (-12)| + |-16|$

54. $|43 + (-73)| + |-20|$
55. −1.3 + [0.5 + (−0.3) + 0.4]
56. −3.7 + [0.1 + (−0.6) + 8.1]

Solve. See Example 8.

57. The low temperature in Anoka, Minnesota, was −15° last night. During the day, it rose only 9°. Find the high temperature for the day.

58. On January 2, 1943, the temperature was −4° at 7:30 a.m. in Spearfish, South Dakota. Incredibly, it got 49° warmer in the next 2 minutes. To what temperature did it rise by 7:32?

59. The lowest point in Africa is −512 feet at Lake Assal in Djibouti. If you are standing at a point 658 feet above Lake Assal, what is your elevation? (*Source:* Microsoft Encarta)

60. The lowest elevation in Australia is −52 feet at Lake Eyre. If you are standing at a point 439 feet above Lake Eyre, what is your elevation? (*Source:* National Geographic Society)

A negative net income results when a company spends more money than it brings in.

61. Johnson Outdoors Inc. had the following quarterly net incomes during its 2009 fiscal year. (Data from Yahoo Finance)

Quarter of Fiscal 2009	Net Income (in millions)
First	2.5
Second	9
Third	−14.2
Fourth	−4.2

What was the total net income for fiscal year 2009?

62. LeapFrog Enterprises Inc. had the following quarterly net incomes during its 2009 fiscal year. (Data from Yahoo Finance)

Quarter of Fiscal 2009	Net Income (in millions)
First	−27.1
Second	−12.2
Third	7.2
Fourth	29.4

What was the total net income for fiscal year 2009?

In golf, scores that are under par for the entire round are shown as negative scores; positive scores are shown for scores that are over par, and 0 is par.

63. Sandra Gal was the winner of the 2011 LPGA Kia Classic in California. Her scores were −6, −5, −3, and −2. What was her overall score? (*Source:* Ladies Professional Golf Association)

64. During the 2011 PGA Waste Management Phoenix Open, Mark Wilson won with scores of −6, −7, −3, and −2. What was his overall score? (*Source:* Professional Golf Association)

Find each additive inverse or opposite. See Example 9.

65. 6　　　　**66.** 4　　　　**67.** −2

68. −8　　　　**69.** 0　　　　**70.** $-\dfrac{1}{4}$

71. $|-6|$　　　　**72.** $|-11|$

Simplify each of the following. See Example 10.

73. $-|-2|$　　　**74.** $-(-3)$　　　**75.** $-|0|$

76. $\left|-\dfrac{2}{3}\right|$　　　**77.** $-\left|-\dfrac{2}{3}\right|$　　　**78.** $-(-7)$

Decide whether the given number is a solution of the given equation.

79. Is −4 a solution of $x + 9 = 5$?

80. Is 10 a solution of $7 = -x + 3$?

81. Is −1 a solution of $y + (-3) = -7$?

82. Is −6 a solution of $1 = y + 7$?

CONCEPT EXTENSIONS

The following bar graph shows each month's average daily low temperature in degrees Fahrenheit for Barrow, Alaska. Use this graph to answer Exercises 83 through 88.

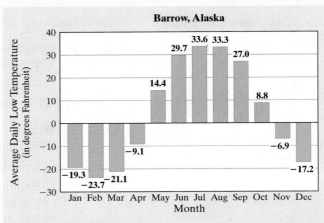

Data from National Climatic Data Center

83. For what month is the graphed temperature the highest?

84. For what month is the graphed temperature the lowest?

85. For what month is the graphed temperature positive *and* closest to 0°?

86. For what month is the graphed temperature negative *and* closest to 0°?

87. Find the average of the temperatures shown for the months of April, May, and October. (To find the average of three temperatures, find their sum and divide by 3.)

88. Find the average of the temperatures shown for the months of January, September, and October.

Each calculation below is incorrect. Find the error and correct it. See the Concept Check in this section.

89. $7 + (-10) \overset{?}{=} 17$　　　　**90.** $-4 + 14 \overset{?}{=} -18$

91. $-10 + (-12) \overset{?}{=} -120$　　　**92.** $-15 + (-17) \overset{?}{=} 32$

If a is a positive number and b is a negative number, fill in the blanks with the words positive or negative.

93. $-a$ is _____.　　　　**94.** $-b$ is _____.

95. $a + a$ is _____.　　　　**96.** $b + b$ is _____.

For Exercises 97 through 100, determine whether each statement is true or false.

97. The sum of two negative numbers is always a negative number.

98. The sum of two positive numbers is always a positive number.

99. The sum of a positive number and a negative number is always a negative number.

100. The sum of zero and a negative number is always a negative number.

101. In your own words, explain how to find the opposite of a number.

102. In your own words, explain why 0 is the only number that is its own opposite.

103. Explain why adding a negative number to another negative number always gives a negative sum.

104. When a positive and a negative number are added, sometimes the sum is positive, sometimes it is zero, and sometimes it is negative. Explain why and when this happens.

1.6 | Subtracting Real Numbers

OBJECTIVES

1 Subtract Real Numbers.

2 Add and Subtract Real Numbers.

3 Evaluate Algebraic Expressions Using Real Numbers.

4 Solve Applications That Involve Subtraction of Real Numbers.

5 Find Complementary and Supplementary Angles.

OBJECTIVE

1   Subtracting Real Numbers

Now that addition of signed numbers has been discussed, we can explore subtraction. We know that $9 - 7 = 2$. Notice that $9 + (-7) = 2$ also. This means that

$$9 - 7 = 9 + (-7)$$

Notice that the difference of 9 and 7 is the same as the sum of 9 and the opposite of 7. In general, we have the following.

> **Subtracting Two Real Numbers**
>
> If a and b are real numbers, then $a - b = a + (-b)$.

In other words, to find the difference of two numbers, add the first number to the opposite of the second number.

EXAMPLE 1   Subtract.

a. $-13 - 4$ **b.** $5 - (-6)$ **c.** $3 - 6$ **d.** $-1 - (-7)$

Solution

a. $-13 - 4 = -13 + (-4)$ Add -13 to the opposite of $+4$, which is -4.

$$= -17$$

b. $5 - (-6) = 5 + (6)$ Add 5 to the opposite of -6, which is 6.

$$= 11$$

c. $3 - 6 = 3 + (-6)$ Add 3 to the opposite of 6, which is -6.

$$= -3$$

d. $-1 - (-7) = -1 + (7) = 6$

PRACTICE

1   Subtract.

a. $-7 - 6$ **b.** $-8 - (-1)$ **c.** $9 - (-3)$ **d.** $5 - 7$

> ▶ **Helpful Hint**
>
> Study the patterns indicated.
>
>
>
> No change ——— Change to addition.
> ——— Change to opposite.
>
> $$5 - 11 = 5 + (-11) = -6$$
> $$-3 - 4 = -3 + (-4) = -7$$
> $$7 - (-1) = 7 + (1) = 8$$

EXAMPLE 2 Subtract.

a. $5.3 - (-4.6)$ **b.** $-\dfrac{3}{10} - \dfrac{5}{10}$ **c.** $-\dfrac{2}{3} - \left(-\dfrac{4}{5}\right)$

Solution

a. $5.3 - (-4.6) = 5.3 + (4.6) = 9.9$

b. $-\dfrac{3}{10} - \dfrac{5}{10} = -\dfrac{3}{10} + \left(-\dfrac{5}{10}\right) = -\dfrac{8}{10} = -\dfrac{4}{5}$

c. $-\dfrac{2}{3} - \left(-\dfrac{4}{5}\right) = -\dfrac{2}{3} + \left(\dfrac{4}{5}\right) = -\dfrac{10}{15} + \dfrac{12}{15} = \dfrac{2}{15}$ The common denominator is 15. ☐

PRACTICE
2 Subtract.

a. $8.4 - (-2.5)$ **b.** $-\dfrac{5}{8} - \left(-\dfrac{1}{8}\right)$ **c.** $-\dfrac{3}{4} - \dfrac{1}{5}$

EXAMPLE 3 Subtract 8 from -4.

Solution Be careful when interpreting this: The order of numbers in subtraction is important. 8 is to be subtracted **from** -4.

$$-4 - 8 = -4 + (-8) = -12 \qquad ☐$$

PRACTICE
3 Subtract 5 from -2.

OBJECTIVE
2 Adding and Subtracting Real Numbers

If an expression contains additions and subtractions, just write the subtractions as equivalent additions. Then simplify from left to right.

EXAMPLE 4 Simplify each expression.

a. $-14 - 8 + 10 - (-6)$ **b.** $1.6 - (-10.3) + (-5.6)$

Solution

a. $-14 - 8 + 10 - (-6) = -14 + (-8) + 10 + 6$
$$= -6$$

b. $1.6 - (-10.3) + (-5.6) = 1.6 + 10.3 + (-5.6)$
$$= 6.3 \qquad ☐$$

PRACTICE
4 Simplify each expression.

a. $-15 - 2 - (-4) + 7$ **b.** $3.5 + (-4.1) - (-6.7)$

When an expression contains parentheses and brackets, remember the order of operations. Start with the innermost set of parentheses or brackets and work your way outward.

EXAMPLE 5   Simplify each expression.

a. $-3 + [(-2 - 5) - 2]$ **b.** $2^3 - |10| + [-6 - (-5)]$

Solution

a. Start with the innermost sets of parentheses. Rewrite $-2 - 5$ as a sum.

$$
\begin{aligned}
-3 + [(-2 - 5) - 2] &= -3 + [(-2 + (-5)) - 2] \\
&= -3 + [(-7) - 2] &&\text{Add: } -2 + (-5). \\
&= -3 + [-7 + (-2)] &&\text{Write } -7 - 2 \text{ as a sum.} \\
&= -3 + [-9] &&\text{Add.} \\
&= -12 &&\text{Add.}
\end{aligned}
$$

b. Start simplifying the expression inside the brackets by writing $-6 - (-5)$ as a sum.

$$
\begin{aligned}
2^3 - |10| + [-6 - (-5)] &= 2^3 - |10| + [-6 + 5] \\
&= 2^3 - |10| + [-1] &&\text{Add.} \\
&= 8 - 10 + (-1) &&\text{Evaluate } 2^3 \text{ and } |10|. \\
&= 8 + (-10) + (-1) &&\text{Write } 8 - 10 \text{ as a sum.} \\
&= -2 + (-1) &&\text{Add.} \\
&= -3 &&\text{Add.} \quad \square
\end{aligned}
$$

PRACTICE
5   Simplify each expression.

a. $-4 + [(-8 - 3) - 5]$ **b.** $|-13| - 3^2 + [2 - (-7)]$

OBJECTIVE
3   Evaluating Algebraic Expressions

Knowing how to evaluate expressions for given replacement values is helpful when checking solutions of equations and when solving problems whose unknowns satisfy given expressions. The next example illustrates this.

EXAMPLE 6   Find the value of each expression when $x = 2$ and $y = -5$.

a. $\dfrac{x - y}{12 + x}$ **b.** $x^2 - 3y$

Solution

a. Replace x with 2 and y with -5. Be sure to put parentheses around -5 to separate signs. Then simplify the resulting expression.

$$
\begin{aligned}
\frac{x - y}{12 + x} &= \frac{2 - (-5)}{12 + 2} \\
&= \frac{2 + 5}{14} \\
&= \frac{7}{14} = \frac{1}{2}
\end{aligned}
$$

b. Replace x with 2 and y with -5 and simplify.

$$
\begin{aligned}
x^2 - 3y &= 2^2 - 3(-5) \\
&= 4 - 3(-5) \\
&= 4 - (-15) \\
&= 4 + 15 \\
&= 19 \quad \square
\end{aligned}
$$

PRACTICE
6   Find the value of each expression when $x = -3$ and $y = 4$.

a. $\dfrac{7 - x}{2y + x}$ **b.** $y^2 + x$

> ▶ Helpful Hint
>
> For additional help when replacing variables with replacement values, first place parentheses around any variables.
>   For Example 6b on the previous page, we have
>
> $$x^2 - 3y = \underbrace{(x)^2 - 3(y)}_{\substack{\text{Place parentheses} \\ \text{around variables}}} = \underbrace{(2)^2 - 3(-5)}_{\substack{\text{Replace variables} \\ \text{with values}}} = 4 - 3(-5) = 4 - (-15) = 4 + 15 = 19$$

OBJECTIVE
4   Solving Applications by Subtracting Real Numbers

One use of positive and negative numbers is in recording altitudes above and below sea level, as shown in the next example.

EXAMPLE 7   **Finding a Change in Elevation**

The highest point in the United States is the top of Mount McKinley, at a height of 20,320 feet above sea level. The lowest point is Death Valley, California, which is 282 feet below sea level. How much higher is Mount McKinley than Death Valley? (*Source:* U.S. Geological Survey)

Solution: To find "how much higher," we subtract. Don't forget that since Death Valley is 282 feet *below* sea level, we represent its height by -282. Draw a diagram to help visualize the problem.

In words: | how much higher is Mt. McKinley | $=$ | height of Mt. McKinley | minus | height of Death Valley
Translate: | how much higher is Mt. McKinley | $=$ | 20,320 | $-$ | (-282)

$$= 20{,}320 + 282$$
$$= 20{,}602$$

Thus, Mount McKinley is 20,602 feet higher than Death Valley.   □

PRACTICE
7   On Tuesday morning, a bank account balance was $282. On Thursday, the account balance had dropped to $-\$75$. Find the overall change in this account balance.

OBJECTIVE

5 Finding Complementary and Supplementary Angles

A knowledge of geometric concepts is needed by many professionals, such as doctors, carpenters, electronic technicians, gardeners, machinists, and pilots, just to name a few. With this in mind, we review the geometric concepts of **complementary** and **supplementary angles.**

Complementary and Supplementary Angles

Two angles are **complementary** if their sum is 90°.

$$x + y = 90°$$

Two angles are **supplementary** if their sum is 180°.

$$x + y = 180°$$

EXAMPLE 8   Find each unknown complementary or supplementary angle.

a.

b.

Solution

a. These angles are complementary, so their sum is 90°. This means that x is 90° − 38°.

$$x = 90° − 38° = 52°$$

b. These angles are supplementary, so their sum is 180°. This means that y is 180° − 62°.

$$y = 180° − 62° = 118°$$ □

PRACTICE

8   Find each unknown complementary or supplementary angle.

a.

b.

···

Vocabulary, Readiness & Video Check

Translate each phrase. Let x represent "a number." Use the choices below to fill in each blank.

$$7 − x \qquad x − 7$$

1. 7 minus a number _____

2. 7 subtracted from a number _____

3. A number decreased by 7 _____

4. 7 less a number _____

5. A number less than 7 _____

6. A number subtracted from 7 _____

Multiple choice: Select the correct lettered response following each exercise.

7. To evaluate $x - y$ for $x = -10$ and $y = -14$, we replace x with -10 and y with -14 and evaluate _____.

   a. $10 - 14$ **b.** $-10 - 14$ **c.** $-14 - 10$ **d.** $-10 - (-14)$

8. The expression $-5 - 10$ equals _____.

   a. $5 - 10$ **b.** $5 + 10$ **c.** $-5 + (-10)$ **d.** $10 - 5$

Martin-Gay Interactive Videos

See Video 1.6

Watch the section lecture video and answer the following questions.

OBJECTIVE 1

9. Complete this statement based on the lecture given before Example 1. To subtract two real numbers, change the operation to _____ and take the _____ of the second number.

OBJECTIVE 2

10. When simplifying Example 5, what is the result of the first step and why is the expression rewritten in this way?

OBJECTIVE 3

11. In Example 7, why are you told to be especially careful when working with the replacement value in the numerator?

OBJECTIVE 4

12. For Example 8, why is the overall vertical change represented as a negative number?

OBJECTIVE 5

13. The definition of supplementary angles is given just before Example 9. Explain how this definition is used to solve Example 9.

1.6 Exercise Set

MyMathLab®

MIXED PRACTICE

Subtract. See Examples 1 and 2.

1. $-6 - 4$
2. $-12 - 8$
3. $4 - 9$
4. $8 - 11$
5. $16 - (-3)$
6. $12 - (-5)$
7. $\dfrac{1}{2} - \dfrac{1}{3}$
8. $\dfrac{3}{4} - \dfrac{7}{8}$
9. $-16 - (-18)$
10. $-20 - (-48)$
11. $-6 - 5$
12. $-8 - 4$
13. $7 - (-4)$
14. $3 - (-6)$
15. $-6 - (-11)$
16. $-4 - (-16)$
17. $16 - (-21)$
18. $15 - (-33)$
19. $9.7 - 16.1$
20. $8.3 - 11.2$
21. $-44 - 27$
22. $-36 - 51$
23. $-21 - (-21)$
24. $-17 - (-17)$
25. $-2.6 - (-6.7)$
26. $-6.1 - (-5.3)$
27. $-\dfrac{3}{11} - \left(-\dfrac{5}{11}\right)$
28. $-\dfrac{4}{7} - \left(-\dfrac{1}{7}\right)$
29. $-\dfrac{1}{6} - \dfrac{3}{4}$
30. $-\dfrac{1}{10} - \dfrac{7}{8}$
31. $8.3 - (-0.62)$
32. $4.3 - (-0.87)$

TRANSLATING

Translate each phrase to an expression and simplify. See Example 3.

33. Subtract -5 from 8.
34. Subtract 3 from -2.
35. Subtract -1 from -6.
36. Subtract 17 from 1.
37. Subtract 8 from 7.
38. Subtract 9 from -4.
39. Decrease -8 by 15.
40. Decrease 11 by -14.

Simplify each expression. (Remember the order of operations.) See Examples 4 and 5.

41. $-10 - (-8) + (-4) - 20$
42. $-16 - (-3) + (-11) - 14$
43. $5 - 9 + (-4) - 8 - 8$
44. $7 - 12 + (-5) - 2 + (-2)$
45. $-6 - (2 - 11)$
46. $-9 - (3 - 8)$
47. $3^3 - 8 \cdot 9$
48. $2^3 - 6 \cdot 3$
49. $2 - 3(8 - 6)$
50. $4 - 6(7 - 3)$
51. $(3 - 6) + 4^2$
52. $(2 - 3) + 5^2$
53. $-2 + [(8 - 11) - (-2 - 9)]$
54. $-5 + [(4 - 15) - (-6) - 8]$
55. $|-3| + 2^2 + [-4 - (-6)]$
56. $|-2| + 6^2 + (-3 - 8)$

Evaluate each expression when x = −5, y = 4, and t = 10. See Example 6.

57. $x - y$

58. $y - x$

59. $|x| + 2t - 8y$

60. $|x + t - 7y|$

61. $\dfrac{9 - x}{y + 6}$

62. $\dfrac{15 - x}{y + 2}$

63. $y^2 - x$

64. $t^2 - x$

65. $\dfrac{|x - (-10)|}{2t}$

66. $\dfrac{|5y - x|}{6t}$

Solve. See Example 7.

67. Within 24 hours in 1916, the temperature in Browning, Montana, fell from 44°F to −56°F. How large a drop in temperature was this?

68. Much of New Orleans is below sea level. If George descends 12 feet from an elevation of 5 feet above sea level, what is his new elevation?

69. The coldest temperature ever recorded on Earth was −129°F in Antarctica. The warmest temperature ever recorded was 136°F in the Sahara Desert. How many degrees warmer is 136°F than −129°F? (*Source: Questions Kids Ask,* Grolier Limited, 1991, and *The World Almanac*)

70. The coldest temperature ever recorded in the United States was −80°F in Alaska. The warmest temperature ever recorded was 134°F in California. How many degrees warmer is 134°F than −80°F? (*Source: The World Almanac*)

71. Mauna Kea in Hawaii has an elevation of 13,796 feet above sea level. The Mid-America Trench in the Pacific Ocean has an elevation of 21,857 feet below sea level. Find the difference in elevation between those two points. (*Source:* National Geographic Society and Defense Mapping Agency)

72. A woman received a statement of her charge account at Old Navy. She spent $93 on purchases last month. She returned an $18 top because she didn't like the color. She also returned a $26 nightshirt because it was damaged. What does she actually owe on her account?

73. A commercial jetliner hits an air pocket and drops 250 feet. After climbing 120 feet, it drops another 178 feet. What is its overall vertical change?

74. In some card games, it is possible to have a negative score. Lavonne Schultz currently has a score of 15 points. She then loses 24 points. What is her new score?

75. The highest point in Africa is Mt. Kilimanjaro, Tanzania, at an elevation of 19,340 feet. The lowest point is Lake Assal, Djibouti, at 512 feet below sea level. How much higher is Mt. Kilimanjaro than Lake Assal? (*Source:* National Geographic Society)

76. The airport in Bishop, California, is at an elevation of 4101 feet above sea level. The nearby Furnace Creek Airport in Death Valley, California, is at an elevation of 226 feet below sea level. How much higher in elevation is the Bishop Airport than the Furnace Creek Airport? (*Source:* National Climatic Data Center)

Find each unknown complementary or supplementary angle. See Example 8.

77.

78.

79.

80.

Decide whether the given number is a solution of the given equation.

81. Is −4 a solution of $x - 9 = 5$?

82. Is 3 a solution of $x - 10 = -7$?

83. Is −2 a solution of $-x + 6 = -x - 1$?

84. Is −10 a solution of $-x - 6 = -x - 1$?

85. Is 2 a solution of $-x - 13 = -15$?

86. Is 5 a solution of $4 = 1 - x$?

MIXED PRACTICE—TRANSLATING (*SECTIONS 1.5, 1.6*)

Translate each phrase to an algebraic expression. Use "x" to represent "a number."

87. The sum of −5 and a number.

88. The difference of −3 and a number.

89. Subtract a number from −20.

90. Add a number and −36.

CONCEPT EXTENSIONS

Recall the bar graph from Section 1.5. It shows each month's average daily low temperature in degrees Fahrenheit for Barrow, Alaska. Use this graph to answer Exercises 91 through 94.

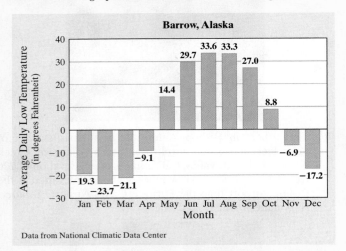

Data from National Climatic Data Center

91. Record the monthly increases and decreases in the low temperature from the previous month.

Month	Monthly Increase or Decrease (from the previous month)
February	
March	
April	
May	
June	

92. Record the monthly increases and decreases in the low temperature from the previous month.

Month	Monthly Increase or Decrease (from the previous month)
July	33.6
August	33.3
September	
October	
November	
December	

93. Which month had the greatest increase in temperature?

94. Which month had the greatest decrease in temperature?

95. Find two numbers whose difference is -5.

96. Find two numbers whose difference is -9.

*Each calculation below is **incorrect**. Find the error and correct it.*

97. $9 - (-7) \overset{?}{=} 2$

98. $-4 - 8 \overset{?}{=} 4$

99. $10 - 30 \overset{?}{=} 20$

100. $-3 - (-10) \overset{?}{=} -13$

If p is a positive number and n is a negative number, determine whether each statement is true or false. Explain your answer.

101. $p - n$ is always a positive number.

102. $n - p$ is always a negative number.

103. $|n| - |p|$ is always a positive number.

104. $|n - p|$ is always a positive number.

Without calculating, determine whether each answer is positive or negative. Then use a calculator to find the exact difference.

105. $56{,}875 - 87{,}262$

106. $4.362 - 7.0086$

Integrated Review OPERATIONS ON REAL NUMBERS

Sections 1.1–1.6

Answer the following with positive, negative, or 0.

1. The opposite of a positive number is a _____ number.

2. The sum of two negative numbers is a _____ number.

3. The absolute value of a negative number is a _____ number.

4. The absolute value of zero is _____.

5. The reciprocal of a positive number is a _____ number.

6. The sum of a number and its opposite is _____.

7. The absolute value of a positive number is a _____ number.

8. The opposite of a negative number is a _____ number.

Fill in the chart:

	Number	Opposite	Absolute Value
9.	$\frac{1}{7}$		
10.	$-\frac{12}{5}$		
11.		-3	
12.		$\frac{9}{11}$	

Perform each indicated operation and simplify.

13. $-19 + (-23)$

14. $7 - (-3)$

15. $-15 + 17$

16. $-8 - 10$

17. $18 + (-25)$

18. $-2 + (-37)$

19. $-14 - (-12)$

20. $5 - 14$

21. $4.5 - 7.9$

22. $-8.6 - 1.2$

23. $-\dfrac{3}{4} - \dfrac{1}{7}$

24. $\dfrac{2}{3} - \dfrac{7}{8}$

25. $-9 - (-7) + 4 - 6$

26. $11 - 20 + (-3) - 12$

27. $24 - 6(14 - 11)$

28. $30 - 5(10 - 8)$

29. $(7 - 17) + 4^2$

30. $9^2 + (10 - 30)$

31. $|-9| + 3^2 + (-4 - 20)$

32. $|-4 - 5| + 5^2 + (-50)$

33. $-7 + [(1 - 2) + (-2 - 9)]$

34. $-6 + [(-3 + 7) + (4 - 15)]$

35. Subtract 5 from 1.

36. Subtract -2 from -3.

37. Subtract $-\dfrac{2}{5}$ from $\dfrac{1}{4}$.

38. Subtract $\dfrac{1}{10}$ from $-\dfrac{5}{8}$.

39. $2(19 - 17)^3 - 3(-7 + 9)^2$

40. $3(10 - 9)^2 + 6(20 - 19)^3$

Evaluate each expression when $x = -2$, $y = -1$, and $z = 9$.

41. $x - y$

42. $x + y$

43. $y + z$

44. $z - y$

45. $\dfrac{|5z - x|}{y - x}$

46. $\dfrac{|-x - y + z|}{2z}$

1.7   Multiplying and Dividing Real Numbers

OBJECTIVES

1. Multiply Real Numbers.

2. Find the Reciprocal of a Real Number.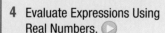

3. Divide Real Numbers.

4. Evaluate Expressions Using Real Numbers.

5. Solve Applications That Involve Multiplication or Division of Real Numbers.

OBJECTIVE

1   Multiplying Real Numbers

In this section, we discover patterns for multiplying and dividing real numbers. To discover sign rules for multiplication, recall that multiplication is repeated addition. Thus $3 \cdot 2$ means that 2 is an addend 3 times. That is,

$$2 + 2 + 2 = 3 \cdot 2$$

which equals 6. Similarly, $3 \cdot (-2)$ means -2 is an addend 3 times. That is,

$$(-2) + (-2) + (-2) = 3 \cdot (-2)$$

Since $(-2) + (-2) + (-2) = -6$, $3 \cdot (-2) = -6$. This suggests that the product of a positive number and a negative number is a negative number.

What about the product of two negative numbers? To find out, consider the following pattern.

Factor decreases by 1 each time

$$\left.\begin{array}{l} -3 \cdot 2 = -6 \\ -3 \cdot 1 = -3 \\ -3 \cdot 0 = 0 \end{array}\right\} \text{Product increases by 3 each time.}$$

This pattern continues as

Factor decreases by 1 each time

$$\left.\begin{array}{l} -3 \cdot -1 = 3 \\ -3 \cdot -2 = 6 \end{array}\right\} \text{Product increases by 3 each time.}$$

This suggests that the product of two negative numbers is a positive number.

Multiplying Real Numbers

1. The product of two numbers with the *same* sign is a positive number.

2. The product of two numbers with *different* signs is a negative number.

EXAMPLE 1 Multiply.

a. $(-8)(4)$ **b.** $14(-1)$ **c.** $-9(-10)$

Solution

a. $-8(4) = -32$ **b.** $14(-1) = -14$ **c.** $-9(-10) = 90$ □

PRACTICE
1 Multiply.

a. $8(-5)$ **b.** $(-3)(-4)$ **c.** $(-6)(9)$

We know that every whole number multiplied by zero equals zero. This remains true for real numbers.

> **Zero as a Factor**
> If b is a real number, then $b \cdot 0 = 0$. Also, $0 \cdot b = 0$.

EXAMPLE 2 Perform the indicated operations.

a. $(7)(0)(-6)$ **b.** $(-2)(-3)(-4)$ **c.** $(-1)(5)(-9)$ **d.** $(-4)(-11) - (5)(-2)$

Solution

a. By the order of operations, we multiply from left to right. Notice that, because one of the factors is 0, the product is 0.

$$(7)(0)(-6) = 0(-6) = 0$$

b. Multiply two factors at a time, from left to right.

$$(-2)(-3)(-4) = (6)(-4) \quad \text{Multiply } (-2)(-3).$$
$$= -24$$

c. Multiply from left to right.

$$(-1)(5)(-9) = (-5)(-9) \quad \text{Multiply } (-1)(5).$$
$$= 45$$

d. Follow the rules for order of operations.

$$(-4)(-11) - (5)(-2) = 44 - (-10) \quad \text{Find each product.}$$
$$= 44 + 10 \quad \text{Add 44 to the opposite of } -10.$$
$$= 54 \quad \text{Add.} \qquad □$$

PRACTICE
2 Perform the indicated operations.

a. $(-1)(-5)(-6)$ **b.** $(-3)(-2)(4)$
c. $(-4)(0)(5)$ **d.** $(-2)(-3) - (-4)(5)$

> ▶ **Helpful Hint**
> You may have noticed from the example that if we multiply:
> • an *even* number of negative numbers, the product is *positive*.
> • an *odd* number of negative numbers, the product is *negative*.

Answer to Concept Check
negative

✓ CONCEPT CHECK
What is the sign of the product of five negative numbers? Explain.

Multiplying signed decimals or fractions is carried out exactly the same way as multiplying integers.

EXAMPLE 3 Multiply.

a. $(-1.2)(0.05)$ **b.** $\dfrac{2}{3} \cdot \left(-\dfrac{7}{10}\right)$ **c.** $\left(-\dfrac{4}{5}\right)(-20)$

Solution

a. The product of two numbers with different signs is negative.

$$(-1.2)(0.05) = -[(1.2)(0.05)]$$
$$= -0.06$$

b. $\dfrac{2}{3} \cdot \left(-\dfrac{7}{10}\right) = -\dfrac{2 \cdot 7}{3 \cdot 10} = -\dfrac{2 \cdot 7}{3 \cdot 2 \cdot 5} = -\dfrac{7}{15}$

c. $\left(-\dfrac{4}{5}\right)(-20) = \dfrac{4 \cdot 20}{5 \cdot 1} = \dfrac{4 \cdot 4 \cdot 5}{5 \cdot 1} = \dfrac{16}{1}$ or 16

PRACTICE
3   Multiply.

a. $(0.23)(-0.2)$ **b.** $\left(-\dfrac{3}{5}\right) \cdot \left(\dfrac{4}{9}\right)$ **c.** $\left(-\dfrac{7}{12}\right)(-24)$

Now that we know how to multiply positive and negative numbers, let's see how we find the values of $(-4)^2$ and -4^2, for example. Although these two expressions look similar, the difference between the two is the parentheses. In $(-4)^2$, the parentheses tell us that the base, or repeated factor, is -4. In -4^2, only 4 is the base. Thus,

$$(-4)^2 = (-4)(-4) = 16 \quad \text{The base is } -4.$$
$$-4^2 = -(4 \cdot 4) = -16 \quad \text{The base is 4.}$$

EXAMPLE 4 Evaluate.

a. $(-2)^3$ **b.** -2^3 **c.** $(-3)^2$ **d.** -3^2

Solution

a. $(-2)^3 = (-2)(-2)(-2) = -8$ The base is -2.
b. $-2^3 = -(2 \cdot 2 \cdot 2) = -8$ The base is 2.
c. $(-3)^2 = (-3)(-3) = 9$ The base is -3.
d. $-3^2 = -(3 \cdot 3) = -9$ The base is 3.

PRACTICE
4   Evaluate.

a. $(-6)^2$ **b.** -6^2 **c.** $(-4)^3$ **d.** -4^3

> ▶ **Helpful Hint**
> Be careful when identifying the base of an exponential expression.
>
> $$(-3)^2 \qquad\qquad -3^2$$
> $$\text{Base is } -3 \qquad\qquad \text{Base is 3}$$
> $$(-3)^2 = (-3)(-3) = 9 \qquad -3^2 = -(3 \cdot 3) = -9$$

OBJECTIVE

2 **Finding Reciprocals**

Just as every difference of two numbers $a - b$ can be written as the sum $a + (-b)$, so too every quotient of two numbers can be written as a product. For example, the quotient $6 \div 3$ can be written as $6 \cdot \frac{1}{3}$. Recall that the pair of numbers 3 and $\frac{1}{3}$ has a special relationship. Their product is 1 and they are called reciprocals or **multiplicative inverses** of each other.

> **Reciprocals or Multiplicative Inverses**
>
> Two numbers whose product is 1 are called reciprocals or multiplicative inverses of each other.

Notice that **0 has no multiplicative inverse** since 0 multiplied by any number is never 1 but always 0.

EXAMPLE 5 Find the reciprocal of each number.

a. 22   **b.** $\frac{3}{16}$ **c.** -10 **d.** $-\frac{9}{13}$

Solution

a. The reciprocal of 22 is $\frac{1}{22}$ since $22 \cdot \frac{1}{22} = 1$.

b. The reciprocal of $\frac{3}{16}$ is $\frac{16}{3}$ since $\frac{3}{16} \cdot \frac{16}{3} = 1$.

c. The reciprocal of -10 is $-\frac{1}{10}$.

d. The reciprocal of $-\frac{9}{13}$ is $-\frac{13}{9}$.   □

PRACTICE

5 Find the reciprocal of each number.

a. $\frac{8}{3}$ **b.** 15   **c.** $-\frac{2}{7}$ **d.** -5

OBJECTIVE

3 **Dividing Real Numbers**

We may now write a quotient as an equivalent product.

> **Quotient of Two Real Numbers**
>
> If a and b are real numbers and b is not 0, then
>
> $$a \div b = \frac{a}{b} = a \cdot \frac{1}{b}$$

In other words, the quotient of two real numbers is the product of the first number and the multiplicative inverse or reciprocal of the second number.

EXAMPLE 6 Use the definition of the quotient of two numbers to divide.

a. $-18 \div 3$ **b.** $\frac{-14}{-2}$ **c.** $\frac{20}{-4}$

Solution

a. $-18 \div 3 = -18 \cdot \frac{1}{3} = -6$ **b.** $\frac{-14}{-2} = -14 \cdot -\frac{1}{2} = 7$

c. $\frac{20}{-4} = 20 \cdot -\frac{1}{4} = -5$ □

PRACTICE
6   Use the definition of the quotient of two numbers to divide.

a. $\dfrac{16}{-2}$ **b.** $24 \div (-6)$ **c.** $\dfrac{-35}{-7}$

Since the quotient $a \div b$ can be written as the product $a \cdot \dfrac{1}{b}$, it follows that sign patterns for dividing two real numbers are the same as sign patterns for multiplying two real numbers.

> **Multiplying and Dividing Real Numbers**
>
> **1.** The product or quotient of two numbers with the *same* sign is a positive number.
> **2.** The product or quotient of two numbers with *different* signs is a negative number.

EXAMPLE 7   Divide.

a. $\dfrac{-24}{-4}$ **b.** $\dfrac{-36}{3}$ **c.** $\dfrac{2}{3} \div \left(-\dfrac{5}{4}\right)$ **d.** $-\dfrac{3}{2} \div 9$

Solution

a. $\dfrac{-24}{-4} = 6$ **b.** $\dfrac{-36}{3} = -12$ **c.** $\dfrac{2}{3} \div \left(-\dfrac{5}{4}\right) = \dfrac{2}{3} \cdot \left(-\dfrac{4}{5}\right) = -\dfrac{8}{15}$

d. $-\dfrac{3}{2} \div 9 = -\dfrac{3}{2} \cdot \dfrac{1}{9} = -\dfrac{3 \cdot 1}{2 \cdot 9} = -\dfrac{3 \cdot 1}{2 \cdot 3 \cdot 3} = -\dfrac{1}{6}$

PRACTICE
7   Divide.

a. $\dfrac{-18}{-6}$ **b.** $\dfrac{-48}{3}$ **c.** $\dfrac{3}{5} \div \left(-\dfrac{1}{2}\right)$ **d.** $-\dfrac{4}{9} \div 8$

> **✓CONCEPT CHECK**
> What is wrong with the following calculation?
> $\dfrac{-36}{-9} = -4$

The definition of the quotient of two real numbers does not allow for division by 0 because 0 does not have a multiplicative inverse. There is no number we can multiply 0 by to get 1. How then do we interpret $\dfrac{3}{0}$? We say that division by 0 is not allowed or not defined and that $\dfrac{3}{0}$ does not represent a real number. The denominator of a fraction can never be 0.

Can the numerator of a fraction be 0? Can we divide 0 by a number? Yes. For example,

$$\dfrac{0}{3} = 0 \cdot \dfrac{1}{3} = 0$$

In general, the quotient of 0 and any nonzero number is 0.

> **Zero as a Divisor or Dividend**
>
> **1.** The quotient of any nonzero real number and 0 is undefined. In symbols, if $a \neq 0, \dfrac{a}{0}$ is **undefined**.
>
> **2.** The quotient of 0 and any real number except 0 is 0. In symbols, if $a \neq 0, \dfrac{0}{a} = 0$.

Answer to Concept Check
$\dfrac{-36}{-9} = 4$

EXAMPLE 8 Perform the indicated operations.

a. $\dfrac{1}{0}$ **b.** $\dfrac{0}{-3}$ **c.** $\dfrac{0(-8)}{2}$

Solution

a. $\dfrac{1}{0}$ is undefined **b.** $\dfrac{0}{-3} = 0$ **c.** $\dfrac{0(-8)}{2} = \dfrac{0}{2} = 0$ ☐

PRACTICE
8 Perform the indicated operations.

a. $\dfrac{0}{-2}$ **b.** $\dfrac{-4}{0}$ **c.** $\dfrac{-5}{6(0)}$

Notice that $\dfrac{12}{-2} = -6$, $-\dfrac{12}{2} = -6$, and $\dfrac{-12}{2} = -6$. This means that

$$\frac{12}{-2} = -\frac{12}{2} = \frac{-12}{2}$$

In words, a single negative sign in a fraction can be written in the denominator, in the numerator, or in front of the fraction without changing the value of the fraction. Thus,

$$\frac{1}{-7} = \frac{-1}{7} = -\frac{1}{7}$$

> In general, if a and b are real numbers, $b \neq 0$, then $\dfrac{a}{-b} = \dfrac{-a}{b} = -\dfrac{a}{b}$.

OBJECTIVE
4 Evaluating Expressions

Examples combining basic arithmetic operations along with the principles of order of operations help us review these concepts.

EXAMPLE 9 Simplify each expression.

a. $\dfrac{(-12)(-3) + 3}{-7 - (-2)}$ **b.** $\dfrac{2(-3)^2 - 20}{-5 + 4}$

Solution

a. First, simplify the numerator and denominator separately, then divide.

$$\frac{(-12)(-3) + 3}{-7 - (-2)} = \frac{36 + 3}{-7 + 2}$$
$$= \frac{39}{-5} \text{ or } -\frac{39}{5}$$

b. Simplify the numerator and denominator separately, then divide.

$$\frac{2(-3)^2 - 20}{-5 + 4} = \frac{2 \cdot 9 - 20}{-5 + 4} = \frac{18 - 20}{-5 + 4} = \frac{-2}{-1} = 2$$ ☐

PRACTICE
9 Simplify each expression.

a. $\dfrac{(-8)(-11) - 4}{-9 - (-4)}$ **b.** $\dfrac{3(-2)^3 - 9}{-6 + 3}$

Using what we have learned about multiplying and dividing real numbers, we continue to practice evaluating algebraic expressions.

EXAMPLE 10   If $x = -2$ and $y = -4$, evaluate each expression.

a. $5x - y$ **b.** $x^4 - y^2$ **c.** $\dfrac{3x}{2y}$

Solution

a. Replace x with -2 and y with -4 and simplify.

$$5x - y = 5(-2) - (-4) = -10 - (-4) = -10 + 4 = -6$$

b. Replace x with -2 and y with -4.

$$x^4 - y^2 = (-2)^4 - (-4)^2 \quad \text{Substitute the given values for the variables.}$$
$$= 16 - (16) \quad \text{Evaluate exponential expressions.}$$
$$= 0 \quad \text{Subtract.}$$

c. Replace x with -2 and y with -4 and simplify.

$$\frac{3x}{2y} = \frac{3(-2)}{2(-4)} = \frac{-6}{-8} = \frac{3}{4}$$

PRACTICE
10   If $x = -5$ and $y = -2$, evaluate each expression.

a. $7y - x$ **b.** $x^2 - y^3$ **c.** $\dfrac{2x}{3y}$

OBJECTIVE
5   **Solving Applications That Involve Multiplying or Dividing Numbers**
Many real-life problems involve multiplication and division of numbers.

EXAMPLE 11   **Calculating a Total Golf Score**

A professional golfer finished seven strokes under par (-7) for each of three days of a tournament. What was her total score for the tournament?

Solution   Although the key word is "total," since this is repeated addition of the same number, we multiply.

In words:

golfer's total score	=	number of days	·	score each day
golfer's total	=	3	·	(-7)

Translate:

$$= -21$$

Thus, the golfer's total score was -21, or 21 strokes under par.

PRACTICE
11   A card player had a score of -13 for each of four games. Find the total score.

Graphing Calculator Explorations

Entering Negative Numbers on a Scientific Calculator

To enter a negative number on a scientific calculator, find a key marked $\boxed{+/-}$. (On some calculators, this key is marked $\boxed{\text{CHS}}$ for "change sign.") To enter -8, for example, press the keys $\boxed{8}\,\boxed{+/-}$. The display will read $\boxed{-8}$.

(Continued on next page)

Entering Negative Numbers on a Graphing Calculator

To enter a negative number on a graphing calculator, find a key marked $\boxed{(-)}$. Do not confuse this key with the key $\boxed{-}$, which is used for subtraction. To enter -8, for example, press the keys $\boxed{(-)}$ $\boxed{8}$. The display will read $\boxed{-8}$.

Operations with Real Numbers

To evaluate $-2(7 - 9) - 20$ on a calculator, press the keys

$$\boxed{2}\,\boxed{+/-}\,\boxed{\times}\,\boxed{(}\,\boxed{(}\,\boxed{7}\,\boxed{-}\,\boxed{9}\,\boxed{)}\,\boxed{-}\,\boxed{2}\,\boxed{0}\,\boxed{=} \text{ or}$$

$$\boxed{(-)}\,\boxed{2}\,\boxed{(}\,\boxed{(}\,\boxed{7}\,\boxed{-}\,\boxed{9}\,\boxed{)}\,\boxed{-}\,\boxed{2}\,\boxed{0}\,\boxed{\text{ENTER}}$$

The display will read $\boxed{-16}$ or $\boxed{\begin{array}{c} -2(7 - 9) - 20 \\ \hline -16 \end{array}}$.

Use a calculator to simplify each expression.

1. $-38(26 - 27)$
2. $-59(-8) + 1726$
3. $134 + 25(68 - 91)$
4. $45(32) - 8(218)$
5. $\dfrac{-50(294)}{175 - 265}$
6. $\dfrac{-444 - 444.8}{-181 - 324}$
7. $9^5 - 4550$
8. $5^8 - 6259$
9. $(-125)^2$ (Be careful.)
10. -125^2 (Be careful.)

Vocabulary, Readiness & Video Check

Use the choices below to fill in each blank.

positive   0   negative   undefined

1. If n is a real number, then $n \cdot 0 = $ _____ and $0 \cdot n = $ _____.

2. If n is a real number, but not 0, then $\dfrac{0}{n} = $ _____ and we say $\dfrac{n}{0}$ is _____.

3. The product of two negative numbers is a _____ number.

4. The quotient of two negative numbers is a _____ number.

5. The quotient of a positive number and a negative number is a _____ number.

6. The product of a positive number and a negative number is a _____ number.

7. The reciprocal of a positive number is a _____ number.

8. The opposite of a positive number is a _____ number.

Martin-Gay Interactive Videos

See Video 1.7

Watch the section lecture video and answer the following questions.

OBJECTIVE 1

9. Explain the significance of the use of parentheses when comparing ⊟ Examples 6 and 7.

OBJECTIVE 2

10. In ⊟ Example 9, why is the reciprocal equal to $\dfrac{3}{2}$ and not $-\dfrac{3}{2}$?

OBJECTIVE 3

11. Before ⊟ Example 11, the sign rules for division of real numbers are discussed. Are the sign rules for division the same as for multiplication? Why or why not?

OBJECTIVE 4

12. In ⊟ Example 17, the importance of placing the replacement values in parentheses when evaluating is emphasized. Why?

OBJECTIVE 5

13. In Example 18, explain why each loss of 4 yards is represented by -4 and not 4.

1.7 Exercise Set   MyMathLab®

Multiply. See Examples 1 through 3.

1. $-6(4)$ **2.** $-8(5)$

3. $2(-1)$ **4.** $7(-4)$

5. $-5(-10)$ **6.** $-6(-11)$

7. $-3 \cdot 4$ **8.** $-2 \cdot 8$

9. $-7 \cdot 0$ **10.** $-6 \cdot 0$

11. $2(-9)$ **12.** $3(-5)$

13. $-\dfrac{1}{2}\left(-\dfrac{3}{5}\right)$ **14.** $-\dfrac{1}{8}\left(-\dfrac{1}{3}\right)$

15. $-\dfrac{3}{4}\left(-\dfrac{8}{9}\right)$ **16.** $-\dfrac{5}{6}\left(-\dfrac{3}{10}\right)$

17. $5(-1.4)$ **18.** $6(-2.5)$

19. $-0.2(-0.7)$ **20.** $-0.5(-0.3)$

21. $-10(80)$ **22.** $-20(60)$

23. $4(-7)$ **24.** $5(-9)$

25. $(-5)(-5)$ **26.** $(-7)(-7)$

27. $\dfrac{2}{3}\left(-\dfrac{4}{9}\right)$ **28.** $\dfrac{2}{7}\left(-\dfrac{2}{11}\right)$

29. $-11(11)$ **30.** $-12(12)$

31. $-\dfrac{20}{25}\left(\dfrac{5}{16}\right)$ **32.** $-\dfrac{25}{36}\left(\dfrac{6}{15}\right)$

33. $(-1)(2)(-3)(-5)$ **34.** $(-2)(-3)(-4)(-2)$

Perform the indicated operations. See Example 2.

35. $(-2)(5) - (-11)(3)$ **36.** $8(-3) - 4(-5)$

37. $(-6)(-1)(-2) - (-5)$ **38.** $20 - (-4)(3)(-2)$

Decide whether each statement is true or false.

39. The product of three negative integers is negative.

40. The product of three positive integers is positive.

41. The product of four negative integers is negative.

42. The product of four positive integers is positive.

Evaluate. See Example 4.

43. $(-2)^4$ **44.** -2^4

45. -1^5 **46.** $(-1)^5$

47. $(-5)^2$ **48.** -5^2

49. -7^2 **50.** $(-7)^2$

Find each reciprocal or multiplicative inverse. See Example 5.

51. 9 **52.** 100 **53.** $\dfrac{2}{3}$

54. $\dfrac{1}{7}$ **55.** -14 **56.** -8

57. $-\dfrac{3}{11}$ **58.** $-\dfrac{6}{13}$ **59.** 0.2

60. 1.5 **61.** $\dfrac{1}{-6.3}$ **62.** $\dfrac{1}{-8.9}$

Divide. See Examples 6 through 8.

63. $\dfrac{18}{-2}$ **64.** $\dfrac{20}{-10}$ **65.** $\dfrac{-16}{-4}$

66. $\dfrac{-18}{-6}$ **67.** $\dfrac{-48}{12}$ **68.** $\dfrac{-60}{5}$

69. $\dfrac{0}{-4}$ **70.** $\dfrac{0}{-9}$ **71.** $-\dfrac{15}{3}$

72. $-\dfrac{24}{8}$ **73.** $\dfrac{5}{0}$ **74.** $\dfrac{3}{0}$

75. $\dfrac{-12}{-4}$ **76.** $\dfrac{-45}{-9}$ **77.** $\dfrac{30}{-2}$

78. $\dfrac{14}{-2}$ **79.** $\dfrac{6}{7} \div \left(-\dfrac{1}{3}\right)$

80. $\dfrac{4}{5} \div \left(-\dfrac{1}{2}\right)$ **81.** $-\dfrac{5}{9} \div \left(-\dfrac{3}{4}\right)$

82. $-\dfrac{1}{10} \div \left(-\dfrac{8}{11}\right)$ **83.** $-\dfrac{4}{9} \div \dfrac{4}{9}$

84. $-\dfrac{5}{12} \div \dfrac{5}{12}$

MIXED PRACTICE

Simplify. See Examples 1 through 9.

85. $\dfrac{-9(-3)}{-6}$ **86.** $\dfrac{-6(-3)}{-4}$

87. $\dfrac{12}{9 - 12}$ **88.** $\dfrac{-15}{1 - 4}$

89. $\dfrac{-6^2 + 4}{-2}$ **90.** $\dfrac{3^2 + 4}{5}$

91. $\dfrac{8 + (-4)^2}{4 - 12}$ **92.** $\dfrac{6 + (-2)^2}{4 - 9}$

93. $\dfrac{22 + (3)(-2)}{-5 - 2}$ **94.** $\dfrac{-20 + (-4)(3)}{1 - 5}$

95. $\dfrac{-3 - 5^2}{2(-7)}$ **96.** $\dfrac{-2 - 4^2}{3(-6)}$

97. $\dfrac{6 - 2(-3)}{4 - 3(-2)}$ **98.** $\dfrac{8 - 3(-2)}{2 - 5(-4)}$

99. $\dfrac{-3 - 2(-9)}{-15 - 3(-4)}$ **100.** $\dfrac{-4 - 8(-2)}{-9 - 2(-3)}$

101. $\dfrac{|5 - 9| + |10 - 15|}{|2(-3)|}$ **102.** $\dfrac{|-3 + 6| + |-2 + 7|}{|-2 \cdot 2|}$

If $x = -5$ and $y = -3$, evaluate each expression. See Example 10.

103. $3x + 2y$ **104.** $4x + 5y$

105. $2x^2 - y^2$ **106.** $x^2 - 2y^2$

107. $x^3 + 3y$ **108.** $y^3 + 3x$

109. $\dfrac{2x - 5}{y - 2}$ **110.** $\dfrac{2y - 12}{x - 4}$

111. $\dfrac{-3 - y}{x - 4}$ **112.** $\dfrac{4 - 2x}{y + 3}$

TRANSLATING

Translate each phrase to an expression. Use x to represent "a number." See Example 11.

113. The product of −71 and a number

114. The quotient of −8 and a number

115. Subtract a number from −16.

116. The sum of a number and −12

117. −29 increased by a number

118. The difference of a number and −10

119. Divide a number by −33.

120. Multiply a number by −17.

Solve. See Example 11.

▷ **121.** A football team lost four yards on each of three consecutive plays. Represent the total loss as a product of signed numbers and find the total loss.

122. Joe Norstrom lost $400 on each of seven consecutive days in the stock market. Represent his total loss as a product of signed numbers and find his total loss.

123. A deep-sea diver must move up or down in the water in short steps to keep from getting a physical condition called the "bends." Suppose a diver moves down from the surface in five steps of 20 feet each. Represent his total movement as a product of signed numbers and find the total depth.

124. A weather forecaster predicts that the temperature will drop five degrees each hour for the next six hours. Represent this drop as a product of signed numbers and find the total drop in temperature.

Decide whether the given number is a solution of the given equation.

125. Is 7 a solution of $-5x = -35$?

126. Is −4 a solution of $2x = x - 1$?

127. Is −20 a solution of $\frac{x}{10} = 2$?

128. Is −3 a solution of $\frac{45}{x} = -15$?

129. Is 5 a solution of $-3x - 5 = -20$?

130. Is −4 a solution of $2x + 4 = x + 8$?

CONCEPT EXTENSIONS

Study the bar graph below showing the average surface temperatures of planets. Use Exercises 131 and 132 to complete the planet temperatures on the graph. (Pluto is now classified as a dwarf planet.)

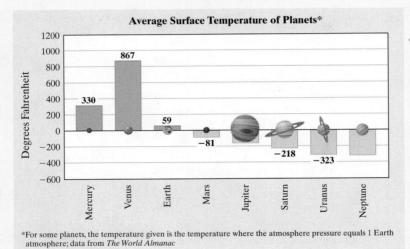

Average Surface Temperature of Planets*

*For some planets, the temperature given is the temperature where the atmosphere pressure equals 1 Earth atmosphere; data from *The World Almanac*

131. The surface temperature of Jupiter is twice the temperature of Mars. Find this temperature.

132. The surface temperature of Neptune is equal to the temperature of Mercury divided by −1. Find this temperature.

133. Explain why the product of an even number of negative numbers is a positive number.

134. If *a* and *b* are any real numbers, is the statement $a \cdot b = b \cdot a$ always true? Why or why not?

135. Find any real numbers that are their own reciprocal.

136. Explain why 0 has no reciprocal.

If q is a negative number, r is a negative number, and t is a positive number, determine whether each expression simplifies to a positive or negative number. If it is not possible to determine, state so.

137. $\dfrac{q}{r \cdot t}$

138. $q^2 \cdot r \cdot t$

139. $q + t$

140. $t + r$

141. $t(q + r)$

142. $r(q - t)$

Write each of the following as an expression and evaluate.

143. The sum of −2 and the quotient of −15 and 3

144. The sum of 1 and the product of −8 and −5

145. Twice the sum of −5 and −3

146. 7 subtracted from the quotient of 0 and 5

1.8 | Properties of Real Numbers

OBJECTIVES

1 Use the Commutative and Associative Properties. ▶

2 Use the Distributive Property. ▶

3 Use the Identity and Inverse Properties. ▶

OBJECTIVE

1 Using the Commutative and Associative Properties ▶

In this section, we give names to properties of real numbers with which we are already familiar. Throughout this section, the variables *a, b*, and *c* represent real numbers.

We know that order does not matter when adding numbers. For example, we know that $7 + 5$ is the same as $5 + 7$. This property is given a special name—the **commutative property of addition.** We also know that order does not matter when multiplying numbers. For example, we know that $-5(6) = 6(-5)$. This property means that multiplication is commutative also and is called the **commutative property of multiplication.**

Commutative Properties	
Addition:	$a + b = b + a$
Multiplication:	$a \cdot b = b \cdot a$

These properties state that the *order* in which any two real numbers are added or multiplied does not change their sum or product. For example, if we let $a = 3$ and $b = 5$, then the commutative properties guarantee that

$$3 + 5 = 5 + 3 \quad \text{and} \quad 3 \cdot 5 = 5 \cdot 3$$

▶ **Helpful Hint**

Is subtraction also commutative? Try an example. Does $3 - 2 = 2 - 3$? **No!** The left side of this statement equals 1; the right side equals -1. There is no commutative property of subtraction. Similarly, there is no commutative property for division. For example, $10 \div 2$ does not equal $2 \div 10$.

EXAMPLE 1   Use a commutative property to complete each statement.

a. $x + 5 = $ _____

b. $3 \cdot x = $ _____

Solution

a. $x + 5 = 5 + x$ By the commutative property of addition

b. $3 \cdot x = x \cdot 3$ By the commutative property of multiplication   □

PRACTICE

1   Use a commutative property to complete each statement.

a. $x \cdot 8 = $ ____

b. $x + 17 = $ _____

✓**CONCEPT CHECK**

Which of the following pairs of actions are commutative?

a. "raking the leaves" and "bagging the leaves"

b. "putting on your left glove" and "putting on your right glove"

c. "putting on your coat" and "putting on your shirt"

d. "reading a novel" and "reading a newspaper"

Let's now discuss grouping numbers. We know that when we add three numbers, the way in which they are grouped or associated does not change their sum. For example, we know that $2 + (3 + 4) = 2 + 7 = 9$. This result is the same if we group the numbers differently. In other words, $(2 + 3) + 4 = 5 + 4 = 9$ also. Thus, ▶ $2 + (3 + 4) = (2 + 3) + 4$. This property is called the **associative property of addition.**

We also know that changing the grouping of numbers when multiplying does not change their product. For example, $2 \cdot (3 \cdot 4) = (2 \cdot 3) \cdot 4$ (check it). This is the **associative property of multiplication.**

Associative Properties

Addition: $(a + b) + c = a + (b + c)$

Multiplication: $(a \cdot b) \cdot c = a \cdot (b \cdot c)$

These properties state that the way in which three numbers are *grouped* does not change their sum or their product.

EXAMPLE 2 Use an associative property to complete each statement.

a. $5 + (4 + 6) = $ _____

b. $(-1 \cdot 2) \cdot 5 = $ _____

Solution

a. $5 + (4 + 6) = (5 + 4) + 6$ By the associative property of addition

b. $(-1 \cdot 2) \cdot 5 = -1 \cdot (2 \cdot 5)$ By the associative property of multiplication □

PRACTICE
2 Use an associative property to complete each statement.

a. $(2 + 9) + 7 = $ _____

b. $-4 \cdot (2 \cdot 7) = $ _____

▶ **Helpful Hint**

Remember the difference between the commutative properties and the associative properties. The commutative properties have to do with the *order* of numbers, and the associative properties have to do with the *grouping* of numbers.

Let's now illustrate how these properties can help us simplify expressions.

EXAMPLE 3 Simplify each expression.

a. $10 + (x + 12)$

b. $-3(7x)$

Solution

a. $10 + (x + 12) = 10 + (12 + x)$ By the commutative property of addition

$\qquad\qquad = (10 + 12) + x$ By the associative property of addition

$\qquad\qquad = 22 + x$ Add.

b. $-3(7x) = (-3 \cdot 7)x$ By the associative property of multiplication

$\qquad\qquad = -21x$ Multiply. □

PRACTICE
3 Simplify each expression.

a. $(5 + x) + 9$

b. $5(-6x)$

OBJECTIVE

2 Using the Distributive Property ▶

The **distributive property of multiplication over addition** is used repeatedly throughout algebra. It is useful because it allows us to write a product as a sum or a sum as a product.

We know that $7(2 + 4) = 7(6) = 42$. Compare that with $7(2) + 7(4) = 14 + 28 = 42$. Since both original expressions equal 42, they must equal each other, or

$$7(2 + 4) = 7(2) + 7(4)$$

This is an example of the distributive property. The product on the left side of the equal sign is equal to the sum on the right side. We can think of the 7 as being distributed to each number inside the parentheses.

Distributive Property of Multiplication Over Addition

$$a(\overparen{b + c}) = ab + ac$$

Since multiplication is commutative, this property can also be written as

$$(\overparen{b + c})a = ba + ca$$

The distributive property can also be extended to more than two numbers inside the parentheses. For example,

$$3(\overparen{x + y + z}) = 3(x) + 3(y) + 3(z)$$
$$= 3x + 3y + 3z$$

Since we define subtraction in terms of addition, the distributive property is also true for subtraction. For example

$$2(\overparen{x - y}) = 2(x) - 2(y)$$
$$= 2x - 2y$$

EXAMPLE 4   Use the distributive property to write each expression without parentheses. Then simplify if possible.

a. $2(x + y)$ **b.** $-5(-3 + 2z)$ **c.** $5(x + 3y - z)$

d. $-1(2 - y)$ **e.** $-(3 + x - w)$ **f.** $\dfrac{1}{2}(6x + 14) + 10$

Solution

a. $2(\overparen{x + y}) = 2 \cdot x + 2 \cdot y$
$\qquad\quad = 2x + 2y$

b. $-5(\overparen{-3 + 2z}) = -5(-3) + (-5)(2z)$
$\qquad\qquad\quad = 15 - 10z$

c. $5(\overparen{x + 3y - z}) = 5(x) + 5(3y) - 5(z)$
$\qquad\qquad\qquad = 5x + 15y - 5z$

d. $-1(2 - y) = (-1)(2) - (-1)(y)$
$\qquad\qquad\; = -2 + y$

e. $-(3 + x - w) = -1(3 + x - w)$
$\qquad\qquad\qquad = (-1)(3) + (-1)(x) - (-1)(w)$
$\qquad\qquad\qquad = -3 - x + w$

> ▶ **Helpful Hint**
> Notice in part (**e**) that $-(3 + x - w)$ is first rewritten as $-1(3 + x - w)$.

f. $\dfrac{1}{2}(6x + 14) + 10 = \dfrac{1}{2}(6x) + \dfrac{1}{2}(14) + 10$ Apply the distributive property.
$\qquad\qquad\qquad\quad = 3x + 7 + 10$ Multiply.
$\qquad\qquad\qquad\quad = 3x + 17$ Add.   □

4 Use the distributive property to write each expression without parentheses. Then simplify if possible.

a. $5(x - y)$

b. $-6(4 + 2t)$

c. $2(3x - 4y - z)$

d. $(3 - y) \cdot (-1)$

e. $-(x - 7 + 2s)$

f. $\dfrac{1}{2}(2x + 4) + 9$

We can use the distributive property in reverse to write a sum as a product.

EXAMPLE 5 Use the distributive property to write each sum as a product.

a. $8 \cdot 2 + 8 \cdot x$

b. $7s + 7t$

Solution

a. $8 \cdot 2 + 8 \cdot x = 8(2 + x)$

b. $7s + 7t = 7(s + t)$

5 Use the distributive property to write each sum as a product.

a. $5 \cdot w + 5 \cdot 3$

b. $9w + 9z$

OBJECTIVE

3 Using the Identity and Inverse Properties

Next, we look at the **identity properties.**

The number 0 is called the identity for addition because when 0 is added to any real number, the result is the same real number. In other words, the *identity* of the real number is not changed.

The number 1 is called the identity for multiplication because when a real number is multiplied by 1, the result is the same real number. In other words, the *identity* of the real number is not changed.

Identities for Addition and Multiplication

0 is the identity element for addition.

$$a + 0 = a \quad \text{and} \quad 0 + a = a$$

1 is the identity element for multiplication.

$$a \cdot 1 = a \quad \text{and} \quad 1 \cdot a = a$$

Notice that 0 is the *only* number that can be added to any real number with the result that the sum is the same real number. Also, 1 is the *only* number that can be multiplied by any real number with the result that the product is the same real number.

Additive inverses or **opposites** were introduced in Section 1.5. Two numbers are called additive inverses or opposites if their sum is 0. The additive inverse or opposite of 6 is -6 because $6 + (-6) = 0$. The additive inverse or opposite of -5 is 5 because $-5 + 5 = 0$.

Reciprocals or **multiplicative inverses** were introduced in Section 1.3. Two nonzero numbers are called reciprocals or multiplicative inverses if their product is 1. The reciprocal or multiplicative inverse of $\frac{2}{3}$ is $\frac{3}{2}$ because $\frac{2}{3} \cdot \frac{3}{2} = 1$. Likewise, the reciprocal of -5 is $-\frac{1}{5}$ because $-5\left(-\frac{1}{5}\right) = 1$.

✓**CONCEPT CHECK**

Which of the following, $1, -\frac{10}{3}, \frac{3}{10}, 0, \frac{10}{3}, -\frac{3}{10}$, is the

a. opposite of $-\frac{3}{10}$?   **b.** reciprocal of $-\frac{3}{10}$?

Additive or Multiplicative Inverses

The numbers a and $-a$ are additive inverses or opposites of each other because their sum is 0; that is,

$$a + (-a) = 0$$

The numbers b and $\frac{1}{b}$ (for $b \neq 0$) are reciprocals or multiplicative inverses of each other because their product is 1; that is,

$$b \cdot \frac{1}{b} = 1$$

EXAMPLE 6   Name the property or properties illustrated by each true statement.

Solution

a. $3 \cdot y = y \cdot 3$ Commutative property of multiplication (order changed)

b. $(x + 7) + 9 = x + (7 + 9)$ Associative property of addition (grouping changed)

c. $(b + 0) + 3 = b + 3$ Identity element for addition

d. $0.2 \cdot (z \cdot 5) = 0.2 \cdot (5 \cdot z)$ Commutative property of multiplication (order changed)

e. $-2 \cdot \left(-\frac{1}{2}\right) = 1$ Multiplicative inverse property

f. $-2 + 2 = 0$ Additive inverse property

g. $-6 \cdot (y \cdot 2) = (-6 \cdot 2) \cdot y$ Commutative and associative properties of multiplication (order and grouping changed)   □

PRACTICE

6   Name the property or properties illustrated by each true statement.

a. $(7 \cdot 3x) \cdot 4 = (3x \cdot 7) \cdot 4$ Commutative property of multiplication

b. $6 + (3 + y) = (6 + 3) + y$ Associative property of addition

c. $8 + (t + 0) = 8 + t$ Identity element for addition

d. $-\frac{3}{4} \cdot \left(-\frac{4}{3}\right) = 1$ Multiplicative inverse property

e. $(2 + x) + 5 = 5 + (2 + x)$ Commutative property of addition

f. $3 + (-3) = 0$ Additive inverse property

g. $(-3b) \cdot 7 = (-3 \cdot 7) \cdot b$ Commutative and associative properties of multiplication

Answers to Concept Check:
a. $\frac{3}{10}$ **b.** $-\frac{10}{3}$

Vocabulary, Readiness & Video Check

Use the choices below to fill in each blank.

distributive property
opposites or additive inverses
reciprocals or multiplicative inverses

associative property of multiplication
associative property of addition
commutative property of multiplication

commutative property of addition

1. $x + 5 = 5 + x$ is a true statement by the _____.

2. $x \cdot 5 = 5 \cdot x$ is a true statement by the _____.

3. $3(y + 6) = 3 \cdot y + 3 \cdot 6$ is true by the _____.

4. $2 \cdot (x \cdot y) = (2 \cdot x) \cdot y$ is a true statement by the _____.

5. $x + (7 + y) = (x + 7) + y$ is a true statement by the _____.

6. The numbers $-\frac{2}{3}$ and $-\frac{3}{2}$ are called _____.

7. The numbers $-\frac{2}{3}$ and $\frac{2}{3}$ are called _____.

Martin-Gay Interactive Videos

See Video 1.8

Watch the section lecture video and answer the following questions.

OBJECTIVE 1

8. The commutative properties are discussed in ▣ Examples 1 and 2 and the associative properties are discussed in ▣ Examples 3–7. What's the one word used again and again to describe the commutative property? The associative property?

OBJECTIVE 2

9. In ▣ Example 10, what point is made about the term 2?

OBJECTIVE 3

10. Complete these statements based on the lecture given before ▣ Example 12.

   • The identify element for addition is _____ because if we add _____ to any real number, the result is that real number.

   • The identify element for multiplication is _____ because any real number times _____ gives a result of that original real number.

1.8 Exercise Set

MyMathLab®

Use a commutative property to complete each statement. See Example 1.

▶ 1. $x + 16 = $ _____   2. $4 + y = $ _____

  3. $-4 \cdot y = $ _____   4. $-2 \cdot x = $ _____

▶ 5. $xy = $ _____   6. $ab = $ _____

  7. $2x + 13 = $ _____   8. $19 + 3y = $ _____

Use an associative property to complete each statement. See Example 2.

▶ 9. $(xy) \cdot z = $ _____   10. $3 \cdot (xy) = $ _____

  11. $2 + (a + b) = $ _____   12. $(y + 4) + z = $ _____

  13. $4 \cdot (ab) = $ _____   14. $(-3y) \cdot z = $ _____

▶ 15. $(a + b) + c = $ _____

  16. $6 + (r + s) = $ _____

Use the commutative and associative properties to simplify each expression. See Example 3.

▶ 17. $8 + (9 + b)$ 18. $(r + 3) + 11$

▶ 19. $4(6y)$ 20. $2(42x)$

  21. $\frac{1}{5}(5y)$ 22. $\frac{1}{8}(8z)$

  23. $(13 + a) + 13$ 24. $7 + (x + 4)$

  25. $-9(8x)$ 26. $-3(12y)$

  27. $\frac{3}{4}\left(\frac{4}{3}s\right)$ 28. $\frac{2}{7}\left(\frac{7}{2}r\right)$

  29. $\frac{2}{3} + \left(\frac{4}{3} + x\right)$ 30. $\frac{7}{9} + \left(\frac{2}{9} + y\right)$

Use the distributive property to write each expression without parentheses. Then simplify the result. See Example 4.

31. $4(x + y)$

32. $7(a + b)$

33. $9(x - 6)$

34. $11(y - 4)$

35. $2(3x + 5)$

36. $5(7 + 8y)$

37. $7(4x - 3)$

38. $3(8x - 1)$

39. $3(6 + x)$

40. $2(x + 5)$

41. $-2(y - z)$

42. $-3(z - y)$

43. $-7(3y + 5)$

44. $-5(2r + 11)$

45. $5(x + 4m + 2)$

46. $8(3y + z - 6)$

47. $-4(1 - 2m + n)$

48. $-4(4 + 2p + 5q)$

49. $-(5x + 2)$

50. $-(9r + 5)$

51. $-(r - 3 - 7p)$

52. $-(q - 2 + 6r)$

53. $\frac{1}{2}(6x + 8)$

54. $\frac{1}{4}(4x - 2)$

55. $-\frac{1}{3}(3x - 9y)$

56. $-\frac{1}{5}(10a - 25b)$

57. $3(2r + 5) - 7$

58. $10(4s + 6) - 40$

59. $-9(4x + 8) + 2$

60. $-11(5x + 3) + 10$

61. $-4(4x + 5) - 5$

62. $-6(2x + 1) - 1$

Use the distributive property to write each sum as a product. See Example 5.

63. $4 \cdot 1 + 4 \cdot y$

64. $14 \cdot z + 14 \cdot 5$

65. $11x + 11y$

66. $9a + 9b$

67. $(-1) \cdot 5 + (-1) \cdot x$

68. $(-3)a + (-3)b$

69. $30a + 30b$

70. $25x + 25y$

Name the properties illustrated by each true statement. See Example 6.

71. $3 \cdot 5 = 5 \cdot 3$

72. $4(3 + 8) = 4 \cdot 3 + 4 \cdot 8$

73. $2 + (x + 5) = (2 + x) + 5$

74. $(x + 9) + 3 = (9 + x) + 3$

75. $9(3 + 7) = 9 \cdot 3 + 9 \cdot 7$

76. $1 \cdot 9 = 9$

77. $(4 \cdot y) \cdot 9 = 4 \cdot (y \cdot 9)$

78. $6 \cdot \frac{1}{6} = 1$

79. $0 + 6 = 6$

80. $(a + 9) + 6 = a + (9 + 6)$

81. $-4(y + 7) = -4 \cdot y + (-4) \cdot 7$

82. $(11 + r) + 8 = (r + 11) + 8$

83. $-4 \cdot (8 \cdot 3) = (8 \cdot -4) \cdot 3$

84. $r + 0 = r$

CONCEPT EXTENSIONS

Fill in the table with the opposite (additive inverse), and the reciprocal (multiplicative inverse). Assume that the value of each expression is not 0.

	Expression	Opposite	Reciprocal
85.	8		
86.	$-\frac{2}{3}$		
87.	x		
88.	$4y$		
89.			$\frac{1}{2x}$
90.		$7x$	

Decide whether each statement is true or false. See the second Concept Check in this section.

91. The opposite of $-\frac{a}{2}$ is $-\frac{2}{a}$.

92. The reciprocal of $-\frac{a}{2}$ is $\frac{a}{2}$.

Determine which pairs of actions are commutative. See the first Concept Check in this section.

93. "taking a test" and "studying for the test"

94. "putting on your shoes" and "putting on your socks"

95. "putting on your left shoe" and "putting on your right shoe"

96. "reading the sports section" and "reading the comics section"

97. "mowing the lawn" and "trimming the hedges"

98. "baking a cake" and "eating the cake"

99. "dialing a number" and "turning on the cell phone"

100. "feeding the dog" and "feeding the cat"

Name the property illustrated by each step.

101. a. $\triangle + (\square + \bigcirc) = (\square + \bigcirc) + \triangle$

    b. $\qquad\qquad = (\bigcirc + \square) + \triangle$

    c. $\qquad\qquad = \bigcirc + (\square + \triangle)$

102. **a.** $(x + y) + z = x + (y + z)$
     b. $\qquad = (y + z) + x$
     c. $\qquad = (z + y) + x$

103. Explain why 0 is called the identity element for addition.

104. Explain why 1 is called the identity element for multiplication.

105. Write an example that shows that division is not commutative.

106. Write an example that shows that subtraction is not commutative.

Chapter 1 Vocabulary Check

Fill in each blank with one of the words or phrases listed below.

set   inequality symbols   opposites   absolute value   numerator

denominator   grouping symbols   exponent   base   reciprocals

variable   equation   solution

1. The symbols $\neq$, $<$, and $>$ are called _____.
2. A mathematical statement that two expressions are equal is called a(n) _____.
3. The _____ of a number is the distance between that number and 0 on the number line.
4. A symbol used to represent a number is called a(n) _____.
5. Two numbers that are the same distance from 0 but lie on opposite sides of 0 are called _____.
6. The number in a fraction above the fraction bar is called the _____.
7. A(n) _____ of an equation is a value for the variable that makes the equation a true statement.
8. Two numbers whose product is 1 are called _____.
9. In 2^3, the 2 is called the _____ and the 3 is called the _____.
10. The number in a fraction below the fraction bar is called the _____.
11. Parentheses and brackets are examples of _____.
12. A(n) _____ is a collection of objects.

Chapter 1 Highlights

DEFINITIONS AND CONCEPTS	EXAMPLES
Section 1.2 Symbols and Sets of Numbers	
A **set** is a collection of objects, called **elements,** enclosed in braces.	$\{a, c, e\}$
Natural Numbers: $\{1, 2, 3, 4, \ldots\}$	Given the set $\left\{-3.4, \sqrt{3}, 0, \frac{2}{3}, 5, -4\right\}$, list the numbers that belong to the set of
Whole Numbers: $\{0, 1, 2, 3, 4, \ldots\}$	Natural numbers: 5
Integers: $\{\ldots, -3, -2, -1, 0, 1, 2, 3, \ldots\}$	Whole numbers: 0, 5 Integers: $-4, 0, 5$
Rational Numbers: {real numbers that can be expressed as a quotient of integers}	Rational numbers: $-4, -3.4, 0, \frac{2}{3}, 5$
Irrational Numbers: {real numbers that cannot be expressed as a quotient of integers}	Irrational Numbers: $\sqrt{3}$
Real Numbers: {all numbers that correspond to a point on the number line}	Real numbers: $-4, -3.4, 0, \frac{2}{3}, \sqrt{3}, 5$

DEFINITIONS AND CONCEPTS	EXAMPLES

Section 1.2 Symbols and Sets of Numbers (continued)

A line used to picture numbers is called a **number line.**

The **absolute value** of a real number a, denoted by $|a|$, is the distance between a and 0 on the number line.

$|5| = 5 \qquad |0| = 0 \qquad |-2| = 2$

Symbols: $=$ is equal to

$-7 = -7$

$\neq$ is not equal to

$3 \neq -3$

$>$ is greater than

$4 > 1$

$<$ is less than

$1 < 4$

$\leq$ is less than or equal to

$6 \leq 6$

$\geq$ is greater than or equal to

$18 \geq -\dfrac{1}{3}$

Order Property for Real Numbers

For any two real numbers a and b, a is less than b if a is to the left of b on a number line.

$-3 < 0 \qquad 0 > -3 \qquad 0 < 2.5 \qquad 2.5 > 0$

Section 1.3 Fractions and Mixed Numbers

A quotient of two integers is called a **fraction.** The **numerator** of a fraction is the top number. The **denominator** of a fraction is the bottom number.

$\dfrac{13}{17} \leftarrow \text{numerator} \\ \phantom{\dfrac{13}{17}} \leftarrow \text{denominator}$

If $a \cdot b = c$, then a and b are **factors** and c is the **product.**

$7 \quad \cdot \quad 9 \quad = \quad 63$
$\downarrow \qquad\quad \downarrow \qquad\qquad \downarrow$
factor $\quad$ factor $\qquad$ product

A fraction is in **lowest terms** or **simplest form** when the numerator and the denominator have no factors in common other than 1.

$\dfrac{13}{17}$ is in simplest form.

To write a fraction in simplest form, factor the numerator and the denominator; then apply the fundamental principle.

Write in simplest form.

$$\frac{6}{14} = \frac{2 \cdot 3}{2 \cdot 7} = \frac{3}{7}$$

Two fractions are **reciprocals** if their product is 1. The reciprocal of $\dfrac{a}{b}$ is $\dfrac{b}{a}$.

The reciprocal of $\dfrac{6}{25}$ is $\dfrac{25}{6}$.

To multiply fractions, numerator times numerator is the numerator of the product and denominator times denominator is the denominator of the product.

Perform the indicated operations.

$$\frac{2}{5} \cdot \frac{3}{7} = \frac{6}{35}$$

To divide fractions, multiply the first fraction by the reciprocal of the second fraction.

$$\frac{5}{9} \div \frac{2}{7} = \frac{5}{9} \cdot \frac{7}{2} = \frac{35}{18}$$

To add fractions with the same denominator, add the numerators and place the sum over the common denominator.

$$\frac{5}{11} + \frac{3}{11} = \frac{8}{11}$$

To subtract fractions with the same denominator, subtract the numerators and place the difference over the common denominator.

$$\frac{13}{15} - \frac{3}{15} = \frac{10}{15} = \frac{2}{3}$$

Fractions that represent the same quantity are called **equivalent fractions.**

$$\frac{1}{5} = \frac{1 \cdot 4}{5 \cdot 4} = \frac{4}{20}$$

$\dfrac{1}{5}$ and $\dfrac{4}{20}$ are equivalent fractions.

DEFINITIONS AND CONCEPTS	EXAMPLES

Section 1.4   Exponents, Order of Operations, Variable Expressions, and Equations

The expression a^n is an **exponential expression.** The number a is called the **base;** it is the repeated factor. The number n is called the **exponent;** it is the number of times that the base is a factor.

$$4^3 = 4 \cdot 4 \cdot 4 = 64$$
$$7^2 = 7 \cdot 7 = 49$$

Order of Operations

Simplify expressions in the following order. If grouping symbols are present, simplify expressions within those first, starting with the innermost set. Also, simplify the numerator and the denominator of a fraction separately.

1. Simplify exponential expressions.
2. Multiply or divide in order from left to right.
3. Add or subtract in order from left to right.

$$\frac{8^2 + 5(7 - 3)}{3 \cdot 7} = \frac{8^2 + 5(4)}{21}$$
$$= \frac{64 + 5(4)}{21}$$
$$= \frac{64 + 20}{21}$$
$$= \frac{84}{21}$$
$$= 4$$

A symbol used to represent a number is called a **variable.**

Examples of variables are:
$$q, x, z$$

An **algebraic expression** is a collection of numbers, variables, operation symbols, and grouping symbols.

Examples of algebraic expressions are:
$$5x, 2(y - 6), \frac{q^2 - 3q + 1}{6}$$

To evaluate an algebraic expression containing a variable, substitute a given number for the variable and simplify.

Evaluate $x^2 - y^2$ if $x = 5$ and $y = 3$.
$$x^2 - y^2 = (5)^2 - 3^2$$
$$= 25 - 9$$
$$= 16$$

A mathematical statement that two expressions are equal is called an **equation.**

Examples of equations are:
$$3x - 9 = 20$$
$$A = \pi r^2$$

A **solution** of an equation is a value for the variable that makes the equation a true statement.

Determine whether 4 is a solution of $5x + 7 = 27$.
$$5x + 7 = 27$$
$$5(4) + 7 \stackrel{?}{=} 27$$
$$20 + 7 \stackrel{?}{=} 27$$
$$27 = 27 \quad \text{True}$$

4 is a solution.

Section 1.5   Adding Real Numbers

To Add Two Numbers with the Same Sign

1. Add their absolute values.
2. Use their common sign as the sign of the sum.

Add.
$$10 + 7 = 17$$
$$-3 + (-8) = -11$$

To Add Two Numbers with Different Signs

1. Subtract their absolute values.
2. Use the sign of the number whose absolute value is larger as the sign of the sum.

$$-25 + 5 = -20$$
$$14 + (-9) = 5$$

DEFINITIONS AND CONCEPTS	EXAMPLES

Section 1.5   Adding Real Numbers (continued)

Two numbers that are the same distance from 0 but lie on opposite sides of 0 are called **opposites** or **additive inverses**. The opposite of a number a is denoted by $-a$.

The sum of a number a and its opposite, $-a$, is 0.

$$a + (-a) = 0$$

If a is a number, then $-(-a) = a$.

The opposite of -7 is 7.
The opposite of 123 is -123.

$$-4 + 4 = 0$$
$$12 + (-12) = 0$$
$$-(-8) = 8$$
$$-(-14) = 14$$

Section 1.6   Subtracting Real Numbers

To subtract two numbers a and b, add the first number a to the opposite of the second number b.

$$a - b = a + (-b)$$

Subtract.

$$3 - (-44) = 3 + 44 = 47$$
$$-5 - 22 = -5 + (-22) = -27$$
$$-30 - (-30) = -30 + 30 = 0$$

Section 1.7   Multiplying and Dividing Real Numbers

Quotient of two real numbers

$$\frac{a}{b} = a \cdot \frac{1}{b}$$

Multiplying and Dividing Real Numbers

The product or quotient of two numbers with the same sign is a positive number. The product or quotient of two numbers with different signs is a negative number.

Products and Quotients Involving Zero

The product of 0 and any number is 0.

$$b \cdot 0 = 0 \quad \text{and} \quad 0 \cdot b = 0$$

The quotient of a nonzero number and 0 is undefined.

$$\frac{b}{0} \text{ is undefined.}$$

The quotient of 0 and any nonzero number is 0.

$$\frac{0}{b} = 0$$

Multiply or divide.

$$\frac{42}{2} = 42 \cdot \frac{1}{2} = 21$$

$$7 \cdot 8 = 56 \quad -7 \cdot (-8) = 56$$
$$-2 \cdot 4 = -8 \quad 2 \cdot (-4) = -8$$
$$\frac{90}{10} = 9 \quad \frac{-90}{-10} = 9$$
$$\frac{42}{-6} = -7 \quad \frac{-42}{6} = -7$$

$$-4 \cdot 0 = 0 \quad 0 \cdot \left(-\frac{3}{4}\right) = 0$$

$$\frac{-85}{0} \text{ is undefined.}$$

$$\frac{0}{18} = 0 \quad \frac{0}{-47} = 0$$

Section 1.8   Properties of Real Numbers

Commutative Properties
Addition: $a + b = b + a$
Multiplication: $a \cdot b = b \cdot a$

Associative Properties
Addition: $(a + b) + c = a + (b + c)$
Multiplication: $(a \cdot b) \cdot c = a \cdot (b \cdot c)$

$$3 + (-7) = -7 + 3$$
$$-8 \cdot 5 = 5 \cdot (-8)$$

$$(5 + 10) + 20 = 5 + (10 + 20)$$
$$(-3 \cdot 2) \cdot 11 = -3 \cdot (2 \cdot 11)$$

(continued)

DEFINITIONS AND CONCEPTS	EXAMPLES

Section 1.8   Properties of Real Numbers (continued)

Two numbers whose product is 1 are called **multiplicative inverses** or **reciprocals.** The reciprocal of a nonzero number a is $\frac{1}{a}$ because $a \cdot \frac{1}{a} = 1$.

The reciprocal of 3 is $\frac{1}{3}$.

The reciprocal of $-\frac{2}{5}$ is $-\frac{5}{2}$.

Distributive Property $a(b + c) = a \cdot b + a \cdot c$

$$5(6 + 10) = 5 \cdot 6 + 5 \cdot 10$$
$$-2(3 + x) = -2 \cdot 3 + (-2)(x)$$

Identities $a + 0 = a$ $\qquad$ $0 + a = a$

$\qquad\qquad$ $a \cdot 1 = a$ $\qquad$ $1 \cdot a = a$

$$5 + 0 = 5 \qquad 0 + (-2) = -2$$
$$-14 \cdot 1 = -14 \qquad 1 \cdot 27 = 27$$

Inverses

Additive or opposite: $a + (-a) = 0$

$$7 + (-7) = 0$$

Multiplicative or reciprocal: $b \cdot \frac{1}{b} = 1$

$$3 \cdot \frac{1}{3} = 1$$

Chapter 1 Review

(1.2) *Insert* $<, >,$ *or* $=$ *in the appropriate space to make the following statements true.*

1. 8 $\quad$ 10

2. 7 $\quad$ 2

3. -4 $\quad$ -5

4. $\frac{12}{2}$ $\quad$ -8

5. $|-7|$ $\quad$ $|-8|$

6. $|-9|$ $\quad$ -9

7. $-|-1|$ $\quad$ -1

8. $|-14|$ $\quad$ $-(-14)$

9. 1.2 $\quad$ 1.02

10. $-\frac{3}{2}$ $\quad$ $-\frac{3}{4}$

TRANSLATING

Translate each statement into symbols.

11. Four is greater than or equal to negative three.

12. Six is not equal to five.

13. 0.03 is less than 0.3.

14. New York City has 155 museums and 400 art galleries. Write an inequality comparing the numbers 155 and 400. (*Source: Absolute Trivia.com*)

Given the following sets of numbers, list the numbers in each set that also belong to the set of:

a. Natural numbers

b. Whole numbers

c. Integers

d. Rational numbers

e. Irrational numbers

f. Real numbers

15. $\left\{ -6, 0, 1, 1\frac{1}{2}, 3, \pi, 9.62 \right\}$

16. $\left\{ -3, -1.6, 2, 5, \frac{11}{2}, 15.1, \sqrt{5}, 2\pi \right\}$

The following chart shows the gains and losses in dollars of Density Oil and Gas stock for a particular week.

Day	Gain or Loss in Dollars
Monday	+1
Tuesday	−2
Wednesday	+5
Thursday	+1
Friday	−4

17. Which day showed the greatest loss?

18. Which day showed the greatest gain?

(1.3) *Write the number as a product of prime factors.*

19. 36

20. 120

Perform the indicated operations. Write results in lowest terms.

21. $\frac{8}{15} \cdot \frac{27}{30}$

22. $\frac{7}{8} \div \frac{21}{32}$

23. $\frac{7}{15} + \frac{5}{6}$

24. $\frac{3}{4} - \frac{3}{20}$

25. $2\frac{3}{4} + 6\frac{5}{8}$

26. $7\frac{1}{6} - 2\frac{2}{3}$

27. $5 \div \frac{1}{3}$

28. $2 \cdot 8\frac{3}{4}$

Each circle represents a whole, or 1. Determine the unknown part of the circle.

29.

30.
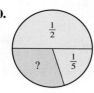

Find the area and the perimeter of each figure.

△ **31.**

△ **32.**
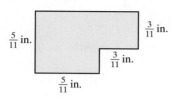

Octuplets were born in the U.S. in 2009. The following chart gives the octuplets' birthweights. The babies are listed in order of birth.

Baby	Gender	Birthweight (pounds)
Baby A	boy	$2\frac{1}{2}$
Baby B	girl	$2\frac{1}{8}$
Baby C	boy	$3\frac{1}{16}$
Baby D	girl	$2\frac{3}{16}$
Baby E	boy	$1\frac{3}{4}$
Baby F	boy	$2\frac{9}{16}$
Baby G	boy	$1\frac{13}{16}$
Baby H	boy	$2\frac{7}{16}$

33. What was the total weight of the boy octuplets?

34. What was the total weight of the girl octuplets?

35. Find the combined weight of all eight octuplets.

36. Which baby weighed the most?

37. Which baby weighed the least?

38. How much more did the heaviest baby weigh than the lightest baby?

(1.4) Choose the correct answer for each statement.

39. The expression $6 \cdot 3^2 + 2 \cdot 8$ simplifies to
   a. -52 **b.** 448   **c.** 70   **d.** 64

40. The expression $68 - 5 \cdot 2^3$ simplifies to
   a. -232 **b.** 28   **c.** 38   **d.** 504

Simplify each expression.

41. $\left(\dfrac{2}{7}\right)^2$

42. $\left(\dfrac{3}{4}\right)^3$

43. $3(1 + 2 \cdot 5) + 4$

44. $8 + 3(2 \cdot 6 - 1)$

45. $\dfrac{4 + |6 - 2| + 8^2}{4 + 6 \cdot 4}$

46. $5[3(2 + 5) - 5]$

TRANSLATING

Translate each word statement to symbols.

47. The difference of twenty and twelve is equal to the product of two and four.

48. The quotient of nine and two is greater than negative five.

Evaluate each expression if $x = 6$, $y = 2$, and $z = 8$.

49. $2x + 3y$

50. $x(y + 2z)$

51. $\dfrac{x}{y} + \dfrac{z}{2y}$

52. $x^2 - 3y^2$

△ **53.** The expression $180 - a - b$ represents the measure of the unknown angle of the given triangle. Replace a with 37 and b with 80 to find the measure of the unknown angle.

△ **54.** The expression $360 - a - b - c$ represents the measure of the unknown angle of the given quadrilateral. Replace a with 93, b with 80, and c with 82 to find the measure of the unknown angle.

Decide whether the given number is a solution to the given equation.

55. Is $x = 3$ a solution of $7x - 3 = 18$?

56. Is $x = 1$ a solution of $3x^2 + 4 = x - 1$?

(1.5) Find the additive inverse or the opposite.

57. -9

58. $\dfrac{2}{3}$

59. $|-2|$

60. $-|-7|$

Find the following sums.

61. $-15 + 4$

62. $-6 + (-11)$

63. $\dfrac{1}{16} + \left(-\dfrac{1}{4}\right)$

64. $-8 + |-3|$

65. $-4.6 + (-9.3)$

66. $-2.8 + 6.7$

(1.6) *Perform the indicated operations.*

67. $6 - 20$

68. $-3.1 - 8.4$

69. $-6 - (-11)$

70. $4 - 15$

71. $-21 - 16 + 3(8 - 2)$

72. $\dfrac{11 - (-9) + 6(8 - 2)}{2 + 3 \cdot 4}$

Evaluate each expression for $x = 3$, $y = -6$, and $z = -9$. Then choose the correct evaluation.

73. $2x^2 - y + z$

    a. 15 **b.** 3 **c.** 27 **d.** -3

74. $\dfrac{|y - 4x|}{2x}$

    a. 3 **b.** 1 **c.** -1 **d.** -3

75. At the beginning of the week, the price of Density Oil and Gas stock from Exercises 17 and 18 is \$50 per share. Find the price of a share of stock at the end of the week.

76. Find the price of a share of stock by the end of the day on Wednesday.

(1.7) *Find the multiplicative inverse or reciprocal.*

77. -6

78. $\dfrac{3}{5}$

Simplify each expression.

79. $6(-8)$

80. $(-2)(-14)$

81. $\dfrac{-18}{-6}$

82. $\dfrac{42}{-3}$

83. $\dfrac{4(-3) + (-8)}{2 + (-2)}$

84. $\dfrac{3(-2)^2 - 5}{-14}$

85. $\dfrac{-6}{0}$

86. $\dfrac{0}{-2}$

87. $-4^2 - (-3 + 5) \div (-1) \cdot 2$

88. $-5^2 - (2 - 20) \div (-3) \cdot 3$

If $x = -5$ and $y = -2$, evaluate each expression.

89. $x^2 - y^4$

90. $x^2 - y^3$

TRANSLATING

Translate each phrase to an expression. Use x to represent a number.

91. The product of -7 and a number

92. The quotient of a number and -13

93. Subtract a number from -20

94. The sum of -1 and a number

(1.8) *Name the property illustrated.*

95. $-6 + 5 = 5 + (-6)$

96. $6 \cdot 1 = 6$

97. $3(8 - 5) = 3 \cdot 8 - 3 \cdot (5)$

98. $4 + (-4) = 0$

99. $2 + (3 + 9) = (2 + 3) + 9$

100. $2 \cdot 8 = 8 \cdot 2$

101. $6(8 + 5) = 6 \cdot 8 + 6 \cdot 5$

102. $(3 \cdot 8) \cdot 4 = 3 \cdot (8 \cdot 4)$

103. $4 \cdot \dfrac{1}{4} = 1$

104. $8 + 0 = 8$

Use the distributive property to write each expression without parentheses.

105. $5(y - 2)$

106. $-3(z + y)$

107. $-(7 - x + 4z)$

108. $\dfrac{1}{2}(6z - 10)$

109. $-4(3x + 5) - 7$

110. $-8(2y + 9) - 1$

MIXED REVIEW

Insert $<$, $>$, or $=$ in the space between each pair of numbers.

111. $-|-11|$ $|11.4|$

112. $-1\dfrac{1}{2}$ $-2\dfrac{1}{2}$

Perform the indicated operations.

113. $-7.2 + (-8.1)$

114. $14 - 20$

115. $4(-20)$

116. $\dfrac{-20}{4}$

117. $-\dfrac{4}{5}\left(\dfrac{5}{16}\right)$

118. $-0.5(-0.3)$

119. $8 \div 2 \cdot 4$

120. $(-2)^4$

121. $\dfrac{-3 - 2(-9)}{-15 - 3(-4)}$

122. $5 + 2[(7 - 5)^2 + (1 - 3)]$

123. $-\dfrac{5}{8} \div \dfrac{3}{4}$

124. $\dfrac{-15 + (-4)^2 + |-9|}{10 - 2 \cdot 5}$

△ **125.** A trim carpenter needs a piece of quarter round molding $6\dfrac{1}{8}$ feet long for a bathroom. She finds a piece $7\dfrac{1}{2}$ feet long. How long a piece does she need to cut from the $7\dfrac{1}{2}$-foot-long molding in order to use it in the bathroom?

Chapter 1 Test MyMathLab® Test Prep VIDEOS YouTube

Translate the statement into symbols.

1. The absolute value of negative seven is greater than five.

2. The sum of nine and five is greater than or equal to four.

Simplify the expression.

3. $-13 + 8$

4. $-13 - (-2)$

5. $12 \div 4 \cdot 3 - 6 \cdot 2$

6. $(13)(-3)$

7. $(-6)(-2)$

8. $\dfrac{|-16|}{-8}$

9. $\dfrac{-8}{0}$

10. $\dfrac{|-6| + 2}{5 - 6}$

11. $\dfrac{1}{2} - \dfrac{5}{6}$

12. $5\dfrac{3}{4} - 1\dfrac{1}{8}$

13. $-0.6 + 1.875$

14. $3(-4)^2 - 80$

15. $6[5 + 2(3 - 8) - 3]$

16. $\dfrac{-12 + 3 \cdot 8}{4}$

17. $\dfrac{(-2)(0)(-3)}{-6}$

Insert $<$, $>$, or $=$ in the appropriate space to make each of the following statements true.

18. $-3 \quad -7$

19. $4 \quad -8$

20. $2 \quad |-3|$

21. $|-2| \quad -1 - (-3)$

22. In the state of Massachusetts, there are 2221 licensed child care centers and 10,993 licensed home-based child care providers. Write an inequality statement comparing the numbers 2221 and 10,993. (*Source:* Children's Foundation)

23. Given $\left\{-5, -1, 0, \dfrac{1}{4}, 1, 7, 11.6, \sqrt{7}, 3\pi\right\}$, list the numbers in this set that also belong to the set of:

   a. Natural numbers

   b. Whole numbers

   c. Integers

   d. Rational numbers

   e. Irrational numbers

   f. Real numbers

If $x = 6$, $y = -2$, and $z = -3$, evaluate each expression.

24. $x^2 + y^2$

25. $x + yz$

26. $2 + 3x - y$

27. $\dfrac{y + z - 1}{x}$

Identify the property illustrated by each expression.

28. $8 + (9 + 3) = (8 + 9) + 3$

29. $6 \cdot 8 = 8 \cdot 6$

30. $-6(2 + 4) = -6 \cdot 2 + (-6) \cdot 4$

31. $\dfrac{1}{6}(6) = 1$

32. Find the opposite of -9.

33. Find the reciprocal of $-\dfrac{1}{3}$.

The New Orleans Saints were 22 yards from the goal when the following series of gains and losses occurred.

	Gains and Losses in Yards
First Down	5
Second Down	-10
Third Down	-2
Fourth Down	29

34. During which down did the greatest loss of yardage occur?

35. Was a touchdown scored?

36. The temperature at the Winter Olympics was a frigid 14 degrees below zero in the morning, but by noon it had risen 31 degrees. What was the temperature at noon?

37. A health insurance provider had net incomes of $356 million, $460 million, and $-$166$ million in 3 consecutive years. What was the health insurance provider's total net income for these three years?

38. A stockbroker decided to sell 280 shares of stock, which decreased in value by $1.50 per share yesterday. How much money did she lose?

Equations, Inequalities, and Problem Solving

Much of mathematics relates to deciding which statements are true and which are false. For example, the statement $x + 7 = 15$ is an equation stating that the sum $x + 7$ has the same value as 15. Is this statement true or false? It is false for some values of x and true for just one value of x, namely 8. Our purpose in this chapter is to learn ways of deciding which values make an equation or an inequality true.

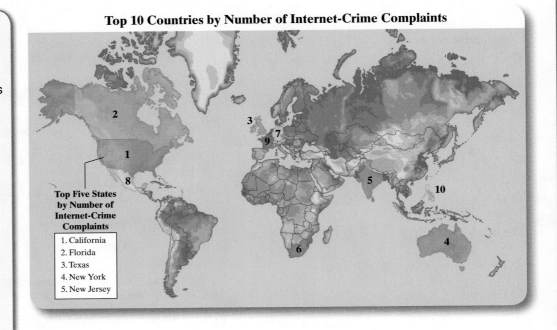

Top 10 Countries by Number of Internet-Crime Complaints

Top Five States by Number of Internet-Crime Complaints

1. California
2. Florida
3. Texas
4. New York
5. New Jersey

Internet Crime

The Internet Crime Complaint Center (IC3) is a joint operation between the FBI and the National White-Collar Crime Center. The IC3 receives and refers criminal complaints occurring on the Internet. Of course, nondelivery of merchandise or payment are the highest reported offenses.

In Section 2.6, Exercises 15 and 16, we analyze a bar graph on the yearly number of complaints received by the IC3.

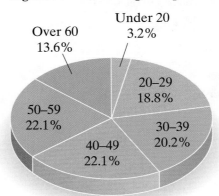

Ages of Persons Filing Complaints

Under 20 3.2%
Over 60 13.6%
20–29 18.8%
50–59 22.1%
30–39 20.2%
40–49 22.1%

2.1 Simplifying Algebraic Expressions

OBJECTIVES

1 Identify Terms, Like Terms, and Unlike Terms.
2 Combine Like Terms.
3 Use the Distributive Property to Remove Parentheses.
4 Write Word Phrases as Algebraic Expressions.

As we explore in this section, an expression such as $3x + 2x$ is not as simple as possible because—even without replacing x by a value—we can perform the indicated addition.

OBJECTIVE

1 Identifying Terms, Like Terms, and Unlike Terms

Before we practice simplifying expressions, some new language of algebra is presented. A **term** is a number or the product of a number and variables raised to powers.

Terms

$$-y, \quad 2x^3, \quad -5, \quad 3xz^2, \quad \frac{2}{y}, \quad 0.8z$$

The **numerical coefficient** (sometimes also simply called the **coefficient**) of a term is the numerical factor. The numerical coefficient of $3x$ is 3. Recall that $3x$ means $3 \cdot x$.

Term	Numerical Coefficient
$3x$	3
$\dfrac{y^3}{5}$	$\dfrac{1}{5}$ since $\dfrac{y^3}{5}$ means $\dfrac{1}{5} \cdot y^3$
$0.7ab^3c^5$	0.7
z	1
$-y$	-1
-5	-5

▶ **Helpful Hint**

The term $-y$ means $-1y$ and thus has a numerical coefficient of -1.
The term z means $1z$ and thus has a numerical coefficient of 1.

EXAMPLE 1 Identify the numerical coefficient in each term.

a. $-3y$ **b.** $22z^4$ **c.** y **d.** $-x$ **e.** $\dfrac{x}{7}$

Solution

a. The numerical coefficient of $-3y$ is -3.

b. The numerical coefficient of $22z^4$ is 22.

c. The numerical coefficient of y is 1, since y is $1y$.

d. The numerical coefficient of $-x$ is -1, since $-x$ is $-1x$.

e. The numerical coefficient of $\dfrac{x}{7}$ is $\dfrac{1}{7}$, since $\dfrac{x}{7}$ means $\dfrac{1}{7} \cdot x$.

PRACTICE

1 Identify the numerical coefficient in each term.

a. t **b.** $-7x$ **c.** $-\dfrac{w}{5}$ **d.** $43x^4$ **e.** $-b$

Terms with the same variables raised to exactly the same powers are called **like terms**. Terms that aren't like terms are called **unlike terms**.

Like Terms	Unlike Terms	Reason
$3x, 2x$	$5x, 5x^2$	Why? Same variable x but different powers x and x^2
$-6x^2y, 2x^2y, 4x^2y$	$7y, 3z, 8x^2$	Why? Different variables
$2ab^2c^3, ac^3b^2$	$6abc^3, 6ab^2$	Why? Different variables and different powers

> ▶ **Helpful Hint**
>
> In like terms, each variable and its exponent must match exactly, but these factors don't need to be in the same order.
>
> $$2x^2y \text{ and } 3yx^2 \text{ are like terms.}$$

EXAMPLE 2   Determine whether the terms are like or unlike.

a. $2x, 3x^2$ **b.** $4x^2y, x^2y, -2x^2y$ **c.** $-2yz, -3zy$ **d.** $-x^4, x^4$

Solution

a. Unlike terms, since the exponents on x are not the same.

b. Like terms, since each variable and its exponent match.

c. Like terms, since $zy = yz$ by the commutative property.

d. Like terms. ☐

PRACTICE

2   Determine whether the terms are like or unlike.

a. $-4xy, 5yx$ **b.** $5q, -3q^2$

c. $3ab^2, -2ab^2, 43ab^2$ **d.** $y^5, \dfrac{y^5}{2}$

OBJECTIVE

2   Combining Like Terms

An algebraic expression containing the sum or difference of like terms can be simplified by applying the distributive property. For example, by the distributive property, we rewrite the sum of the like terms $3x + 2x$ as

$$3x + 2x = (3 + 2)x = 5x$$

Also,

$$-y^2 + 5y^2 = -1y^2 + 5y^2 = (-1 + 5)y^2 = 4y^2$$

Simplifying the sum or difference of like terms is called **combining like terms.**

EXAMPLE 3   Simplify each expression by combining like terms.

a. $7x - 3x$ **b.** $10y^2 + y^2$ **c.** $8x^2 + 2x - 3x$ **d.** $9n^2 - 5n^2 + n^2$

Solution

a. $7x - 3x = (7 - 3)x = 4x$

b. $10y^2 + y^2 = 10y^2 + 1y^2 = (10 + 1)y^2 = 11y^2$

c. $8x^2 + 2x - 3x = 8x^2 + (2 - 3)x = 8x^2 - x$

d. $9n^2 - 5n^2 + n^2 = (9 - 5 + 1)n^2 = 5n^2$ ☐

PRACTICE

3   Simplify each expression by combining like terms.

a. $-3y + 11y$ **b.** $4x^2 + x^2$

c. $5x - 3x^2 + 8x^2$ **d.** $20y^2 + 2y^2 - y^2$

The previous example suggests the following:

> **Combining Like Terms**
>
> To **combine like terms,** add the numerical coefficients and multiply the result by the common variable factors.

EXAMPLE 4 Simplify each expression by combining like terms.

a. $2x + 3x + 5 + 2$ **b.** $-5a - 3 + a + 2$ **c.** $4y - 3y^2$

d. $2.3x + 5x - 6$ **e.** $-\frac{1}{2}b + b$

Solution Use the distributive property to combine like terms.

a. $2x + 3x + 5 + 2 = (2 + 3)x + (5 + 2)$
$$= 5x + 7$$

b. $-5a - 3 + a + 2 = -5a + 1a + (-3 + 2)$
$$= (-5 + 1)a + (-3 + 2)$$
$$= -4a - 1$$

c. $4y - 3y^2$ These two terms cannot be combined because they are unlike terms.

d. $2.3x + 5x - 6 = (2.3 + 5)x - 6$
$$= 7.3x - 6$$

e. $-\frac{1}{2}b + b = -\frac{1}{2}b + 1b = \left(-\frac{1}{2} + 1\right)b = \frac{1}{2}b$

PRACTICE
4 Use the distributive property to combine like terms.

a. $3y + 8y - 7 + 2$ **b.** $6x - 3 - x - 3$ **c.** $\frac{3}{4}t - t$

d. $9y + 3.2y + 10 + 3$ **e.** $5z - 3z^4$

OBJECTIVE
3 Using the Distributive Property

Simplifying expressions makes frequent use of the distributive property to also remove parentheses.

It may be helpful to study the examples below.

$$+(3a + 2) = +1(3a + 2) = +1(3a) + (+1)(2) = 3a + 2$$
means

$$-(3a + 2) = -1(3a + 2) = -1(3a) + (-1)(2) = -3a - 2$$
means

EXAMPLE 5 Find each product by using the distributive property to remove parentheses.

a. $5(3x + 2)$ **b.** $-2(y + 0.3z - 1)$ **c.** $-(9x + y - 2z + 6)$

Solution

a. $5(3x + 2) = 5 \cdot 3x + 5 \cdot 2$ Apply the distributive property.
$$= 15x + 10$$ Multiply.

b. $-2(y + 0.3z - 1) = -2(y) + (-2)(0.3z) + (-2)(-1)$ — Apply the distributive property.

$= -2y - 0.6z + 2$ — Multiply.

c. $-(9x + y - 2z + 6) = -1(9x + y - 2z + 6)$ — Distribute -1 over each term.

$= -1(9x) - 1(y) - 1(-2z) - 1(6)$

$= -9x - y + 2z - 6$ □

PRACTICE

5 Find each product by using the distributive property to remove parentheses.

a. $3(2x - 7)$ **b.** $-5(x - 0.5z - 5)$

c. $-(2x - y + z - 2)$

> **Helpful Hint**
>
> If a "$-$" sign precedes parentheses, the sign of each term inside the parentheses is changed when the distributive property is applied to remove parentheses.
>
> **Examples:**
>
> $-(2x + 1) = -2x - 1$ $-(-5x + y - z) = 5x - y + z$
>
> $-(x - 2y) = -x + 2y$ $-(-3x - 4y - 1) = 3x + 4y + 1$

When simplifying an expression containing parentheses, we often use the distributive property in both directions—first to remove parentheses and then again to combine any like terms.

EXAMPLE 6 Simplify each expression.

a. $3(2x - 5) + 1$ **b.** $-2(4x + 7) - (3x - 1)$ **c.** $9 + 3(4x - 10)$

Solution

a. $3(2x - 5) + 1 = 6x - 15 + 1$ — Apply the distributive property.

$= 6x - 14$ — Combine like terms.

b. $-2(4x + 7) - (3x - 1) = -8x - 14 - 3x + 1$ — Apply the distributive property.

$= -11x - 13$ — Combine like terms.

c. $9 + 3(4x - 10) = 9 + 12x - 30$ — Apply the distributive property.

$= -21 + 12x$ — Combine like terms.

or $12x - 21$ □

> **Helpful Hint**
>
> Don't forget to use the distributive property and multiply before adding or subtracting like terms.

PRACTICE

6 Simplify each expression.

a. $4(9x + 1) + 6$ **b.** $-7(2x - 1) - (6 - 3x)$ **c.** $8 - 5(6x + 5)$

EXAMPLE 7 Write the phrase below as an algebraic expression. Then simplify if possible.

"Subtract $4x - 2$ from $2x - 3$."

Solution "Subtract $4x - 2$ **from** $2x - 3$" translates to $(2x - 3) - (4x - 2)$. Next, simplify the algebraic expression.

$(2x - 3) - (4x - 2) = 2x - 3 - 4x + 2$ — Apply the distributive property.

$= -2x - 1$ — Combine like terms. □

PRACTICE
7   Write the phrase below as an algebraic expression. Then simplify if possible.

"Subtract $7x - 1$ from $2x + 3$."

OBJECTIVE

4   **Writing Word Phrases as Algebraic Expressions**

Next, we practice writing word phrases as algebraic expressions.

EXAMPLE 8   Write the following phrases as algebraic expressions and simplify if possible. Let x represent the unknown number.

a. Twice a number, plus 6

b. The difference of a number and 4, divided by 7

c. Five added to triple the sum of a number and 1

d. The sum of twice a number, 3 times the number, and 5 times the number

Solution

a. In words: twice a number   plus   6

Translate: $2x$ $+$ 6

b. In words: the difference of a number and 4   divided by   7

Translate: $x - 4$ $\div$ 7 or $\dfrac{x - 4}{7}$

c. In words: five   added to   triple   the sum of a number and 1

Translate: 5 $+$ $3 \cdot$ $(x + 1)$

Next, we simplify this expression.

$$5 + 3(x + 1) = 5 + 3x + 3 \quad \text{Use the distributive property.}$$
$$= 8 + 3x \quad \text{Combine like terms.}$$

d. The phrase "the sum of" means that we add.

In words: twice a number   added to   3 times the number   added to   5 times the number

Translate: $2x$ $+$ $3x$ $+$ $5x$

Now let's simplify.

$$2x + 3x + 5x = 10x \quad \text{Combine like terms.}$$

PRACTICE
8   Write the following phrases as algebraic expressions and simplify if possible. Let x represent the unknown number.

a. Three added to double a number

b. Six subtracted from the sum of 5 and a number

c. Two times the sum of 3 and a number, increased by 4

d. The sum of a number, half the number, and 5 times the number

Vocabulary, Readiness & Video Check

Use the choices below to fill in each blank. Some choices may be used more than once.

like	numerical coefficient	term	distributive
unlike	combine like terms	expression	

1. $23y^2 + 10y - 6$ is called a(n) _____ while $23y^2$, $10y$, and -6 are each called a(n) _____.

2. To simplify $x + 4x$, we ___Combine like terms___.

3. The term y has an understood ___numerical coefficient___ of 1.

4. The terms $7z$ and $7y$ are ___unlike___ terms and the terms $7z$ and $-z$ are ___like___ terms.

5. For the term $-\frac{1}{2}xy^2$, the number $-\frac{1}{2}$ is the ___num co___.

6. $5(3x - y)$ equals $15x - 5y$ by the ___dis___ property.

Martin-Gay Interactive Videos

See Video 2.1

Watch the section lecture video and answer the following questions.

OBJECTIVE 1
7. Example 7 shows two terms with exactly the same variables. Why are these terms not considered like terms?

OBJECTIVE 2
8. Example 8 shows us that when combining like terms, we are actually applying what property?

OBJECTIVE 3
9. The expression in ⊞ Example 11 shows a minus sign before parentheses. When using the distributive property to multiply and remove parentheses, what number are we actually distributing to each term within the parentheses?

OBJECTIVE 4
10. Write the phrase given in ⊞ Example 14, translate it to an algebraic expression, then simplify it. Why are we able to simplify it?

2.1 Exercise Set   MyMathLab®

Identify the numerical coefficient of each term. See Example 1.

1. $-7y$
2. $3x$
3. x
4. $-y$
5. $17x^2y$
6. $1.2xyz$

Indicate whether the terms in each list are like or unlike. See Example 2.

▶ 7. $5y, -y$
▶ 8. $-2x^2y, 6xy$
9. $2z, 3z^2$
10. $ab^2, -7ab^2$
11. $8wz, \frac{1}{7}zw$
12. $7.4p^3q^2, 6.2p^3q^2r$

Simplify each expression by combining any like terms. See Examples 3 and 4.

13. $7y + 8y$
▶ 14. $3x + 2x$
15. $8w - w + 6w$
16. $c - 7c + 2c$

17. $3b - 5 - 10b - 4$
18. $6g + 5 - 3g - 7$
19. $m - 4m + 2m - 6$
20. $a + 3a - 2 - 7a$
21. $5g - 3 - 5 - 5g$
22. $8p + 4 - 8p - 15$
23. $6.2x - 4 + x - 1.2$
24. $7.9y - 0.7 - y + 0.2$
25. $6x - 5x + x - 3 + 2x$
26. $8h + 13h - 6 + 7h - h$
27. $7x^2 + 8x^2 - 10x^2$
▶ 28. $8x^3 + x^3 - 11x^3$
▶ 29. $6x + 0.5 - 4.3x - 0.4x + 3$
30. $0.4y - 6.7 + y - 0.3 - 2.6y$

Simplify each expression. First use the distributive property to remove any parentheses. See Examples 5 and 6.

31. $5(y - 4)$ $5y - 4$

32. $7(r - 3)$ $7r - 21$

33. $-2(x + 2)$ $-2x - 4$

34. $-4(y + 6)$ $-4x + -24$

35. $7(d - 3) + 10$ $7d - 21 + 10 = 7d - 11$

36. $9(z + 7) - 15$ $9z + 63 - 15 \quad 9z + 48$

37. $-5(2x - 3y + 6)$

38. $-2(4x - 3z - 1)$

39. $-(3x - 2y + 1)$

40. $-(y + 5z - 7)$

▶ **41.** $5(x + 2) - (3x - 4)$

42. $4(2x - 3) - 2(x + 1)$

Write each of the following as an algebraic expression. Simplify if possible. See Example 7.

43. Add $6x + 7$ to $4x - 10$. $(6x + 7) + (4x - 10)$

44. Add $3y - 5$ to $y + 16$.

45. Subtract $7x + 1$ from $3x - 8$.

46. Subtract $4x - 7$ from $12 + x$.

▶ **47.** Subtract $5m - 6$ from $m - 9$.

48. Subtract $m - 3$ from $2m - 6$.

MIXED PRACTICE

Simplify each expression. See Examples 3 through 7.

49. $2k - k - 6$

50. $7c - 8 - c$

51. $-9x + 4x + 18 - 10x$

52. $5y - 14 + 7y - 20y$

53. $-4(3y - 4) + 12y$

54. $-3(2x + 5) - 6x$

55. $3(2x - 5) - 5(x - 4)$

56. $2(6x - 1) - (x - 7)$

57. $-2(3x - 4) + 7x - 6$

58. $8y - 2 - 3(y + 4)$

59. $5k - (3k - 10)$

60. $-11c - (4 - 2c)$

61. Subtract $6x - 1$ from $3x + 4$

62. Subtract $4 + 3y$ from $8 - 5y$

63. $3.4m - 4 - 3.4m - 7$

64. $2.8w - 0.9 - 0.5 - 2.8w$

65. $\frac{1}{3}(7y - 1) + \frac{1}{6}(4y + 7)$

66. $\frac{1}{5}(9y + 2) + \frac{1}{10}(2y - 1)$

67. $2 + 4(6x - 6)$

68. $8 + 4(3x - 4)$

69. $0.5(m + 2) + 0.4m$

70. $0.2(k + 8) - 0.1k$

71. $10 - 3(2x + 3y)$

72. $14 - 11(5m + 3n)$

73. $6(3x - 6) - 2(x + 1) - 17x$

74. $7(2x + 5) - 4(x + 2) - 20x$

75. $\frac{1}{2}(12x - 4) - (x + 5)$

76. $\frac{1}{3}(9x - 6) - (x - 2)$

TRANSLATING

Write each phrase as an algebraic expression and simplify if possible. Let x represent the unknown number. See Examples 7 and 8.

▶ **77.** Twice a number, decreased by four

78. The difference of a number and two, divided by five

79. Seven added to double a number

80. Eight more than triple a number

81. Three-fourths of a number, increased by twelve

82. Eleven, increased by two-thirds of a number

▶ **83.** The sum of 5 times a number and −2, added to 7 times a number

84. The sum of 3 times a number and 10, subtracted from 9 times a number

85. Eight times the sum of a number and six

86. Six times the difference of a number and five

87. Double a number, minus the sum of the number and ten

88. Half a number, minus the product of the number and eight

89. The sum of 2, three times a number, −9, and four times a number

90. The sum of twice a number, −1, five times a number, and −12

REVIEW AND PREVIEW

Evaluate the following expressions for the given values. See Section 1.6.

91. If $x = -1$ and $y = 3$, find $y - x^2$.

92. If $g = 0$ and $h = -4$, find $gh - h^2$.

93. If $a = 2$ and $b = -5$, find $a - b^2$.

94. If $x = -3$, find $x^3 - x^2 + 4$.

95. If $y = -5$ and $z = 0$, find $yz - y^2$.

96. If $x = -2$, find $x^3 - x^2 - x$.

CONCEPT EXTENSIONS

△ **97.** Recall that the perimeter of a figure is the total distance around the figure. Given the following rectangle, express the perimeter as an algebraic expression containing the variable x.

5x feet

(4x − 1) feet   (4x − 1) feet

5x feet

△ **98.** Given the following triangle, express its perimeter as an algebraic expression containing the variable x.

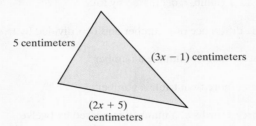

5 centimeters

(3x − 1) centimeters

(2x + 5) centimeters

Given the following two rules, determine whether each scale in Exercises 99 through 102 is balanced.

1 cone balances 1 cube

1 cylinder balances 2 cubes

99.

100.

101.

102.

Write each algebraic expression described.

103. Write an expression with 4 terms that simplifies to $3x - 4$.

104. Write an expression of the form ____ (____ + ____) whose product is $6x + 24$.

105. To convert from feet to inches, we multiply by 12. For example, the number of inches in 2 feet is $12 \cdot 2$ inches. If one board has a length of $(x + 2)$ *feet* and a second board has a length of $(3x - 1)$ *inches,* express their total length in inches as an algebraic expression.

106. The value of 7 nickels is $5 \cdot 7$ cents. Likewise, the value of x nickels is $5x$ cents. If the money box in a drink machine contains x *nickels,* $3x$ *dimes,* and $(30x - 1)$ *quarters,* express their total value in cents as an algebraic expression.

107. In your own words, explain how to combine like terms.

108. Do like terms always contain the same numerical coefficients? Explain your answer.

For Exercises 109 through 114, see the example below.

Example

Simplify $-3xy + 2x^2y - (2xy - 1)$.

Solution

$$-3xy + 2x^2y - (2xy - 1)$$
$$= -3xy + 2x^2y - 2xy + 1 = -5xy + 2x^2y + 1$$

Simplify each expression.

109. $5b^2c^3 + 8b^3c^2 - 7b^3c^2$

110. $4m^4p^2 + m^4p^2 - 5m^2p^4$

111. $3x - (2x^2 - 6x) + 7x^2$

112. $9y^2 - (6xy^2 - 5y^2) - 8xy^2$

113. $-(2x^2y + 3z) + 3z - 5x^2y$

114. $-(7c^3d - 8c) - 5c - 4c^3d$

2.2 The Addition and Multiplication Properties of Equality

OBJECTIVE

1   Defining Linear Equations and Using the Addition Property ▶

Recall from Section 1.4 that an equation is a statement that two expressions have the same value. Also, a value of the variable that makes an equation a true statement is called a solution or root of the equation. The process of finding the solution of an equation is called **solving** the equation for the variable. In this section we concentrate on solving **linear equations** in one variable.

Linear Equation in One Variable

A linear equation in one variable can be written in the form

$$ax + b = c$$

where a, b, and c are real numbers and $a \neq 0$.

Evaluating a linear equation for a given value of the variable, as we did in Section 1.4, can tell us whether that value is a solution, but we can't rely on evaluating an equation as our method of solving it.

   Instead, to solve a linear equation in x, we write a series of simpler equations, all *equivalent* to the original equation, so that the final equation has the form

$$x = \textbf{number} \quad \text{or} \quad \textbf{number} = x$$

Equivalent equations are equations that have the same solution. This means that the "number" above is the solution to the original equation.

   The first property of equality that helps us write simpler equivalent equations is the **addition property of equality.**

Addition Property of Equality

If a, b, and c are real numbers, then

$$a = b \quad \text{and} \quad a + c = b + c$$

are equivalent equations.

This property guarantees that adding the same number to both sides of an equation does not change the solution of the equation. Since subtraction is defined in terms of addition, we may also **subtract the same number from both sides** without changing the solution.

   A good way to picture a true equation is as a balanced scale. Since it is balanced, each side of the scale weighs the same amount.

If the same weight is added to or subtracted from each side, the scale remains balanced.

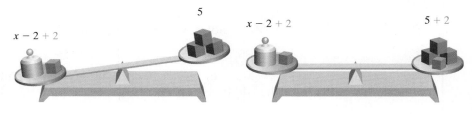

We use the addition property of equality to write equivalent equations until the variable is by itself on one side of the equation, and the equation looks like "x = number" or "number = x."

EXAMPLE 1 Solve $x - 7 = 10$ for x.

Solution To solve for x, we want x alone on one side of the equation. To do this, we add 7 to both sides of the equation.

$$x - 7 = 10$$
$$x - 7 + 7 = 10 + 7 \quad \text{Add 7 to both sides.}$$
$$x = 17 \quad \text{Simplify.}$$

The solution of the equation $x = 17$ is obviously 17. Since we are writing equivalent equations, the solution of the equation $x - 7 = 10$ is also 17.

Check: To check, replace x with 17 in the original equation.

$$x - 7 = 10$$
$$17 - 7 \stackrel{?}{=} 10 \quad \text{Replace } x \text{ with 17 in the original equation.}$$
$$10 = 10 \quad \text{True}$$

Since the statement is true, 17 is the solution. □

PRACTICE
1 Solve: $x + 3 = -5$ for x.

✓**CONCEPT CHECK**
Use the addition property to fill in the blanks so that the middle equation simplifies to the last equation.

$$x - 5 = 3$$
$$x - 5 + \underline{\quad} = 3 + \underline{\quad}$$
$$x = 8$$

EXAMPLE 2 Solve $y + 0.6 = -1.0$ for y.

Solution To get y alone on one side of the equation, subtract 0.6 from both sides of the equation.

$$y + 0.6 = -1.0$$
$$y + 0.6 - 0.6 = -1.0 - 0.6 \quad \text{Subtract 0.6 from both sides.}$$
$$y = -1.6 \quad \text{Combine like terms.}$$

Check: To check the proposed solution, -1.6, replace y with -1.6 in the original equation.

$$y + 0.6 = -1.0$$
$$-1.6 + 0.6 \stackrel{?}{=} -1.0 \quad \text{Replace } y \text{ with } -1.6 \text{ in the original equation.}$$
$$-1.0 = -1.0 \quad \text{True}$$

The solution is -1.6. □

PRACTICE
2 Solve: $y - 0.3 = -2.1$ for y.

Many times, it is best to simplify one or both sides of an equation before applying the addition property of equality.

EXAMPLE 3   Solve: $2x + 3x - 5 + 7 = 10x + 3 - 6x - 4$

Solution   First we simplify both sides of the equation.

$$2x + 3x - 5 + 7 = 10x + 3 - 6x - 4$$
$$5x + 2 = 4x - 1 \qquad \text{Combine like terms on}$$
$$\text{each side of the equation.}$$

Next, we want all terms with a variable on one side of the equation and all numbers on the other side.

$$5x + 2 - 4x = 4x - 1 - 4x \quad \text{Subtract } 4x \text{ from both sides.}$$
$$x + 2 = -1 \qquad\qquad \text{Combine like terms.}$$
$$x + 2 - 2 = -1 - 2 \qquad \text{Subtract 2 from both sides to get } x \text{ alone.}$$
$$x = -3 \qquad\qquad \text{Combine like terms.}$$

Check: $\qquad 2x + 3x - 5 + 7 = 10x + 3 - 6x - 4 \qquad$ Original equation

$$2(-3) + 3(-3) - 5 + 7 \stackrel{?}{=} 10(-3) + 3 - 6(-3) - 4 \quad \text{Replace } x \text{ with } -3.$$
$$-6 - 9 - 5 + 7 \stackrel{?}{=} -30 + 3 + 18 - 4 \qquad \text{Multiply.}$$
$$-13 = -13 \qquad\qquad\qquad \text{True}$$

The solution is -3.

PRACTICE
3   Solve: $8x - 5x - 3 + 9 = x + x + 3 - 7$

If an equation contains parentheses, we use the distributive property to remove them.

EXAMPLE 4   Solve: $7 = -5(2a - 1) - (-11a + 6)$.

Solution
$$7 = -5(2a - 1) - (-11a + 6)$$
$$7 = -10a + 5 + 11a - 6 \qquad \text{Apply the distributive property.}$$
$$7 = a - 1 \qquad\qquad\qquad \text{Combine like terms.}$$
$$7 + 1 = a - 1 + 1 \qquad\qquad \text{Add 1 to both sides to get } a \text{ alone.}$$
$$8 = a \qquad\qquad\qquad\qquad \text{Combine like terms.}$$

Check to see that 8 is the solution.

PRACTICE
4   Solve: $2 = 4(2a - 3) - (7a + 4)$

▶ **Helpful Hint**
We may solve an equation so that the variable is alone on either side of the equation. For example, $8 = a$ is equivalent to $a = 8$.

When solving equations, we may sometimes encounter an equation such as

$$-x = 5.$$

This equation is not solved for x because x is not isolated. One way to solve this equation for x is to recall that

"$-$" can be read as "the opposite of."

We can read the equation $-x = 5$ then as "the opposite of $x = 5$." If the opposite of x is 5, this means that x is the opposite of 5 or -5.

In summary,

$$-x = 5 \quad \text{and} \quad x = -5$$

are equivalent equations and $x = -5$ is solved for x.

OBJECTIVE

2   Using the Multiplication Property

As useful as the addition property of equality is, it cannot help us solve every type of linear equation in one variable. For example, adding or subtracting a value on both sides of the equation does not help solve

$$\frac{5}{2}x = 15.$$

Instead, we apply another important property of equality, the **multiplication property of equality.**

> **Multiplication Property of Equality**
>
> If a, b, and c are real numbers and $c \neq 0$, then
>
> $$a = b \quad \text{and} \quad ac = bc$$
>
> are equivalent equations.

This property guarantees that multiplying both sides of an equation by the same non-zero number does not change the solution of the equation. Since division is defined in terms of multiplication, we may also **divide both sides of the equation by the same nonzero number** without changing the solution.

EXAMPLE 5   Solve: $\dfrac{5}{2}x = 15.$

___**Solution**___   To get x alone, multiply both sides of the equation by the reciprocal of $\dfrac{5}{2}$, which is $\dfrac{2}{5}$.

$$\frac{5}{2}x = 15$$

> ▶ **Helpful Hint**
> Don't forget to multiply *both sides* by $\dfrac{2}{5}$.

$$\frac{2}{5} \cdot \frac{5}{2}x = \frac{2}{5} \cdot 15 \quad \text{Multiply both sides by } \frac{2}{5}.$$

$$\left(\frac{2}{5} \cdot \frac{5}{2}\right)x = \frac{2}{5} \cdot 15 \quad \text{Apply the associative property.}$$

$$1x = 6 \quad \text{Simplify.}$$

or

$$x = 6$$

Check: Replace x with 6 in the original equation.

$$\frac{5}{2}x = 15 \quad \text{Original equation}$$

$$\frac{5}{2}(6) \stackrel{?}{=} 15 \quad \text{Replace } x \text{ with 6.}$$

$$15 = 15 \quad \text{True}$$

The solution is 6.

PRACTICE

5   Solve: $\dfrac{4}{5}x = 16$

In the equation $\frac{5}{2}x = 15$, $\frac{5}{2}$ is the coefficient of x. When the coefficient of x is a *fraction,* we will get x alone by multiplying by the reciprocal. When the coefficient of x is an integer or a decimal, it is usually more convenient to divide both sides by the coefficient. (Dividing by a number is, of course, the same as multiplying by the reciprocal of the number.)

EXAMPLE 6   Solve: $-3x = 33$

Solution   Recall that $-3x$ means $-3 \cdot x$. To get x alone, we divide both sides by the coefficient of x, that is, -3.

$$-3x = 33$$
$$\frac{-3x}{-3} = \frac{33}{-3} \quad \text{Divide both sides by } -3.$$
$$1x = -11 \quad \text{Simplify.}$$
$$x = -11$$

Check:
$$-3x = 33 \quad \text{Original equation}$$
$$-3(-11) \stackrel{?}{=} 33 \quad \text{Replace } x \text{ with } -11.$$
$$33 = 33 \quad \text{True}$$

The solution is -11.   □

PRACTICE
6   Solve: $8x = -96$

EXAMPLE 7   Solve: $\frac{y}{7} = 20$

Solution   Recall that $\frac{y}{7} = \frac{1}{7}y$. To get y alone, we multiply both sides of the equation by 7, the reciprocal of $\frac{1}{7}$.

$$\frac{y}{7} = 20$$
$$\frac{1}{7}y = 20$$
$$7 \cdot \frac{1}{7}y = 7 \cdot 20 \quad \text{Multiply both sides by 7.}$$
$$1y = 140 \quad \text{Simplify.}$$
$$y = 140$$

Check:
$$\frac{y}{7} = 20 \quad \text{Original equation}$$
$$\frac{140}{7} \stackrel{?}{=} 20 \quad \text{Replace } y \text{ with 140.}$$
$$20 = 20 \quad \text{True}$$

The solution is 140.   □

PRACTICE
7   Solve: $\frac{x}{5} = 13$

OBJECTIVE
3   Using Both the Addition and Multiplication Properties

Next, we practice solving equations using both properties.

EXAMPLE 8 Solve: $12a - 8a = 10 + 2a - 13 - 7$

Solution First, simplify both sides of the equation by combining like terms.

$$12a - 8a = 10 + 2a - 13 - 7$$
$$4a = 2a - 10 \qquad \text{Combine like terms.}$$

To get all terms containing a variable on one side, subtract $2a$ from both sides.

$$4a - 2a = 2a - 10 - 2a \qquad \text{Subtract } 2a \text{ from both sides.}$$
$$2a = -10 \qquad \text{Simplify.}$$
$$\frac{2a}{2} = \frac{-10}{2} \qquad \text{Divide both sides by 2.}$$
$$a = -5 \qquad \text{Simplify.}$$

Check: Check by replacing a with -5 in the original equation. The solution is -5. □

PRACTICE
8 Solve: $6b - 11b = 18 + 2b - 6 + 9$

OBJECTIVE
4 Writing Word Phrases as Algebraic Expressions

Next, we practice writing word phrases as algebraic expressions.

EXAMPLE 9

a. The sum of two numbers is 8. If one number is 3, find the other number.

b. The sum of two numbers is 8. If one number is x, write an expression representing the other number.

c. An 8-foot board is cut into two pieces. If one piece is x feet, express the length of the other piece in terms of x.

Solution

a. If the sum of two numbers is 8 and one number is 3, we find the other number by subtracting 3 from 8. The other number is $8 - 3$ or 5.

b. If the sum of two numbers is 8 and one number is x, we find the other number by subtracting x from 8. The other number is represented by $8 - x$.

c. If an 8-foot board is cut into two pieces and one piece is x feet, we find the other length by subtracting x from 8. The other piece is $(8 - x)$ feet.

□

PRACTICE
9

a. The sum of two numbers is 9. If one number is 2, find the other number.

b. The sum of two numbers is 9. If one number is x, write an expression representing the other number.

c. A 9-foot rope is cut into two pieces. If one piece is x feet, express the length of the other piece in terms of x.

EXAMPLE 10   If x is the first of three consecutive integers, express the sum of the three integers in terms of x. Simplify if possible.

Solution   An example of three consecutive integers is

The second consecutive integer is always 1 more than the first, and the third consecutive integer is 2 more than the first. If x is the first of three consecutive integers, the three consecutive integers are

Their sum is

In words:	first integer	$+$	second integer	$+$	third integer
	$\downarrow$		$\downarrow$		$\downarrow$
Translate:	x	$+$	$(x + 1)$	$+$	$(x + 2)$

which simplifies to $3x + 3$.

PRACTICE
10   If x is the first of three consecutive *even* integers, express their sum in terms of x.

Below are examples of consecutive even and odd integers.

Consecutive Even integers: *Consecutive Odd integers:*

> ▶ Helpful Hint
>
> If x is an odd integer, then $x + 2$ is the next odd integer. This 2 simply means that odd integers are always 2 units from each other. (The same is true for even integers. They are always 2 units from each other.)
>
>

Vocabulary, Readiness & Video Check

Use the choices below to fill in each blank. Some choices will be used more than once.

addition   solving ✓   expression ✓   true ✓   multiplication ✓

equivalent ✓   equation ✓   solution   false ✓

1. The difference between an equation and an expression is that a(n) *equation* contains an equal sign, whereas an ___*ex*___ does not.

2. ___*eca*___ equations are equations that have the same solution.

3. A value of the variable that makes the equation a true statement is called a(n) _____ of the equation.

4. The process of finding the solution of an equation is called ___*solving*___ the equation for the variable.

5. By the ___*addition*___ property of equality, $x = -2$ and $x + 10 = -2 + 10$ are equivalent equations.

6. By the ___*addition*___ property of equality, $x = -7$ and $x - 5 = -7 - 5$ are equivalent equations.

7. By the ___*mult*___ property of equality, $y = \dfrac{1}{2}$ and $5 \cdot y = 5 \cdot \dfrac{1}{2}$ are equivalent equations.

8. By the ___*mult*___ property of equality, $9x = -63$ and $\dfrac{9x}{9} = \dfrac{-63}{9}$ are equivalent equations.

9. True or false: The equations $x = \dfrac{1}{2}$ and $\dfrac{1}{2} = x$ are equivalent equations. ___*true*___

10. True or false: The equations $\dfrac{z}{4} = 10$ and $4 \cdot \dfrac{z}{4} = 10$ are equivalent equations. ___*false*___

Martin-Gay Interactive Videos

See Video 2.2

Watch the section lecture video and answer the following questions.

OBJECTIVE 1
11. Complete this statement based on the lecture given before Example 1. The addition property of equality means that if we have an equation, we can add the same real number to _____ of the equation and have an equivalent equation.

OBJECTIVE 2
12. Complete this statement based on the lecture given before Example 4. We can multiply both sides of an equation by _____ nonzero number and have an equivalent equation.

OBJECTIVE 3
13. Both the addition and multiplication properties of equality are used to solve ⊞ Examples 6 and 7. In each of these examples, what property is applied first? What property is applied last? What conclusion, if any, can you make?

OBJECTIVE 4
14. Let x be the first of four consecutive integers, as in ⊞ Example 10. Now express the sum of the second integer and the fourth integer as an algebraic expression containing x.

2.2   Exercise Set   MyMathLab®

Solve each equation. Check each solution. See Examples 1 and 2.

1. $x + 7 = 10$
2. $x + 14 = 25$
3. $x - 2 = -4$
4. $y - 9 = 1$
5. $3 + x = -11$
6. $8 + z = -8$
7. $r - 8.6 = -8.1$
8. $t - 9.2 = -6.8$
9. $8x = 7x - 3$
10. $2x = x - 5$
11. $5b - 0.7 = 6b$
12. $9x + 5.5 = 10x$
13. $7x - 3 = 6x$
14. $18x - 9 = 19x$

Solve each equation. See Examples 3 and 4.

15. $2x + x - 6 = 2x + 5$
16. $7y + 2 = 2y + 4y + 2$
17. $3t - t - 7 = t - 7$
18. $4c + 8 - c = 8 + 2c$
19. $7x + 2x = 8x - 3$
20. $3n + 2n = 7 + 4n$
21. $-2(x + 1) + 3x = 14$
22. $10 = 8(3y - 4) - 23y + 20$

Solve each equation. See Example 6.

23. $-5x = 20$
24. $-7x = -49$

25. $3x = 0$

26. $-2x = 0$

27. $-x = -12$

28. $-y = 8$

29. $3x + 2x = 50$

30. $-y + 4y = 33$

Solve each equation. See Examples 5 and 7.

31. $\dfrac{2}{3}x = -8$

32. $\dfrac{3}{4}n = -15$

33. $\dfrac{1}{6}d = \dfrac{1}{2}$

34. $\dfrac{1}{8}v = \dfrac{1}{4}$

35. $\dfrac{a}{-2} = 1$

36. $\dfrac{d}{15} = 2$

37. $\dfrac{k}{7} = 0$

38. $\dfrac{f}{-5} = 0$

39. In your own words, explain the addition property of equality.

40. In your own words, explain the multiplication property of equality.

MIXED PRACTICE

Solve each equation. Check each solution. See Examples 1 through 8.

41. $2x - 4 = 16$

42. $3x - 1 = 26$

43. $-x + 2 = 22$

44. $-x + 4 = -24$

45. $6a + 3 = 3$

46. $8t + 5 = 5$

47. $6x + 10 = -20$

48. $-10y + 15 = 5$

49. $5 - 0.3k = 5$

50. $2 + 0.4p = 2$

51. $-2x + \dfrac{1}{2} = \dfrac{7}{2}$

52. $-3n - \dfrac{1}{3} = \dfrac{8}{3}$

53. $\dfrac{x}{3} + 2 = -5$

54. $\dfrac{b}{4} - 1 = -7$

55. $10 = 2x - 1$

56. $12 = 3j - 4$

57. $6z - 8 - z + 3 = 0$

58. $4a + 1 + a - 11 = 0$

59. $10 - 3x - 6 - 9x = 7$

60. $12x + 30 + 8x - 6 = 10$

61. $\dfrac{5}{6}x = 10$

62. $-\dfrac{3}{4}x = 9$

63. $1 = 0.3x - 0.5x - 5$

64. $19 = 0.4x - 0.9x - 6$

65. $z - 5z = 7z - 9 - z$

66. $t - 6t = -13 + t - 3t$

67. $0.4x - 0.6x - 5 = 1$

68. $0.1x - 0.6x - 6 = 19$

69. $6 - 2x + 8 = 10$

70. $-5 - 6y + 6 = 19$

71. $-3a + 6 + 5a = 7a - 8a$

72. $4b - 8 - b = 10b - 3b$

73. $20 = -3(2x + 1) + 7x$

74. $-3 = -5(4x + 3) + 21x$

See Example 9.

75. Two numbers have a sum of 20. If one number is p, express the other number in terms of p.

76. Two numbers have a sum of 13. If one number is y, express the other number in terms of y.

77. A 10-foot board is cut into two pieces. If one piece is x feet long, express the other length in terms of x.

78. A 5-foot piece of string is cut into two pieces. If one piece is x feet long, express the other length in terms of x.

79. Two angles are *supplementary* if their sum is 180°. If one angle measures $x°$, express the measure of its supplement in terms of x.

80. Two angles are *complementary* if their sum is 90°. If one angle measures $x°$, express the measure of its complement in terms of x.

81. In a mayoral election, April Catarella received 284 more votes than Charles Pecot. If Charles received n votes, how many votes did April receive?

82. The length of the top of a computer desk is $1\dfrac{1}{2}$ feet longer than its width. If its width measures m feet, express its length as an algebraic expression in m.

83. The Verrazano-Narrows Bridge in New York City is the longest suspension bridge in North America. The Golden Gate Bridge in San Francisco is 60 feet shorter than the Verrazano-Narrows Bridge. If the length of the Verrazano-Narrows Bridge is m feet, express the length of the Golden Gate Bridge as an algebraic expression in m. (*Source: World Almanac*, 2000).

84. The longest interstate highway in the U.S. is I-90, which connects Seattle, Washington, and Boston, Massachusetts. The second longest interstate highway, I-80 (connecting San Francisco, California, and Teaneck, New Jersey), is 178.5 miles shorter than I-90. If the length of I-80 is m miles, express the length of I-90 as an algebraic expression in m. (*Source:* U.S. Department of Transportation–Federal Highway Administration)

85. In a recent year, the number of graduate students at the University of Texas at Austin was approximately 28,000 fewer than the number of undergraduate students. If the number of undergraduate students was n, how many graduate students attend UT Austin? (*Source:* University of Texas at Austin)

86. The Missouri River is the longest river in the United States. The Mississippi River is 200 miles shorter than the Missouri River. If the length of the Missouri River is r miles, express the length of the Mississippi River as an algebraic expression in r. (*Source:* U.S. Geological Survey)

87. The area of the Sahara Desert in Africa is 7 times the area of the Gobi Desert in Asia. If the area of the Gobi Desert is x square miles, express the area of the Sahara Desert as an algebraic expression in x.

88. The largest meteorite in the world is the Hoba West located in Namibia. Its weight is 3 times the weight of the Armanty meteorite located in Outer Mongolia. If the weight of the Armanty meteorite is y kilograms, express the weight of the Hoba West meteorite as an algebraic expression in y.

Write each algebraic expression described. Simplify if possible. See Example 10.

89. If x represents the first of two consecutive odd integers, express the sum of the two integers in terms of x.

90. If x is the first of four consecutive even integers, write their sum as an algebraic expression in x.

91. If x is the first of four consecutive integers, express the sum of the first integer and the third integer as an algebraic expression containing the variable x.

92. If x is the first of two consecutive integers, express the sum of 20 and the second consecutive integer as an algebraic expression containing the variable x.

93. Classrooms on one side of the science building are all numbered with consecutive even integers. If the first room on this side of the building is numbered x, write an expression in x for the sum of five classroom numbers in a row. Then simplify this expression.

94. Two sides of a quadrilateral have the same length, x, while the other two sides have the same length, both being the next consecutive odd integer. Write the sum of these lengths. Then simplify this expression.

REVIEW AND PREVIEW

Simplify each expression. See Section 2.1.

95. $5x + 2(x - 6)$ **96.** $-7y + 2y - 3(y + 1)$

97. $-(x - 1) + x$ **98.** $-(3a - 3) + 2a - 6$

Insert $<$, $>$, or $=$ in the appropriate space to make each statement true. See Sections 1.2 and 1.7.

99. $(-3)^2$ -3^2 **100.** $(-2)^4$ -2^4

101. $(-2)^3$ -2^3 **102.** $(-4)^3$ -4^3

CONCEPT EXTENSIONS

103. The sum of the angles of a triangle is 180°. If one angle of a triangle measures $x°$ and a second angle measures $(2x + 7)°$, express the measure of the third angle in terms of x. Simplify the expression.

104. A quadrilateral is a four-sided figure like the one shown below whose angle sum is 360°. If one angle measures $x°$, a second angle measures $3x°$, and a third angle measures $5x°$, express the measure of the fourth angle in terms of x. Simplify the expression.

105. Write two terms whose sum is $-3x$.

106. Write four terms whose sum is $2y - 6$.

Use the addition property to fill in each blank so that the middle equation simplifies to the last equation. See the Concept Check in this section.

107.
$$x - 4 = -9$$
$$x - 4 + (\quad) = -9 + (\quad)$$
$$x = -5$$

108.
$$a + 9 = 15$$
$$a + 9 + (\quad) = 15 + (\quad)$$
$$a = 6$$

Fill in the blanks with numbers of your choice so that each equation has the given solution. Note: Each blank may be replaced with a different number.

109. _____ $+ x =$ _____; Solution: -3

110. $x -$ _____ $=$ _____; Solution: -10

111. Let $x = 1$ and then $x = 2$ in the equation $x + 5 = x + 6$. Is either number a solution? How many solutions do you think this equation has? Explain your answer.

112. Let $x = 1$ and then $x = 2$ in the equation $x + 3 = x + 3$. Is either number a solution? How many solutions do you think this equation has? Explain your answer.

Fill in the blank with a number so that each equation has the given solution.

113. $6x =$ _____; solution: -8

114. _____ $x = 10$; solution: $\dfrac{1}{2}$

115. A licensed nurse practitioner is instructed to give a patient 2100 milligrams of an antibiotic over a period of 36 hours. If the antibiotic is to be given every 4 hours starting immediately, how much antibiotic should be given in each dose? To answer this question, solve the equation $9x = 2100$.

116. Suppose you are a pharmacist and a customer asks you the following question. His child is to receive 13.5 milliliters of a nausea medicine over a period of 54 hours. If the nausea medicine is to be administered every 6 hours starting immediately, how much medicine should be given in each dose?

Use a calculator to determine whether the given value is a solution of the given equation.

117. $8.13 + 5.85y = 20.05y - 8.91$; $y = 1.2$

118. $3(a + 4.6) = 5a + 2.5$; $a = 6.3$

Solve each equation.

119. $-3.6x = 10.62$

120. $4.95y = -31.185$

121. $7x - 5.06 = -4.92$

122. $0.06y + 2.63 = 2.5562$

2.3 Solving Linear Equations

OBJECTIVES

1 Apply a General Strategy for Solving a Linear Equation.

2 Solve Equations Containing Fractions.

3 Solve Equations Containing Decimals.

4 Recognize Identities and Equations with No Solution.

OBJECTIVE

1 Apply a General Strategy for Solving a Linear Equation

We now present a general strategy for solving linear equations. One new piece of strategy is a suggestion to "clear an equation of fractions" as a first step. Doing so makes the equation less tedious, since operating on integers is usually more convenient than operating on fractions.

Solving Linear Equations in One Variable

Step 1. Multiply on both sides by the LCD to clear the equation of fractions if they occur.

Step 2. Use the distributive property to remove parentheses if they occur.

Step 3. Simplify each side of the equation by combining like terms.

Step 4. Get all variable terms on one side and all numbers on the other side by using the addition property of equality.

Step 5. Get the variable alone by using the multiplication property of equality.

Step 6. Check the solution by substituting it into the original equation.

EXAMPLE 1   Solve: $4(2x - 3) + 7 = 3x + 5$

Solution   There are no fractions, so we begin with Step 2.

$$4(2x - 3) + 7 = 3x + 5$$

Step 2. $\quad\quad\quad 8x - 12 + 7 = 3x + 5 \quad\quad$ Apply the distributive property.

Step 3. $\quad\quad\quad\quad\quad 8x - 5 = 3x + 5 \quad\quad$ Combine like terms.

Step 4. Get all variable terms on the same side of the equation by subtracting $3x$ from both sides, then adding 5 to both sides.

$$8x - 5 - 3x = 3x + 5 - 3x \quad \text{Subtract } 3x \text{ from both sides.}$$
$$5x - 5 = 5 \quad\quad \text{Simplify.}$$
$$5x - 5 + 5 = 5 + 5 \quad\quad \text{Add 5 to both sides.}$$
$$5x = 10 \quad\quad \text{Simplify.}$$

Step 5. Use the multiplication property of equality to get x alone.

$$\frac{5x}{5} = \frac{10}{5} \quad\quad \text{Divide both sides by 5.}$$
$$x = 2 \quad\quad \text{Simplify.}$$

Step 6. Check.

> ▶ **Helpful Hint**
> When checking solutions, remember to use the original written equation.

$$4(2x - 3) + 7 = 3x + 5 \quad\quad \text{Original equation}$$
$$4[2(2) - 3] + 7 \stackrel{?}{=} 3(2) + 5 \quad\quad \text{Replace } x \text{ with 2.}$$
$$4(4 - 3) + 7 \stackrel{?}{=} 6 + 5$$
$$4(1) + 7 \stackrel{?}{=} 11$$
$$4 + 7 \stackrel{?}{=} 11$$
$$11 = 11 \quad\quad \text{True}$$

The solution is 2 or the solution set is $\{2\}$. $\quad\quad\quad\quad\quad\quad\quad\quad\quad\quad$ □

PRACTICE
1   Solve: $2(4a - 9) + 3 = 5a - 6$

EXAMPLE 2   Solve: $8(2 - t) = -5t$

Solution   First, we apply the distributive property.

$$8(2 - t) = -5t$$

Step 2. $\quad\quad 16 - 8t = -5t \quad\quad$ Use the distributive property.

Step 4. $16 - 8t + 8t = -5t + 8t \quad\quad$ To get variable terms on one side, add $8t$ to both sides.

$$16 = 3t \quad\quad \text{Combine like terms.}$$

Step 5. $\quad\quad\quad \dfrac{16}{3} = \dfrac{3t}{3} \quad\quad$ Divide both sides by 3.

$$\frac{16}{3} = t \quad\quad \text{Simplify.}$$

Step 6. Check.

$$8(2 - t) = -5t \quad\quad \text{Original equation}$$
$$8\left(2 - \frac{16}{3}\right) \stackrel{?}{=} -5\left(\frac{16}{3}\right) \quad\quad \text{Replace } t \text{ with } \frac{16}{3}.$$
$$8\left(\frac{6}{3} - \frac{16}{3}\right) \stackrel{?}{=} -\frac{80}{3} \quad\quad \text{The LCD is 3.}$$

$$8\left(-\frac{10}{3}\right) \overset{?}{=} -\frac{80}{3}$$ Subtract fractions.

$$-\frac{80}{3} = -\frac{80}{3}$$ True

The solution is $\frac{16}{3}$. □

PRACTICE
2   Solve: $7(x - 3) = -6x$

OBJECTIVE
2   **Solving Equations Containing Fractions**

If an equation contains fractions, we can clear the equation of fractions by multiplying both sides by the LCD of all denominators. By doing this, we avoid working with time-consuming fractions.

EXAMPLE 3   Solve: $\dfrac{x}{2} - 1 = \dfrac{2}{3}x - 3$

Solution   We begin by clearing fractions. To do this, we multiply both sides of the equation by the LCD of 2 and 3, which is 6.

$$\frac{x}{2} - 1 = \frac{2}{3}x - 3$$

Step 1. $6\left(\dfrac{x}{2} - 1\right) = 6\left(\dfrac{2}{3}x - 3\right)$ Multiply both sides by the LCD, 6.

Step 2. $6\left(\dfrac{x}{2}\right) - 6(1) = 6\left(\dfrac{2}{3}x\right) - 6(3)$ Apply the distributive property.

$$3x - 6 = 4x - 18$$ Simplify.

> ▶ **Helpful Hint**
> Don't forget to multiply *each* term by the LCD.

There are no longer grouping symbols and no like terms on either side of the equation, so we continue with Step 4.

$$3x - 6 = 4x - 18$$

Step 4. $3x - 6 - 3x = 4x - 18 - 3x$ To get variable terms on one side, subtract $3x$ from both sides.

$$-6 = x - 18$$ Simplify.

$$-6 + 18 = x - 18 + 18$$ Add 18 to both sides.

$$12 = x$$ Simplify.

Step 5.   The variable is now alone, so there is no need to apply the multiplication property of equality.

Step 6.   Check.

$$\frac{x}{2} - 1 = \frac{2}{3}x - 3$$ Original equation

$$\frac{12}{2} - 1 \overset{?}{=} \frac{2}{3} \cdot 12 - 3$$ Replace x with 12.

$$6 - 1 \overset{?}{=} 8 - 3$$ Simplify.

$$5 = 5$$ True

The solution is 12. □

PRACTICE
3   Solve: $\dfrac{3}{5}x - 2 = \dfrac{2}{3}x - 1$

EXAMPLE 4 Solve: $\dfrac{2(a + 3)}{3} = 6a + 2$

Solution We clear the equation of fractions first.

$$\frac{2(a + 3)}{3} = 6a + 2$$

Step 1. $\quad 3 \cdot \dfrac{2(a + 3)}{3} = 3(6a + 2)$ Clear the fraction by multiplying both sides by the LCD, 3.

$$2(a + 3) = 3(6a + 2)$$

Step 2. Next, we use the distributive property and remove parentheses.

$$2a + 6 = 18a + 6 \qquad \text{Apply the distributive property.}$$

Step 4. $\quad 2a + 6 - 6 = 18a + 6 - 6$ Subtract 6 from both sides.

$$2a = 18a$$
$$2a - 18a = 18a - 18a \qquad \text{Subtract } 18a \text{ from both sides.}$$
$$-16a = 0$$

Step 5. $\quad \dfrac{-16a}{-16} = \dfrac{0}{-16}$ Divide both sides by -16.

$$a = 0 \qquad \text{Write the fraction in simplest form.}$$

Step 6. To check, replace a with 0 in the original equation. The solution is 0. □

PRACTICE
4   Solve: $\dfrac{4(y + 3)}{3} = 5y - 7$

▶ **Helpful Hint**
Remember: When solving an equation, it makes no difference on which side of the equation variable terms lie. Just make sure that constant terms lie on the other side.

OBJECTIVE
3 **Solving Equations Containing Decimals**

When solving a problem about money, you may need to solve an equation containing decimals. If you choose, you may multiply to clear the equation of decimals.

EXAMPLE 5   Solve: $0.25x + 0.10(x - 3) = 0.05(22)$

Solution   First we clear this equation of decimals by multiplying both sides of the equation by 100. Recall that multiplying a decimal number by 100 has the effect of moving the decimal point 2 places to the right.

$$0.25x + 0.10(x - 3) = 0.05(22)$$

▶ **Helpful Hint**
By the distributive property, 0.10 is multiplied by x and -3. Thus to multiply each term here by 100, we only need to multiply 0.10 by 100.

Step 1. $0.25x + 0.10(x - 3) = 0.05(22)$ Multiply both sides by 100.

$$25x + 10(x - 3) = 5(22)$$

Step 2. $25x + 10x - 30 = 110$ Apply the distributive property.

Step 3. $35x - 30 = 110$ Combine like terms.

Step 4. $35x - 30 + 30 = 110 + 30$ Add 30 to both sides.

$$35x = 140 \qquad \text{Combine like terms.}$$

Step 5.
$$\frac{35x}{35} = \frac{140}{35}$$ Divide both sides by 35.

$$x = 4$$

Step 6. To check, replace x with 4 in the original equation. The solution is 4.   □

PRACTICE
5   Solve: $0.35x + 0.09(x + 4) = 0.03(12)$

OBJECTIVE

4   Recognizing Identities and Equations with No Solution

So far, each equation that we have solved has had a single solution. However, not every equation in one variable has a single solution. Some equations have no solution, while others have an infinite number of solutions. For example,

$$x + 5 = x + 7$$

has no solution since no matter which **real number** we replace x with, the equation is false.

real number + 5 = same **real number** + 7   **FALSE**

On the other hand,

$$x + 6 = x + 6$$

has infinitely many solutions since x can be replaced by any real number and the equation is always true.

real number + 6 = same **real number** + 6   **TRUE**

The equation $x + 6 = x + 6$ is called an **identity.** The next two examples illustrate special equations like these.

EXAMPLE 6   Solve: $-2(x - 5) + 10 = -3(x + 2) + x$

Solution

$$-2(x - 5) + 10 = -3(x + 2) + x$$
$$-2x + 10 + 10 = -3x - 6 + x \quad \text{Apply the distributive property on both sides.}$$
$$-2x + 20 = -2x - 6 \quad \text{Combine like terms.}$$
$$-2x + 20 + 2x = -2x - 6 + 2x \quad \text{Add } 2x \text{ to both sides.}$$
$$20 = -6 \quad \text{Combine like terms.}$$

The final equation contains no variable terms, and there is no value for x that makes $20 = -6$ a true equation. We conclude that there is **no solution** to this equation. In set notation, we can indicate that there is no solution with the empty set, $\{ \ \}$, or use the empty set or null set symbol, $\varnothing$. In this chapter, we will simply write *no solution*.   □

PRACTICE
6   Solve: $4(x + 4) - x = 2(x + 11) + x$

EXAMPLE 7   Solve: $3(x - 4) = 3x - 12$

Solution

$$3(x - 4) = 3x - 12$$
$$3x - 12 = 3x - 12 \quad \text{Apply the distributive property.}$$

The left side of the equation is now identical to the right side. Every real number may be substituted for x and a true statement will result. We arrive at the same conclusion if we continue.

$$3x - 12 = 3x - 12$$
$$3x - 12 + 12 = 3x - 12 + 12 \quad \text{Add 12 to both sides.}$$
$$3x = 3x \quad\quad\quad\quad\quad \text{Combine like terms.}$$
$$3x - 3x = 3x - 3x \quad\quad \text{Subtract } 3x \text{ from both sides.}$$
$$0 = 0$$

Again, one side of the equation is identical to the other side. Thus, $3(x - 4) = 3x - 12$ is an **identity** and **all real numbers** are solutions. In set notation, this is $\{\text{all real numbers}\}$.

☐

PRACTICE

7   Solve: $12x - 18 = 9(x - 2) + 3x$

── ■

✓**CONCEPT CHECK**

Suppose you have simplified several equations and obtain the following results. What can you conclude about the solutions to the original equation?

a. $7 = 7$ **b.** $x = 0$ **c.** $7 = -4$

Graphing Calculator Explorations

Checking Equations

We can use a calculator to check possible solutions of equations. To do this, replace the variable by the possible solution and evaluate both sides of the equation separately.

Equation: $3x - 4 = 2(x + 6)$ *Solution:* $x = 16$
$$3x - 4 = 2(x + 6) \quad\quad \text{Original equation}$$
$$3(16) - 4 \overset{?}{=} 2(16 + 6) \quad \text{Replace } x \text{ with 16.}$$

Now evaluate each side with your calculator.

Evaluate left side:

$\boxed{3}\ \boxed{\times}\ \boxed{16}\ \boxed{-}\ \boxed{4}\ \boxed{=}$ or $\boxed{\text{ENTER}}$ Display: $\boxed{44}$ or $\boxed{\begin{array}{r}3*16 - 4 \\ 44\end{array}}$

Evaluate right side:

$\boxed{2}\ \boxed{(}\ \boxed{16}\ \boxed{+}\ \boxed{6}\ \boxed{)}\ \boxed{=}$ or $\boxed{\text{ENTER}}$ Display: $\boxed{44}$ or $\boxed{\begin{array}{r}2(16 + 6) \\ 44\end{array}}$

Since the left side equals the right side, the solution checks.

Use a calculator to check the possible solutions to each equation.

1. $2x = 48 + 6x;\quad x = -12$ **2.** $-3x - 7 = 3x - 1;\quad x = -1$

3. $5x - 2.6 = 2(x + 0.8);\quad x = 4.4$ **4.** $-1.6x - 3.9 = -6.9x - 25.6;\quad x = 5$

5. $\dfrac{564x}{4} = 200x - 11(649);\quad x = 121$ **6.** $20(x - 39) = 5x - 432;\quad x = 23.2$

Answers to Concept Check:
a. Every real number is a solution.
b. The solution is 0.
c. There is no solution.

Vocabulary, Readiness & Video Check

Throughout algebra, it is important to be able to identify equations and expressions.

Remember,
- an equation contains an equal sign and
- an expression does not.

Also,
- we solve equations and
- we simplify or perform operations on expressions.

Identify each as an equation or an expression.

1. $x = -7$ _____

2. $x - 7$ _____

3. $4y - 6 + 9y + 1$ _____

4. $4y - 6 = 9y + 1$ _____

5. $\dfrac{1}{x} - \dfrac{x-1}{8}$ _____

6. $\dfrac{1}{x} - \dfrac{x-1}{8} = 6$ _____

7. $0.1x + 9 = 0.2x$ _____

8. $0.1x^2 + 9y - 0.2x^2$ _____

Martin-Gay Interactive Videos

See Video 2.3 🍊

Watch the section lecture video and answer the following questions.

OBJECTIVE 1

9. The general strategy for solving linear equations in one variable is discussed after ▣ Example 1. How many properties are mentioned in this strategy and what are they?

OBJECTIVE 2

10. In the first step for solving ▣ Example 2, both sides of the equation are being multiplied by the LCD. Why is the distributive property mentioned?

OBJECTIVE 3

11. In ▣ Example 3, why is the number of decimal places in each term of the equation important?

OBJECTIVE 4

12. Complete each statement based on ▣ Examples 4 and 5.

When solving an equation and all variable terms subtract out:

a. If you have a true statement, then the equation has _____ solution(s).

b. If you have a false statement, then the equation has _____ solution (s).

2.3   Exercise Set   MyMathLab®

Solve each equation. See Examples 1 and 2.

1. $-4y + 10 = -2(3y + 1)$

2. $-3x + 1 = -2(4x + 2)$

3. $15x - 8 = 10 + 9x$

4. $15x - 5 = 7 + 12x$

5. $-2(3x - 4) = 2x$

6. $-(5x - 10) = 5x$

 7. $5(2x - 1) - 2(3x) = 1$

8. $3(2 - 5x) + 4(6x) = 12$

9. $-6(x - 3) - 26 = -8$

10. $-4(n - 4) - 23 = -7$

11. $8 - 2(a + 1) = 9 + a$

12. $5 - 6(2 + b) = b - 14$

13. $4x + 3 = -3 + 2x + 14$

14. $6y - 8 = -6 + 3y + 13$

15. $-2y - 10 = 5y + 18$

16. $-7n + 5 = 8n - 10$

Solve each equation. See Examples 3 through 5.

17. $\dfrac{2}{3}x + \dfrac{4}{3} = -\dfrac{2}{3}$

18. $\dfrac{4}{5}x - \dfrac{8}{5} = -\dfrac{16}{5}$

19. $\dfrac{3}{4}x - \dfrac{1}{2} = 1$

20. $\dfrac{2}{9}x - \dfrac{1}{3} = 1$

 21. $0.50x + 0.15(70) = 35.5$

22. $0.40x + 0.06(30) = 9.8$

23. $\dfrac{2(x + 1)}{4} = 3x - 2$

24. $\dfrac{3(y + 3)}{5} = 2y + 6$

25. $x + \dfrac{7}{6} = 2x - \dfrac{7}{6}$

26. $\dfrac{5}{2}x - 1 = x + \dfrac{1}{4}$

27. $0.12(y - 6) + 0.06y = 0.08y - 0.70$

28. $0.60(z - 300) + 0.05z = 0.70z - 205$

Solve each equation. See Examples 6 and 7.

29. $4(3x + 2) = 12x + 8$

30. $14x + 7 = 7(2x + 1)$

31. $\dfrac{x}{4} + 1 = \dfrac{x}{4}$

32. $\dfrac{x}{3} - 2 = \dfrac{x}{3}$

33. $3x - 7 = 3(x + 1)$

34. $2(x - 5) = 2x + 10$

35. $-2(6x - 5) + 4 = -12x + 14$

36. $-5(4y - 3) + 2 = -20y + 17$

MIXED PRACTICE

Solve. See Examples 1 through 7.

37. $\dfrac{6(3 - z)}{5} = -z$

38. $\dfrac{4(5 - w)}{3} = -w$

39. $-3(2t - 5) + 2t = 5t - 4$

40. $-(4a - 7) - 5a = 10 + a$

41. $5y + 2(y - 6) = 4(y + 1) - 2$

42. $9x + 3(x - 4) = 10(x - 5) + 7$

43. $\dfrac{3(x - 5)}{2} = \dfrac{2(x + 5)}{3}$

44. $\dfrac{5(x - 1)}{4} = \dfrac{3(x + 1)}{2}$

45. $0.7x - 2.3 = 0.5$

46. $0.9x - 4.1 = 0.4$

▶ **47.** $5x - 5 = 2(x + 1) + 3x - 7$

48. $3(2x - 1) + 5 = 6x + 2$

49. $4(2n + 1) = 3(6n + 3) + 1$

50. $4(4y + 2) = 2(1 + 6y) + 8$

51. $x + \dfrac{5}{4} = \dfrac{3}{4}x$

52. $\dfrac{7}{8}x + \dfrac{1}{4} = \dfrac{3}{4}x$

▶ **53.** $\dfrac{x}{2} - 1 = \dfrac{x}{5} + 2$

54. $\dfrac{x}{5} - 7 = \dfrac{x}{3} - 5$

▶ **55.** $2(x + 3) - 5 = 5x - 3(1 + x)$

56. $4(2 + x) + 1 = 7x - 3(x - 2)$

57. $0.06 - 0.01(x + 1) = -0.02(2 - x)$

58. $-0.01(5x + 4) = 0.04 - 0.01(x + 4)$

59. $\dfrac{9}{2} + \dfrac{5}{2}y = 2y - 4$

60. $3 - \dfrac{1}{2}x = 5x - 8$

61. $-2y - 10 = 5y + 18$

62. $7n + 5 = 10n - 10$

63. $0.6x - 0.1 = 0.5x + 0.2$

64. $0.2x - 0.1 = 0.6x - 2.1$

65. $0.02(6t - 3) = 0.12(t - 2) + 0.18$

66. $0.03(2m + 7) = 0.06(5 + m) - 0.09$

TRANSLATING

Write each phrase as an algebraic expression. Use x for the unknown number. See Section 2.1.

67. A number subtracted from -8

68. Three times a number

69. The sum of -3 and twice a number

70. The difference of 8 and twice a number

71. The product of 9 and the sum of a number and 20

72. The quotient of -12 and the difference of a number and 3

See Section 2.1.

73. A plot of land is in the shape of a triangle. If one side is x meters, a second side is $(2x - 3)$ meters, and a third side is $(3x - 5)$ meters, express the perimeter of the lot as a simplified expression in x.

$(3x - 5)$ meters

$(2x - 3)$ meters

x meters

See Section 2.2.

74. A portion of a board has length x feet. The other part has length $(7x - 9)$ feet. Express the total length of the board as a simplified expression in x.

?

x feet

$(7x - 9)$ feet

CONCEPT EXTENSIONS

See the Concept Check in this section.

75. a. Solve: $x + 3 = x + 3$

   b. If you simplify an equation and get $0 = 0$, what can you conclude about the solution(s) of the original equation?

   c. On your own, construct an equation for which every real number is a solution.

76. a. Solve: $x + 3 = x + 5$

   b. If you simplify an equation and get $3 = 5$, what can you conclude about the solution(s) of the original equation?

   c. On your own, construct an equation that has no solution.

For Exercises 77 through 82, match each equation in the first column with its solution in the second column. Items in the second column may be used more than once.

77. $5x + 1 = 5x + 1$ **A.** all real numbers

78. $3x + 1 = 3x + 2$ **B.** no solution

79. $2x - 6x - 10 = -4x + 3 - 10$ **C.** 0

80. $x - 11x - 3 = -10x - 1 - 2$

81. $9x - 20 = 8x - 20$

82. $-x + 15 = x + 15$

83. Explain the difference between simplifying an expression and solving an equation.

84. On your own, write an expression and then an equation. Label each.

For Exercises 85 and 86, **a.** Write an equation for perimeter. **b.** Solve the equation in part (a). **c.** Find the length of each side.

△ **85.** The perimeter of a geometric figure is the sum of the lengths of its sides. The perimeter of the following pentagon (five-sided figure) is 28 centimeters.

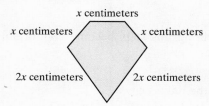

△ **86.** The perimeter of the following triangle is 35 meters.

Fill in the blanks with numbers of your choice so that each equation has the given solution. Note: Each blank may be replaced by a different number.

87. $x + \underline{\hspace{1cm}} = 2x - \underline{\hspace{1cm}}$; solution: 9

88. $-5x - \underline{\hspace{1cm}} = \underline{\hspace{1cm}}$; solution: 2

Solve.

89. $1000(7x - 10) = 50(412 + 100x)$

90. $1000(x + 40) = 100(16 + 7x)$

91. $0.035x + 5.112 = 0.010x + 5.107$

92. $0.127x - 2.685 = 0.027x - 2.38$

For Exercises 93 through 96, see the example below.

Example

Solve: $t(t + 4) = t^2 - 2t + 6$.

Solution

$$t(t + 4) = t^2 - 2t + 6$$
$$t^2 + 4t = t^2 - 2t + 6$$
$$t^2 + 4t - t^2 = t^2 - 2t + 6 - t^2$$
$$4t = -2t + 6$$
$$4t + 2t = -2t + 6 + 2t$$
$$6t = 6$$
$$t = 1$$

Solve each equation.

93. $x(x - 3) = x^2 + 5x + 7$

94. $t^2 - 6t = t(8 + t)$

95. $2z(z + 6) = 2z^2 + 12z - 8$

96. $y^2 - 4y + 10 = y(y - 5)$

Integrated Review   SOLVING LINEAR EQUATIONS

Sections 2.1–2.3

Solve. Feel free to use the steps given in Section 2.3.

1. $x - 10 = -4$ **2.** $y + 14 = -3$

3. $9y = 108$ **4.** $-3x = 78$

5. $-6x + 7 = 25$ **6.** $5y - 42 = -47$

7. $\frac{2}{3}x = 9$ **8.** $\frac{4}{5}z = 10$

9. $\frac{r}{-4} = -2$ **10.** $\frac{y}{-8} = 8$

11. $6 - 2x + 8 = 10$ **12.** $-5 - 6y + 6 = 19$

13. $2x - 7 = 2x - 27$

14. $3 + 8y = 8y - 2$

15. $-3a + 6 + 5a = 7a - 8a$

16. $4b - 8 - b = 10b - 3b$

17. $-\frac{2}{3}x = \frac{5}{9}$ **18.** $-\frac{3}{8}y = -\frac{1}{16}$

19. $10 = -6n + 16$ **20.** $-5 = -2m + 7$

21. $3(5c - 1) - 2 = 13c + 3$

22. $4(3t + 4) - 20 = 3 + 5t$

23. $\frac{2(z + 3)}{3} = 5 - z$

24. $\frac{3(w + 2)}{4} = 2w + 3$

25. $-2(2x - 5) = -3x + 7 - x + 3$

26. $-4(5x - 2) = -12x + 4 - 8x + 4$

27. $0.02(6t - 3) = 0.04(t - 2) + 0.02$

28. $0.03(m + 7) = 0.02(5 - m) + 0.03$

29. $-3y = \dfrac{4(y-1)}{5}$

30. $-4x = \dfrac{5(1-x)}{6}$

35. $\dfrac{1}{10}(3x - 7) = \dfrac{3}{10}x + 5$

31. $\dfrac{5}{3}x - \dfrac{7}{3} = x$

32. $\dfrac{7}{5}n + \dfrac{3}{5} = -n$

36. $\dfrac{1}{7}(2x - 5) = \dfrac{2}{7}x + 1$

33. $9(3x - 1) = -4 + 49$

34. $12(2x + 1) = -6 + 66$

37. $5 + 2(3x - 6) = -4(6x - 7)$

38. $3 + 5(2x - 4) = -7(5x + 2)$

2.4   An Introduction to Problem Solving

OBJECTIVES

Apply the steps for problem solving as we

1 Solve Problems Involving Direct Translations.

2 Solve Problems Involving Relationships Among Unknown Quantities.

3 Solve Problems Involving Consecutive Integers.

OBJECTIVE

1   Solving Direct Translation Problems

In previous sections, we practiced writing word phrases and sentences as algebraic expressions and equations to help prepare for problem solving. We now use these translations to help write equations that model a problem. The problem-solving steps given next may be helpful.

> **General Strategy for Problem Solving**
>
> **1.** UNDERSTAND the problem. During this step, become comfortable with the problem. Some ways of doing this are to:
>
>   Read and reread the problem.
>
>   Choose a variable to represent the unknown.
>
>   Construct a drawing whenever possible.
>
>   Propose a solution and check. Pay careful attention to how you check your proposed solution. This will help when writing an equation to model the problem.
>
> **2.** TRANSLATE the problem into an equation.
>
> **3.** SOLVE the equation.
>
> **4.** INTERPRET the results: *Check* the proposed solution in the stated problem and state your conclusion.

Much of problem solving involves a direct translation from a sentence to an equation.

EXAMPLE 1   Finding an Unknown Number

Twice a number, added to seven, is the same as three subtracted from the number. Find the number.

Solution   Translate the sentence into an equation and solve.

In words:	twice a number	added to	seven	is the same as	three subtracted from the number
	↓	↓	↓	↓	↓
Translate:	$2x$	$+$	7	$=$	$x - 3$

> **Helpful Hint**
> Order matters when subtracting (and dividing), so be especially careful with these translations.

To solve, begin by subtracting x from both sides to get all variable terms on one side.

$$2x + 7 = x - 3$$

$2x + 7 - x = x - 3 - x$ Subtract x from both sides.

$x + 7 = -3$ Combine like terms.

$x + 7 - 7 = -3 - 7$ Subtract 7 from both sides.

$x = -10$ Combine like terms.

Check the solution in the problem as it was originally stated. To do so, replace "number" in the sentence with -10. Twice "-10" added to 7 is the same as 3 subtracted from "-10."

$$2(-10) + 7 = -10 - 3$$
$$-13 = -13$$

The unknown number is -10.

PRACTICE
1　Three times a number, minus 6, is the same as two times a number, plus 3. Find the number.

> ▶ **Helpful Hint**
> When checking solutions, go back to the original stated problem, rather than to your equation, in case errors have been made in translating to an equation.

EXAMPLE 2　**Finding an Unknown Number**

Twice the sum of a number and 4 is the same as four times the number, decreased by 12. Find the number.

Solution

1. UNDERSTAND. Read and reread the problem. If we let

$$x = \text{the unknown number, then}$$

"the sum of a number and 4" translates to "$x + 4$" and "four times the number" translates to "$4x$."

2. TRANSLATE.

twice	the sum of a number and 4	is the same as	four times the number	decreased by	12
↓	↓	↓	↓	↓	↓
2	$(x + 4)$	=	$4x$	$-$	12

3. SOLVE.

$$2(x + 4) = 4x - 12$$
$$2x + 8 = 4x - 12 \quad \text{Apply the distributive property.}$$
$$2x + 8 - 4x = 4x - 12 - 4x \quad \text{Subtract } 4x \text{ from both sides.}$$
$$-2x + 8 = -12$$
$$-2x + 8 - 8 = -12 - 8 \quad \text{Subtract 8 from both sides.}$$
$$-2x = -20$$
$$\frac{-2x}{-2} = \frac{-20}{-2} \quad \text{Divide both sides by } -2.$$
$$x = 10$$

4. INTERPRET.

Check:　Check this solution in the problem as it was originally stated. To do so, replace "number" with 10. Twice the sum of "10" and 4 is 28, which is the same as 4 times "10" decreased by 12.

State:　The number is 10.

PRACTICE
2　Three times a number, decreased by 4, is the same as double the difference of the number and 1.

2 Solving Problems Involving Relationships Among Unknown Quantities

The next three examples have to do with relationships among unknown quantities.

> **EXAMPLE 3** **Finding the Length of a Board**

Balsa wood sticks are commonly used for building models (for example, bridge models). A 48-inch balsa wood stick is to be cut into two pieces so that the longer piece is 3 times the shorter. Find the length of each piece.

Solution

1. **UNDERSTAND** the problem. To do so, read and reread the problem. You may also want to propose a solution. For example, if 10 inches represents the length of the shorter piece, then $3(10) = 30$ inches is the length of the longer piece, since it is 3 times the length of the shorter piece. This guess gives a total stick length of 10 inches + 30 inches = 40 inches, too short. However, the purpose of proposing a solution is not to guess correctly but to help understand the problem better and how to model it.

    Since the length of the longer piece is given in terms of the length of the shorter piece, let's let

$$x = \text{length of shorter piece; then}$$
$$3x = \text{length of longer piece}$$

48 inches

3x inches

x inches

2. **TRANSLATE** the problem. First, we write the equation in words.

length of shorter piece	added to	length of longer piece	equals	total length of stick
↓	↓	↓	↓	↓
x	$+$	$3x$	$=$	48

3. **SOLVE.**

$$x + 3x = 48$$
$$4x = 48 \quad \text{Combine like terms.}$$
$$\frac{4x}{4} = \frac{48}{4} \quad \text{Divide both sides by 4.}$$
$$x = 12$$

4. **INTERPRET.**

Check: Check the solution in the stated problem. If the shorter piece of stick is 12 inches, the longer piece is $3 \cdot (12 \text{ inches}) = 36$ inches, and the sum of the two pieces is 12 inches + 36 inches = 48 inches.

State: The shorter piece of balsa wood is 12 inches, and the longer piece of balsa wood is 36 inches.

▶ **Helpful Hint**
Make sure that units are included in your answer, if appropriate.

PRACTICE

3 A 45-inch board is to be cut into two pieces so that the longer piece is 4 times the shorter. Find the length of each piece.

EXAMPLE 4 **Finding the Number of Republican and Democratic Representatives**

The 112th Congress began on January 3, 2011, and had a total of 435 Democrat and Republican representatives. There were 49 fewer Democratic representatives than Republican. Find the number of representatives from each party. (*Source:* Wikipedia.com)

Solution:

1. UNDERSTAND the problem. Read and reread the problem. Let's suppose that there were 200 Republican representatives. Since there were 49 fewer Democrats than Republicans, there must have been $200 - 49 = 151$ Democrats. The total number of Republicans and Democrats was then $200 + 151 = 351$. This is incorrect since the total should be 435, but we now have a better understanding of the problem.

In general, if we let

$$x = \text{number of Republicans, then}$$
$$x - 49 = \text{number of Democrats}$$

2. TRANSLATE the problem. First, we write the equation in words.

number of Republicans	added to	number of Democrats	equals	435
↓	↓	↓	↓	↓
x	$+$	$(x - 49)$	$=$	435

3. SOLVE.

$$x + (x - 49) = 435$$
$$2x - 49 = 435 \qquad \text{Combine like terms.}$$
$$2x - 49 + 49 = 435 + 49 \qquad \text{Add 49 to both sides.}$$
$$2x = 484$$
$$\frac{2x}{2} = \frac{484}{2} \qquad \text{Divide both sides by 2.}$$
$$x = 242$$

4. INTERPRET.

Check: If there were 242 Republican representatives, then there were $242 - 49 = 193$ Democratic representatives. The total number of representatives was then $242 + 193 = 435$. The results check.

State: There were 242 Republican and 193 Democratic representatives at the beginning of the 112th Congress. ☐

PRACTICE

4 In 2011, there were 9 fewer Democratic State Governors than Republican State Governors. Find the number of State Governors from each party. Rhode Island had an independent governor, so use a total of 49, representing the other 49 states. (*Source:* National Conference of State Legislatures).

△ **EXAMPLE 5** **Finding Angle Measures**

If the two walls of the Vietnam Veterans Memorial in Washington, D.C., were connected, an isosceles triangle would be formed. The measure of the third angle is 97.5° more than the measure of either of the other two equal angles. Find the measure of the third angle. (*Source:* National Park Service)

Solution

1. UNDERSTAND. Read and reread the problem. We then draw a diagram (recall that an isosceles triangle has two angles with the same measure) and let

$$x = \text{degree measure of one angle}$$
$$x = \text{degree measure of the second equal angle}$$
$$x + 97.5 = \text{degree measure of the third angle}$$

2. TRANSLATE. Recall that the sum of the measures of the angles of a triangle equals 180.

measure of first angle	measure of second angle	measure of third angle	equals	180
↓	↓	↓	↓	↓
x +	x	+ $(x + 97.5)$	=	180

3. SOLVE.

$$x + x + (x + 97.5) = 180$$
$$3x + 97.5 = 180 \qquad \text{Combine like terms.}$$
$$3x + 97.5 - 97.5 = 180 - 97.5 \qquad \text{Subtract 97.5 from both sides.}$$
$$3x = 82.5$$
$$\frac{3x}{3} = \frac{82.5}{3} \qquad \text{Divide both sides by 3.}$$
$$x = 27.5$$

4. INTERPRET.

Check: If $x = 27.5$, then the measure of the third angle is $x + 97.5 = 125$. The sum of the angles is then $27.5 + 27.5 + 125 = 180$, the correct sum.

State: The third angle measures 125°.*

PRACTICE

5 The second angle of a triangle measures three times as large as the first. If the third angle measures 55° more than the first, find the measures of all three angles.

OBJECTIVE

3 Solving Consecutive Integer Problems

The next example has to do with consecutive integers. Recall what we have learned thus far about these integers.

	Example	General Representation
Consecutive Integers	11, 12, 13 ⌣+1⌢+1⌢	Let x be an integer. $\quad x, \; x + 1, \; x + 2$ ⌣+1⌢+1⌢
Consecutive Even Integers	38, 40, 42 ⌣+2⌢+2⌢	Let x be an even integer. $\; x, \; x + 2, \; x + 4$ ⌣+2⌢+2⌢
Consecutive Odd Integers	57, 59, 61 ⌣+2⌢+2⌢	Let x be an odd integer. $\; x, \; x + 2, \; x + 4$ ⌣+2⌢+2⌢

*The two walls actually meet at an angle of 125 degrees 12 minutes. The measurement of 97.5° given in the problem is an approximation.

EXAMPLE 6   Some states have a single area code for the entire state. Two such states have area codes that are consecutive odd integers. If the sum of these integers is 1208, find the two area codes. (*Source:* North American Numbering Plan Administration)

Solution:

1. UNDERSTAND. Read and reread the problem. If we let

$$x = \text{the first odd integer, then}$$
$$x + 2 = \text{the next odd integer}$$

2. TRANSLATE.

> ▶ **Helpful Hint**
> Remember, the 2 here means that odd integers are 2 units apart, for example, the odd integers 13 and 13 + 2 = 15.

first odd integer	the sum of	next odd integer	is	1208
↓	↓	↓	↓	↓
x	$+$	$(x + 2)$	$=$	1208

3. SOLVE.

$$x + x + 2 = 1208$$
$$2x + 2 = 1208$$
$$2x + 2 - 2 = 1208 - 2$$
$$2x = 1206$$
$$\frac{2x}{2} = \frac{1206}{2}$$
$$x = 603$$

4. INTERPRET.

Check: If $x = 603$, then the next odd integer $x + 2 = 603 + 2 = 605$. Notice their sum, $603 + 605 = 1208$, as needed.

State: The area codes are 603 and 605.

Note: New Hampshire's area code is 603 and South Dakota's area code is 605.

PRACTICE
6   The sum of three consecutive even integers is 144. Find the integers.

Vocabulary, Readiness & Video Check

Fill in the table.

1.	A number: → x	Double the number:	→ Double the number, decreased by 31:
2.	A number: → x	Three times the number:	→ Three times the number, increased by 17:
3.	A number: → x	The sum of the number and 5:	→ Twice the sum of the number and 5:
4.	A number: → x	The difference of the number and 11: →	Seven times the difference of a number and 11:
5.	A number: → y	The difference of 20 and the number: →	The difference of 20 and the number, divided by 3:
6.	A number: → y	The sum of −10 and the number: →	The sum of −10 and the number, divided by 9:

Martin-Gay Interactive Videos

See Video 2.4

Watch the section lecture video and answer the following questions.

OBJECTIVE 1
7. At the end of Example 1, where are you told is the best place to check the solution of an application problem?

OBJECTIVE 2
8. The solution of the equation for Example 3 is $x = 43$. Why is this not the solution to the application?

OBJECTIVE 3
9. What are two things that should be checked to make sure the solution of Example 4 is correct?

2.4 Exercise Set MyMathLab®

TRANSLATING

Write each of the following as an equation. Then solve. See Examples 1 and 2.

1. The sum of six times a number, and 1, is equal to five times the number. Find the number.

2. The difference of three times a number, and 1, is the same as twice the number. Find the number.

3. Three times a number, minus 6, is equal to two times the number, plus 8. Find the number.

4. The sum of 4 times a number, and −2, is equal to the sum of 5 times the number, and −2. Find the number.

5. Twice the difference of a number and 8 is equal to three times the sum of the number and 3. Find the number.

6. Five times the sum of a number and −1 is the same as 6 times the difference of the number and 5. Find the number.

7. Twice the sum of −2 and a number is the same as the number decreased by $\frac{1}{2}$. Find the number.

8. If the difference of a number and four is doubled, the result is $\frac{1}{4}$ less than the number. Find the number.

Solve. For Exercises 9 and 10, the solutions have been started for you. See Examples 3 through 5.

9. A 25-inch piece of steel is cut into three pieces so that the second piece is twice as long as the first piece, and the third piece is one inch more than five times the length of the first piece. Find the lengths of the pieces.

Start the solution:

1. UNDERSTAND the problem. Reread it as many times as needed.

2. TRANSLATE into an equation. (Fill in the blanks below.)

total length of steel	equals	length of first piece	plus	length of second piece	plus	length of third piece
↓	↓	↓	↓	↓	↓	↓
25	=	———	+	———	+	———

Finish with:

3. SOLVE and **4.** INTERPRET

10. A 46-foot piece of rope is cut into three pieces so that the second piece is three times as long as the first piece, and the third piece is two feet more than seven times the length of the first piece. Find the lengths of the pieces.

Start the solution:

1. UNDERSTAND the problem. Reread it as many times as needed.

2. TRANSLATE into an equation. (Fill in the blanks below.)

total length of rope	equals	length of first piece	plus	length of second piece	plus	length of third piece
↓	↓	↓	↓	↓	↓	↓
46	=	———	+	———	+	———

Finish with:

3. SOLVE and **4.** INTERPRET

11. A 40-inch board is to be cut into three pieces so that the second piece is twice as long as the first piece, and the third piece is 5 times as long as the first piece. If x represents the length of the first piece, find the lengths of all three pieces.

40 inches

x inches

12. A 21-foot beam is to be cut into three pieces so that the second and the third piece are each 3 times the length of the first piece. If x represents the length of the shorter piece, find the lengths of all three pieces.

21 feet

x feet

For Exercises 13 and 14, use each table to find the value of x. Then write a sentence to explain, in words, the meaning and the value of x. (Source: IHS Screen Digest)

13. The fastest growing type of movie screen in 2010 was 3D.

Type of Screen	Number of Screens
3D	x
Non-3D	23,873 more than x
Total screens	39,547

14. The majority of movie screens in the United States in 2010 were located at sites with five or more screens.

Type of Site	Number of Screens
Smaller (1–4 screens)	x
Larger (5 or more screens)	22,857 more than x
Total screens	39,547

15. The flag of Equatorial Guinea contains an isosceles triangle. (Recall that an isosceles triangle contains two angles with the same measure.) If the measure of the third angle of the triangle is 30° more than twice the measure of either of the other two angles, find the measure of each angle of the triangle. (*Hint:* Recall that the sum of the measures of the angles of a triangle is 180°.)

16. The flag of Brazil contains a parallelogram. One angle of the parallelogram is 15° less than twice the measure of the angle next to it. Find the measure of each angle of the parallelogram. (*Hint:* Recall that opposite angles of a parallelogram have the same measure and that the sum of the measures of the angles is 360°.)

Solve. See Example 6. For Exercises 17 through 24, fill in the table. Most of the first row has been completed for you.

	First Integer →	Next Integers	→		Indicated Sum
17. Three consecutive integers:	Integer: x	$x + 1$	$x + 2$		Sum of the three consecutive integers, simplified:
18. Three consecutive integers:	Integer: x				Sum of the second and third consecutive integers, simplified:
19. Three consecutive even integers:	Even integer: x				Sum of the first and third even consecutive integers, simplified:
20. Three consecutive odd integers:	Odd integer: x				Sum of the three consecutive odd integers, simplified:
21. Four consecutive integers:	Integer: x				Sum of the four consecutive integers, simplified:
22. Four consecutive integers:	Integer: x				Sum of the first and fourth consecutive integers, simplified:
23. Three consecutive odd integers:	Odd integer: x				Sum of the second and third consecutive odd integers, simplified:
24. Three consecutive even integers:	Even integer: x				Sum of the three consecutive even integers, simplified:

25. The left and right page numbers of an open book are two consecutive integers whose sum is 469. Find these page numbers.

26. The room numbers of two adjacent classrooms are two consecutive even numbers. If their sum is 654, find the classroom numbers.

27. To make an international telephone call, you need the code for the country you are calling. The codes for Belgium, France, and Spain are three consecutive integers whose sum is 99. Find the code for each country. (*Source: The World Almanac and Book of Facts*, 2007)

28. To make an international telephone call, you need the code for the country you are calling. The codes for Mali Republic, Côte d'Ivoire, and Niger are three consecutive odd integers whose sum is 675. Find the code for each country.

MIXED PRACTICE

Solve. See Examples 1 through 6.

29. The area of the Sahara Desert is 7 times the area of the Gobi Desert. If the sum of their areas is 4,000,000 square miles, find the area of each desert.

30. The largest meteorite in the world is the Hoba West, located in Namibia. Its weight is 3 times the weight of the Armanty meteorite, located in Outer Mongolia. If the sum of their weights is 88 tons, find the weight of each.

31. A 17-foot piece of string is cut into two pieces so that the longer piece is 2 feet longer than twice the length of the shorter piece. Find the lengths of both pieces.

32. A 25-foot wire is to be cut so that the longer piece is one foot longer than 5 times the length of the shorter piece. Find the length of each piece.

33. Five times a number, subtracted from ten, is triple the number. Find the number.

34. Nine is equal to ten subtracted from double a number. Find the number.

35. The greatest producer of diamonds in carats is Botswana. This country produces about four times the amount produced in Angola. If the total produced in both countries is 40,000,000 carats, find the amount produced in each country. (*Source: Diamond Facts.*)

36. Beetles have the greatest number of different species. There are twenty times the number of beetle species as grasshopper species, and the total number of species for both is 420,000. Find the number of species for each type of insect.

 37. The measures of the angles of a triangle are 3 consecutive even integers. Find the measure of each angle.

 38. A quadrilateral is a polygon with 4 sides. The sum of the measures of the 4 angles in a quadrilateral is 360°. If the measures of the angles of a quadrilateral are consecutive odd integers, find the measures.

39. For the 2010 Winter Olympics, the total number of medals won by athletes from each of the countries of South Korea, Russia, and Austria are three consecutive integers whose sum is 45. Find the number of medals for each country.

40. The code to unlock a student's combination lock happens to be three consecutive odd integers whose sum is 51. Find the integers.

41. If the sum of a number and five is tripled, the result is one less than twice the number. Find the number.

42. Twice the sum of a number and six equals three times the sum of the number and four. Find the number.

43. Two angles are supplementary if their sum is 180°. The larger angle measures eight degrees more than three times the measure of a smaller angle. If x represents the measure of the smaller angle and these two angles are supplementary, find the measure of each angle.

44. Two angles are complementary if their sum is 90°. The larger angle measures three degrees less than twice the measure of a smaller angle. If x represents the measure of the smaller angle and these two angles are complementary, find the measure of each angle.

45. If the quotient of a number and 4 is added to $\frac{1}{2}$, the result is $\frac{3}{4}$. Find the number.

46. The sum of $\frac{1}{5}$ and twice a number is equal to $\frac{4}{5}$ subtracted from three times the number. Find the number.

47. The sum of $\frac{2}{3}$ and four times a number is equal to $\frac{5}{6}$ subtracted from five times the number. Find the number.

48. If $\frac{3}{4}$ is added to three times a number, the result is $\frac{1}{2}$ subtracted from twice the number. Find the number.

49. Currently, the two fastest trains are the Japanese Maglev and the French TGV. The sum of their fastest speeds is 718.2 miles per hour. If the speed of the Maglev is 3.8 mph faster than the speed of the TGV, find the speeds of each.

50. The Pentagon is the world's largest office building in terms of floor space. It has three times the amount of floor space as the Empire State Building. If the total floor space for these two buildings is approximately 8700 thousand square feet, find the floor space of each building.

51. One-third of a number is five-sixths. Find the number.

52. Seven-eighths of a number is one-half. Find the number.

53. The number of counties in California and the number of counties in Montana are consecutive even integers whose sum is 114. If California has more counties than Montana, how many counties does each state have? (*Source: The World Almanac and Book of Facts*)

54. A student is building a bookcase with stepped shelves for her dorm room. She buys a 48-inch board and wants to cut the board into three pieces with lengths equal to three consecutive even integers. Find the three board lengths.

55. A geodesic dome, based on the design by Buckminster Fuller, is composed of two types of triangular panels. One of these is an isosceles triangle. In one geodesic dome, the measure of the third angle is 76.5° more than the measure of either of the two equal angles. Find the measure of the third angle. (*Source:* Buckminster Fuller Institute)

56. The measures of the angles of a particular triangle are such that the second and third angles are each four times larger than the smallest angle. Find the measures of the angles of this triangle.

57. A 30-foot piece of siding is cut into three pieces so that the second piece is four times as long as the first piece and the third piece is five times as long as the first piece. If x represents the length of the first piece, find the lengths of all three pieces.

58. A 48-foot-long piece of cable wire is to be cut into three pieces so that the second piece is five times as long as the first piece and the third piece is six times as long as the first piece. If x represents the length of the first piece, find the lengths of all three pieces.

The graph below shows the best-selling albums of all time. Use this graph for Exercises 59 through 64.

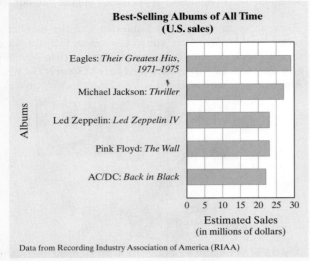

Best-Selling Albums of All Time
(U.S. sales)

Data from Recording Industry Association of America (RIAA)

(*Note:* These numbers are before the death of Michael Jackson.)

59. Which album is the best-selling album of all time?

60. Which albums had total sales between $20 million and $25 million?

61. *Thriller* and *The Wall* had sales worth a total of $50 million. *Thriller* brought in $4 million more than *The Wall*. Find the amount of sales that each album brought in.

62. Eagles: *Their Greatest Hits, 1971–1975*, and AC/DC: *Back in Black* had sales worth $51 million. Eagles: *Their Greatest Hits, 1971–1975*, sold $7 million more than AC/DC: *Back in Black*. Find the amount of sales for each album.

Compare the lengths of the bars in the graph with your results for the exercises below. Are your answers reasonable?

63. Exercise 61   **64.** Exercise 62

REVIEW AND PREVIEW

Evaluate each expression for the given values. See Section 1.4.

65. $2W + 2L$; $W = 7$ and $L = 10$

66. $\frac{1}{2}Bh$; $B = 14$ and $h = 22$

67. πr^2; $r = 15$ **68.** $r \cdot t$; $r = 15$ and $t = 2$

CONCEPT EXTENSIONS

69. A golden rectangle is a rectangle whose length is approximately 1.6 times its width. The early Greeks thought that a rectangle with these dimensions was the most pleasing to the eye, and examples of the golden rectangle are found in many early works of art. For example, the Parthenon in Athens contains many examples of golden rectangles.

Mike Hallahan would like to plant a rectangular garden in the shape of a golden rectangle. If he has 78 feet of fencing available, find the dimensions of the garden.

70. Dr. Dorothy Smith gave the students in her geometry class at the University of New Orleans the following question. Is it possible to construct a triangle such that the second angle of the triangle has a measure that is twice the measure of the first angle and the measure of the third angle is 5 times the measure of the first? If so, find the measure of each angle. (*Hint:* Recall that the sum of the measures of the angles of a triangle is 180°.)

71. Only male crickets chirp. They chirp at different rates depending on their species and the temperature of their environment. Suppose a certain species is currently chirping at a rate of 90 chirps per minute. At this rate, how many chirps occur in one hour? In one 24-hour day? In one year?

72. The human eye blinks once every 5 seconds on average. How many times does the average eye blink in one hour? In one 16-hour day while awake? In one year while awake?

73. In your own words, explain why a solution of a word problem should be checked using the original wording of the problem and not the equation written from the wording.

74. Give an example of how you recently solved a problem using mathematics.

Recall from Exercise 69 that a golden rectangle is a rectangle whose length is approximately 1.6 times its width.

75. It is thought that for about 75% of adults, a rectangle in the shape of the golden rectangle is the most pleasing to the eye. Draw three rectangles, one in the shape of the golden rectangle, and poll your class. Do the results agree with the percentage given above?

76. Examples of golden rectangles can be found today in architecture and manufacturing packaging. Find an example of a golden rectangle in your home. A few suggestions: the front face of a book, the floor of a room, the front of a box of food.

For Exercises 77 and 78, measure the dimensions of each rectangle and decide which one best approximates the shape of a golden rectangle.

77.

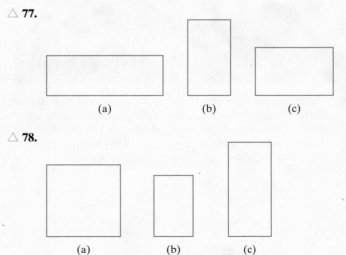

(a)   (b)   (c)

78.

(a)   (b)   (c)

2.5 Formulas and Problem Solving

OBJECTIVES

1 Use Formulas to Solve Problems.

2 Solve a Formula or Equation for One of Its Variables.

OBJECTIVE

1   Using Formulas to Solve Problems

An equation that describes a known relationship among quantities, such as distance, time, volume, weight, and money, is called a **formula.** These quantities are represented by letters and are thus variables of the formula. Here are some common formulas and their meanings.

Formulas	Their Meanings
$A = lw$	Area of a rectangle = length · width
$I = PRT$	Simple interest = principal · rate · time
$P = a + b + c$	Perimeter of a triangle = side a + side b + side c
$d = rt$	distance = rate · time
$V = lwh$	Volume of a rectangular solid = length · width · height
$F = \left(\dfrac{9}{5}\right)C + 32$ or $F = 1.8C + 32$	degrees Fahrenheit = $\left(\dfrac{9}{5}\right)$ · degrees Celsius + 32

Formulas are valuable tools because they allow us to calculate measurements as long as we know certain other measurements. For example, if we know we traveled a distance of 100 miles at a rate of 40 miles per hour, we can replace the variables d and r in the formula $d = rt$ and find our time, t.

$$d = rt \qquad \text{Formula.}$$
$$100 = 40t \qquad \text{Replace } d \text{ with 100 and } r \text{ with 40.}$$

This is a linear equation in one variable, t. To solve for t, divide both sides of the equation by 40.

$$\frac{100}{40} = \frac{40t}{40} \qquad \text{Divide both sides by 40.}$$

$$\frac{5}{2} = t \qquad \text{Simplify.}$$

The time traveled is $\dfrac{5}{2}$ hours, or $2\dfrac{1}{2}$ hours, or 2.5 hours.

In this section, we solve problems that can be modeled by known formulas. We use the same problem-solving steps that were introduced in the previous section. These steps have been slightly revised to include formulas.

EXAMPLE 1   **Finding Time Given Rate and Distance**

A glacier is a giant mass of rocks and ice that flows downhill like a river. Portage Glacier in Alaska is about 6 miles, or 31,680 *feet,* long and moves 400 *feet* per year. Icebergs are created when the front end of the glacier flows into Portage Lake. How long does it take for ice at the head (beginning) of the glacier to reach the lake?

Solution

1. UNDERSTAND. Read and reread the problem. The appropriate formula needed to solve this problem is the distance formula, $d = rt$. To become familiar with this formula, let's find the distance that ice traveling at a rate of 400 feet per year travels in 100 years. To do so, we let time t be 100 years and rate r be the given 400 feet per year and substitute these values into the formula $d = rt$. We then have that distance $d = 400(100) = 40,000$ feet. Since we are interested in finding how long it takes ice to travel 31,680 feet, we now know that it is less than 100 years.

   Since we are using the formula $d = rt$, we let

   t = the time in years for ice to reach the lake

   r = rate or speed of ice

   d = distance from beginning of glacier to lake

2. TRANSLATE. To translate to an equation, we use the formula $d = rt$ and let distance $d = 31,680$ feet and rate $r = 400$ feet per year.

$$d = r \cdot t$$
$$31{,}680 = 400 \cdot t \quad \text{Let } d = 31{,}680 \text{ and } r = 400.$$

3. SOLVE. Solve the equation for t. To solve for t, divide both sides by 400.

$$\frac{31{,}680}{400} = \frac{400 \cdot t}{400} \quad \text{Divide both sides by 400.}$$

$$79.2 = t \quad \text{Simplify.}$$

4. INTERPRET.

Check: To check, substitute 79.2 for t and 400 for r in the distance formula and check to see that the distance is 31,680 feet.

State: It takes 79.2 years for the ice at the head of Portage Glacier to reach the lake. □

> **Helpful Hint**
> Don't forget to include units if appropriate.

PRACTICE

1 The Stromboli Volcano, in Italy, began erupting in 2002 after a dormant period of over 17 years. In 2007, a volcanologist measured the lava flow to be moving at 5 meters/second. If the path the lava follows to the sea is 580 meters long, how long does it take the lava to reach the sea? *(Source:* Thorsten Boeckel and CNN)

⚠ **EXAMPLE 2**   **Calculating the Length of a Garden**

Charles Pecot can afford enough fencing to enclose a rectangular garden with a perimeter of 140 feet. If the width of his garden must be 30 feet, find the length.

$w = 30$ feet

l

Solution

1. **UNDERSTAND.** Read and reread the problem. The formula needed to solve this problem is the formula for the perimeter of a rectangle, $P = 2l + 2w$. Before continuing, let's become familiar with this formula.

   $l = $ the length of the rectangular garden
   $w = $ the width of the rectangular garden
   $P = $ perimeter of the garden

2. **TRANSLATE.** To translate to an equation, we use the formula $P = 2l + 2w$ and let perimeter $P = 140$ feet and width $w = 30$ feet.

$$P = 2l + 2w$$
$$\downarrow \qquad\qquad \downarrow$$
$$140 = 2l + 2(30) \quad \text{Let } P = 140 \text{ and } w = 30.$$

3. **SOLVE.**

$$140 = 2l + 2(30)$$
$$140 = 2l + 60 \qquad\qquad \text{Multiply } 2(30).$$
$$140 - 60 = 2l + 60 - 60 \quad \text{Subtract 60 from both sides.}$$
$$80 = 2l \qquad\qquad\qquad \text{Combine like terms.}$$
$$40 = l \qquad\qquad\qquad \text{Divide both sides by 2.}$$

4. **INTERPRET.**

Check: Substitute 40 for l and 30 for w in the perimeter formula and check to see that the perimeter is 140 feet.

State: The length of the rectangular garden is 40 feet.   □

PRACTICE

2   Evelyn Gryk fenced in part of her backyard for a dog run. The dog run was 40 feet in length and used 98 feet of fencing. Find the width of the dog run.

EXAMPLE 3   **Finding an Equivalent Temperature**

The average minimum temperature for July in Shanghai, China, is 77° Fahrenheit. Find the equivalent temperature in degrees Celsius.

Solution

1. **UNDERSTAND.** Read and reread the problem. A formula that can be used to solve this problem is the formula for converting degrees Celsius to degrees Fahrenheit, $F = \dfrac{9}{5}C + 32$. Before continuing, become familiar with this formula. Using this formula, we let

$$C = \text{temperature in degrees Celsius, and}$$
$$F = \text{temperature in degrees Fahrenheit.}$$

2. TRANSLATE. To translate to an equation, we use the formula $F = \frac{9}{5}C + 32$ and let degrees Fahrenheit $F = 77$.

Formula: $\qquad F = \frac{9}{5}C + 32$

Substitute: $\quad 77 = \frac{9}{5}C + 32 \quad$ Let $F = 77$.

3. SOLVE.

$$77 = \frac{9}{5}C + 32$$

$$77 - 32 = \frac{9}{5}C + 32 - 32 \quad \text{Subtract 32 from both sides.}$$

$$45 = \frac{9}{5}C \qquad\qquad \text{Combine like terms.}$$

$$\frac{5}{9} \cdot 45 = \frac{5}{9} \cdot \frac{9}{5}C \qquad \text{Multiply both sides by } \frac{5}{9}.$$

$$25 = C \qquad\qquad \text{Simplify.}$$

4. INTERPRET.

Check: To check, replace C with 25 and F with 77 in the formula and see that a true statement results.

State: Thus, 77° Fahrenheit is equivalent to 25° Celsius.

Note: There is a formula for directly converting degrees Fahrenheit to degrees Celsius. It is $C = \frac{5}{9}(F - 32)$, as we shall see in Example 8. □

PRACTICE

3 The average minimum temperature for July in Sydney, Australia, is 8° Celsius. Find the equivalent temperature in degrees Fahrenheit.

In the next example, we again use the formula for perimeter of a rectangle as in Example 2. In Example 2, we knew the width of the rectangle. In this example, both the length and width are unknown.

△ **EXAMPLE 4**   **Finding Road Sign Dimensions**

The length of a rectangular road sign is 2 feet less than three times its width. Find the dimensions if the perimeter is 28 feet.

Solution

1. UNDERSTAND. Read and reread the problem. Recall that the formula for the perimeter of a rectangle is $P = 2l + 2w$. Draw a rectangle and guess the solution. If the width of the rectangular sign is 5 feet, its length is 2 feet less than 3 times the width or 3(5 feet) − 2 feet = 13 feet. The perimeter P of the rectangle is then 2(13 feet) + 2(5 feet) = 36 feet, too much. We now know that the width is less than 5 feet.

Proposed rectangle:

5 feet

13 feet

Let

$$w = \text{the width of the rectangular sign; then}$$
$$3w - 2 = \text{the length of the sign.}$$

$3w - 2$

Draw a rectangle and label it with the assigned variables.

2. TRANSLATE.

Formula: $P = 2l + 2w$ or

Substitute: $28 = 2(3w - 2) + 2w.$

3. SOLVE.

$$28 = 2(3w - 2) + 2w$$
$$28 = 6w - 4 + 2w \qquad \text{Apply the distributive property.}$$
$$28 = 8w - 4$$
$$28 + 4 = 8w - 4 + 4 \qquad \text{Add 4 to both sides.}$$
$$32 = 8w$$
$$\frac{32}{8} = \frac{8w}{8} \qquad \text{Divide both sides by 8.}$$
$$4 = w$$

4. INTERPRET.

Check: If the width of the sign is 4 feet, the length of the sign is 3(4 feet) − 2 feet = 10 feet. This gives a perimeter of $P = 2(4 \text{ feet}) + 2(10 \text{ feet}) = 28$ feet, the correct perimeter.

State: The width of the sign is 4 feet, and the length of the sign is 10 feet.   □

PRACTICE

4   The new street signs along Route 114 have a length that is 3 inches more than 5 times the width. Find the dimensions of the signs if the perimeter of the signs is 66 inches.

OBJECTIVE

2   Solving a Formula for One of Its Variables ▶

We say that the formula

$$F = \frac{9}{5}C + 32$$

is solved for F because F is alone on one side of the equation, and the other side of the equation contains no F's. Suppose that we need to convert many Fahrenheit temperatures to equivalent degrees Celsius. In this case, it is easier to perform this task by solving the formula $F = \frac{9}{5}C + 32$ for C. (See Example 8.) For this reason, it is important to be able to solve an equation for any one of its specified variables. For example, the formula $d = rt$ is solved for d in terms of r and t. We can also solve $d = rt$ for t in terms of d and r. To solve for t, divide both sides of the equation by r.

$$d = rt$$
$$\frac{d}{r} = \frac{rt}{r} \qquad \text{Divide both sides by } r.$$
$$\frac{d}{r} = t \qquad \text{Simplify.}$$

To solve a formula or an equation for a specified variable, we use the same steps as for solving a linear equation. These steps are listed next.

Solving Equations for a Specified Variable

Step 1. Multiply on both sides to clear the equation of fractions if they occur.

Step 2. Use the distributive property to remove parentheses if they occur.

Step 3. Simplify each side of the equation by combining like terms.

Step 4. Get all terms containing the specified variable on one side and all other terms on the other side by using the addition property of equality.

Step 5. Get the specified variable alone by using the multiplication property of equality.

EXAMPLE 5   Solve $V = lwh$ for l.

Solution   This formula is used to find the volume of a box. To solve for l, divide both sides by wh.

$$V = lwh$$

$$\frac{V}{wh} = \frac{lwh}{wh} \qquad \text{Divide both sides by } wh.$$

$$\frac{V}{wh} = l \qquad \text{Simplify.}$$

Since we have l alone on one side of the equation, we have solved for l in terms of V, w, and h. Remember that it does not matter on which side of the equation we isolate the variable. □

PRACTICE
5   Solve $I = Prt$ for r.

EXAMPLE 6   Solve $y = mx + b$ for x.

Solution   The term containing the variable we are solving for, mx, is on the right side of the equation. Get mx alone by subtracting b from both sides.

$$y = mx + b$$

$$y - b = mx + b - b \qquad \text{Subtract } b \text{ from both sides.}$$

$$y - b = mx \qquad \text{Combine like terms.}$$

Next, solve for x by dividing both sides by m.

$$\frac{y - b}{m} = \frac{mx}{m}$$

$$\frac{y - b}{m} = x \qquad \text{Simplify.}$$ □

PRACTICE
6   Solve $H = 5as + 10a$ for s.

✓**CONCEPT CHECK**

Solve:

a. ⬤ = ◼ − ◼ for ◼

b. ⬤ = ◼ · ▲ − ◼ for ◼

Answers to Concept Check:

a. ◼ = ⬤ + ◼   b. ◼ = (⬤ + ◼)/▲

EXAMPLE 7   Solve $P = 2l + 2w$ for w.

Solution   This formula relates the perimeter of a rectangle to its length and width. Find the term containing the variable w. To get this term, $2w$, alone subtract $2l$ from both sides.

l

w

Helpful Hint

The 2's may *not* be divided out here. Although 2 is a factor of the denominator, 2 is *not* a factor of the numerator since it is not a factor of both terms in the numerator.

$$P = 2l + 2w$$

$P - 2l = 2l + 2w - 2l$ Subtract $2l$ from both sides.

$P - 2l = 2w$ Combine like terms.

$\dfrac{P - 2l}{2} = \dfrac{2w}{2}$ Divide both sides by 2.

$\dfrac{P - 2l}{2} = w$ Simplify.   □

PRACTICE

7   Solve $N = F + d(n - 1)$ for d.

The next example has an equation containing a fraction. We will first clear the equation of fractions and then solve for the specified variable.

EXAMPLE 8   Solve $F = \dfrac{9}{5}C + 32$ for C.

Solution

$$F = \dfrac{9}{5}C + 32$$

$5(F) = 5\left(\dfrac{9}{5}C + 32\right)$ Clear the fraction by multiplying both sides by the LCD.

$5F = 9C + 160$ Distribute the 5.

$5F - 160 = 9C + 160 - 160$ To get the term containing the variable C alone, subtract 160 from both sides.

$5F - 160 = 9C$ Combine like terms.

$\dfrac{5F - 160}{9} = \dfrac{9C}{9}$ Divide both sides by 9.

$\dfrac{5F - 160}{9} = C$ Simplify.

Note: An equivalent way to write this formula is $C = \dfrac{5}{9}(F - 32)$.   □

PRACTICE

8   Solve $A = \dfrac{1}{2}a(b + B)$ for B.

Vocabulary, Readiness & Video Check

Martin-Gay Interactive Videos

See Video 2.5

Watch the section lecture video and answer the following questions.

OBJECTIVE 1

1. Complete this statement based on the lecture given before Example 1. A formula is an equation that describes known _____ among quantities.

OBJECTIVE 1

2. In Example 2, how are the units for the solution determined?

OBJECTIVE 2

3. During Example 4, why is the equation $5x = 30$?

2.5   Exercise Set   MyMathLab®

Substitute the given values into each given formula and solve for the unknown variable. If necessary, round to one decimal place. See Examples 1 through 4.

△ 1. $A = bh$; $A = 45, b = 15$ (Area of a parallelogram)

2. $d = rt$; $d = 195, t = 3$ (Distance formula)

△ 3. $S = 4lw + 2wh$; $S = 102, l = 7, w = 3$ (Surface area of a special rectangular box)

△ 4. $V = lwh$; $l = 14, w = 8, h = 3$ (Volume of a rectangular box)

△ 5. $A = \frac{1}{2}h(B + b)$; $A = 180, B = 11, b = 7$ (Area of a trapezoid)

△ 6. $A = \frac{1}{2}h(B + b)$; $A = 60, B = 7, b = 3$ (Area of a trapezoid)

△ 7. $P = a + b + c$; $P = 30, a = 8, b = 10$ (Perimeter of a triangle)

△ 8. $V = \frac{1}{3}Ah$; $V = 45, h = 5$ (Volume of a pyramid)

9. $C = 2\pi r$; $C = 15.7$ (use the approximation 3.14 or a calculator approximation for π) (Circumference of a circle)

10. $A = \pi r^2$; $r = 4.5$ (use the approximation 3.14 or a calculator approximation for π) (Area of a circle)

11. $I = PRT$; $I = 3750, P = 25,000, R = 0.05$ (Simple interest formula)

12. $I = PRT$; $I = 1,056,000, R = 0.055, T = 6$ (Simple interest formula)

13. $V = \frac{1}{3}\pi r^2 h$; $V = 565.2, r = 6$ (use a calculator approximation for π) (Volume of a cone)

14. $V = \frac{4}{3}\pi r^3$; $r = 3$ (use a calculator approximation for π) (Volume of a sphere)

Solve each formula for the specified variable. See Examples 5 through 8.

15. $f = 5gh$ for h △ 16. $A = \pi ab$ for b

▶ 17. $V = lwh$ for w 18. $T = mnr$ for n

19. $3x + y = 7$ for y

20. $-x + y = 13$ for y

21. $A = P + PRT$ for R

22. $A = P + PRT$ for T

23. $V = \frac{1}{3}Ah$ for A

24. $D = \frac{1}{4}fk$ for k

25. $P = a + b + c$ for a

26. $PR = x + y + z + w$ for z

▶ 27. $S = 2\pi rh + 2\pi r^2$ for h
△

△ 28. $S = 4lw + 2wh$ for h

Solve. For Exercises 29 and 30, the solutions have been started for you. See Examples 1 through 4.

△ 29. The iconic NASDAQ sign in New York's Times Square has a width of 84 feet and an area of 10,080 square feet. Find the height (or length) of the sign. (*Source:* livedesignonline.com)

Start the solution:

1. UNDERSTAND the problem. Reread it as many times as needed.

2. TRANSLATE into an equation. (Fill in the blanks below.)

Area	=	length	times	width
↓	↓	↓	↓	↓
___	=	x	·	___

Finish with:

3. SOLVE and   4. INTERPRET

△ 30. The world's largest sign for Coca-Cola is located in Arica, Chile. The rectangular sign has a length of 400 feet and an area of 52,400 square feet. Find the width of the sign. (*Source:* Fabulous Facts about Coca-Cola, Atlanta, GA)

Start the solution:

1. UNDERSTAND the problem. Reread it as many times as needed.

2. TRANSLATE into an equation. (Fill in the blanks below.)

Area	=	length	times	width
↓	↓	↓	↓	↓
___	=	___	·	x

Finish with:

3. SOLVE and   4. INTERPRET

31. For the purpose of purchasing new baseboard and carpet,

   a. Find the area and perimeter of the room below (neglecting doors).

   b. Identify whether baseboard has to do with area or perimeter and the same with carpet.

11.5 ft   9 ft

32. For the purpose of purchasing lumber for a new fence and seed to plant grass,

  a. Find the area and perimeter of the yard below.

  b. Identify whether a fence has to do with area or perimeter and the same with grass seed.

27 ft   45 ft   36 ft

33. A frame shop charges according to both the amount of framing needed to surround the picture and the amount of glass needed to cover the picture.

  a. Find the area and perimeter of the trapezoid-shaped framed picture below.

  b. Identify whether the amount of framing has to do with perimeter or area and the same with the amount of glass.

24 in.

20 in.   12 in.   20 in.

56 in.

34. A decorator is painting and placing a border completely around the parallelogram-shaped wall.

  a. Find the area and perimeter of the wall below.

  b. Identify whether the border has to do with perimeter or area and the same with paint.

7 ft   11.7 ft   9.3 ft

▶ **35.** Convert Nome, Alaska's 14°F high temperature to Celsius.

36. Convert Paris, France's low temperature of −5°C to Fahrenheit.

▶ **37.** An architect designs a rectangular flower garden such that the width is exactly two-thirds of the length. If 260 feet of antique picket fencing are to be used to enclose the garden, find the dimensions of the garden.

x feet

△ **38.** If the length of a rectangular parking lot is 10 meters less than twice its width, and the perimeter is 400 meters, find the length of the parking lot.

x meters

△ **39.** A flower bed is in the shape of a triangle with one side twice the length of the shortest side, and the third side is 30 feet more than the length of the shortest side. Find the dimensions if the perimeter is 102 feet.

? x ?

△ **40.** The perimeter of a yield sign in the shape of an isosceles triangle is 22 feet. If the shortest side is 2 feet less than the other two sides, find the length of the shortest side. (*Hint:* An isosceles triangle has two sides the same length.)

? x feet   x feet

▶ **41.** The Cat is a high-speed catamaran auto ferry that operates between Bar Harbor, Maine, and Yarmouth, Nova Scotia. The Cat can make the 138-mile trip in about $2\frac{1}{2}$ hours. Find the catamaran speed for this trip. (*Source:* Bay Ferries)

42. A family is planning their vacation to Disney World. They will drive from a small town outside New Orleans, Louisiana, to Orlando, Florida, a distance of 700 miles. They plan to average a rate of 55 mph. How long will this trip take?

△ **43.** Piranha fish require 1.5 cubic feet of water per fish to maintain a healthy environment. Find the maximum number of piranhas you could put in a tank measuring 8 feet by 3 feet by 6 feet.

6 feet

3 feet   8 feet

△ **44.** Find the maximum number of goldfish you can put in a cylindrical tank whose diameter is 8 meters and whose height is 3 meters if each goldfish needs 2 cubic meters of water.

8 meters

3 meters

Dolbear's Law states the relationship between the rate at which Snowy Tree crickets chirp and the air temperature of their environment. The formula is

$$T = 50 + \frac{N - 40}{4}, \text{ where}$$

T = temperature in degrees Fahrenheit and
N = number of chirps per minute

45. If $N = 86$, find the temperature in degrees Fahrenheit, T.

46. If $N = 94$, find the temperature in degrees Fahrenheit, T.

47. If $T = 55°F$, find the number of chirps per minute.

48. If $T = 65°F$, find the number of chirps per minute.

Use the results of Exercises 45–48 to complete each sentence with "increases" or "decreases."

49. As the number of cricket chirps per minute increases, the air temperature of their environment _____.

50. As the air temperature of their environment decreases, the number of cricket chirps per minute _____.

△ **51.** A lawn is in the shape of a trapezoid with a height of 60 feet and bases of 70 feet and 130 feet. How many whole bags of fertilizer must be purchased to cover the lawn if each bag covers 4000 square feet?

70 feet

60 feet

130 feet

△ **52.** If the area of a right-triangularly shaped sail is 20 square feet and its base is 5 feet, find the height of the sail.

?

5 feet

△ **53.** Maria's Pizza sells one 16-inch cheese pizza or two 10-inch cheese pizzas for $9.99. Determine which size gives more pizza.

16 inches   10 inches   10 inches

△ **54.** Find how much rope is needed to wrap around the earth at the equator if the radius of the earth is 4000 miles. (*Hint:* Use 3.14 for π and the formula for circumference.)

△ **55.** The perimeter of a geometric figure is the sum of the lengths of its sides. If the perimeter of the following pentagon (five-sided figure) is 48 meters, find the length of each side.

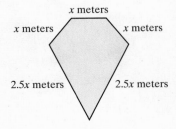

x meters

x meters   *x* meters

2.5*x* meters   2.5*x* meters

△ **56.** The perimeter of the following triangle is 82 feet. Find the length of each side.

$(2x − 8)$ feet

x feet

$(3x − 12)$ feet

57. The Hawaiian volcano Kilauea is one of the world's most active volcanoes and has had continuous eruptive activity since 1983. Erupting lava flows through a tube system about 11 kilometers to the sea. Assume a lava flow speed of 0.5 kilometer per hour and calculate how long it takes to reach the sea.

58. The world's largest pink ribbon, the sign of the fight against breast cancer, was erected out of pink Post-it® notes on a billboard in New York City in October 2004. If the area of the rectangular billboard covered by the ribbon was approximately 3990 square feet, and the width of the billboard was approximately 57 feet, what was the height of this billboard?

△ **59.** The perimeter of an equilateral triangle is 7 inches more than the perimeter of a square, and the side of the triangle is 5 inches longer than the side of the square. Find the side of the triangle. (*Hint:* An equilateral triangle has three sides the same length.)

△ **60.** A square animal pen and a pen shaped like an equilateral triangle have equal perimeters. Find the length of the sides of each pen if the sides of the triangular pen are fifteen less than twice a side of the square pen.

61. Find how long it takes a person to drive 135 miles on I-10 if she merges onto I-10 at 10 a.m. and drives nonstop with her cruise control set on 60 mph.

62. Beaumont, Texas, is about 150 miles from Toledo Bend. If Leo Miller leaves Beaumont at 4 a.m. and averages 45 mph, when should he arrive at Toledo Bend?

△ **63.** The longest runway at Los Angeles International Airport has the shape of a rectangle and an area of 1,813,500 square feet. This runway is 150 feet wide. How long is the runway? (*Source:* Los Angeles World Airports)

64. Normal room temperature is about 78°F. Convert this temperature to Celsius.

65. The highest temperature ever recorded in Europe was 122°F in Seville, Spain, in August 1881. Convert this record high temperature to Celsius. (*Source:* National Climatic Data Center)

66. The lowest temperature ever recorded in Oceania was −10°C at the Haleakala Summit in Maui, Hawaii, in January 1961. Convert this record low temperature to Fahrenheit. (*Source:* National Climatic Data Center)

67. The average temperature on the planet Mercury is 167°C. Convert this temperature to degrees Fahrenheit. (*Source:* National Space Science Data Center)

68. The average temperature on the planet Jupiter is −227°F. Convert this temperature to degrees Celsius. Round to the nearest degree. (*Source:* National Space Science Data Center)

△ **69.** The Hoberman Sphere is a toy ball that expands and contracts. When it is completely closed, it has a diameter of 9.5 inches. Find the volume of the Hoberman Sphere when it is

completely closed. Use 3.14 for π. Round to the nearest whole cubic inch. (*Hint:* Volume of a sphere $= \frac{4}{3}\pi r^3$. *Source:* Hoberman Designs, Inc.)

△ **70.** When the Hoberman Sphere (see Exercise 69) is completely expanded, its diameter is 30 inches. Find the volume of the Hoberman Sphere when it is completely expanded. Use 3.14 for π. (*Source:* Hoberman Designs, Inc.)

REVIEW AND PREVIEW

Write each percent as a decimal. See Appendix B.2.

71. 32%   **72.** 8%

73. 200%   **74.** 0.5%

Write each decimal as a percent. See Appendix B.2.

75. 0.17   **76.** 0.03

77. 7.2   **78.** 5

CONCEPT EXTENSIONS

△ **79.** The formula $V = lwh$ is used to find the volume of a box. If the length of a box is doubled, the width is doubled, and the height is doubled, how does this affect the volume? Explain your answer.

△ **80.** The formula $A = bh$ is used to find the area of a parallelogram. If the base of a parallelogram is doubled and its height is doubled, how does this affect the area? Explain your answer.

81. Use the Dolbear's Law formula for Exercises 45–48 and calculate when the number of cricket chirps per minute is the same as the temperature in degrees Fahrenheit. (*Hint:* Replace T with N and solve for N or replace N with T and solve for T.)

82. Find the temperature at which the Celsius measurement and the Fahrenheit measurement are the same number.

Solve.

83. $N = R + \dfrac{V}{G}$ for V (Urban forestry: tree plantings per year)

84. $B = \dfrac{F}{P − V}$ for V (Business: break-even point)

Solve. See the Concept Check in this section.

85. ■ − ● · ■ = ▲ for ●

86. ⬟ · ■ + ▲ = ● for ■

87. The distance from the sun to the earth is approximately 93,000,000 miles. If light travels at a rate of 186,000 miles per second, how long does it take light from the sun to reach us?

88. Light travels at a rate of 186,000 miles per second. If our moon is 238,860 miles from the earth, how long does it take light from the moon to reach us? (Round to the nearest tenth of a second.)

238,860 miles

89. A glacier is a giant mass of rocks and ice that flows downhill like a river. Exit Glacier, near Seward, Alaska, moves at a rate of 20 inches a day. Find the distance in feet the glacier moves in a year. (Assume 365 days a year. Round to 2 decimal places.)

90. Flying fish do not *actually* fly, but glide. They have been known to travel a distance of 1300 feet at a rate of 20 miles per hour. How many seconds does it take to travel this distance? (*Hint:* First convert miles per hour to feet per second. Recall that 1 mile = 5280 feet. Round to the nearest tenth of a second.)

91. A Japanese "bullet" train set a new world record for train speed at 581 kilometers per hour during a manned test run on the Yamanashi Maglev Test Line in 2003. The Yamanashi Maglev Test Line is 42.8 kilometers long. How many *minutes* would a test run on the Yamanashi Line last at this record-setting speed? Round to the nearest hundredth of a minute. (*Source:* Japan Railways Central Co.)

92. The Boeing X-51 is an unmanned demonstration aircraft for hypersonic flight testing. In May 2010, it successfully completed a free flight at about 3800 mph. Neglecting altitude, if the circumference of Earth is approximately 25,000 miles, how long would it take for the X-51 to travel around Earth? Give your answer in hours and minutes rounded to the nearest whole minute.

93. In the United States, a notable hang glider flight was a 303-mile, $8\frac{1}{2}$-hour flight from New Mexico to Kansas. What was the average rate during this flight?

94. Stalactites join stalagmites to form columns. A column found at Natural Bridge Caverns near San Antonio, Texas, rises 15 feet and has a *diameter* of only 2 inches. Find the volume of this column in cubic inches. (*Hint:* Use the formula for volume of a cylinder and use a calculator approximation for π. Round to the nearest tenth of an inch.)

2.8 | Solving Linear Inequalities

OBJECTIVE

1   Graphing Solution Sets to Linear Inequalities and Using Interval Notation

In Chapter 1, we reviewed these inequality symbols and their meanings:

$<$ means "is less than" $\leq$ means "is less than or equal to"

$>$ means "is greater than" $\geq$ means "is greater than or equal to"

Equations	Inequalities
$x = 3$	$x \leq 3$
$5n - 6 = 14$	$5n - 6 < 14$
$12 = 7 - 3y$	$12 \geq 7 - 3y$
$\dfrac{x}{4} - 6 = 1$	$\dfrac{x}{4} - 6 > 1$

A linear inequality is similar to a linear equation except that the equality symbol is replaced with an inequality symbol.

Linear Inequality in One Variable

A **linear inequality in one variable** is an inequality that can be written in the form

$$ax + b < c$$

where a, b, and c are real numbers and a is not 0.

This definition and all other definitions, properties, and steps in this section also hold true for the inequality symbols $>$, $\geq$, and $\leq$.

A **solution of an inequality** is a value of the variable that makes the inequality a true statement. The solution set is the set of all solutions. For the inequality $x < 3$, replacing x with any number less than 3, that is, to the left of 3 on a number line, makes the resulting inequality true. This means that any number less than 3 is a solution of the inequality $x < 3$.

Since there are infinitely many such numbers, we cannot list all the solutions of the inequality. We *can* use set notation and write

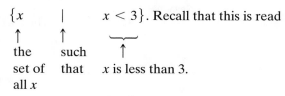

$\{x \qquad | \qquad x < 3\}$. Recall that this is read

the set of all x such that x is less than 3.

We can also picture the solutions on a number line. If we use open/closed-circle notation, the graph of $\{x \mid x < 3\}$ looks like the following.

In this text, a convenient notation, called **interval notation,** will be used to write solution sets of inequalities. To help us understand this notation, a different graphing notation will be used. Instead of an open circle, we use a parenthesis; instead of a closed circle, we use a bracket. With this new notation, the graph of $\{x \mid x < 3\}$ now looks like

and can be represented in interval notation as $(-\infty, 3)$. The symbol $-\infty$, read as "negative infinity," does not indicate a number but does indicate that the shaded arrow to the left never ends. In other words, the interval $(-\infty, 3)$ includes *all* numbers less than 3.

Picturing the solutions of an inequality on a number line is called **graphing** the solutions or graphing the inequality, and the picture is called the **graph** of the inequality.

To graph $\{x \mid x \leq 3\}$ or simply $x \leq 3$, shade the numbers to the left of 3 and place a bracket at 3 on the number line. The bracket indicates that 3 **is** a solution: 3 **is** less than or equal to 3. In interval notation, we write $(-\infty, 3]$.

> ▶ **Helpful Hint**
>
> When writing an inequality in interval notation, it may be easier to graph the inequality first, then write it in interval notation. To help, think of the number line as approaching $-\infty$ to the left and $+\infty$ or ∞ to the right. Then simply write the interval notation by following your shading from left to right.

EXAMPLE 1   Graph $x \geq -1$. Then write the solutions in interval notation.

Solution   We place a bracket at -1 since the inequality symbol is $\geq$ and -1 is greater than or equal to -1. Then we shade to the right of -1.

In interval notation, this is $[-1, \infty)$.   □

PRACTICE

1   Graph $x < 5$. Then write the solutions in interval notation.

OBJECTIVE

2 Solving Linear Inequalities ▶

When solutions of a linear inequality are not immediately obvious, they are found through a process similar to the one used to solve a linear equation. Our goal is to get the variable alone, and we use properties of inequality similar to properties of equality.

> **Addition Property of Inequality**
>
> If a, b, and c are real numbers, then
>
> $$a < b \quad \text{and} \quad a + c < b + c$$
>
> are equivalent inequalities.

This property also holds true for subtracting values, since subtraction is defined in terms of addition. In other words, adding or subtracting the same quantity from both sides of an inequality does not change the solution of the inequality.

EXAMPLE 2   Solve $x + 4 \leq -6$ for x. Graph the solution set and write it in interval notation.

Solution   To solve for x, subtract 4 from both sides of the inequality.

$$
\begin{array}{ll}
x + 4 \leq -6 & \text{Original inequality} \\
x + 4 - 4 \leq -6 - 4 & \text{Subtract 4 from both sides.} \\
x \leq -10 & \text{Simplify.}
\end{array}
$$

The solution set is $(-\infty, -10]$.

PRACTICE

2   Solve $x + 11 \geq 6$. Graph the solution set and write it in interval notation.

> ▶ **Helpful Hint**
>
> Notice that any number less than or equal to -10 is a solution to $x \leq -10$. For example, solutions include
>
> $$-10,\ -200,\ -11\tfrac{1}{2},\ -7\pi,\ -\sqrt{130},\ -50.3$$

An important difference between linear equations and linear inequalities is shown when we multiply or divide both sides of an inequality by a nonzero real number. For example, start with the true statement $6 < 8$ and multiply both sides by 2. As we see below, the resulting inequality is also true.

$$
\begin{array}{ll}
6 < 8 & \text{True} \\
2(6) < 2(8) & \text{Multiply both sides by 2.} \\
12 < 16 & \text{True}
\end{array}
$$

But if we start with the same true statement $6 < 8$ and multiply both sides by -2, the resulting inequality is not a true statement.

$$
\begin{array}{ll}
6 < 8 & \text{True} \\
-2(6) < -2(8) & \text{Multiply both sides by } -2. \\
-12 < -16 & \text{False}
\end{array}
$$

Notice, however, that if we reverse the direction of the inequality symbol, the resulting inequality is true.

$$
\begin{array}{ll}
-12 < -16 & \text{False} \\
-12 > -16 & \text{True}
\end{array}
$$

This demonstrates the multiplication property of inequality.

> **Multiplication Property of Inequality**
>
> **1.** If a, b, and c are real numbers, and c is **positive,** then
>
> $$a < b \quad \text{and} \quad ac < bc$$
>
> are equivalent inequalities.
>
> **2.** If a, b, and c are real numbers, and c is **negative,** then
>
> $$a < b \quad \text{and} \quad ac > bc$$
>
> are equivalent inequalities.

Because division is defined in terms of multiplication, this property also holds true when dividing both sides of an inequality by a nonzero number. If we multiply or divide both sides of an inequality by a negative number, **the direction of the inequality symbol must be reversed for the inequalities to remain equivalent.**

> ▶ **Helpful Hint**
> Whenever both sides of an inequality are multiplied or divided by a negative number, the direction of the inequality symbol **must be** reversed to form an equivalent inequality.

EXAMPLE 3 Solve $-2x \le -4$. Graph the solution set and write it in interval notation.

Solution Remember to reverse the direction of the inequality symbol when dividing by a negative number.

> ▶ **Helpful Hint**
> Don't forget to reverse the direction of the inequality symbol.

$$-2x \le -4$$

$$\frac{-2x}{-2} \ge \frac{-4}{-2} \quad \text{Divide both sides by } -2 \text{ and reverse the direction of the inequality symbol.}$$

$$x \ge 2 \quad \text{Simplify.}$$

The solution set $[2, \infty)$ is graphed as shown.

PRACTICE
3 Solve $-5x \ge -15$. Graph the solution set and write it in interval notation.

▶ **EXAMPLE 4** Solve $2x < -4$. Graph the solution set and write it in interval notation.

Solution

> ▶ **Helpful Hint**
> Do not reverse the inequality sign.

$$2x < -4$$

$$\frac{2x}{2} < \frac{-4}{2} \quad \text{Divide both sides by 2.} \quad \text{Do not reverse the direction of the inequality sign.}$$

$$x < -2 \quad \text{Simplify.}$$

The solution set $(-\infty, -2)$ is graphed as shown.

PRACTICE
4 Solve $3x > -9$. Graph the solution set and write it in interval notation.

✓**CONCEPT CHECK**
Fill in the blank with $<$, $>$, $\le$, or $\ge$.

a. Since $-8 < -4$, then $3(-8)$ _____ $3(-4)$.

b. Since $5 \ge -2$, then $\dfrac{5}{-7}$ _____ $\dfrac{-2}{-7}$.

c. If $a < b$, then $2a$ _____ $2b$.

d. If $a \ge b$, then $\dfrac{a}{-3}$ _____ $\dfrac{b}{-3}$.

The following steps may be helpful when solving inequalities. Notice that these steps are similar to the ones given in Section 2.3 for solving equations.

Solving Linear Inequalities in One Variable

Step 1. Clear the inequality of fractions by multiplying both sides of the inequality by the lowest common denominator (LCD) of all fractions in the inequality.

Step 2. Remove grouping symbols such as parentheses by using the distributive property.

Step 3. Simplify each side of the inequality by combining like terms.

Step 4. Write the inequality with variable terms on one side and numbers on the other side by using the addition property of inequality.

Step 5. Get the variable alone by using the multiplication property of inequality.

▶ **Helpful Hint**

Don't forget that if both sides of an inequality are multiplied or divided by a negative number, the direction of the inequality symbol must be reversed.

EXAMPLE 5   Solve $-4x + 7 \geq -9$. Graph the solution set and write it in interval notation.

Solution

$$-4x + 7 \geq -9$$

$$-4x + 7 - 7 \geq -9 - 7 \quad \text{Subtract 7 from both sides.}$$

$$-4x \geq -16 \quad \text{Simplify.}$$

$$\frac{-4x}{-4} \leq \frac{-16}{-4} \quad \begin{array}{l}\text{Divide both sides by } -4 \text{ and reverse}\\\text{the direction of the inequality symbol.}\end{array}$$

$$x \leq 4 \quad \text{Simplify.}$$

The solution set $(-\infty, 4]$ is graphed as shown.

PRACTICE

5   Solve $45 - 7x \leq -4$. Graph the solution set and write it in interval notation.

EXAMPLE 6   Solve $2x + 7 \leq x - 11$. Graph the solution set and write it in interval notation.

Solution

$$2x + 7 \leq x - 11$$

$$2x + 7 - x \leq x - 11 - x \quad \text{Subtract } x \text{ from both sides.}$$

$$x + 7 \leq -11 \quad \text{Combine like terms.}$$

$$x + 7 - 7 \leq -11 - 7 \quad \text{Subtract 7 from both sides.}$$

$$x \leq -18 \quad \text{Combine like terms.}$$

The graph of the solution set $(-\infty, -18]$ is shown.

PRACTICE

6   Solve $3x + 20 \leq 2x + 13$. Graph the solution set and write it in interval notation.

EXAMPLE 7 Solve $-5x + 7 < 2(x - 3)$. Graph the solution set and write it in interval notation.

Solution

$$-5x + 7 < 2(x - 3)$$

$-5x + 7 < 2x - 6$	Apply the distributive property.
$-5x + 7 - 2x < 2x - 6 - 2x$	Subtract $2x$ from both sides.
$-7x + 7 < -6$	Combine like terms.
$-7x + 7 - 7 < -6 - 7$	Subtract 7 from both sides.
$-7x < -13$	Combine like terms.
$\dfrac{-7x}{-7} > \dfrac{-13}{-7}$	Divide both sides by -7 and reverse the direction of the inequality symbol.
$x > \dfrac{13}{7}$	Simplify.

The graph of the solution set $\left(\dfrac{13}{7}, \infty\right)$ is shown.

PRACTICE
7 Solve $6 - 5x > 3(x - 4)$. Graph the solution set and write it in interval notation.

EXAMPLE 8 Solve $2(x - 3) - 5 \le 3(x + 2) - 18$. Graph the solution set and write it in interval notation.

Solution

$$2(x - 3) - 5 \le 3(x + 2) - 18$$

$2x - 6 - 5 \le 3x + 6 - 18$	Apply the distributive property.
$2x - 11 \le 3x - 12$	Combine like terms.
$-x - 11 \le -12$	Subtract $3x$ from both sides.
$-x \le -1$	Add 11 to both sides.
$\dfrac{-x}{-1} \ge \dfrac{-1}{-1}$	Divide both sides by -1 and reverse the direction of the inequality symbol.
$x \ge 1$	Simplify.

The graph of the solution set $[1, \infty)$ is shown.

PRACTICE
8 Solve $3(x - 4) - 5 \le 5(x - 1) - 12$. Graph the solution set and write it in interval notation.

OBJECTIVE
3 Solving Compound Inequalities

Inequalities containing one inequality symbol are called **simple inequalities,** while inequalities containing two inequality symbols are called **compound inequalities.** A compound inequality is really two simple inequalities in one. The compound inequality

$$3 < x < 5 \quad \text{means} \quad 3 < x \text{ and } x < 5$$

This can be read "x is greater than 3 and less than 5."

A solution of a compound inequality is a value that is a solution of both of the simple inequalities that make up the compound inequality. For example,

$$4\frac{1}{2} \text{ is a solution of } 3 < x < 5 \text{ since } 3 < 4\frac{1}{2} \text{ and } 4\frac{1}{2} < 5.$$

To graph $3 < x < 5$, place parentheses at both 3 and 5 and shade between.

EXAMPLE 9 Graph $2 < x \leq 4$. Write the solutions in interval notation.

Solution Graph all numbers greater than 2 and less than or equal to 4. Place a parenthesis at 2, a bracket at 4, and shade between.

In interval notation, this is $(2, 4]$. □

PRACTICE
9 Graph $-3 \leq x < 1$. Write the solutions in interval notation.

When we solve a simple inequality, we isolate the variable on one side of the inequality. When we solve a compound inequality, we isolate the variable in the middle part of the inequality. Also, when solving a compound inequality, we must perform the same operation to all **three** parts of the inequality: left, middle, and right.

EXAMPLE 10 Solve $-1 \leq 2x - 3 < 5$. Graph the solution set and write it in interval notation.

Solution
$$-1 \leq 2x - 3 < 5$$
$$-1 + 3 \leq 2x - 3 + 3 < 5 + 3 \qquad \text{Add 3 to all three parts.}$$
$$2 \leq 2x < 8 \qquad \text{Combine like terms.}$$
$$\frac{2}{2} \leq \frac{2x}{2} < \frac{8}{2} \qquad \text{Divide all three parts by 2.}$$
$$1 \leq x < 4 \qquad \text{Simplify.}$$

The graph of the solution set $[1, 4)$ is shown.

PRACTICE
10 Solve $-4 < 3x + 2 \leq 8$. Graph the solution set and write it in interval notation.

EXAMPLE 11 Solve $3 \leq \frac{3x}{2} + 4 \leq 5$. Graph the solution set and write it in interval notation.

Solution
$$3 \leq \frac{3x}{2} + 4 \leq 5$$

$$2(3) \leq 2\left(\frac{3x}{2} + 4\right) \leq 2(5) \qquad \text{Multiply all three parts by 2 to clear the fraction.}$$
$$6 \leq 3x + 8 \leq 10 \qquad \text{Distribute.}$$
$$-2 \leq 3x \leq 2 \qquad \text{Subtract 8 from all three parts.}$$
$$\frac{-2}{3} \leq \frac{3x}{3} \leq \frac{2}{3} \qquad \text{Divide all three parts by 3.}$$
$$-\frac{2}{3} \leq x \leq \frac{2}{3} \qquad \text{Simplify.}$$

The graph of the solution set $\left[-\dfrac{2}{3}, \dfrac{2}{3}\right]$ is shown.

PRACTICE
11 Solve $1 < \dfrac{3}{4}x + 5 < 6$. Graph the solution set and write it in interval notation.

OBJECTIVE
4 Solving Inequality Applications

Problems containing words such as "at least," "at most," "between," "no more than," and "no less than" usually indicate that an inequality should be solved instead of an equation. In solving applications involving linear inequalities, use the same procedure you use to solve applications involving linear equations.

Some Inequality Translations			
$\geq$	$\leq$	$<$	$>$
at least	at most	is less than	is greater than
no less than	no more than		

EXAMPLE 12 12 subtracted from 3 times a number is less than 21. Find all numbers that make this statement true.

Solution

1. UNDERSTAND. Read and reread the problem. This is a direct translation problem, and let's let
   x = the unknown number

2. TRANSLATE.

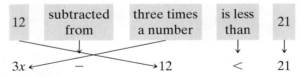

3. SOLVE. $3x - 12 < 21$

$\qquad\qquad 3x < 33$ Add 12 to both sides.

$\qquad\qquad \dfrac{3x}{3} < \dfrac{33}{3}$ Divide both sides by 3 and do not reverse the direction of the inequality symbol.

$\qquad\qquad x < 11$ Simplify.

4. INTERPRET.

Check: Check the translation; then let's choose a number less than 11 to see if it checks. For example, let's check 10. 12 subtracted from 3 times 10 is 12 subtracted from 30, or 18. Since 18 is less than 21, the number 10 checks.

State: All numbers less than 11 make the original statement true.

PRACTICE
12 Twice a number, subtracted from 35, is greater than 15. Find all numbers that make this true.

EXAMPLE 13 **Staying within Budget**

Marie Chase and Jonathan Edwards are having their wedding reception at the Gallery Reception Hall. They may spend at most $2000 for the reception. If the reception hall charges a $100 cleanup fee plus $36 per person, find the greatest number of people that they can invite and still stay within their budget.

Solution

1. UNDERSTAND. Read and reread the problem. Next, guess a solution. If 40 people attend the reception, the cost is $100 + $36(40) = $100 + $1440 = $1540. Let x = the number of people who attend the reception.

2. TRANSLATE.

In words:	cleanup fee	+	cost per person	must be less than or equal to	2000
	↓		↓	↓	↓
Translate:	100	+	36x	≤	2000

3. SOLVE.

$$100 + 36x \le 2000$$
$$36x \le 1900 \quad \text{Subtract 100 from both sides.}$$
$$x \le 52\frac{7}{9} \quad \text{Divide both sides by 36.}$$

4. INTERPRET.

Check: Since x represents the number of people, we round down to the nearest whole, or 52. Notice that if 52 people attend, the cost is

$100 + $36(52) = $1972. If 53 people attend, the cost is

$100 + $36(53) = $2008, which is more than the given 2000.

State: Marie Chase and Jonathan Edwards can invite at most 52 people to the reception. □

PRACTICE

13 Kasonga is eager to begin his education at his local community college. He has budgeted $1500 for college this semester. His local college charges a $300 matriculation fee and costs an average of $375 for tuition, fees, and books for each three-credit course. Find the greatest number of classes Kasonga can afford to take this semester.

Vocabulary, Readiness & Video Check

Use the choices below to fill in each blank.

expression   inequality   equation

1. $6x - 7(x + 9)$ _____

2. $6x = 7(x + 9)$ _____

3. $6x < 7(x + 9)$ _____

4. $5y - 2 \ge -38$ _____

Decide which number listed is not a solution to each given inequality.

5. $x \ge -3; -3, 0, -5, \pi$ _____

6. $x < 6; -6, |-6|, 0, -3.2$ _____

Martin-Gay Interactive Videos

See Video 2.8

Watch the section lecture video and answer the following questions.

OBJECTIVE 1

7. Using ▣ Example 1 from the video as a reference, explain the connection between the graph of an inequality and interval notation.

OBJECTIVE 2

8. The steps for solving a linear inequality in one variable are discussed in the lecture before ▣ Example 6. Why are you told to be very careful when you use Step 5?

OBJECTIVE 3

9. For ▣ Example 8, explain how the solving would change if the compound inequality simplified to $0 < -3x < 14$ instead of $0 < 3x < 14$.

OBJECTIVE 4

10. What is the phrase in ▣ Example 9 that tells you to translate to an *inequality*? What does this phrase translate to?

2.8 Exercise Set   MyMathLab®

Graph each set of numbers given in interval notation. Then write an inequality statement in x describing the numbers graphed.

1. $[2, \infty)$
2. $(-3, \infty)$
3. $(-\infty, -5)$
4. $(-\infty, 4]$

Graph each inequality on a number line. Then write the solutions in interval notation. See Example 1.

▶ 5. $x \le -1$
6. $y < 0$
7. $x < \dfrac{1}{2}$
8. $z < -\dfrac{2}{3}$
9. $y \ge 5$
▶ 10. $x > 3$

Solve each inequality. Graph the solution set and write it in interval notation. See Examples 2 through 4.

11. $2x < -6$
12. $3x > -9$
▶ 13. $x - 2 \ge -7$
14. $x + 4 \le 1$
▶ 15. $-8x \le 16$
16. $-5x < 20$

Solve each inequality. Graph the solution set and write it in interval notation. See Examples 5 and 6.

17. $3x - 5 > 2x - 8$
18. $3 - 7x \ge 10 - 8x$
19. $4x - 1 \le 5x - 2x$
20. $7x + 3 < 9x - 3x$

Solve each inequality. Graph the solution set and write it in interval notation. See Examples 7 and 8.

21. $x - 7 < 3(x + 1)$
22. $3x + 9 \le 5(x - 1)$
23. $-6x + 2 \ge 2(5 - x)$
24. $-7x + 4 > 3(4 - x)$
25. $4(3x - 1) \le 5(2x - 4)$

26. $3(5x - 4) \le 4(3x - 2)$
27. $3(x + 2) - 6 > -2(x - 3) + 14$
28. $7(x - 2) + x \le -4(5 - x) - 12$

MIXED PRACTICE

Solve the following inequalities. Graph each solution set and write it in interval notation.

29. $-2x \le -40$
30. $-7x > 21$
31. $-9 + x > 7$
32. $y - 4 \le 1$
33. $3x - 7 < 6x + 2$
34. $2x - 1 \ge 4x - 5$
35. $5x - 7x \ge x + 2$
36. $4 - x < 8x + 2x$
37. $\dfrac{3}{4}x > 2$
38. $\dfrac{5}{6}x \ge -8$
39. $3(x - 5) < 2(2x - 1)$
40. $5(x + 4) < 4(2x + 3)$
41. $4(2x + 1) < 4$
42. $6(2 - x) \ge 12$
43. $-5x + 4 \ge -4(x - 1)$
44. $-6x + 2 < -3(x + 4)$
▶ 45. $-2(x - 4) - 3x < -(4x + 1) + 2x$
46. $-5(1 - x) + x \le -(6 - 2x) + 6$
47. $\dfrac{1}{4}(x + 4) < \dfrac{1}{5}(2x + 3)$
48. $\dfrac{1}{3}(3x - 1) < \dfrac{1}{2}(x + 4)$

Graph each inequality. Then write the solutions in interval notation. See Example 9.

49. $-1 < x < 3$

50. $2 \le y \le 3$

▶ **51.** $0 \le y < 2$

52. $-1 \le x \le 4$

Solve each inequality. Graph the solution set and write it in interval notation. See Examples 10 and 11.

53. $-3 < 3x < 6$

54. $-5 < 2x < -2$

55. $2 \le 3x - 10 \le 5$

56. $4 \le 5x - 6 \le 19$

57. $-4 < 2(x - 3) \le 4$

58. $0 < 4(x + 5) \le 8$

59. $-2 < 3x - 5 < 7$

60. $1 < 4 + 2x \le 7$

▶ **61.** $-6 < 3(x - 2) \le 8$

62. $-5 \le 2(x + 4) < 8$

Solve the following. For Exercises 65 and 66, the solutions have been started for you. See Examples 12 and 13.

63. Six more than twice a number is greater than negative fourteen. Find all numbers that make this statement true.

64. One more than five times a number is less than or equal to ten. Find all such numbers.

▶ △ **65.** The perimeter of a rectangle is to be no greater than 100 centimeters and the width must be 15 centimeters. Find the maximum length of the rectangle.

15 cm

x cm

Start the solution:

1. UNDERSTAND the problem. Reread it as many times as needed.

2. TRANSLATE into an equation. (Fill in the blanks below.)

the perimeter of the rectangle	is no greater than	100
↓	↓	↓
$x + 15 + x + 15$	_____	100

Finish with:

3. SOLVE and 4. INTERPRET

△ **66.** One side of a triangle is three times as long as another side, and the third side is 12 inches long. If the perimeter can be no longer than 32 inches, find the maximum lengths of the other two sides.

12 in.   *x* in.

3*x* in.

Start the solution:

1. UNDERSTAND the problem. Reread it as many times as needed.

2. TRANSLATE into an equation. (Fill in the blanks below.)

the perimeter of the rectangle	is no longer than	32
↓	↓	↓
$12 + 3x + x$	_____	32

Finish with:

3. SOLVE and 4. INTERPRET

67. Ben Holladay bowled 146 and 201 in his first two games. What must he bowl in his third game to have an average of at least 180? (*Hint:* The average of a list of numbers is their sum divided by the number of numbers in the list.)

68. On an NBA team, the two forwards measure 6′8″ and 6′6″ tall and the two guards measure 6′0″ and 5′9″ tall. How tall should the center be if they wish to have a starting team average height of at least 6′5″?

69. Dennis and Nancy Wood are celebrating their 30th wedding anniversary by having a reception at Tiffany Oaks reception hall. They have budgeted $3000 for their reception. If the reception hall charges a $50.00 cleanup fee plus $34 per person, find the greatest number of people that they may invite and still stay within their budget.

70. A surprise retirement party is being planned for Pratap Puri. A total of $860 has been collected for the event, which is to be held at a local reception hall. This reception hall charges a cleanup fee of $40 and $15 per person for drinks and light snacks. Find the greatest number of people that may be invited and still stay within the $860 budget.

71. A 150-pound person uses 5.8 calories per minute when walking at a speed of 4 mph. How long must a person walk at this speed to use at least 200 calories? Round up to the nearest minute. (*Source:* Home & Garden Bulletin No. 72)

72. A 170-pound person uses 5.3 calories per minute when bicycling at a speed of 5.5 mph. How long must a person ride a bike at this speed to use at least 200 calories? Round up to the nearest minute. (*Source:* Same as Exercise 71)

73. Twice a number, increased by one, is between negative five and seven. Find all such numbers.

74. Half a number, decreased by four, is between two and three. Find all such numbers.

REVIEW AND PREVIEW

Evaluate the following. See Section 1.4.

75. $(2)^3$

76. $(3)^3$

77. $(1)^{12}$ **78.** 0^5

79. $\left(\dfrac{4}{7}\right)^2$ **80.** $\left(\dfrac{2}{3}\right)^3$

CONCEPT EXTENSIONS

Fill in the box with $<$, $>$, $\leq$, or $\geq$. See the Concept Check in this section.

81. Since $3 < 5$, then $3(-4) \square 5(-4)$.

82. If $m \leq n$, then $2m \square 2n$.

83. If $m \leq n$, then $-2m \square -2n$.

84. If $-x < y$, then $x \square -y$.

85. When solving an inequality, when must you reverse the direction of the inequality symbol?

86. If both sides of the inequality $-3x < 30$ are divided by -3, do you reverse the direction of the inequality symbol? Why or why not?

Solve.

87. Eric Daly has scores of 75, 83, and 85 on his history tests. Use an inequality to find the scores he can make on his final exam to receive a B in the class. The final exam counts as **two** tests, and a B is received if the final course average is greater than or equal to 80.

88. Maria Lipco has scores of 85, 95, and 92 on her algebra tests. Use an inequality to find the scores she can make on her final exam to receive an A in the course. The final exam counts as **three** tests, and an A is received if the final course average is greater than or equal to 90. Round to one decimal place.

89. Explain how solving a linear inequality is similar to solving a linear equation.

90. Explain how solving a linear inequality is different from solving a linear equation.

91. Explain how solving a linear inequality is different from solving a compound inequality.

92. Explain how solving a linear inequality is similar to solving a compound inequality.

93. The formula $C = 3.14d$ can be used to approximate the circumference of a circle given its diameter. Waldo Manufacturing manufactures and sells a certain washer with an outside circumference of 3 centimeters. The company has decided that a washer whose actual circumference is in the interval $2.9 \leq C \leq 3.1$ centimeters is acceptable. Use a compound inequality and find the corresponding interval for diameters of these washers. (Round to 3 decimal places.)

94. Bunnie Supplies manufactures plastic Easter eggs that open. The company has determined that if the circumference of the opening of each part of the egg is in the interval $118 \leq C \leq 122$ millimeters, the eggs will open and close comfortably. Use a compound inequality and find the corresponding interval for diameters of these openings. (Round to 2 decimal places.)

For Exercises 95 through 98, see the example below.

Solve $x(x - 6) > x^2 - 5x + 6$. Graph the solution set and write it in interval notation.

Solution

$$x(x - 6) > x^2 - 5x + 6$$
$$x^2 - 6x > x^2 - 5x + 6$$
$$x^2 - 6x - x^2 > x^2 - 5x + 6 - x^2$$
$$-6x > -5x + 6$$
$$-x > 6$$
$$\dfrac{-x}{-1} < \dfrac{6}{-1}$$
$$x < -6$$

The solution set $(-\infty, -6)$ is graphed as shown.

$$\xleftarrow{\quad} \overset{}{\underset{-7}{}}\ \overset{}{\underset{-6}{}}\ \overset{}{\underset{-5}{}}\ \overset{}{\underset{-4}{}}\ \overset{}{\underset{-3}{}}\ \overset{}{\underset{-2}{}}\ \overset{}{\underset{-1}{}}\ \xrightarrow{\quad}$$

Solve each inequality. Graph the solution set and write it in interval notation.

95. $x(x + 4) > x^2 - 2x + 6$

96. $x(x - 3) \geq x^2 - 5x - 8$

97. $x^2 + 6x - 10 < x(x - 10)$

98. $x^2 - 4x + 8 < x(x + 8)$

Chapter 2 Vocabulary Check

Fill in each blank with one of the words or phrases listed below.

like terms   numerical coefficient   linear inequality in one variable   no solution

equivalent equations   formula   compound inequalities   reversed

linear equation in one variable   unlike terms   all real numbers   the same

1. Terms with the same variables raised to exactly the same powers are called _____.

2. If terms are not like terms, they are _____.

3. A(n) _____ can be written in the form $ax + b = c$.

4. A(n) _____ can be written in the form $ax + b < c$ (or $>, \leq, \geq$).

5. Inequalities containing two inequality symbols are called _____.

6. An equation that describes a known relationship among quantities is called a(n) _____.

7. The _____ of a term is its numerical factor.

8. Equations that have the same solution are called _____.

9. The solution(s) to the equation $x + 5 = x + 5$ is/are _____.

10. The solution(s) to the equation $x + 5 = x + 4$ is/are _____.

11. If both sides of an inequality are multiplied or divided by the same positive number, the direction of the inequality symbol is _____.

12. If both sides of an inequality are multiplied by the same negative number, the direction of the inequality symbol is _____.

Chapter 2 Highlights

DEFINITIONS AND CONCEPTS	EXAMPLES

Section 2.1   Simplifying Algebraic Expressions

The **numerical coefficient** of a **term** is its numerical factor.

Term	Numerical Coefficient
$-7y$	-7
x	1
$\frac{1}{5}a^2b$	$\frac{1}{5}$

Terms with the same variables raised to exactly the same powers are **like terms.**

Like Terms	Unlike Terms
$12x, -x$	$3y, 3y^2$
$-2xy, 5yx$	$7a^2b, -2ab^2$

To combine like terms, add the numerical coefficients and multiply the result by the common variable factor.

$$9y + 3y = 12y$$
$$-4z^2 + 5z^2 - 6z^2 = -5z^2$$

To remove parentheses, apply the distributive property.

$$-4(x + 7) + 10(3x - 1)$$
$$= -4x - 28 + 30x - 10$$
$$= 26x - 38$$

DEFINITIONS AND CONCEPTS	EXAMPLES

Section 2.2   The Addition and Multiplication Properties of Equality

A **linear equation in one variable** can be written in the form $ax + b = c$ where $a, b,$ and c are real numbers and $a \neq 0$.

Linear Equations

$$-3x + 7 = 2$$

$$3(x - 1) = -8(x + 5) + 4$$

Equivalent equations are equations that have the same solution.

$x - 7 = 10$ and $x = 17$
are equivalent equations.

Addition Property of Equality

Adding the same number to or subtracting the same number from both sides of an equation does not change its solution.

$$y + 9 = 3$$
$$y + 9 - 9 = 3 - 9$$
$$y = -6$$

Multiplication Property of Equality

Multiplying both sides or dividing both sides of an equation by the same nonzero number does not change its solution.

$$\frac{2}{3}a = 18$$

$$\frac{3}{2}\left(\frac{2}{3}a\right) = \frac{3}{2}(18)$$

$$a = 27$$

Section 2.3   Solving Linear Equations

To Solve Linear Equations

Solve: $\dfrac{5(-2x + 9)}{6} + 3 = \dfrac{1}{2}$

1. Clear the equation of fractions.

1. $6 \cdot \dfrac{5(-2x + 9)}{6} + 6 \cdot 3 = 6 \cdot \dfrac{1}{2}$

$$5(-2x + 9) + 18 = 3$$

2. Remove any grouping symbols such as parentheses.

2. $\quad -10x + 45 + 18 = 3 \qquad$ Distributive property

3. Simplify each side by combining like terms.

3. $\quad -10x + 63 = 3 \qquad$ Combine like terms.

4. Write variable terms on one side and numbers on the other side using the addition property of equality.

4. $\quad -10x + 63 - 63 = 3 - 63 \quad$ Subtract 63.

$$-10x = -60$$

5. Get the variable alone using the multiplication property of equality.

5. $\quad \dfrac{-10x}{-10} = \dfrac{-60}{-10} \qquad$ Divide by -10.

$$x = 6$$

6. Check by substituting in the original equation.

6. $\dfrac{5(-2x + 9)}{6} + 3 = \dfrac{1}{2}$

$$\frac{5(-2 \cdot 6 + 9)}{6} + 3 \overset{?}{=} \frac{1}{2}$$

$$\frac{5(-3)}{6} + 3 \overset{?}{=} \frac{1}{2}$$

$$-\frac{5}{2} + \frac{6}{2} \overset{?}{=} \frac{1}{2}$$

$$\frac{1}{2} = \frac{1}{2} \qquad \text{True}$$

DEFINITIONS AND CONCEPTS	EXAMPLES

Section 2.4   An Introduction to Problem Solving

Problem-Solving Steps

The height of the Hudson volcano in Chile is twice the height of the Kiska volcano in the Aleutian Islands. If the sum of their heights is 12,870 feet, find the height of each.

1. UNDERSTAND the problem.

1. Read and reread the problem. Guess a solution and check your guess.

Let x be the height of the Kiska volcano. Then $2x$ is the height of the Hudson volcano.

x⏋ $2x$⏋
Kiska Hudson

2. TRANSLATE the problem.

2. In words:

height of Kiska	added to	height of Hudson	is	12,870
↓	↓	↓	↓	↓
x	$+$	$2x$	$=$	12,870

Translate:

3. SOLVE.

3.
$$x + 2x = 12{,}870$$
$$3x = 12{,}870$$
$$x = 4290$$

4. INTERPRET the results.

4. *Check:* If x is 4290, then $2x$ is 2(4290) or 8580. Their sum is 4290 + 8580 or 12,870, the required amount.

State: The Kiska volcano is 4290 feet high and the Hudson volcano is 8580 feet high.

Section 2.5   Formulas and Problem Solving

An equation that describes a known relationship among quantities is called a **formula.**

If all values for the variables in a formula are known except for one, this unknown value may be found by substituting in the known values and solving.

Formulas
$$A = lw \text{ (area of a rectangle)}$$
$$I = PRT \text{ (simple interest)}$$

If $d = 182$ miles and $r = 52$ miles per hour in the formula $d = r \cdot t$, find t.

$$d = r \cdot t$$
$$182 = 52 \cdot t \quad \text{Let } d = 182 \text{ and } r = 52.$$
$$3.5 = t$$

The time is 3.5 hours.

To solve a formula for a specified variable, use the same steps as for solving a linear equation. Treat the specified variable as the only variable of the equation.

Solve: $P = 2l + 2w$ for l.
$$P = 2l + 2w$$
$$P - 2w = 2l + 2w - 2w \quad \text{Subtract } 2w.$$
$$P - 2w = 2l$$
$$\frac{P - 2w}{2} = \frac{2l}{2} \quad \text{Divide by 2.}$$
$$\frac{P - 2w}{2} = l \quad \text{Simplify.}$$

DEFINITIONS AND CONCEPTS	EXAMPLES

Section 2.8   Solving Linear Inequalities

A **linear inequality in one variable** is an inequality that can be written in one of the forms:

$$ax + b < c \qquad ax + b \le c$$
$$ax + b > c \qquad ax + b \ge c$$

where a, b, and c are real numbers and a is not 0.

Linear Inequalities

$$2x + 3 < 6 \qquad 5(x-6) \ge 10$$
$$\frac{x-2}{5} > \frac{5x+7}{2} \qquad \frac{-(x+8)}{9} \le \frac{-2x}{11}$$

Addition Property of Inequality

Adding the same number to or subtracting the same number from both sides of an inequality does not change the solutions.

$$y + 4 \le -1$$
$$y + 4 - 4 \le -1 - 4 \quad \text{Subtract 4.}$$
$$y \le -5$$

$(-\infty, -5)$

Multiplication Property of Inequality

Multiplying or dividing both sides of an inequality by the same positive number does not change its solutions.

$$\frac{1}{3}x > -2$$
$$3\left(\frac{1}{3}x\right) > 3\cdot -2 \quad \text{Multiply by 3.}$$
$$x > -6 \quad (-6, \infty)$$

Multiplying or dividing both sides of an inequality by the same **negative number and reversing the direction of the inequality symbol** does not change its solutions.

$$-2x \le 4$$
$$\frac{-2x}{-2} \ge \frac{4}{-2} \quad \text{Divide by } -2, \text{ reverse inequality symbol.}$$
$$x \ge -2 \quad [-2, \infty)$$

(continued)

DEFINITIONS AND CONCEPTS	EXAMPLES

Section 2.8   Solving Linear Inequalities (continued)

To Solve Linear Inequalities

1. Clear the equation of fractions.
2. Remove grouping symbols.
3. Simplify each side by combining like terms.
4. Write variable terms on one side and numbers on the other side, using the addition property of inequality.
5. Get the variable alone, using the multiplication property of inequality.

Solve: $3(x + 2) \le -2 + 8$

1. No fractions to clear. $3(x + 2) \le -2 + 8$

2. $\qquad\qquad 3x + 6 \le -2 + 8$ Distributive property

3. $\qquad\qquad 3x + 6 \le 6$ Combine like terms.

4. $\qquad 3x + 6 - 6 \le 6 - 6$ Subtract 6.

$\qquad\qquad\qquad 3x \le 0$

5. $\qquad\qquad \dfrac{3x}{3} \le \dfrac{0}{3}$ Divide by 3.

$x \le 0 \quad (-\infty, 0)$

Inequalities containing two inequality symbols are called **compound inequalities.**

Compound Inequalities

$$-2 < x < 6$$

$$5 \le 3(x - 6) < \frac{20}{3}$$

To solve a compound inequality, isolate the variable in the middle part of the inequality. Perform the same operation to all three parts of the inequality: left, middle, right.

Solve: $\quad -2 < 3x + 1 < 7$

$-2 - 1 < 3x + 1 - 1 < 7 - 1$ Subtract 1.

$-3 < 3x < 6$

$\dfrac{-3}{3} < \dfrac{3x}{3} < \dfrac{6}{3}$ Divide by 3.

$-1 < x < 2 \quad (-1, 2)$

Chapter 2 Review

(2.1) Simplify the following expressions.

1. $5x - x + 2x$

2. $0.2z - 4.6x - 7.4z$

3. $\dfrac{1}{2}x + 3 + \dfrac{7}{2}x - 5$

4. $\dfrac{4}{5}y + 1 + \dfrac{6}{5}y + 2$

5. $2(n - 4) + n - 10$

6. $3(w + 2) - (12 - w)$

7. Subtract $7x - 2$ from $x + 5$.

8. Subtract $1.4y - 3$ from $y - 0.7$.

Write each of the following as algebraic expressions.

9. Three times a number decreased by 7

10. Twice the sum of a number and 2.8 added to 3 times the number

(2.2) Solve each equation.

11. $8x + 4 = 9x$

12. $5y - 3 = 6y$

13. $\dfrac{2}{7}x + \dfrac{5}{7}x = 6$

14. $3x - 5 = 4x + 1$

15. $2x - 6 = x - 6$

16. $4(x + 3) = 3(1 + x)$

17. $6(3 + n) = 5(n - 1)$

18. $5(2 + x) - 3(3x + 2) = -5(x - 6) + 2$

Use the addition property to fill in the blank so that the middle equation simplifies to the last equation.

19. $\qquad x - 5 = 3$

$x - 5 + \underline{\quad} = 3 + \underline{\quad}$

$x = 8$

20. $\qquad x + 9 = -2$

$x + 9 - \underline{\quad} = -2 - \underline{\quad}$

$x = -11$

Choose the correct algebraic expression.

21. The sum of two numbers is 10. If one number is x, express the other number in terms of x.

    a. $x - 10$ **b.** $10 - x$

    c. $10 + x$ **d.** $10x$

22. Mandy is 5 inches taller than Melissa. If x inches represents the height of Mandy, express Melissa's height in terms of x.

    a. $x - 5$ **b.** $5 - x$

    c. $5 + x$ **d.** $5x$

△ 23. If one angle measures $x°$, express the measure of its complement in terms of x.

    a. $(180 - x)°$ **b.** $(90 - x)°$

    c. $(x - 180)°$ **d.** $(x - 90)°$

△ **24.** If one angle measures $(x + 5)°$, express the measure of its supplement in terms of x.

    a. $(185 + x)°$

    b. $(95 + x)°$

    c. $(175 - x)°$

    d. $(x - 170)°$

Solve each equation.

25. $\dfrac{3}{4}x = -9$ **26.** $\dfrac{x}{6} = \dfrac{2}{3}$

27. $-5x = 0$ **28.** $-y = 7$

29. $0.2x = 0.15$ **30.** $\dfrac{-x}{3} = 1$

31. $-3x + 1 = 19$ **32.** $5x + 25 = 20$

33. $7(x - 1) + 9 = 5x$ **34.** $7x - 6 = 5x - 3$

35. $-5x + \dfrac{3}{7} = \dfrac{10}{7}$ **36.** $5x + x = 9 + 4x - 1 + 6$

37. Write the sum of three consecutive integers as an expression in x. Let x be the first integer.

38. Write the sum of the first and fourth of four consecutive even integers. Let x be the first even integer.

(2.3) *Solve each equation.*

39. $\dfrac{5}{3}x + 4 = \dfrac{2}{3}x$ **40.** $\dfrac{7}{8}x + 1 = \dfrac{5}{8}x$

41. $-(5x + 1) = -7x + 3$ **42.** $-4(2x + 1) = -5x + 5$

43. $-6(2x - 5) = -3(9 + 4x)$

44. $3(8y - 1) = 6(5 + 4y)$

45. $\dfrac{3(2 - z)}{5} = z$ **46.** $\dfrac{4(n + 2)}{5} = -n$

47. $0.5(2n - 3) - 0.1 = 0.4(6 + 2n)$

48. $-9 - 5a = 3(6a - 1)$ **49.** $\dfrac{5(c + 1)}{6} = 2c - 3$

50. $\dfrac{2(8 - a)}{3} = 4 - 4a$

▦ **51.** $200(70x - 3560) = -179(150x - 19{,}300)$

52. $1.72y - 0.04y = 0.42$

(2.4) *Solve each of the following.*

53. The height of the Washington Monument is 50.5 inches more than 10 times the length of a side of its square base. If the sum of these two dimensions is 7327 inches, find the height of the Washington Monument. (*Source:* National Park Service)

54. A 12-foot board is to be divided into two pieces so that one piece is twice as long as the other. If x represents the length of the shorter piece, find the length of each piece.

55. In a recent year, Kellogg Company acquired Keebler Foods Company. After the merger, the total number of Kellogg and Keebler manufacturing plants was 53. The number of Kellogg plants was one less than twice the number of Keebler plants. How many of each type of plant were there? (*Source: Kellogg Company 2000 Annual Report*)

56. Find three consecutive integers whose sum is -114.

57. The quotient of a number and 3 is the same as the difference of the number and two. Find the number.

58. Double the sum of a number and 6 is the opposite of the number. Find the number.

(2.5) *Substitute the given values into the given formulas and solve for the unknown variable.*

59. $P = 2l + 2w$; $P = 46, l = 14$

60. $V = lwh$; $V = 192, l = 8, w = 6$

Solve each equation as indicated.

61. $y = mx + b$ for m

62. $r = vst - 5$ for s

63. $2y - 5x = 7$ for x

64. $3x - 6y = -2$ for y

△ **65.** $C = \pi D$ for π

△ **66.** $C = 2\pi r$ for π

△ **67.** A swimming pool holds 900 cubic meters of water. If its length is 20 meters and its height is 3 meters, find its width.

68. The perimeter of a rectangular billboard is 60 feet and has a length 6 feet longer than its width. Find the dimensions of the billboard.

69. A charity 10K race is given annually to benefit a local hospice organization. How long will it take to run/walk a 10K race (10 kilometers or 10,000 meters) if your average pace is 125 **meters** per minute? Give your time in hours and minutes.

70. On April 28, 2001, the highest temperature recorded in the United States was 104°F, which occurred in Death Valley, California. Convert this temperature to degrees Celsius. (*Source:* National Weather Service)

(2.6) Find each of the following.

71. The number 9 is what percent of 45?

72. The number 59.5 is what percent of 85?

73. The number 137.5 is 125% of what number?

74. The number 768 is 60% of what number?

75. The price of a small diamond ring was recently increased by 11%. If the ring originally cost $1900, find the mark-up and the new price of the ring.

76. A recent survey found that 79% of Americans use the Internet. If a city has a population of 76,000 how many people in that city would you expect to use the Internet? (*Source:* PEW)

77. Thirty gallons of a 20% acid solution is needed for an experiment. Only 40% and 10% acid solutions are available. How much of each should be mixed to form the needed solution?

78. The ACT Assessment is a college entrance exam taken by about 60% of college-bound students. The national average score was 20.7 in 1993 and rose to 21.0 in 2008. Find the percent increase. (Round to the nearest hundredth of a percent.)

The graph below shows the percent(s) of cell phone users who have engaged in various behaviors while driving and talking on their cell phones. Use this graph to answer Exercises 79 through 82.

Effects of Cell Phone Use on Driving

Data from Progressive Casualty Insurance Company

79. What percent of motorists who use a cell phone while driving have almost hit another car?

80. What is the most common effect of cell phone use on driving?

Suppose that a cell phone service has an estimated 4600 customers who use their cell phones while driving. Use this information for Exercises 81 and 82.

81. How many of these customers would you expect to have cut someone off while driving and talking on their cell phones?

82. How many of these customers would you expect to have sped up while driving and talking on their cell phones?

83. If a price decreases from $250 to $170, what is the percent decrease?

84. Find the original price of a DVD if the sale price is $19.20 after a 20% discount.

85. In 2005, Lance Armstrong incredibly won his seventh Tour de France, the first man in history to win more than five Tour de France Championships. Suppose he rides a bicycle up a category 2 climb at 10 km/hr and rides down the same distance at a speed of 50 km/hr. Find the distance traveled if the total time on the mountain was 3 hours.

(2.7) Solve.

86. A $50,000 retirement pension is to be invested into two accounts: a money market fund that pays 8.5% and a certificate of deposit that pays 10.5%. How much should be invested at each rate to provide a yearly interest income of $4550?

87. A pay phone is holding its maximum number of 500 coins consisting of nickels, dimes, and quarters. The number of quarters is twice the number of dimes. If the value of all the coins is $88.00, how many nickels are in the pay phone?

88. How long will it take an Amtrak passenger train to catch up to a freight train if their speeds are 60 and 45 mph and the freight train had an hour and a half head start?

(2.8) Solve and graph the solutions of each of the following inequalities.

89. $x > 0$

90. $x \leq -2$

91. $0.5 \leq y < 1.5$

92. $-1 < x < 1$

93. $-3x > 12$

94. $-2x \geq -20$

95. $x + 4 \geq 6x - 16$

96. $5x - 7 > 8x + 5$

97. $-3 < 4x - 1 < 2$

98. $2 \leq 3x - 4 < 6$

99. $4(2x - 5) \leq 5x - 1$

100. $-2(x - 5) > 2(3x - 2)$

101. Tina earns $175 per week plus a 5% commission on all her sales. Find the minimum amount of sales to ensure that she earns at least $300 per week.

102. Ellen Catarella shot rounds of 76, 82, and 79 golfing. What must she shoot on her next round so that her average will be below 80?

MIXED REVIEW

Solve each equation.

103. $6x + 2x - 1 = 5x + 11$

104. $2(3y - 4) = 6 + 7y$

105. $4(3 - a) - (6a + 9) = -12a$

106. $\frac{x}{3} - 2 = 5$

107. $2(y + 5) = 2y + 10$

108. $7x - 3x + 2 = 2(2x - 1)$

Solve.

109. The sum of six and twice a number is equal to seven less than the number. Find the number.

110. A 23-inch piece of string is to be cut into two pieces so that the length of the longer piece is three more than four times the shorter piece. If x represents the length of the shorter piece, find the lengths of both pieces.

Solve for the specified variable.

111. $V = \frac{1}{3}Ah$ for h

112. What number is 26% of 85?

113. The number 72 is 45% of what number?

114. A company recently increased its number of employees from 235 to 282. Find the percent increase.

Solve each inequality. Graph the solution set.

115. $4x - 7 > 3x + 2$

116. $-5x < 20$

117. $-3(1 + 2x) + x \geq -(3 - x)$

Chapter 2 Test

Simplify each of the following expressions.

1. $2y - 6 - y - 4$

2. $2.7x + 6.1 + 3.2x - 4.9$

3. $4(x - 2) - 3(2x - 6)$

4. $7 + 2(5y - 3)$

Solve each of the following equations.

5. $-\frac{4}{5}x = 4$

6. $4(n - 5) = -(4 - 2n)$

7. $5y - 7 + y = -(y + 3y)$

8. $4z + 1 - z = 1 + z$

9. $\frac{2(x + 6)}{3} = x - 5$

10. $\frac{1}{2} - x + \frac{3}{2} = x - 4$

11. $-0.3(x - 4) + x = 0.5(3 - x)$

12. $-4(a + 1) - 3a = -7(2a - 3)$

13. $-2(x - 3) = x + 5 - 3x$

14. Find the value of x if $y = -14, m = -2$, and $b = -2$ in the formula $y = mx + b$.

Solve each of the following equations for the indicated variable.

15. $V = \pi r^2 h$ for h

16. $3x - 4y = 10$ for y

Solve each of the following inequalities. Graph each solution set and write it in interval notation.

17. $3x - 5 \geq 7x + 3$

18. $x + 6 > 4x - 6$

19. $-2 < 3x + 1 < 8$

20. $\frac{2(5x + 1)}{3} > 2$

Solve each of the following applications.

21. A number increased by two-thirds of the number is 35. Find the number.

22. A rectangular deck is to be built so that the width and length are two consecutive even integers and the perimeter is 252 feet. Find the dimensions of the deck.

23. Some states have a single area code for the entire state. Two such states have area codes where one is double the other. If the sum of these integers is 1203, find the two area codes. *(Source:* North American Numbering Plan Administration*)*

24. Sedric Angell invested an amount of money in Amoxil stock that earned an annual 10% return, and then he invested twice that amount in IBM stock that earned an annual 12% return. If his total return from both investments was $2890, find how much he invested in each stock.

The following graph shows the breakdown of tornadoes occurring in the United States by strength. The corresponding Fujita Tornado Scale categories are shown in parentheses. Use this graph to answer Exercise 26.

Data from National Climatic Data Center

25. Two trains leave Los Angeles simultaneously traveling on the same track in opposite directions at speeds of 50 and 64 mph. How long will it take before they are 285 miles apart?

26. According to the National Climatic Data Center, in an average year, about 800 tornadoes are reported in the United States. How many of these would you expect to be classified as "weak" tornadoes?

27. The number 72 is what percent of 180?

28. The number of employees of a company decreased from 225 to 189. Find this percent decrease.

Chapter 2 **Cumulative Review**

1. Given the set $\left\{-2, 0, \frac{1}{4}, -1.5, 112, -3, 11, \sqrt{2}\right\}$, list the numbers in this set that belong to the set of:

a. Natural numbers

b. Whole numbers

c. Integers

d. Rational numbers

e. Irrational numbers

f. Real numbers

2. Given the set $\left\{7, 2, -\frac{1}{5}, 0, \sqrt{3}, -185, 8\right\}$, list the numbers in this set that belong to the set of:

a. Natural numbers

b. Whole numbers

c. Integers

d. Rational numbers

e. Irrational numbers

f. Real numbers

3. Find the absolute value of each number.

a. $|4|$ **b.** $|-5|$

c. $|0|$ **d.** $\left|-\frac{1}{2}\right|$

e. $|5.6|$

4. Find the absolute value of each number.

a. $|5|$ **b.** $|-8|$ **c.** $\left|-\frac{2}{3}\right|$

5. Write each of the following numbers as a product of primes.

a. 40   **b.** 63

6. Write each number as a product of primes.

a. 44   **b.** 90

7. Write $\frac{2}{5}$ as an equivalent fraction with a denominator of 20.

8. Write $\frac{2}{3}$ as an equivalent fraction with a denominator of 24.

9. Simplify $3[4 + 2(10 - 1)]$.

10. Simplify $5[16 - 4(2 + 1)]$.

11. Decide whether 2 is a solution of $3x + 10 = 8x$.

12. Decide whether 3 is a solution of $5x - 2 = 4x$.

Add.

13. $-1 + (-2)$ **14.** $(-2) + (-8)$

15. $-4 + 6$ **16.** $-3 + 10$

17. Simplify each expression.

a. $-(-10)$ **b.** $-\left(-\frac{1}{2}\right)$

c. $-(-2x)$ **d.** $-|-6|$

18. Simplify each expression.

a. $-(-5)$ **b.** $-\left(-\frac{2}{3}\right)$

c. $-(-a)$ **d.** $-|-3|$

19. Subtract.

a. $5.3 - (-4.6)$ **b.** $-\frac{3}{10} - \frac{5}{10}$

c. $-\frac{2}{3} - \left(-\frac{4}{5}\right)$

20. Subtract

a. $-2.7 - 8.4$

b. $-\dfrac{4}{5} - \left(-\dfrac{3}{5}\right)$

c. $\dfrac{1}{4} - \left(-\dfrac{1}{2}\right)$

21. Find each unknown complementary or supplementary angle.

a.

b.

22. Find each unknown complementary or supplementary angle.

a.

b.

23. Multiply.

a. $(-1.2)(0.05)$

b. $\dfrac{2}{3} \cdot \left(-\dfrac{7}{10}\right)$

c. $\left(-\dfrac{4}{5}\right)(-20)$

24. Multiply.

a. $(4.5)(-0.08)$

b. $-\dfrac{3}{4} \cdot \left(-\dfrac{8}{17}\right)$

25. Divide.

a. $\dfrac{-24}{-4}$

b. $\dfrac{-36}{3}$

c. $\dfrac{2}{3} \div \left(-\dfrac{5}{4}\right)$

d. $-\dfrac{3}{2} \div 9$

26. Divide.

a. $\dfrac{-32}{8}$

b. $\dfrac{-108}{-12}$

c. $\dfrac{-5}{7} \div \left(\dfrac{-9}{2}\right)$

27. Use a commutative property to complete each statement.

a. $x + 5 = $ _____

b. $3 \cdot x = $ _____

28. Use a commutative property to complete each statement.

a. $y + 1 = $ _____

b. $y \cdot 4 = $ _____

29. Use the distributive property to write each sum as a product.

a. $8 \cdot 2 + 8 \cdot x$

b. $7s + 7t$

30. Use the distributive property to write each sum as a product.

a. $4 \cdot y + 4 \cdot \dfrac{1}{3}$

b. $0.10x + 0.10y$

31. Subtract $4x - 2$ from $2x - 3$.

32. Subtract $10x + 3$ from $-5x + 1$.

Solve.

33. $y + 0.6 = -1.0$

34. $\dfrac{5}{6} + x = \dfrac{2}{3}$

35. $7 = -5(2a - 1) - (-11a + 6)$

36. $-3x + 1 - (-4x - 6) = 10$

37. $\dfrac{y}{7} = 20$

38. $\dfrac{x}{4} = 18$

39. $4(2x - 3) + 7 = 3x + 5$

40. $6x + 5 = 4(x + 4) - 1$

41. Twice the sum of a number and 4 is the same as four times the number, decreased by 12. Find the number.

42. A number increased by 4 is the same as 3 times the number decreased by 8. Find the number.

43. Solve $V = lwh$ for l.

44. Solve $C = 2\pi r$ for r.

45. Solve $x + 4 \le -6$ for x. Graph the solution set and write it in interval notation.

46. Solve $x - 3 > 2$ for x. Graph the solution set and write it in interval notation.

CHAPTER 3 Graphing

In the previous chapter, we learned to solve and graph the solutions of linear equations and inequalities in one variable. Now we define and present techniques for solving and graphing linear equations and inequalities in two variables.

Tourism 2020 Vision is the World Tourism Organization's long-term forecast of world tourism through 2020. The broken-line graph below shows the forecasts. In Section 3.1, Exercises 1 through 6, we read a bar graph showing the top tourist destinations by country.

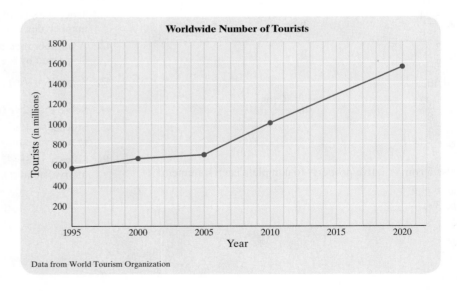

Data from World Tourism Organization

3.1 | Reading Graphs and the Rectangular Coordinate System

OBJECTIVES

1 Read Bar and Line Graphs.

2 Define the Rectangular Coordinate System and Plot Ordered Pairs of Numbers.

3 Graph Paired Data to Create a Scatter Diagram.

4 Determine Whether an Ordered Pair Is a Solution of an Equation in Two Variables.

5 Find the Missing Coordinate of an Ordered Pair Solution, Given One Coordinate of the Pair.

In today's world, where the exchange of information must be fast and entertaining, graphs are becoming increasingly popular. They provide a quick way of making comparisons, drawing conclusions, and approximating quantities.

OBJECTIVE

1   Reading Bar and Line Graphs

A **bar graph** consists of a series of bars arranged vertically or horizontally. The bar graph in Example 1 shows a comparison of worldwide Internet users by region. The names of the regions are listed vertically and a bar is shown for each region. Corresponding to the length of the bar for each region is a number along a horizontal axis. These horizontal numbers are numbers of Internet users in millions.

EXAMPLE 1   The following bar graph shows the estimated number of Internet users worldwide by region as of a recent year.

a. Find the region that has the most Internet users and approximate the number of users.

b. How many more users are in the North America region than the Latin America/Caribbean region?

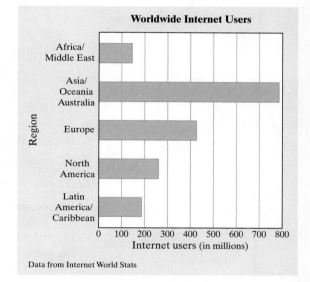

Solution

a. Since these bars are arranged horizontally, we look for the longest bar, which is the bar representing Asia/Oceania/ Australia. To approximate the number associated with this region, we move from the right edge of this bar vertically downward to the Internet user axis. This region has approximately 785 million Internet users.

b. The North America region has approximately 260 million Internet users. The Latin America/Caribbean region has approximately 187 million Internet users. To find how many more users are in the North America region, we subtract $260 - 187 = 73$ million more Internet users.   □

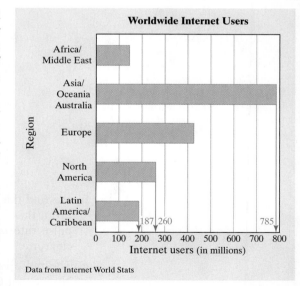

PRACTICE

1   Use the graph from Example 1 to answer the following.

a. Find the region with the fewest Internet users and approximate the number of users.

b. How many more users are in the Asia/Oceania/Australia region than in the Africa/ Middle East region?

A **line graph** consists of a series of points connected by a line. The next graph is an example of a line graph. It is also sometimes called a **broken-line graph.**

EXAMPLE 2   The line graph shows the relationship between time spent smoking a cigarette and pulse rate. Time is recorded along the horizontal axis in minutes, with 0 minutes being the moment a smoker lights a cigarette. Pulse is recorded along the vertical axis in heartbeats per minute.

a. What is the pulse rate 15 minutes after a cigarette is lit?

b. When is the pulse rate the lowest?

c. When does the pulse rate show the greatest change?

Solution

a. We locate the number 15 along the time axis and move vertically upward until the line is reached. From this point on the line, we move horizontally to the left until the pulse rate axis is reached. Reading the number of beats per minute, we find that the pulse rate is 80 beats per minute 15 minutes after a cigarette is lit.

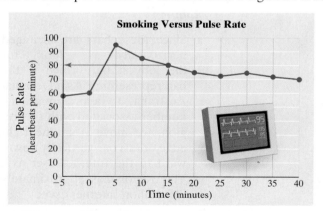

b. We find the lowest point of the line graph, which represents the lowest pulse rate. From this point, we move vertically downward to the time axis. We find that the pulse rate is the lowest at −5 minutes, which means 5 minutes *before* lighting a cigarette.

c. The pulse rate shows the greatest change during the 5 minutes between 0 and 5. Notice that the line graph is *steepest* between 0 and 5 minutes.   □

PRACTICE

2   Use the graph from Example 2 to answer the following.

a. What is the pulse rate 40 minutes after lighting a cigarette?

b. What is the pulse rate when the cigarette is being lit?

c. When is the pulse rate the highest?

2   Defining the Rectangular Coordinate System and Plotting Ordered Pairs of Numbers

Notice in the previous graph that two numbers are associated with each point of the graph. For example, we discussed earlier that 15 minutes after lighting a cigarette, the pulse rate is 80 beats per minute. If we agree to write the time first and the pulse rate second, we can say there is a point on the graph corresponding to the **ordered pair** of numbers (15, 80). A few more ordered pairs are listed alongside their corresponding points.

In general, we use this same ordered pair idea to describe the location of a point in a plane (such as a piece of paper). We start with a horizontal and a vertical axis. Each axis is a number line and, for the sake of consistency, we construct our axes to intersect at the 0 coordinate of both. This point of intersection is called the **origin.** Notice that these two number lines or axes divide the plane into four regions called **quadrants.** The quadrants are usually numbered with Roman numerals as shown. The axes are not considered to be in any quadrant.

It is helpful to label axes, so we label the horizontal axis the **x-axis** and the vertical axis the **y-axis.** We call the system described above the **rectangular coordinate system.**

Just as with the pulse rate graph, we can then describe the locations of points by ordered pairs of numbers. We list the horizontal **x-axis** measurement first and the vertical **y-axis** measurement second.

To plot or graph the point corresponding to the ordered pair

$$(a, b)$$

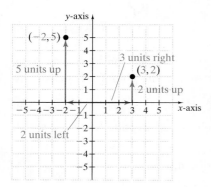

we start at the origin. We then move a units left or right (right if a is positive, left if a is negative). From there, we move b units up or down (up if b is positive, down if b is negative). For example, to plot the point corresponding to the ordered pair (3, 2), we start at the origin, move 3 units right and from there move 2 units up. (See the figure to the left.) The x-value, 3, is called the **x-coordinate** and the y-value, 2, is called the **y-coordinate.** From now on, we will call the point with coordinates (3, 2) simply the point (3, 2). The point $(-2, 5)$ is graphed to the left also.

Does the order in which the coordinates are listed matter? Yes! Notice below that the point corresponding to the ordered pair (2, 3) is in a different location than the point corresponding to (3, 2). These two ordered pairs of numbers describe two different points of the plane.

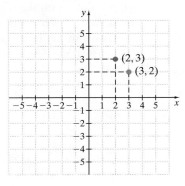

✓CONCEPT CHECK

Is the graph of the point $(-5, 1)$ in the same location as the graph of the point $(1, -5)$? Explain.

> ▶ **Helpful Hint**
>
> Don't forget that **each ordered pair corresponds to exactly one point in the plane and that each point in the plane corresponds to exactly one ordered pair.**

EXAMPLE 3 On a single coordinate system, plot each ordered pair. State in which quadrant, if any, each point lies.

a. $(5, 3)$ **b.** $(-5, 3)$ **c.** $(-2, -4)$ **d.** $(1, -2)$ **e.** $(0, 0)$

f. $(0, 2)$ **g.** $(-5, 0)$ **h.** $\left(0, -5\frac{1}{2}\right)$ **i.** $\left(4\frac{2}{3}, -3\right)$

Solution

a. Point $(5, 3)$ lies in quadrant I.

b. Point $(-5, 3)$ lies in quadrant II.

c. Point $(-2, -4)$ lies in quadrant III.

d. Point $(1, -2)$ lies in quadrant IV.

e.–h. Points $(0, 0)$, $(0, 2)$, $(-5, 0)$, and $\left(0, -5\frac{1}{2}\right)$ lie on axes, so they are not in any quadrant.

i. Point $\left(4\frac{2}{3}, -3\right)$ lies in quadrant IV.

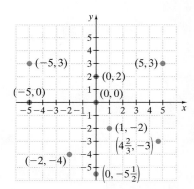

From Example 3, notice that the y-coordinate of any point on the x-axis is 0. For example, the point $(-5, 0)$ lies on the x-axis. Also, the x-coordinate of any point on the y-axis is 0. For example, the point $(0, 2)$ lies on the y-axis. □

PRACTICE

3 On a single coordinate system, plot each ordered pair. State in which quadrant, if any, each point lies.

a. $(4, -3)$ **b.** $(-3, 5)$ **c.** $(0, 4)$ **d.** $(-6, 1)$

e. $(-2, 0)$ **f.** $(5, 5)$ **g.** $\left(3\frac{1}{2}, 1\frac{1}{2}\right)$ **h.** $(-4, -5)$

Answer to Concept Check:
The graph of point $(-5, 1)$ lies in quadrant II and the graph of point $(1, -5)$ lies in quadrant IV. They are *not* in the same location.

✓CONCEPT CHECK

For each description of a point in the rectangular coordinate system, write an ordered pair that represents it.

a. Point A is located three units to the left of the *y*-axis and five units above the *x*-axis.

b. Point B is located six units below the origin.

OBJECTIVE

3   **Graphing Paired Data**

Data that can be represented as an ordered pair is called **paired data.** Many types of data collected from the real world are paired data. For instance, the annual measurement of a child's height can be written as an ordered pair of the form (year, height in inches) and is paired data. The graph of paired data as points in the rectangular coordinate system is called a **scatter diagram.** Scatter diagrams can be used to look for patterns and trends in paired data.

EXAMPLE 4   The table gives the annual net sales (in billions of dollars) for Target stores for the years shown. (Data from www.retailsales.com)

Year	Target Net Sales (in billions of dollars)
2006	58
2007	61
2008	63
2009	63
2010	66

a. Write this paired data as a set of ordered pairs of the form (year, sales in billions of dollars).

b. Create a scatter diagram of the paired data.

c. What trend in the paired data does the scatter diagram show?

Solution

a. The ordered pairs are (2006, 58), (2007, 61), (2008, 63), (2009, 63), (2010, 66).

b. We begin by plotting the ordered pairs. Because the *x*-coordinate in each ordered pair is a year, we label the *x*-axis "Year" and mark the horizontal axis with the years given. Then we label the *y*-axis or vertical axis "Net Sales (in billions of dollars)." In this case we can mark the vertical axis in multiples of 2. Since no net sale is less than 58, we use the notation ⌇ to skip to 58, then proceed by multiples of 2.

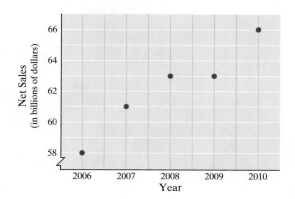

Answers to Concept Check:
a. $(-3, 5)$ **b.** $(0, -6)$

c. The scatter diagram shows that Target net sales were constant or steadily increased over the years 2006–2010. □

PRACTICE
4 The table gives the approximate annual number of wildfires (in thousands) that have occurred in the United States for the years shown. (Data from National Interagency Fire Center)

Year	Wildfires (in thousands)
2004	65
2005	67
2006	96
2007	86
2008	79
2009	79
2010	72

a. Write this paired data as a set of ordered pairs of the form (year, number of wildfires in thousands).

b. Create a scatter diagram of the paired data.

OBJECTIVE
4 Determining Whether an Ordered Pair Is a Solution

Let's see how we can use ordered pairs to record solutions of equations containing two variables. An equation in one variable such as $x + 1 = 5$ has one solution, which is 4: The number 4 is the value of the variable x that makes the equation true.

An equation in two variables, such as $2x + y = 8$, has solutions consisting of two values, one for x and one for y. For example, $x = 3$ and $y = 2$ is a solution of $2x + y = 8$ because, if x is replaced with 3 and y with 2, we get a true statement.

$$2x + y = 8$$
$$2(3) + 2 = 8$$
$$8 = 8 \quad \text{True}$$

The solution $x = 3$ and $y = 2$ can be written as $(3, 2)$, an **ordered pair** of numbers. The first number, 3, is the x-value and the second number, 2, is the y-value.

In general, an ordered pair is a **solution** of an equation in two variables if replacing the variables by the values of the ordered pair results in a true statement.

EXAMPLE 5 Determine whether each ordered pair is a solution of the equation $x - 2y = 6$.

a. $(6, 0)$ **b.** $(0, 3)$ **c.** $\left(1, -\dfrac{5}{2}\right)$

Solution

a. Let $x = 6$ and $y = 0$ in the equation $x - 2y = 6$.

$$x - 2y = 6$$
$$6 - 2(0) = 6 \quad \text{Replace } x \text{ with 6 and } y \text{ with 0.}$$
$$6 - 0 = 6 \quad \text{Simplify.}$$
$$6 = 6 \quad \text{True}$$

$(6, 0)$ is a solution, since $6 = 6$ is a true statement.

b. Let $x = 0$ and $y = 3$.

$$x - 2y = 6$$
$$0 - 2(3) = 6 \quad \text{Replace } x \text{ with 0 and } y \text{ with 3.}$$
$$0 - 6 = 6$$
$$-6 = 6 \quad \text{False}$$

$(0, 3)$ is *not* a solution, since $-6 = 6$ is a false statement.

c. Let $x = 1$ and $y = -\dfrac{5}{2}$ in the equation.

$$x - 2y = 6$$
$$1 - 2\left(-\frac{5}{2}\right) = 6 \quad \text{Replace } x \text{ with 1 and } y \text{ with } -\frac{5}{2}.$$
$$1 + 5 = 6$$
$$6 = 6 \quad \text{True}$$

$\left(1, -\dfrac{5}{2}\right)$ is a solution, since $6 = 6$ is a true statement.   □

PRACTICE

5   Determine whether each ordered pair is a solution of the equation $x + 3y = 6$.

a. $(3, 1)$ **b.** $(6, 0)$ **c.** $\left(-2, \dfrac{2}{3}\right)$

OBJECTIVE

5   Completing Ordered Pair Solutions ▶

If one value of an ordered pair solution of an equation is known, the other value can be determined. To find the unknown value, replace one variable in the equation by its known value. Doing so results in an equation with just one variable that can be solved for the variable using the methods of Chapter 2.

EXAMPLE 6   Complete the following ordered pair solutions for the equation $3x + y = 12$.

a. $(0, \ )$ **b.** $(\ , 6)$ **c.** $(-1, \ )$

Solution

a. In the ordered pair $(0, \ )$, the x-value is 0. Let $x = 0$ in the equation and solve for y.

$$3x + y = 12$$
$$3(0) + y = 12 \quad \text{Replace } x \text{ with 0.}$$
$$0 + y = 12$$
$$y = 12$$

The completed ordered pair is $(0, 12)$.

b. In the ordered pair $(\ , 6)$, the y-value is 6. Let $y = 6$ in the equation and solve for x.

$$3x + y = 12$$
$$3x + 6 = 12 \quad \text{Replace } y \text{ with 6.}$$
$$3x = 6 \quad \text{Subtract 6 from both sides.}$$
$$x = 2 \quad \text{Divide both sides by 3.}$$

The ordered pair is $(2, 6)$.

c. In the ordered pair $(-1, \ )$, the x-value is -1. Let $x = -1$ in the equation and solve for y.

$$3x + y = 12$$
$$3(-1) + y = 12 \quad \text{Replace } x \text{ with } -1.$$
$$-3 + y = 12$$
$$y = 15 \quad \text{Add 3 to both sides.}$$

The ordered pair is $(-1, 15)$. ☐

PRACTICE
6 Complete the following ordered pair solutions for the equation $2x - y = 8$.

a. $(0, \ )$ **b.** $(\ , 4)$ **c.** $(-3, \ )$

Solutions of equations in two variables can also be recorded in a **table of values,** as shown in the next example.

EXAMPLE 7 Complete the table for the equation $y = 3x$.

	x	y
a.	-1	
b.		0
c.		-9

Solution
a. Replace x with -1 in the equation and solve for y.

$$y = 3x$$
$$y = 3(-1) \quad \text{Let } x = -1.$$
$$y = -3$$

The ordered pair is $(-1, -3)$.
b. Replace y with 0 in the equation and solve for x.

$$y = 3x$$
$$0 = 3x \quad \text{Let } y = 0.$$
$$0 = x \quad \text{Divide both sides by 3.}$$

The ordered pair is $(0, 0)$.
c. Replace y with -9 in the equation and solve for x.

$$y = 3x$$
$$-9 = 3x \quad \text{Let } y = -9.$$
$$-3 = x \quad \text{Divide both sides by 3.}$$

x	y
-1	-3
0	0
-3	-9

The ordered pair is $(-3, -9)$. The completed table is shown to the left. ☐

PRACTICE
7 Complete the table for the equation $y = -4x$.

	x	y
a.	-2	
b.		-12
c.	0	

EXAMPLE 8   Complete the table for the equation

$$y = \frac{1}{2}x - 5.$$

	x	y
a.	-2	
b.	0	
c.		0

Solution

a. Let $x = -2$.

$$y = \frac{1}{2}x - 5$$

$$y = \frac{1}{2}(-2) - 5$$

$$y = -1 - 5$$

$$y = -6$$

b. Let $x = 0$.

$$y = \frac{1}{2}x - 5$$

$$y = \frac{1}{2}(0) - 5$$

$$y = 0 - 5$$

$$y = -5$$

c. Let $y = 0$.

$$y = \frac{1}{2}x - 5$$

$$0 = \frac{1}{2}x - 5 \quad \text{Now, solve for } x.$$

$$5 = \frac{1}{2}x \quad \text{Add 5.}$$

$$10 = x \quad \text{Multiply by 2.}$$

Ordered Pairs: $(-2, -6)$ $(0, -5)$ $(10, 0)$

The completed table is

x	y
-2	-6
0	-5
10	0

PRACTICE
8   Complete the table for the equation $y = \frac{1}{5}x - 2$.

	x	y
a.	-10	
b.	0	
c.		0

EXAMPLE 9   **Finding the Value of a Computer**

A computer was recently purchased for a small business for $2000. The business manager predicts that the computer will be used for 5 years and the value in dollars y of the computer in x years is $y = -300x + 2000$. Complete the table.

x	0	1	2	3	4	5
y						

Solution   To find the value of y when x is 0, replace x with 0 in the equation. We use this same procedure to find y when x is 1 and when x is 2.

When $x = 0$,

$$y = -300x + 2000$$

$$y = -300 \cdot 0 + 2000$$

$$y = 0 + 2000$$

$$y = 2000$$

When $x = 1$,

$$y = -300x + 2000$$

$$y = -300 \cdot 1 + 2000$$

$$y = -300 + 2000$$

$$y = 1700$$

When $x = 2$,

$$y = -300x + 2000$$

$$y = -300 \cdot 2 + 2000$$

$$y = -600 + 2000$$

$$y = 1400$$

We have the ordered pairs $(0, 2000)$, $(1, 1700)$, and $(2, 1400)$. This means that in 0 years, the value of the computer is $2000, in 1 year the value of the computer is $1700, and in

2 years the value is $1400. To complete the table of values, we continue the procedure for $x = 3$, $x = 4$, and $x = 5$.

When x = 3,
$y = -300x + 2000$
$y = -300 \cdot 3 + 2000$
$y = -900 + 2000$
$y = 1100$

When x = 4,
$y = -300x + 2000$
$y = -300 \cdot 4 + 2000$
$y = -1200 + 2000$
$y = 800$

When x = 5,
$y = -300x + 2000$
$y = -300 \cdot 5 + 2000$
$y = -1500 + 2000$
$y = 500$

The completed table is

x	0	1	2	3	4	5
y	2000	1700	1400	1100	800	500

PRACTICE

9 A college student purchased a used car for $12,000. The student predicted that she would need to use the car for four years and the value in dollars y of the car in x years is $y = -1800x + 12,000$. Complete this table.

x	0	1	2	3	4
y					

The ordered pair solutions recorded in the completed table for the example above are graphed below. Notice that the graph gives a visual picture of the decrease in value of the computer.

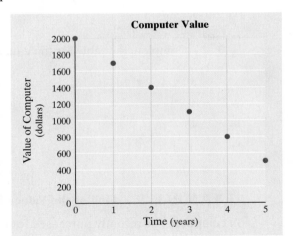

x	y
0	2000
1	1700
2	1400
3	1100
4	800
5	500

Vocabulary, Readiness & Video Check

Use the choices below to fill in each blank. The exercises below all have to do with the rectangular coordinate system.

origin   x-coordinate   x-axis   one   four
quadrants   y-coordinate   y-axis   solution

1. The horizontal axis is called the _____ and the vertical axis is called the _____.
2. The intersection of the horizontal axis and the vertical axis is a point called the _____.
3. The axes divide the plane into regions called _____. There are _____ of these regions.
4. In the ordered pair of numbers $(-2, 5)$, the number -2 is called the _____ and the number 5 is called the _____.
5. Each ordered pair of numbers corresponds to _____ point in the plane.
6. An ordered pair is a(n) _____ of an equation in two variables if replacing the variables by the coordinates of the ordered pair results in a true statement.

Martin-Gay Interactive Videos

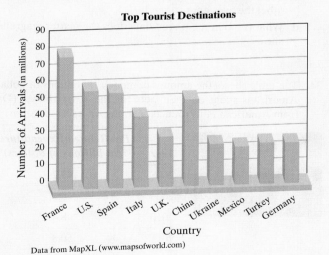

See Video 3.1

Watch the section lecture video and answer the following questions.

OBJECTIVE 1

7. Examples 1–3 ask you to answer questions about a bar graph. What information is provided on the horizontal axis of this bar graph? On the vertical axis?

OBJECTIVE 2

8. Several points are plotted in Examples 4–11. Where do you always start when plotting a point? How does the 1st coordinate tell you to move? How does the 2nd coordinate tell you to move?

OBJECTIVE 3

9. In the lecture before Example 12, what connection is made between data and graphing?

OBJECTIVE 4

10. An ordered pair is a solution of an equation if, when the variables are replaced with their values, a true statement results. In Example 13, three ordered pairs are tested. What are the last two points to be tested? What lesson can be learned by the results of testing these two points and why?

OBJECTIVE 5

11. In Example 14, when one variable of a linear equation in two variables is replaced by a replacement value, what type of equation results?

3.1 Exercise Set   MyMathLab®

The following bar graph shows the top 10 tourist destinations and the number of tourists that visit each country per year. Use this graph to answer Exercises 1 through 6. See Example 1.

Top Tourist Destinations

Data from MapXL (www.mapsofworld.com)

1. Which country shown is the most popular tourist destination?

2. Which country shown is the least popular tourist destination?

3. Which countries shown have more than 40 million tourists per year?

4. Which countries shown have fewer than 30 million tourists per year?

5. Estimate the number of tourists per year whose destination is Italy.

6. Estimate the number of tourists per year whose destination is the U.K.

The following line graph shows the paid attendance at each Super Bowl game from 2005 through 2011. Use this graph to answer Exercises 7 through 10. See Example 2.

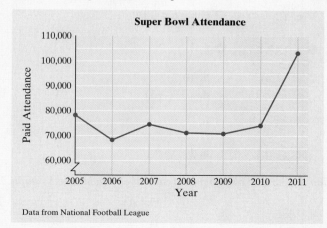

Super Bowl Attendance

Data from National Football League

7. Estimate the Super Bowl attendance in 2009.

8. Estimate the Super Bowl attendance in 2010.

9. Find the year on the graph with the greatest Super Bowl attendance and approximate that attendance.

10. Find the year on the graph with the least Super Bowl attendance and approximate that attendance.

The line graph below shows the number of students per teacher in U.S. public elementary and secondary schools. Use this graph for Exercises 11 through 16. See Example 2.

Students per Teacher in Elementary and Secondary Public Schools

Data from National Center for Education Statistics * Some years are projected.

11. Approximate the number of students per teacher in 2000.

12. Approximate the number of students per teacher in 2012.

13. Between what years shown did the greatest decrease in number of students per teacher occur?

14. What was the first year shown that the number of students per teacher fell below 16?

15. What was the first year shown that the number of students per teacher fell below 15?

16. Discuss any trends shown by this line graph.

Plot each ordered pair. State in which quadrant or on which axis each point lies. See Example 3.

17. a. $(1, 5)$ **b.** $(-5, -2)$
   c. $(-3, 0)$ **d.** $(0, -1)$
   e. $(2, -4)$ **f.** $\left(-1, 4\frac{1}{2}\right)$
   g. $(3.7, 2.2)$ **h.** $\left(\frac{1}{2}, -3\right)$

18. a. $(2, 4)$ **b.** $(0, 2)$
   c. $(-2, 1)$ **d.** $(-3, -3)$
   e. $\left(3\frac{3}{4}, 0\right)$ **f.** $(5, -4)$
   g. $(-3.4, 4.8)$ **h.** $\left(\frac{1}{3}, -5\right)$

Find the x- and y-coordinates of each labeled point. See Example 3.

19. A
20. B
21. C
22. D
23. E
24. F
25. G

26. A
27. B
28. C
29. D
30. E
31. F
32. G

Solve. See Example 4.

33. The table shows the worldwide box office (in billions of dollars) for the movie industry during the years shown. (Data from Motion Picture Association of America)

Year	Box Office (in billions of dollars)
2006	25.5
2007	26.3
2008	27.7
2009	29.4
2010	31.8

a. Write this paired data as a set of ordered pairs of the form (year, box office).

b. In your own words, write the meaning of the ordered pair (2010, 31.8).

c. Create a scatter diagram of the paired data. Be sure to label the axes appropriately.

d. What trend in the paired data does the scatter diagram show?

34. The table shows the amount of money (in billions of dollars) Americans spent on their pets for the years shown. (Data from American Pet Products Manufacturers Association)

Year	Pet-Related Expenditures (in billions of dollars)
2008	43.2
2009	45.5
2010	48.4
2011	50.8

a. Write this paired data as a set of ordered pairs of the form (year, pet-related expenditures).

b. In your own words, write the meaning of the ordered pair (2011, 50.8).

c. Create a scatter diagram of the paired data. Be sure to label the axes appropriately.

d. What trend in the paired data does the scatter diagram show?

▶ **35.** Minh, a psychology student, kept a record of how much time she spent studying for each of her 20-point psychology quizzes and her score on each quiz.

Hours Spent Studying	0.50	0.75	1.00	1.25	1.50	1.50	1.75	2.00
Quiz Score	10	12	15	16	18	19	19	20

a. Write the data as ordered pairs of the form (hours spent studying, quiz score).

b. In your own words, write the meaning of the ordered pair (1.25, 16).

c. Create a scatter diagram of the paired data. Be sure to label the axes appropriately.

d. What might Minh conclude from the scatter diagram?

36. A local lumberyard uses quantity pricing. The table shows the price per board for different amounts of lumber purchased.

Price per Board (in dollars)	Number of Boards Purchased
8.00	1
7.50	10
6.50	25
5.00	50
2.00	100

a. Write the data as ordered pairs of the form (price per board, number of boards purchased).

b. In your own words, write the meaning of the ordered pair (2.00, 100).

c. Create a scatter diagram of the paired data. Be sure to label the axes appropriately.

d. What trend in the paired data does the scatter diagram show?

▶ **37.** The table shows the distance from the equator (in miles) and the average annual snowfall (in inches) for each of eight selected U.S. cities. (Data from National Climatic Data Center, Wake Forest University Albatross Project)

City	Distance from Equator (in miles)	Average Annual Snowfall (in inches)
1. Atlanta, GA	2313	2
2. Austin, TX	2085	1
3. Baltimore, MD	2711	21
4. Chicago, IL	2869	39
5. Detroit, MI	2920	42
6. Juneau, AK	4038	99
7. Miami, FL	1783	0
8. Winston-Salem, NC	2493	9

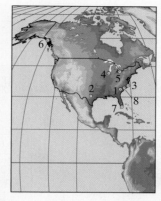

a. Write this paired data as a set of ordered pairs of the form (distance from equator, average annual snowfall).

b. Create a scatter diagram of the paired data. Be sure to label the axes appropriately.

c. What trend in the paired data does the scatter diagram show?

38. The table shows the average farm size (in acres) in the United States during the years shown. (Data from National Agricultural Statistics Service)

Year	Average Farm Size (in acres)
2001	438
2002	440
2003	441
2004	443
2005	445
2006	446

a. Write this paired data as a set of ordered pairs of the form (year, average farm size).

b. Create a scatter diagram of the paired data. Be sure to label the axes appropriately.

Determine whether each ordered pair is a solution of the given linear equation. See Example 5.

▶ **39.** $2x + y = 7$; $(3, 1), (7, 0), (0, 7)$

40. $3x + y = 8$; $(2, 3), (0, 8), (8, 0)$

41. $x = -\frac{1}{3}y$; $(0, 0), (3, -9)$

42. $y = -\frac{1}{2}x$; $(0, 0), (4, 2)$

43. $x = 5$; $(4, 5), (5, 4), (5, 0)$

44. $y = -2$; $(-2, 2), (2, -2), (0, -2)$

Complete each ordered pair so that it is a solution of the given linear equation. See Examples 6 through 8.

▶ **45.** $x - 4y = 4$; $(\quad, -2), (4, \quad)$

46. $x - 5y = -1$; $(\quad, -2), (4, \quad)$

47. $y = \frac{1}{4}x - 3; (-8, \quad), (\quad, 1)$

48. $y = \frac{1}{5}x - 2; (-10, \quad), (\quad, 1)$

Complete the table of ordered pairs for each linear equation. See Examples 6 through 8.

49. $y = -7x$

x	y
0	
-1	
	2

50. $y = -9x$

x	y
	0
-3	
	2

51. $y = -x + 2$

x	y
0	
	0
-3	

52. $x = -y + 4$

x	y
	0
0	
	-3

53. $y = \frac{1}{2}x$

x	y
0	
-6	
	1

54. $y = \frac{1}{3}x$

x	y
0	
-6	
	1

55. $x + 3y = 6$

x	y
0	
	0
	1

56. $2x + y = 4$

x	y
	4
2	
	2

57. $y = 2x - 12$

x	y
0	
	-2
3	

58. $y = 5x + 10$

x	y
	0
	5
0	

59. $2x + 7y = 5$

x	y
0	
	0
	1

60. $x - 6y = 3$

x	y
0	
1	
	-1

MIXED PRACTICE

Complete the table of ordered pairs for each equation. Then plot the ordered pair solutions. See Examples 1 through 7.

61. $x = -5y$

x	y
	0
	1
10	

62. $y = -3x$

x	y
	0
-2	
	9

63. $y = \frac{1}{3}x + 2$

x	y
0	
-3	
	0

64. $y = \frac{1}{2}x + 3$

x	y
0	
-4	
	0

Solve. See Example 9.

65. The cost in dollars y of producing x computer desks is given by $y = 80x + 5000$.

   a. Complete the table.

x	100	200	300
y			

   b. Find the number of computer desks that can be produced for $8600. (*Hint:* Find x when $y = 8600$.)

66. The hourly wage y of an employee at a certain production company is given by $y = 0.25x + 9$ where x is the number of units produced by the employee in an hour.

   a. Complete the table.

x	0	1	5	10
y				

   b. Find the number of units that an employee must produce each hour to earn an hourly wage of $12.25. (*Hint:* Find x when $y = 12.25$.)

67. The average annual cinema admission price y (in dollars) from 2001 through 2010 is given by $y = 0.24x + 5.28$. In this equation, x represents the number of years after 2000. (*Source:* Motion Picture Association of America)

   a. Complete the table.

x	1	3	5
y			

   b. Find the year in which the average cinema admission price was approximately $7.50.

   (*Hint:* Find x when $y = 7.50$ and round to the nearest whole number.)

   c. Use the given equation to predict when the cinema admission price might be $9.00. (Use the hint for part b.)

   d. In your own words, write the meaning of the ordered pair (5, 6.48).

68. The average amount of money y spent per person on recorded music from 2002 to 2009 is given by $y = -4.22x + 65.70$. In this equation, x represents the number of years after 2000. (*Source:* edgeqld.org)

a. Complete the table.

x	1	5	9
y			

b. Find the year in which the yearly average amount of money per person spent on recorded music was approximately $30. (*Hint:* Find x when $y = 30$ and round to the nearest whole number.)

The graph below shows the number of U.S. Walmart stores for each year. Use this graph to answer Exercises 69 through 72.

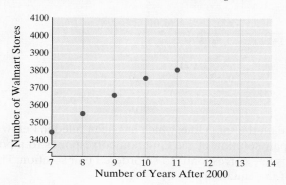

Data from Walmart

69. The ordered pair $(10, 3755)$ is a point of the graph. Write a sentence describing the meaning of this ordered pair.

70. The ordered pair $(11, 3804)$ is a point of the graph. Write a sentence describing the meaning of this ordered pair.

71. Estimate the increase in Walmart stores for years 8, 9, and 10.

72. Use a straightedge or ruler and this graph to predict the number of Walmart stores in the year 2014.

73. Describe what is similar about the coordinates of points whose graph lies on the x-axis.

74. Describe what is similar about the coordinates of points whose graph lies on the y-axis.

REVIEW AND PREVIEW

Solve each equation for y. See Section 2.5.

75. $x + y = 5$ **76.** $x - y = 3$

77. $2x + 4y = 5$ **78.** $5x + 2y = 7$

79. $10x = -5y$ **80.** $4y = -8x$

81. $x - 3y = 6$ **82.** $2x - 9y = -20$

CONCEPT EXTENSIONS

Answer each exercise with true or false.

83. Point $(-1, 5)$ lies in quadrant IV.

84. Point $(3, 0)$ lies on the y-axis.

85. For the point $\left(-\frac{1}{2}, 1.5\right)$, the first value, $-\frac{1}{2}$, is the x-coordinate and the second value, 1.5, is the y-coordinate.

86. The ordered pair $\left(2, \frac{2}{3}\right)$ is a solution of $2x - 3y = 6$.

For Exercises 87 through 91, fill in each blank with "0," "positive," or "negative." For Exercises 92 and 93, fill in each blank with "x" or "y."

	Point	Location
87.	(_____ , _____)	quadrant III
88.	(_____ , _____)	quadrant I
89.	(_____ , _____)	quadrant IV
90.	(_____ , _____)	quadrant II
91.	(_____ , _____)	origin
92.	(number, 0)	___-axis
93.	(0, number)	___-axis

94. Give an example of an ordered pair whose location is in (or on)

a. quadrant I   **b.** quadrant II

c. quadrant III   **d.** quadrant IV

e. x-axis   **f.** y-axis

Solve. See the first Concept Check in this section.

95. Is the graph of $(3, 0)$ in the same location as the graph of $(0, 3)$? Explain why or why not.

96. Give the coordinates of a point such that if the coordinates are reversed, their location is the same.

97. In general, what points can have coordinates reversed and still have the same location?

98. In your own words, describe how to plot or graph an ordered pair of numbers.

Write an ordered pair for each point described. See the second Concept Check in this section.

99. Point C is four units to the right of the y-axis and seven units below the x-axis.

100. Point D is three units to the left of the origin.

Solve.

△ **101.** Find the perimeter of the rectangle whose vertices are the points with coordinates $(-1, 5), (3, 5), (3, -4)$, and $(-1, -4)$.

△ **102.** Find the area of the rectangle whose vertices are the points with coordinates $(5, 2), (5, -6), (0, -6)$, and $(0, 2)$.

103. Three vertices of a rectangle are $(-2, -3), (-7, -3)$, and $(-7, 6)$.

a. Find the coordinates of the fourth vertex of the rectangle.

b. Find the perimeter of the rectangle.

c. Find the area of the rectangle.

104. Three vertices of a square are $(-4, -1), (-4, 8)$, and $(5, 8)$.

a. Find the coordinates of the fourth vertex of the square.

b. Find the perimeter of the square.

c. Find the area of the square.

3.2 | Graphing Linear Equations

OBJECTIVES

1 Identify Linear Equations.

2 Graph a Linear Equation by Finding and Plotting Ordered Pair Solutions.

OBJECTIVE

1   Identifying Linear Equations

In the previous section, we found that equations in two variables may have more than one solution. For example, both $(6, 0)$ and $(2, -2)$ are solutions of the equation $x - 2y = 6$. In fact, this equation has an infinite number of solutions. Other solutions include $(0, -3)$, $(4, -1)$, and $(-2, -4)$. If we graph these solutions, notice that a pattern appears.

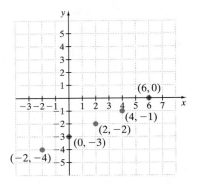

These solutions all appear to lie on the same line, which has been filled in below. It can be shown that every ordered pair solution of the equation corresponds to a point on this line, and every point on this line corresponds to an ordered pair solution. Thus, we say that this line is the **graph of the equation** $x - 2y = 6$.

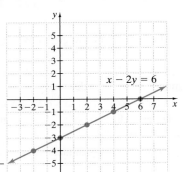

Helpful Hint

Notice that we can only show a part of a line on a graph. The arrowheads on each end of the line remind us that the line actually extends indefinitely in both directions.

The equation $x - 2y = 6$ is called a **linear equation in two variables** and **the graph of every linear equation in two variables is a line.**

Linear Equation in Two Variables

A linear equation in two variables is an equation that can be written in the form

$$Ax + By = C$$

where A, B, and C are real numbers and A and B are not both 0. **The graph of a linear equation in two variables is a straight line.**

The form $Ax + By = C$ is called **standard form.**

Helpful Hint

Notice in the form $Ax + By = C$, the understood exponent on both x and y is 1.

Examples of Linear Equations in Two Variables

$$2x + y = 8 \qquad -2x = 7y \qquad y = \frac{1}{3}x + 2 \qquad y = 7$$
(Standard Form)

Before we graph linear equations in two variables, let's practice identifying these equations.

EXAMPLE 1 Determine whether each equation is a linear equation in two variables.

a. $x - 1.5y = -1.6$ **b.** $y = -2x$ **c.** $x + y^2 = 9$ **d.** $x = 5$

Solution

a. This is a linear equation in two variables because it is written in the form $Ax + By = C$ with $A = 1$, $B = -1.5$, and $C = -1.6$.

b. This is a linear equation in two variables because it can be written in the form $Ax + By = C$.

$$y = -2x$$
$$2x + y = 0 \qquad \text{Add } 2x \text{ to both sides.}$$

c. This is *not* a linear equation in two variables because y is squared.

d. This is a linear equation in two variables because it can be written in the form $Ax + By = C$.

$$x = 5$$
$$x + 0y = 5 \qquad \text{Add } 0 \cdot y.$$

PRACTICE

1 Determine whether each equation is a linear equation in two variables.

a. $3x + 2.7y = -5.3$ **b.** $x^2 + y = 8$ **c.** $y = 12$ **d.** $5x = -3y$

OBJECTIVE

2 Graphing Linear Equations by Plotting Ordered Pair Solutions

From geometry, we know that a straight line is determined by just two points. Graphing a linear equation in two variables, then, requires that we find just two of its infinitely many solutions. Once we do so, we plot the solution points and draw the line connecting the points. Usually, we find a third solution as well, as a check.

EXAMPLE 2 Graph the linear equation $2x + y = 5$.

Solution Find three ordered pair solutions of $2x + y = 5$. To do this, choose a value for one variable, x or y, and solve for the other variable. For example, let $x = 1$. Then $2x + y = 5$ becomes

$$2x + y = 5$$
$$2(1) + y = 5 \qquad \text{Replace } x \text{ with 1.}$$
$$2 + y = 5 \qquad \text{Multiply.}$$
$$y = 3 \qquad \text{Subtract 2 from both sides.}$$

Since $y = 3$ when $x = 1$, the ordered pair $(1, 3)$ is a solution of $2x + y = 5$. Next, let $x = 0$.

$$2x + y = 5$$
$$2(0) + y = 5 \qquad \text{Replace } x \text{ with 0.}$$
$$0 + y = 5$$
$$y = 5$$

The ordered pair $(0, 5)$ is a second solution.

The two solutions found so far allow us to draw the straight line that is the graph of all solutions of $2x + y = 5$. However, we find a third ordered pair as a check. Let $y = -1$.

$$2x + y = 5$$
$$2x + (-1) = 5 \quad \text{Replace } y \text{ with } -1.$$
$$2x - 1 = 5$$
$$2x = 6 \quad \text{Add 1 to both sides.}$$
$$x = 3 \quad \text{Divide both sides by 2.}$$

The third solution is $(3, -1)$. These three ordered pair solutions are listed in table form as shown. The graph of $2x + y = 5$ is the line through the three points.

x	y
1	3
0	5
3	-1

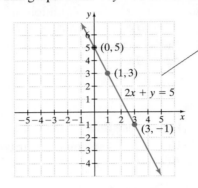

> ▶ **Helpful Hint**
> All three points should fall on the same straight line. If not, check your ordered pair solutions for a mistake.

PRACTICE
2 Graph the linear equation $x + 3y = 9$.

EXAMPLE 3 Graph the linear equation $-5x + 3y = 15$.

Solution Find three ordered pair solutions of $-5x + 3y = 15$.

Let $x = 0$.
$$-5x + 3y = 15$$
$$-5 \cdot 0 + 3y = 15$$
$$0 + 3y = 15$$
$$3y = 15$$
$$y = 5$$

Let $y = 0$.
$$-5x + 3y = 15$$
$$-5x + 3 \cdot 0 = 15$$
$$-5x + 0 = 15$$
$$-5x = 15$$
$$x = -3$$

Let $x = -2$.
$$-5x + 3y = 15$$
$$-5(-2) + 3y = 15$$
$$10 + 3y = 15$$
$$3y = 5$$
$$y = \frac{5}{3}$$

The ordered pairs are $(0, 5)$, $(-3, 0)$, and $\left(-2, \frac{5}{3}\right)$. The graph of $-5x + 3y = 15$ is the line through the three points.

x	y
0	5
-3	0
-2	$\frac{5}{3} = 1\frac{2}{3}$

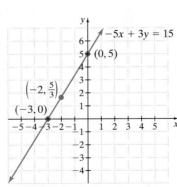

PRACTICE
3 Graph the linear equation $3x - 4y = 12$.

EXAMPLE 4   Graph the linear equation $y = 3x$.

Solution   To graph this linear equation, we find three ordered pair solutions. Since this equation is solved for y, choose three x values.

If $x = 2, y = 3 \cdot 2 = 6$.
If $x = 0, y = 3 \cdot 0 = 0$.
If $x = -1, y = 3 \cdot -1 = -3$.

x	y
2	6
0	0
-1	-3

Next, graph the ordered pair solutions listed in the table above and draw a line through the plotted points as shown below. The line is the graph of $y = 3x$. Every point on the graph represents an ordered pair solution of the equation and every ordered pair solution is a point on this line.

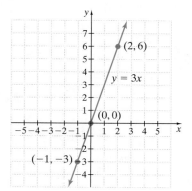

PRACTICE
4   Graph the linear equation $y = -2x$.

▶ **Helpful Hint**

When graphing a linear equation in two variables, if it is
• solved for y, it may be easier to find ordered pair solutions by choosing x-values. If it is
• solved for x, it may be easier to find ordered pair solutions by choosing y-values.

EXAMPLE 5   Graph the linear equation $y = -\frac{1}{3}x + 2$.

Solution   Find three ordered pair solutions, graph the solutions, and draw a line through the plotted solutions. To avoid fractions, choose x values that are multiples of 3 to substitute in the equation. When a multiple of 3 is multiplied by $-\frac{1}{3}$, the result is an integer. See the calculations shown above the table.

If $x = 6$, then $y = -\frac{1}{3} \cdot 6 + 2 = -2 + 2 = 0$

If $x = 0$, then $y = -\frac{1}{3} \cdot 0 + 2 = 0 + 2 = 2$

If $x = -3$, then $y = -\frac{1}{3} \cdot -3 + 2 = 1 + 2 = 3$

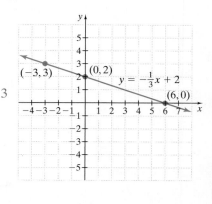

x	y
6	0
0	2
-3	3

PRACTICE
5   Graph the linear equation $y = \frac{1}{2}x + 3$.

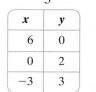

Let's compare the graphs in Examples 4 and 5. The graph of $y = 3x$ tilts upward (as we follow the line from left to right) and the graph of $y = -\frac{1}{3}x + 2$ tilts downward (as we follow the line from left to right). We will learn more about the tilt, or slope, of a line in Section 3.4.

EXAMPLE 6 Graph the linear equation $y = -2$.

Solution: The equation $y = -2$ can be written in standard form as $0x + y = -2$. No matter what value we replace x with, y is always -2.

x	y
0	−2
3	−2
−2	−2

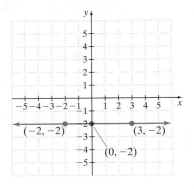

Notice that the graph of $y = -2$ is a horizontal line. □

PRACTICE
6 Graph the linear equation $x = -2$.

EXAMPLE 7 Graph the linear equation $y = 3x + 6$ and compare this graph with the graph of $y = 3x$ in Example 4.

Solution Find ordered pair solutions, graph the solutions, and draw a line through the plotted solutions. We choose x values and substitute in the equation $y = 3x + 6$.

If $x = -3$, then $y = 3(-3) + 6 = -3$.
If $x = 0$, then $y = 3(0) + 6 = 6$.
If $x = 1$, then $y = 3(1) + 6 = 9$.

x	y
−3	−3
0	6
1	9

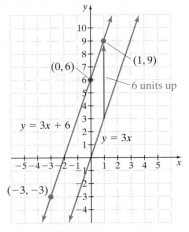

The most startling similarity is that both graphs appear to have the same upward tilt as we move from left to right. Also, the graph of $y = 3x$ crosses the y-axis at the origin, while the graph of $y = 3x + 6$ crosses the y-axis at 6. In fact, the graph of $y = 3x + 6$ is the same as the graph of $y = 3x$ moved vertically upward 6 units. □

PRACTICE

7   Graph the linear equation $y = -2x + 3$ and compare this graph with the graph of $y = -2x$ in Practice 4.

Notice that the graph of $y = 3x + 6$ crosses the y-axis at 6. This happens because when $x = 0$, $y = 3x + 6$ becomes $y = 3 \cdot 0 + 6 = 6$. The graph contains the point $(0, 6)$, which is on the y-axis.

In general, if a linear equation in two variables is solved for y, we say that it is written in the form $y = mx + b$. The graph of this equation contains the point $(0, b)$ because when $x = 0$, $y = mx + b$ is $y = m \cdot 0 + b = b$.

> The graph of $y = mx + b$ crosses the y-axis at $(0, b)$.

We will review this again in Section 3.5.

Linear equations are often used to model real data as seen in the next example.

EXAMPLE 8   **Estimating the Number of Registered Nurses**

The occupation expected to have the most employment growth in the next few years is registered nurse. The number of people y (in thousands) employed as registered nurses in the United States can be estimated by the linear equation $y = 58.1x + 2619$, where x is the number of years after the year 2008. (Data from U.S. Bureau of Labor Statistics)

a. Graph the equation.

b. Use the graph to predict the number of registered nurses in the year 2018.

Solution:

a. To graph $y = 58.1x + 2619$, choose x-values and substitute in the equation.

If $x = 0$, then $y = 58.1(0) + 2619 = 2619$.
If $x = 2$, then $y = 58.1(2) + 2619 = 2735.2$.
If $x = 5$, then $y = 58.1(5) + 2619 = 2909.5$.

x	y
0	2619
2	2735.2
5	2909.5

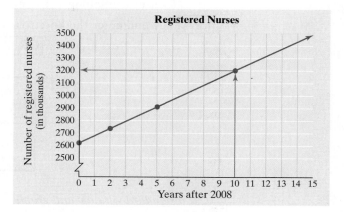

b. To use the graph to *predict* the number of registered nurses in the year 2018, we need to find the y-coordinate that corresponds to $x = 10$. (10 years after 2008 is the year 2018.) To do so, find 10 on the x-axis. Move vertically upward to the graphed line and then horizontally to the left. We approximate the number on the y-axis to be 3200. Thus, in the year 2018, we predict that there will be 3200 thousand registered nurses. (The actual value, using 10 for x, is 3200.)

8 One of the occupations expected to have a large growth in employment in the next few years is computer software application engineers. The number of people y (in thousands) employed as computer software application engineers in the United States can be estimated by the linear equation $y = 17.5x + 515$, where x is the number of years after 2008. (*Source:* Based on data from the Bureau of Labor Statistics)

a. Graph the equation.

b. Use the graph to predict the number of computer software application engineers in the year 2020.

> **Helpful Hint**
>
> Make sure you understand that models are mathematical approximations of the data for the known years. (For example, see the model in Example 8.) Any number of unknown factors can affect future years, so be cautious when using models to predict.

Graphing Calculator Explorations

In this section, we begin an optional study of graphing calculators and graphing software packages for computers. These graphers use the same point plotting technique that was introduced in this section. The advantage of this graphing technology is, of course, that graphing calculators and computers can find and plot ordered pair solutions much faster than we can. Note, however, that the features described in these boxes may not be available on all graphing calculators.

The rectangular screen where a portion of the rectangular coordinate system is displayed is called a **window**. We call it a **standard window** for graphing when both the x- and y-axes show coordinates between -10 and 10. This information is often displayed in the window menu on a graphing calculator as

$$\text{Xmin} = -10$$
$$\text{Xmax} = 10$$
$$\text{Xscl} = 1 \qquad \text{The scale on the } x\text{-axis is one unit per tick mark.}$$
$$\text{Ymin} = -10$$
$$\text{Ymax} = 10$$
$$\text{Yscl} = 1 \qquad \text{The scale on the } y\text{-axis is one unit per tick mark.}$$

To use a graphing calculator to graph the equation $y = 2x + 3$, press the $\boxed{\text{Y=}}$ key and enter the keystrokes $\boxed{2}\ \boxed{x}\ \boxed{+}\ \boxed{3}$. The top row should now read $Y_1 = 2x + 3$. Next press the $\boxed{\text{GRAPH}}$ key, and the display should look like this:

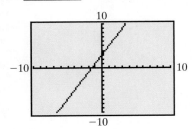

Use a standard window and graph the following linear equations. (Unless otherwise stated, use a standard window when graphing.) See graphing answer section.

1. $y = -3x + 7$

2. $y = -x + 5$

3. $y = 2.5x - 7.9$

4. $y = -1.3x + 5.2$

5. $y = -\dfrac{3}{10}x + \dfrac{32}{5}$

6. $y = \dfrac{2}{9}x - \dfrac{22}{3}$

Vocabulary, Readiness & Video Check

Martin-Gay Interactive Videos

See Video 3.2

Watch the section lecture video and answer the following questions.

OBJECTIVE
1

1. Exponents aren't mentioned in the definition of a linear equation in two variables. However, in determining whether Example 3 is a linear equation in two variables, the exponents or powers on the variables are discussed. Explain.

OBJECTIVE
2

2. In the lecture before Example 5, it's mentioned that you need only two points to determine a line. Why then are three ordered pair solutions found in Examples 5–7?

OBJECTIVE
2

3. What does a graphed line represent as discussed at the end of Examples 5 and 7?

3.2 Exercise Set MyMathLab®

Determine whether each equation is a linear equation in two variables. See Example 1.

1. $-x = 3y + 10$

2. $y = x - 15$

3. $x = y$

4. $x = y^3$

5. $x^2 + 2y = 0$

6. $0.01x - 0.2y = 8.8$

7. $y = -1$

8. $x = 25$

For each equation, find three ordered pair solutions by completing the table. Then use the ordered pairs to graph the equation. See Examples 2 through 7.

9. $x - y = 6$

x	y
	0
4	
	-1

10. $x - y = 4$

x	y
	0
	2
-1	

11. $y = -4x$

x	y
1	
0	
-1	

12. $y = -5x$

x	y
1	
0	
-1	

13. $y = \frac{1}{3}x$

x	y
0	
6	
-3	

14. $y = \frac{1}{2}x$

x	y
0	
-4	
2	

15. $y = -4x + 3$

x	y
0	
1	
2	

16. $y = -5x + 2$

x	y
0	
1	
2	

MIXED PRACTICE

Graph each linear equation. See Examples 2 through 7.

17. $x + y = 1$

18. $x + y = 7$

19. $x - y = -2$

20. $-x + y = 6$

21. $x - 2y = 6$

22. $-x + 5y = 5$

23. $y = 6x + 3$

24. $y = -2x + 7$

25. $x = -4$

26. $y = 5$

27. $y = 3$

28. $x = -1$

29. $y = x$

30. $y = -x$

31. $x = -3y$

32. $x = -5y$

33. $x + 3y = 9$

34. $2x + y = 2$

35. $y = \frac{1}{2}x + 2$

36. $y = \frac{1}{4}x + 3$

37. $3x - 2y = 12$

38. $2x - 7y = 14$

39. $y = -3.5x + 4$

40. $y = -1.5x - 3$

Graph each pair of linear equations on the same set of axes. Discuss how the graphs are similar and how they are different. See Example 7.

41. $y = 5x; y = 5x + 4$

42. $y = 2x; y = 2x + 5$

43. $y = -2x; y = -2x - 3$

44. $y = x; y = x - 7$

45. $y = \frac{1}{2}x; y = \frac{1}{2}x + 2$

46. $y = -\frac{1}{4}x; y = -\frac{1}{4}x + 3$

The graph of $y = 5x$ is given below as well as Figures a–d. For Exercises 47 through 50, match each equation with its graph. Hint: Recall that if an equation is written in the form $y = mx + b$, its graph crosses the y-axis at $(0, b)$.

47. $y = 5x + 5$ c

49. $y = 5x - 1$ d

48. $y = 5x - 4$ b

50. $y = 5x + 2$ a

a.

b.

c.

d.

Solve. See Example 8.

51. Jogging is one of the few sports that has been consistently increasing over the past few years. The number of people jogging (in millions) from the years 2000 to 2009 is given by the equation $y = x + 23$, where x is the number of years after 2000. (*Source:* Based on data from the National Sporting Goods Association)

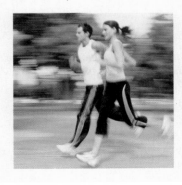

a. Use this equation or a graph of it to complete the ordered pair (8,   ).

b. Write a sentence explaining the meaning of the answer to part (a).

c. If this trend continues, how many joggers will there be in 2017?

52. The revenue y (in billions of dollars) for Home Depot stores during the years 2006 through 2010 is given by the equation $y = -3x + 79$, where x is the number of years after 2006. (*Source:* Based on data from Home Depot stores)

a. Use this equation or a graph of it to complete the ordered pair (4,   ).

b. Write a sentence explaining the meaning of the answer to part (a).

c. If this trend continues, predict the revenue for Home Depot stores for the year 2015.

53. One American rite of passage is a driver's license. The number of people y (in millions) who have a driver's license can be estimated by the linear equation $y = 2.2x + 190$, where x is the number of years after 2000. (Data from Federal Highway Administration)

a. Use this equation to complete the ordered pair (8,   ).

b. Write a sentence explaining the meaning of the ordered pair in part (a).

c. If this trend continues, predict the number of people with driver's licenses in 2016.

54. The percent of U.S. households y with at least one computer can be approximated by the linear equation $y = 4.3x + 51$, where x is the number of years since 2000. (Data from *Statistical Abstract of the United States*)

a. Use the equation to complete the ordered pair (9,   ).

b. Write a sentence explaining the meaning of the ordered pair found in part (a).

c. If this trend continues, predict the percent of U.S. households that have at least one computer in 2012.

d. Explain any issues with your answer to part (c).

REVIEW AND PREVIEW

△ **55.** The coordinates of three vertices of a rectangle are $(-2, 5)$, $(4, 5)$, and $(-2, -1)$. Find the coordinates of the fourth vertex. See Section 3.1.

△ **56.** The coordinates of two vertices of a square are $(-3, -1)$ and $(2, -1)$. Find the coordinates of two pairs of points possible for the third and fourth vertices. See Section 3.1.

Complete each table. See Section 3.1.

57. $x - y = -3$

x	y
0	
	0

58. $y - x = 5$

x	y
0	
	0

59. $y = 2x$

x	y
0	
	0

60. $x = -3y$

x	y
0	
	0

CONCEPT EXTENSIONS

Write each statement as an equation in two variables. Then graph the equation.

61. The y-value is 5 more than the x-value.

62. The y-value is twice the x-value.

63. Two times the x-value, added to three times the y-value, is 6.

64. Five times the x-value, added to twice the y-value, is -10.

△ **65.** The perimeter of the trapezoid below is 22 centimeters. Write a linear equation in two variables for the perimeter. Find y if x is 3 cm.

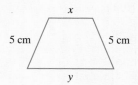

△ **66.** The perimeter of the rectangle below is 50 miles. Write a linear equation in two variables for this perimeter. Use this equation to find x when y is 20.

67. Explain how to find ordered pair solutions of linear equations in two variables.

68. If (a, b) is an ordered pair solution of $x + y = 5$, is (b, a) also a solution? Explain why or why not.

69. Graph the nonlinear equation $y = x^2$ by completing the table shown. Plot the ordered pairs and connect them with a smooth curve.

x	y
0	
1	
-1	
2	
-2	

70. Graph the nonlinear equation $y = |x|$ by completing the table shown. Plot the ordered pairs and connect them. This curve is "V" shaped.

$$y = |x|$$

x	y
0	
1	
-1	
2	
-2	

3.3 | Intercepts

OBJECTIVES

1 Identify Intercepts of a Graph.

2 Graph a Linear Equation by Finding and Plotting Intercepts.

3 Identify and Graph Vertical and Horizontal Lines.

OBJECTIVE

1   Identifying Intercepts

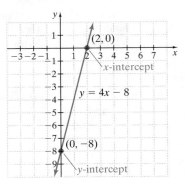

In this section, we graph linear equations in two variables by identifying intercepts. For example, the graph of $y = 4x - 8$ is shown on the right. Notice that this graph crosses the y-axis at the point $(0, -8)$. This point is called the **y-intercept.** Likewise, the graph crosses the x-axis at $(2, 0)$, and this point is called the **x-intercept.**

The intercepts are $(2, 0)$ and $(0, -8)$.

▶ **Helpful Hint**

If a graph crosses the x-axis at $(-3, 0)$ and the y-axis at $(0, 7)$, then

$$\underbrace{(-3, 0)}_{x\text{-intercept}} \qquad \underbrace{(0, 7)}_{y\text{-intercept}}$$

Notice that for the y-intercept, the x-value is 0 and for the x-intercept, the y-value is 0.
Note: Sometimes in mathematics, you may see just the number 7 stated as the y-intercept, and -3 stated as the x-intercept.

EXAMPLES   Identify the x- and y-intercepts.

1.

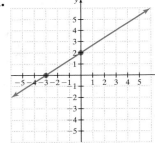

Solution

x-intercept: $(-3, 0)$
y-intercept: $(0, 2)$

2.

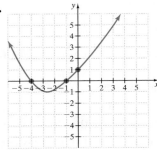

Solution

x-intercepts: $(-4, 0)$, $(-1, 0)$
y-intercept: $(0, 1)$

▶ **Helpful Hint**

Notice that any time $(0, 0)$ is a point of a graph, then it is an x-intercept and a y-intercept. Why? It is the only point that lies on both axes.

3.

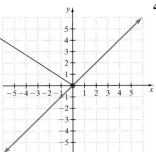

Solution

x-intercept: $(0, 0)$
y-intercept: $(0, 0)$

4.

Solution

x-intercept: $(2, 0)$
y-intercept: none

5.

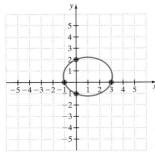

Solution

x-intercepts:
$(-1, 0)$, $(3, 0)$
y-intercepts:
$(0, 2)$, $(0, -1)$

□

1–5   Identify the *x*- and *y*-intercepts.

1.

2.

3.

4.

5.

OBJECTIVE

2   Using Intercepts to Graph a Linear Equation ▶

Given the equation of a line, intercepts are usually easy to find since one coordinate is 0.

One way to find the *y*-intercept of a line, given its equation, is to let $x = 0$, since a point on the *y*-axis has an *x*-coordinate of 0. To find the *x*-intercept of a line, let $y = 0$, since a point on the *x*-axis has a *y*-coordinate of 0.

Finding *x*- and *y*-intercepts

To find the *x*-intercept, let $y = 0$ and solve for *x*.
To find the *y*-intercept, let $x = 0$ and solve for *y*.

EXAMPLE 6   Graph $x - 3y = 6$ by finding and plotting intercepts.

Solution   Let $y = 0$ to find the *x*-intercept and let $x = 0$ to find the *y*-intercept.

$$
\begin{array}{ll}
\text{Let } y = 0 & \text{Let } x = 0 \\
x - 3y = 6 & x - 3y = 6 \\
x - 3(0) = 6 & 0 - 3y = 6 \\
x - 0 = 6 & -3y = 6 \\
x = 6 & y = -2
\end{array}
$$

The *x*-intercept is $(6, 0)$ and the *y*-intercept is $(0, -2)$. We find a third ordered pair solution to check our work. If we let $y = -1$, then $x = 3$. Plot the points $(6, 0)$, $(0, -2)$, and $(3, -1)$. The graph of $x - 3y = 6$ is the line drawn through these points, as shown on page 196.

x	*y*
6	0
0	−2
3	−1

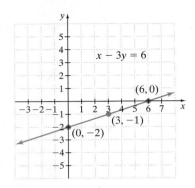

6   Graph $x + 2y = -4$ by finding and plotting intercepts.

EXAMPLE 7   Graph $x = -2y$ by plotting intercepts.

Solution   Let $y = 0$ to find the x-intercept and $x = 0$ to find the y-intercept.

$$\text{Let } y = 0 \qquad\qquad \text{Let } x = 0$$
$$x = -2y \qquad\qquad\qquad x = -2y$$
$$x = -2(0) \qquad\qquad\quad 0 = -2y$$
$$x = 0 \qquad\qquad\qquad\quad 0 = y$$

Both the x-intercept and y-intercept are $(0, 0)$. In other words, when $x = 0$, then $y = 0$, which gives the ordered pair $(0, 0)$. Also, when $y = 0$, then $x = 0$, which gives the same ordered pair $(0, 0)$. This happens when the graph passes through the origin. Since two points are needed to determine a line, we must find at least one more ordered pair that satisfies $x = -2y$. We will let $y = -1$ to find a second ordered pair solution and let $y = 1$ as a checkpoint.

$$\text{Let } y = -1 \qquad\qquad \text{Let } y = 1$$
$$x = -2(-1) \qquad\qquad\quad x = -2(1)$$
$$x = 2 \qquad\qquad\qquad\quad x = -2$$

The ordered pairs are $(0, 0)$, $(2, -1)$, and $(-2, 1)$. Plot these points to graph $x = -2y$.

x	*y*
0	0
2	−1
−2	1

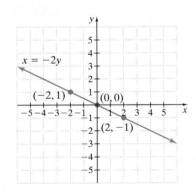

7   Graph $x = 3y$ by plotting intercepts.

EXAMPLE 8   Graph $4x = 3y - 9$.

Solution   Find the x- and y-intercepts, and then choose $x = 2$ to find a checkpoint.

Let $y = 0$	Let $x = 0$	Let $x = 2$
$4x = 3(0) - 9$	$4 \cdot 0 = 3y - 9$	$4(2) = 3y - 9$
$4x = -9$	$9 = 3y$	$8 = 3y - 9$
Solve for x.	Solve for y.	Solve for y.
	$3 = y$	$17 = 3y$
$x = -\dfrac{9}{4}$ or $-2\dfrac{1}{4}$		$\dfrac{17}{3} = y$ or $y = 5\dfrac{2}{3}$

The ordered pairs are $\left(-2\dfrac{1}{4}, 0\right)$, $(0, 3)$, and $\left(2, 5\dfrac{2}{3}\right)$. The equation $4x = 3y - 9$ is graphed as follows.

x	y
$-2\dfrac{1}{4}$	0
0	3
2	$5\dfrac{2}{3}$

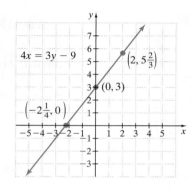

PRACTICE
8   Graph $3x = 2y + 4$.

OBJECTIVE
3   Graphing Vertical and Horizontal Lines ▶

The equation $x = c$, where c is a real number constant, is a linear equation in two variables because it can be written in the form $x + 0y = c$. The graph of this equation is a vertical line as shown in the next example.

EXAMPLE 9   Graph $x = 2$.

Solution   The equation $x = 2$ can be written as $x + 0y = 2$. For any y-value chosen, notice that x is 2. No other value for x satisfies $x + 0y = 2$. Any ordered pair whose x-coordinate is 2 is a solution of $x + 0y = 2$. We will use the ordered pair solutions $(2, 3)$, $(2, 0)$, and $(2, -3)$ to graph $x = 2$.

x	y
2	3
2	0
2	-3

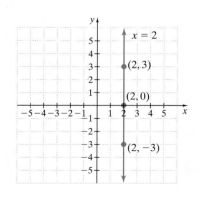

The graph is a vertical line with x-intercept $(2, 0)$. Note that this graph has no y-intercept because x is never 0. □

PRACTICE
9   Graph $x = -2$.

Vertical Lines

The graph of $x = c$, where c is a real number, is a vertical line with x-intercept $(c, 0)$.

EXAMPLE 10   Graph $y = -3$.

Solution   The equation $y = -3$ can be written as $0x + y = -3$. For any x-value chosen, y is -3. If we choose 4, 1, and -2 as x-values, the ordered pair solutions are $(4, -3)$, $(1, -3)$, and $(-2, -3)$. Use these ordered pairs to graph $y = -3$. The graph is a horizontal line with y-intercept $(0, -3)$ and no x-intercept.

x	y
4	-3
1	-3
-2	-3

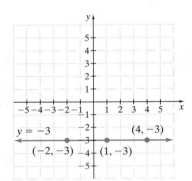

□

PRACTICE
10   Graph $y = 2$.

Horizontal Lines

The graph of $y = c$, where c is a real number, is a horizontal line with y-intercept $(0, c)$.

Graphing Calculator Explorations

You may have noticed that to use the $\boxed{Y=}$ key on a grapher to graph an equation, the equation must be solved for y. For example, to graph $2x + 3y = 7$, we solve this equation for y.

$$2x + 3y = 7$$
$$3y = -2x + 7 \quad \text{Subtract } 2x \text{ from both sides.}$$
$$\frac{3y}{3} = -\frac{2x}{3} + \frac{7}{3} \quad \text{Divide both sides by 3.}$$
$$y = -\frac{2}{3}x + \frac{7}{3} \quad \text{Simplify.}$$

$2x + 3y = 7$ or $y = -\frac{2}{3}x + \frac{7}{3}$

To graph $2x + 3y = 7$ or $y = -\frac{2}{3}x + \frac{7}{3}$, press the $\boxed{Y =}$ key and enter

$$Y_1 = -\frac{2}{3}x + \frac{7}{3}$$

Graph each linear equation.

1. $x = 3.78y$ 　　　　　**2.** $-2.61y = x$ 　　　　　**3.** $3x + 7y = 21$

4. $-4x + 6y = 21$ 　　　**5.** $-2.2x + 6.8y = 15.5$ 　**6.** $5.9x - 0.8y = -10.4$

Vocabulary, Readiness & Video Check

Use the choices below to fill in each blank. Some choices may be used more than once. Exercises 1 and 2 come from Section 3.2.

x	vertical	x-intercept	linear
y	horizontal	y-intercept	standard

1. An equation that can be written in the form $Ax + By = C$ is called a(n) _____ equation in two variables.

2. The form $Ax + By = C$ is called _____ form.

3. The graph of the equation $y = -1$ is a _____ line.

4. The graph of the equation $x = 5$ is a _____ line.

5. A point where a graph crosses the y-axis is called a(n) _____.

6. A point where a graph crosses the x-axis is called a(n) _____.

7. Given an equation of a line, to find the x-intercept (if there is one), let _____ $= 0$ and solve for _____.

8. Given an equation of a line, to find the y-intercept (if there is one), let _____ $= 0$ and solve for _____.

Martin-Gay Interactive Videos

See Video 3.3

Watch the section lecture video and answer the following questions.

OBJECTIVE 1

9. At the end of Example 2, patterns are discussed. What reason is given for why x-intercepts have y-values of 0? For why y-intercepts have x-values of 0?

OBJECTIVE 2

10. In Example 3, the goal is to use the x- and y-intercepts to graph a line. Yet once the two intercepts are found, a third point is also found before the line is graphed. Why do think this practice of finding a third point is continued?

OBJECTIVE 3

11. From Examples 5 and 6, what can you say about the coefficient of x when the equation of a horizontal line is written as $Ax + By = C$? What about the coefficient of y when the equation of a vertical line is written as $Ax + By = C$?

3.3 Exercise Set MyMathLab®

Identify the intercepts. See Examples 1 through 5.

1.

2.

3.

4.

5.

6.

7.

8.

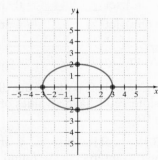

Solve. See Examples 1 through 5.

9. What is the greatest number of intercepts for a line?

10. What is the least number of intercepts for a line?

11. What is the least number of intercepts for a circle?

12. What is the greatest number of intercepts for a circle?

Graph each linear equation by finding and plotting its intercepts. See Examples 6 through 8.

13. $x - y = 3$
14. $x - y = -4$
15. $x = 5y$

16. $x = 2y$
17. $-x + 2y = 6$
18. $x - 2y = -8$

19. $2x - 4y = 8$
20. $2x + 3y = 6$
21. $y = 2x$

22. $y = -2x$
23. $y = 3x + 6$
24. $y = 2x + 10$

Graph each linear equation. See Examples 9 and 10.

25. $x = -1$
26. $y = 5$
27. $y = 0$

28. $x = 0$
29. $y + 7 = 0$
30. $x - 2 = 0$

31. $x + 3 = 0$
32. $y - 6 = 0$

MIXED PRACTICE

Graph each linear equation. See Examples 6 through 10.

33. $x = y$
34. $x = -y$

35. $x + 8y = 8$
36. $x + 3y = 9$

37. $5 = 6x - y$
38. $4 = x - 3y$

39. $-x + 10y = 11$
40. $-x + 9y = 10$

41. $x = -4\frac{1}{2}$
42. $x = -1\frac{3}{4}$

43. $y = 3\frac{1}{4}$
44. $y = 2\frac{1}{2}$

45. $y = -\frac{2}{3}x + 1$
46. $y = -\frac{3}{5}x + 3$

47. $4x - 6y + 2 = 0$
48. $9x - 6y + 3 = 0$

For Exercises 49 through 54, match each equation with its graph. See Graphs A.–F. below and on the next page.

49. $y = 3$
50. $y = 2x + 2$

51. $x = -1$
52. $x = 3$

53. $y = 2x + 3$
54. $y = -2x$

A.

B.

C.

D.

E.

F.

REVIEW AND PREVIEW

Simplify. See Sections 1.4 through 1.7.

55. $\dfrac{-6 - 3}{2 - 8}$

56. $\dfrac{4 - 5}{-1 - 0}$

57. $\dfrac{-8 - (-2)}{-3 - (-2)}$

58. $\dfrac{12 - 3}{10 - 9}$

59. $\dfrac{0 - 6}{5 - 0}$

60. $\dfrac{2 - 2}{3 - 5}$

CONCEPT EXTENSIONS

Answer the following true or false.

61. All lines have an x-intercept *and* a y-intercept.

62. The graph of $y = 4x$ contains the point $(0, 0)$.

63. The graph of $x + y = 5$ has an x-intercept of $(5, 0)$ and a y-intercept of $(0, 5)$.

64. The graph of $y = 5x$ contains the point $(5, 1)$.

The production supervisor at Alexandra's Office Products finds that it takes 3 hours to manufacture a particular office chair and 6 hours to manufacture an office desk. A total of 1200 hours is available to produce office chairs and desks of this style. The linear equation that models this situation is $3x + 6y = 1200$, where x represents the number of chairs produced and y the number of desks manufactured. Use this information for Exercises 65 through 68.

65. Complete the ordered pair solution $(0,\ \ )$ of this equation. Describe the manufacturing situation that corresponds to this solution.

66. Complete the ordered pair solution $(\ \ , 0)$ of this equation. Describe the manufacturing situation that corresponds to this solution.

67. If 50 desks are manufactured, find the greatest number of chairs that can be made.

68. If 50 chairs are manufactured, find the greatest number of desks that can be made.

69. Since 2002, admissions at movie theaters in the U.S. and Canada have mostly been in a decline. The number of people y (in billions) who go to movie theaters each year can be estimated by the equation $y = -0.025x + 1.55$, where x represents the number of years since 2002. (*Source:* Based on data from Motion Picture Association of America)

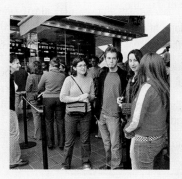

a. Find the x-intercept of this equation.

b. What does this x-intercept mean?

c. Use part (b) to comment on your opinion of the limitations of using equations to model real data.

70. The price of admission to a movie theater has been steadily increasing. The price of regular admission y (in dollars) to a movie theater may be represented by the equation $y = 0.24x + 5.28$, where x is the number of years after 2000. (*Source:* Based on data from Motion Picture Association of America)

a. Find the x-intercept of this equation.

b. What does this x-intercept mean?

c. Use part (b) to comment on your opinion of the limitations of using equations to model real data.

Two lines in the same plane that do not intersect are called **parallel lines.**

△ **71.** Draw a line parallel to the line $x = 5$ that intersects the x-axis at $(1, 0)$. What is the equation of this line?

△ **72.** Draw a line parallel to the line $y = -1$ that intersects the y-axis at $(0, -4)$. What is the equation of this line?

73. Discuss whether a vertical line ever has a y-intercept.

74. Explain why it is a good idea to use three points to graph a linear equation.

75. Discuss whether a horizontal line ever has an x-intercept.

76. Explain how to find intercepts.

3.4 | Slope and Rate of Change

OBJECTIVE

1 Finding the Slope of a Line Given Two Points of the Line

Thus far, much of this chapter has been devoted to graphing lines. You have probably noticed by now that a key feature of a line is its slant or steepness. In mathematics, the slant or steepness of a line is formally known as its **slope.** We measure the slope of a line by the ratio of vertical change to the corresponding horizontal change as we move along the line.

On the line below, for example, suppose that we begin at the point $(1, 2)$ and move to the point $(4, 6)$. The vertical change is the change in y-coordinates: $6 - 2$ or 4 units. The corresponding horizontal change is the change in x-coordinates: $4 - 1 = 3$ units. The ratio of these changes is

$$\text{slope} = \frac{\text{change in } y \text{ (vertical change)}}{\text{change in } x \text{ (horizontal change)}} = \frac{4}{3}$$

The slope of this line, then, is $\frac{4}{3}$. This means that for every 4 units of change in y-coordinates, there is a corresponding change of 3 units in x-coordinates.

> ▶ **Helpful Hint**
>
> It makes no difference what two points of a line are chosen to find its slope. The slope of a line is the same everywhere on the line.

To find the slope of a line, then, choose two points of the line. Label the two x-coordinates of two points x_1 and x_2 (read "x sub one" and "x sub two"), and label the corresponding y-coordinates y_1 and y_2.

The vertical change or **rise** between these points is the difference in the y-coordinates: $y_2 - y_1$. The horizontal change or **run** between the points is the difference of the x-coordinates: $x_2 - x_1$. The slope of the line is the ratio of $y_2 - y_1$ to $x_2 - x_1$, and we traditionally use the letter m to denote slope: $m = \dfrac{y_2 - y_1}{x_2 - x_1}$.

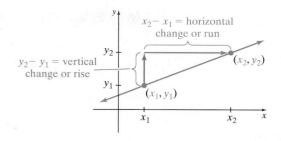

Slope of a Line

The slope m of the line containing the points (x_1, y_1) and (x_2, y_2) is given by

$$m = \frac{\text{rise}}{\text{run}} = \frac{\text{change in } y}{\text{change in } x} = \frac{y_2 - y_1}{x_2 - x_1}, \qquad \text{as long as } x_2 \neq x_1$$

EXAMPLE 1   Find the slope of the line through $(-1, 5)$ and $(2, -3)$. Graph the line.

Solution   If we let (x_1, y_1) be $(-1, 5)$, then $x_1 = -1$ and $y_1 = 5$. Also, let (x_2, y_2) be $(2, -3)$ so that $x_2 = 2$ and $y_2 = -3$. Then, by the definition of slope,

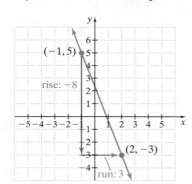

$$m = \frac{y_2 - y_1}{x_2 - x_1}$$

$$= \frac{-3 - 5}{2 - (-1)}$$

$$= \frac{-8}{3} = -\frac{8}{3}$$

The slope of the line is $-\dfrac{8}{3}$.   ☐

PRACTICE

1   Find the slope of the line through $(-4, 11)$ and $(2, 5)$.

▶ **Helpful Hint**

When finding slope, it makes no difference which point is identified as (x_1, y_1) and which is identified as (x_2, y_2). Just remember that whatever y-value is first in the numerator, its corresponding x-value must be first in the denominator. Another way to calculate the slope in Example 1 is:

$$m = \frac{y_2 - y_1}{x_2 - x_1} = \frac{5 - (-3)}{-1 - 2} = \frac{8}{-3} \quad \text{or} \quad -\frac{8}{3} \quad \leftarrow \text{Same slope as found in Example 1}$$

✓CONCEPT CHECK

The points $(-2, -5)$, $(0, -2)$, $(4, 4)$, and $(10, 13)$ all lie on the same line. Work with a partner and verify that the slope is the same no matter which points are used to find slope.

Answer to Concept Check:

$$m = \frac{3}{2}$$

EXAMPLE 2   Find the slope of the line through $(-1, -2)$ and $(2, 4)$. Graph the line.

Solution   Let (x_1, y_1) be $(2, 4)$ and (x_2, y_2) be $(-1, -2)$.

$$m = \frac{y_2 - y_1}{x_2 - x_1}$$

$$= \frac{-2 - 4}{-1 - 2} \quad \begin{array}{l} y\text{-value} \\ \text{corresponding } x\text{-value} \end{array}$$

$$= \frac{-6}{-3} = 2$$

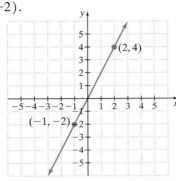

> **Helpful Hint**
> The slope for Example 2 is the same if we let (x_1, y_1) be $(-1, -2)$ and (x_2, y_2) be $(2, 4)$.
>
> $$m = \frac{\overset{y\text{-value}}{\overbrace{4 - (-2)}}}{\underset{\uparrow}{2 - (-1)}} = \frac{6}{3} = 2$$
>
> corresponding x-value

PRACTICE

2   Find the slope of the line through $(-3, -1)$ and $(3, 1)$.

✓**CONCEPT CHECK**

What is wrong with the following slope calculation for the points $(3, 5)$ and $(-2, 6)$?

$$m = \frac{5 - 6}{-2 - 3} = \frac{-1}{-5} = \frac{1}{5}$$

Notice that the slope of the line in Example 1 is negative, whereas the slope of the line in Example 2 is positive. Let your eye follow the line with negative slope from left to right and notice that the line "goes down." Following the line with positive slope from left to right, notice that the line "goes up." This is true in general.

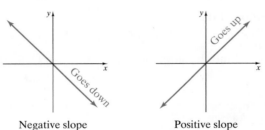

Negative slope   Positive slope

> **Helpful Hint**
> To decide whether a line "goes up" or "goes down," always follow the line from left to right.

OBJECTIVE

2   Finding the Slope of a Line Given Its Equation ▶

As we have seen, the slope of a line is defined by two points on the line. Thus, if we know the equation of a line, we can find its slope by finding two of its points. For example, let's find the slope of the line

$$y = 3x + 2$$

To find two points, we can choose two values for x and substitute to find corresponding y-values. If $x = 0$, for example, $y = 3 \cdot 0 + 2$ or $y = 2$. If $x = 1$, $y = 3 \cdot 1 + 2$ or $y = 5$. This gives the ordered pairs $(0, 2)$ and $(1, 5)$. Using the definition for slope, we have

$$m = \frac{5 - 2}{1 - 0} = \frac{3}{1} = 3 \qquad \text{The slope is 3.}$$

Notice that the slope, 3, is the same as the coefficient of x in the equation $y = 3x + 2$.
Also, recall from Section 3.2 that the graph of an equation of the form $y = mx + b$ has y-intercept $(0, b)$.

Answer to Concept Check:
The order in which the x- and y-values are used must be the same.

$$m = \frac{5 - 6}{3 - (-2)} = \frac{-1}{5} = -\frac{1}{5}$$

This means that the y-intercept of the graph of $y = 3x + 2$ is $(0, 2)$. This is true in general and the form $y = mx + b$ is appropriately called the **slope-intercept form.**

$$y = \underset{\uparrow}{m}x + \underset{\uparrow}{b}$$

slope y-intercept
$$(0, b)$$

> **Slope-Intercept Form**
>
> When a linear equation in two variables is written in slope-intercept form,
>
> $$y = mx + b$$
>
> m is the slope of the line and $(0, b)$ is the y-intercept of the line.

EXAMPLE 3   Find the slope and y-intercept of the line whose equation is $y = \dfrac{3}{4}x + 6$

Solution   The equation is in slope-intercept form, $y = mx + b$.

$$y = \frac{3}{4}x + 6$$

The coefficient of x, $\dfrac{3}{4}$, is the slope and the constant term, 6, is the y-value of the y-intercept, $(0, 6)$.   ☐

PRACTICE
3   Find the slope and y-intercept of the line whose equation is $y = \dfrac{2}{3}x - 2$.

EXAMPLE 4   Find the slope and the y-intercept of the line whose equation is $-y = 5x - 2$.

Solution: Remember, the equation must be solved for y (not $-y$) in order for it to be written in slope-intercept form.

To solve for y, let's divide both sides of the equation by -1.

$$-y = 5x - 2$$
$$\frac{-y}{-1} = \frac{5x}{-1} - \frac{2}{-1} \qquad \text{Divide both sides by } -1.$$
$$y = -5x + 2 \qquad \text{Simplify.}$$

The coefficient of x, -5, is the slope and the constant term, 2, is the y-value of the y-intercept, $(0, 2)$.   ☐

PRACTICE
4   Find the slope and y-intercept of the line whose equation is $-y = -6x + 5$.

EXAMPLE 5   Find the slope and the y-intercept of the line whose equation is $3x - 4y = 4$.

Solution   Write the equation in slope-intercept form by solving for y.

$$3x - 4y = 4$$
$$-4y = -3x + 4 \qquad \text{Subtract } 3x \text{ from both sides.}$$
$$\frac{-4y}{-4} = \frac{-3x}{-4} + \frac{4}{-4} \qquad \text{Divide both sides by } -4.$$
$$y = \frac{3}{4}x - 1 \qquad \text{Simplify.}$$

The coefficient of x, $\dfrac{3}{4}$, is the slope, and the y-intercept is $(0, -1)$.   ☐

PRACTICE
5 Find the slope and the *y*-intercept of the line whose equation is $5x + 2y = 8$.

OBJECTIVE
3 Finding Slopes of Horizontal and Vertical Lines

Recall that if a line tilts upward from left to right, its slope is positive. If a line tilts downward from left to right, its slope is negative. Let's now find the slopes of two special lines, horizontal and vertical lines.

EXAMPLE 6 Find the slope of the line $y = -1$.

Solution Recall that $y = -1$ is a horizontal line with *y*-intercept $(0, -1)$. To find the slope, find two ordered pair solutions of $y = -1$. Solutions of $y = -1$ must have a *y*-value of -1. Let's use points $(2, -1)$ and $(-3, -1)$, which are on the line.

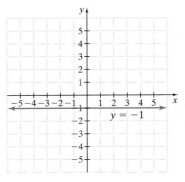

$$m = \frac{y_2 - y_1}{x_2 - x_1} = \frac{-1 - (-1)}{-3 - 2} = \frac{0}{-5} = 0$$

The slope of the line $y = -1$ is 0 and its graph is shown.

PRACTICE
6 Find the slope of the line $y = 3$.

Any two points of a horizontal line will have the same *y*-values. This means that the *y*-values will always have a difference of 0 for all horizontal lines. Thus, **all horizontal lines have a slope 0.**

EXAMPLE 7 Find the slope of the line $x = 5$.

Solution Recall that the graph of $x = 5$ is a vertical line with *x*-intercept $(5, 0)$.

To find the slope, find two ordered pair solutions of $x = 5$. Solutions of $x = 5$ must have an *x*-value of 5. Let's use points $(5, 0)$ and $(5, 4)$, which are on the line.

$$m = \frac{y_2 - y_1}{x_2 - x_1} = \frac{4 - 0}{5 - 5} = \frac{4}{0}$$

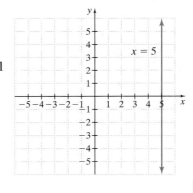

Since $\frac{4}{0}$ is undefined, we say the slope of the vertical line $x = 5$ is undefined, and its graph is shown.

PRACTICE
7 Find the slope of the line $x = -4$.

Any two points of a vertical line will have the same *x*-values. This means that the *x*-values will always have a difference of 0 for all vertical lines. Thus **all vertical lines have undefined slope.**

> ▶ **Helpful Hint**
> Slope of 0 and undefined slope are not the same. Vertical lines have undefined slope or no slope, while horizontal lines have a slope of 0.

Here is a general review of slope.

Summary of Slope

Slope m of the line through (x_1, y_1) and (x_2, y_2) is given by the equation $m = \dfrac{y_2 - y_1}{x_2 - x_1}$.

Positive slope: $m > 0$

Negative slope: $m < 0$

Zero slope: $m = 0$

Undefined slope or no slope

OBJECTIVE
4 Slopes of Parallel and Perpendicular Lines

Two lines in the same plane are **parallel** if they do not intersect. Slopes of lines can help us determine whether lines are parallel. Parallel lines have the same steepness, so it follows that they have the same slope.

For example, the graphs of

$$y = -2x + 4$$

and

$$y = -2x - 3$$

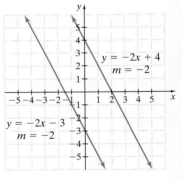

are shown. These lines have the same slope, -2. They also have different y-intercepts, so the lines are distinct and parallel. (If the y-intercepts were the same also, the lines would be the same.)

Parallel Lines

Nonvertical parallel lines have the same slope and different y-intercepts.

Two lines are **perpendicular** if they lie in the same plane and meet at a 90° (right) angle. How do the slopes of perpendicular lines compare? The product of the slopes of two perpendicular lines is -1.

For example, the graphs of

$$y = 4x + 1$$

and

$$y = -\frac{1}{4}x - 3$$

are shown. The slopes of the lines are 4 and $-\frac{1}{4}$. Their product is $4\left(-\frac{1}{4}\right) = -1$, so the lines are perpendicular.

Perpendicular Lines

If the product of the slopes of two lines is -1, then the lines are perpendicular.

   (Two nonvertical lines are perpendicular if the slope of one is the negative reciprocal of the slope of the other.)

▶ **Helpful Hint**

Here are examples of numbers that are negative (opposite) reciprocals.

Number	Negative Reciprocal	Their Product Is −1.
$\frac{2}{3}$	$-\frac{3}{2}$	$\frac{2}{3} \cdot -\frac{3}{2} = -\frac{6}{6} = -1$
-5 or $-\frac{5}{1}$	$\frac{1}{5}$	$-5 \cdot \frac{1}{5} = -\frac{5}{5} = -1$

▶ **Helpful Hint**

Here are a few important facts about vertical and horizontal lines.

- Two distinct vertical lines are parallel.
- Two distinct horizontal lines are parallel.
- A horizontal line and a vertical line are always perpendicular.

△ **EXAMPLE 8**   Determine whether each pair of lines is parallel, perpendicular, or neither.

a. $y = -\frac{1}{5}x + 1$ **b.** $x + y = 3$ **c.** $3x + y = 5$

 $2x + 10y = 3$ $-x + y = 4$ $2x + 3y = 6$

Solution

a. The slope of the line $y = -\frac{1}{5}x + 1$ is $-\frac{1}{5}$. We find the slope of the second line by solving its equation for y.

$$2x + 10y = 3$$

$$10y = -2x + 3 \qquad \text{Subtract } 2x \text{ from both sides.}$$

$$y = \frac{-2}{10}x + \frac{3}{10} \qquad \text{Divide both sides by 10.}$$

$$y = -\frac{1}{5}x + \frac{3}{10} \qquad \text{Simplify.}$$

The slope of this line is $-\frac{1}{5}$ also. Since the lines have the same slope and different y-intercepts, they are parallel, as shown in the figure on the next page.

b. To find each slope, we solve each equation for y.

$$x + y = 3 \qquad\qquad -x + y = 4$$
$$y = -x + 3 \qquad\qquad y = x + 4$$
$$\uparrow \qquad\qquad\qquad\qquad \uparrow$$
The slope is -1.   The slope is 1.

The slopes are not the same, so the lines are not parallel. Next we check the product of the slopes: $(-1)(1) = -1$. Since the product is -1, the lines are perpendicular, as shown in the figure.

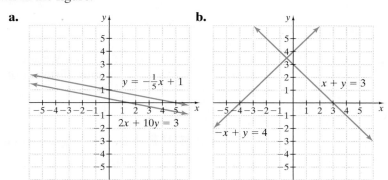

c. We solve each equation for y to find each slope. The slopes are -3 and $-\dfrac{2}{3}$. The slopes are not the same and their product is not -1. Thus, the lines are neither parallel nor perpendicular.   □

PRACTICE
8   Determine whether each pair of lines is parallel, perpendicular, or neither.

a. $y = -5x + 1$ **b.** $x + y = 11$ **c.** $2x + 3y = 21$
$\quad\;\; x - 5y = 10$ $2x + y = 11$ $6y = -4x - 2$

✓CONCEPT CHECK
Consider the line $-6x + 2y = 1$.
a. Write the equations of two lines parallel to this line.
b. Write the equations of two lines perpendicular to this line.

OBJECTIVE
5   Slope as a Rate of Change ▶

Slope can also be interpreted as a rate of change. In other words, slope tells us how fast y is changing with respect to x. To see this, let's look at a few of the many real-world applications of slope. For example, the pitch of a roof, used by builders and architects,

is its slope. The pitch of the roof on the left is $\dfrac{7}{10}\left(\dfrac{\text{rise}}{\text{run}}\right)$. This means that the roof rises vertically 7 feet for every horizontal 10 feet. The rate of change for the roof is 7 vertical feet (y) per 10 horizontal feet (x).

The grade of a road is its slope written as a percent. A 7% grade, as shown below, means that the road rises (or falls) 7 feet for every horizontal 100 feet. $\Big($ Recall that $7\% = \dfrac{7}{100}.\Big)$ Here, the slope of $\dfrac{7}{100}$ gives us the rate of change. The road rises (in our diagram) 7 vertical feet (y) for every 100 horizontal feet (x).

Answers to Concept Check:
a. any two lines with $m = 3$ and
y-intercept not $\left(0, \dfrac{1}{2}\right)$
b. any two lines with $m = -\dfrac{1}{3}$

EXAMPLE 9 Finding the Grade of a Road

At one part of the road to the summit of Pikes Peak, the road rises at a rate of 15 vertical feet for a horizontal distance of 250 feet. Find the grade of the road.

Solution Recall that the grade of a road is its slope written as a percent.

$$\text{grade} = \frac{\text{rise}}{\text{run}} = \frac{15}{250} = 0.06 = 6\%$$

15 feet

250 feet

The grade is 6%.

PRACTICE

9 One part of the Mt. Washington (New Hampshire) cog railway rises about 1794 feet over a horizontal distance of 7176 feet. Find the grade of this part of the railway.

EXAMPLE 10 Finding the Slope of a Line

The following graph shows annual food and drink sales y (in billions of dollars) for year x. Find the slope of the line and attach the proper units for the rate of change. Then write a sentence explaining the meaning of the slope for this application.

Solution Use (1990, 240) and (2011, 597) to calculate slope.

$$m = \frac{597 - 240}{2011 - 1990} = \frac{357}{21} = \frac{17 \text{ billion dollars}}{1 \text{ year}}$$

This means that the rate of change of restaurant food and drink sales increases by 17 billion dollars every 1 year, or \$17 billion per year.

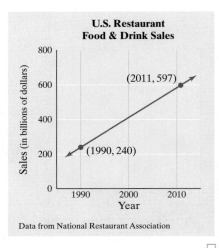

U.S. Restaurant Food & Drink Sales

Sales (in billions of dollars)

(2011, 597)

(1990, 240)

Year

Data from National Restaurant Association

PRACTICE

10 The following graph shows the cost y (in dollars) of having laundry done at the Wash-n-Fold, where x is the number of pounds of laundry. Find the slope of the line, and attach the proper units for the rate of change.

Cost of Laundry

Cost of Laundry (in dollars)

(6, 5)

(2, 2)

Pounds of Laundry

Graphing Calculator Explorations

It is possible to use a grapher to sketch the graph of more than one equation on the same set of axes. This feature can be used to confirm our findings from Section 3.2 when we learned that the graph of an equation written in the form $y = mx + b$ has a y-intercept of b. For example, graph the equations $y = \frac{2}{5}x$, $y = \frac{2}{5}x + 7$, and

$y = \dfrac{2}{5}x - 4$ on the same set of axes. To do so, press the $\boxed{Y=}$ key and enter the equations on the first three lines.

$$Y_1 = \left(\dfrac{2}{5}\right)x$$

$$Y_2 = \left(\dfrac{2}{5}\right)x + 7$$

$$Y_3 = \left(\dfrac{2}{5}\right)x - 4$$

The screen should look like:

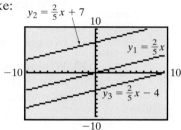

Notice that all three graphs appear to have the same positive slope. The graph of $y = \dfrac{2}{5}x + 7$ is the graph of $y = \dfrac{2}{5}x$ moved 7 units upward with a y-intercept of 7. Also, the graph of $y = \dfrac{2}{5}x - 4$ is the graph of $y = \dfrac{2}{5}x$ moved 4 units downward with a y-intercept of -4.

Graph the equations on the same set of axes. Describe the similarities and differences in their graphs.

1. $y = 3.8x,\ y = 3.8x - 3,\ y = 3.8x + 9$

2. $y = -4.9x,\ y = -4.9x + 1,\ y = -4.9x + 8$

3. $y = \dfrac{1}{4}x;\ y = \dfrac{1}{4}x + 5,\ y = \dfrac{1}{4}x - 8$

4. $y = -\dfrac{3}{4}x,\ y = -\dfrac{3}{4}x - 5,\ y = -\dfrac{3}{4}x + 6$

Vocabulary, Readiness & Video Check

Use the choices below to fill in each blank. Not all choices will be used.

m	x	0	positive	undefined
b	y	slope	negative	

1. The measure of the steepness or tilt of a line is called _____ .

2. If an equation is written in the form $y = mx + b$, the value of the letter _____ is the value of the slope of the graph.

3. The slope of a horizontal line is _____ .

4. The slope of a vertical line is _____ .

5. If the graph of a line moves upward from left to right, the line has _____ slope.

6. If the graph of a line moves downward from left to right, the line has _____ slope.

7. Given two points of a line, slope $= \dfrac{\text{change in}\_\_}{\text{change in}\_\_}$.

Martin-Gay Interactive Videos

See Video 3.4 🍎

Watch the section lecture video and answer the following questions.

OBJECTIVE
1

8. What important point is made during Example 1 having to do with the order of the points in the slope formula?

OBJECTIVE
2

9. From Example 5, how do you write an equation in "slope-intercept form"? Once the equation is in slope-intercept form, how do you identify the slope?

OBJECTIVE
3

10. In the lecture after 🔲 Example 8, different slopes are summarized. What is the difference between zero slope and undefined slope? What does "no slope" mean?

OBJECTIVE
4

11. From 🔲 Example 10, what form of the equations is best to determine if two lines are parallel or perpendicular? Why?

OBJECTIVE
5

12. Writing the slope as a rate of change in 🔲 Example 11 gave real-life meaning to the slope. What step in the general strategy for problem solving does this correspond to?

3.4 Exercise Set

MyMathLab®

Find the slope of the line that passes through the given points. See Examples 1 and 2.

1. $(-1, 5)$ and $(6, -2)$

2. $(3, 1)$ and $(2, 6)$

3. $(-4, 3)$ and $(-4, 5)$

4. $(6, -6)$ and $(6, 2)$

5. $(-2, 8)$ and $(1, 6)$

6. $(4, -3)$ and $(2, 2)$

7. $(5, 1)$ and $(-2, 1)$

8. $(0, 13)$ and $(-4, 13)$

Find the slope of each line if it exists. See Examples 1 and 2.

9.

10.

11.

12.

13.

14.

State whether the slope of the line is positive, negative, 0, or is undefined. See the top box on p. 207.

15.

16.

17.

18.

Decide whether a line with the given slope is upward, downward, horizontal, or vertical. See the top box on p. 207.

19. $m = \dfrac{7}{6}$ _____

20. $m = -3$ _____

21. $m = 0$ _____

22. m is undefined. _____

For each graph, determine which line has the greater slope. See the top box on p. 207.

23.

24.

25.

26.

In Exercises 27 through 32, match each line with its slope. See Examples 1 and 2 and the top box on p. 207.

A. $m = 0$ **B.** undefined slope   **C.** $m = 3$

D. $m = 1$ **E.** $m = -\dfrac{1}{2}$ **F.** $m = -\dfrac{3}{4}$

27.

28.

29.

30.

31.

32.

Find the slope of each line. See Examples 6 and 7.

33. $x = 6$ | **34.** $y = 4$
35. $y = -4$ | **36.** $x = 2$
37. $x = -3$ | **38.** $y = -11$
39. $y = 0$ | **40.** $x = 0$

MIXED PRACTICE

Find the slope of each line. See Examples 3 through 7.

41. $y = 5x - 2$ | **42.** $y = -2x + 6$
43. $y = -0.3x + 2.5$ | **44.** $y = -7.6x - 0.1$
45. $2x + y = 7$ | **46.** $-5x + y = 10$
47. $2x - 3y = 10$ | **48.** $3x - 5y = 1$
49. $x = 1$ | **50.** $y = -2$
51. $x = 2y$ | **52.** $x = -4y$
53. $y = -3$ | **54.** $x = 5$
55. $-3x - 4y = 6$ | **56.** $-4x - 7y = 9$
57. $20x - 5y = 1.2$ | **58.** $24x - 3y = 5.7$

△ *Find the slope of the line that is (a) parallel and (b) perpendicular to the line through each pair of points. See Example 8.*

59. $(-3, -3)$ and $(0,0)$

60. $(6, -2)$ and $(1,4)$

61. $(-8, -4)$ and $(3,5)$

62. $(6, -1)$ and $(-4, -10)$

△ *Determine whether each pair of lines is parallel, perpendicular, or neither. See Example 8.*

63. $y = \dfrac{2}{9}x + 3$
$y = -\dfrac{2}{9}x$ | **64.** $y = \dfrac{1}{5}x + 20$
$y = -\dfrac{1}{5}x$
65. $x - 3y = -6$
$y = 3x - 9$ | **66.** $y = 4x - 2$
$4x + y = 5$
67. $6x = 5y + 1$
$-12x + 10y = 1$ | **68.** $-x + 2y = -2$
$2x = 4y + 3$
69. $6 + 4x = 3y$
$3x + 4y = 8$ | **70.** $10 + 3x = 5y$
$5x + 3y = 1$

The pitch of a roof is its slope. Find the pitch of each roof shown. See Example 9.

71.

72.

The grade of a road is its slope written as a percent. Find the grade of each road shown. See Example 9.

73.

74.

75. One of Japan's superconducting "bullet" trains is researched and tested at the Yamanashi Maglev Test Line near Otsuki City. The steepest section of the track has a rise of 2580 meters for a horizontal distance of 6450 meters. What is the grade of this section of track? (*Source:* Japan Railways Central Co.)

76. Professional plumbers suggest that a sewer pipe should rise 0.25 inch for every horizontal foot. Find the recommended slope for a sewer pipe. Round to the nearest hundredth.

77. There has been controversy over the past few years about the world's steepest street. The *Guinness Book of Records* actually listed Baldwin Street, in Dunedin, New Zealand, as the world's steepest street, but Canton Avenue in the

Pittsburgh neighborhood of Beechview may be steeper. Calculate each grade to the nearest percent.

		Grade (%)
Canton Avenue	for every 30 meters of horizontal distance, the vertical change is 11 meters	
Baldwin Street	for every 2.86 meters of horizontal distance, the vertical change is 1 meter	

78. According to federal regulations, a wheelchair ramp should rise no more than 1 foot for a horizontal distance of 12 feet. Write the slope as a grade. Round to the nearest tenth of a percent.

Find the slope of each line and write the slope as a rate of change. Don't forget to attach the proper units. See Example 10.

79. This graph approximates the number of U.S. households that have televisions y (in millions) for year x.

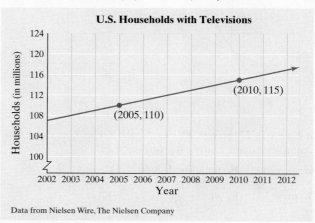

Data from Nielsen Wire, The Nielsen Company

80. The graph approximates the amount of money y (in billions of dollars) spent worldwide on tourism for year x. (Data from World Tourism Organization)

For Exercises 81 and 82, write the slope as a decimal.

▶ **81.** The graph below shows the total cost y (in dollars) of owning and operating a compact car where x is the number of miles driven.

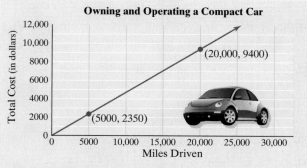

Owning and Operating a Compact Car

(20,000, 9400)

(5000, 2350)

Total Cost (in dollars)

Miles Driven

Data from Federal Highway Administration

82. Americans are keeping their cars longer. The graph below shows the median age y (in years) of automobiles in the United States for the years shown. (Data from Bureau of Transportation Statistics)

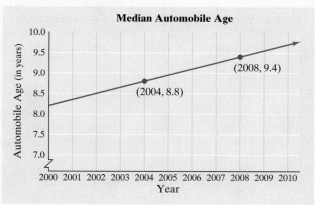

Median Automobile Age

(2008, 9.4)

(2004, 8.8)

Automobile Age (in years)

Year

REVIEW AND PREVIEW

Solve each equation for y. See Section 2.5.

83. $y - (-6) = 2(x - 4)$

84. $y - 7 = -9(x - 6)$

85. $y - 1 = -6(x - (-2))$

86. $y - (-3) = 4(x - (-5))$

CONCEPT EXTENSIONS

Solve. See a Concept Check in this section.

87. Verify that the points $(2, 1)$, $(0, 0)$, $(-2, -1)$ and $(-4, -2)$ are all on the same line by computing the slope between each pair of points. (See the first Concept Check.)

88. Given the points $(2, 3)$ and $(-5, 1)$, can the slope of the line through these points be calculated by $\dfrac{1 - 3}{2 - (-5)}$? Why or why not? (See the second Concept Check.)

89. Write the equations of three lines parallel to $10x - 5y = -7$. (See the third Concept Check.)

90. Write the equations of two lines perpendicular to $10x - 5y = -7$. (See the third Concept Check.)

The following line graph shows the average fuel economy (in miles per gallon) of passenger automobiles produced during each of the model years shown. Use this graph to answer Exercises 91 through 96.

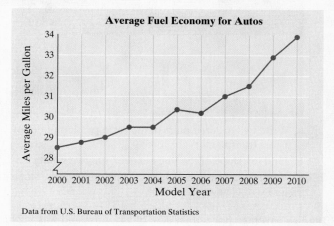

Average Fuel Economy for Autos

Average Miles per Gallon

Model Year

Data from U.S. Bureau of Transportation Statistics

91. Between what two years shown was there a decrease in average fuel economy for automobiles?

92. What was the average fuel economy (in miles per gallon) for automobiles produced during 2008?

93. During which of the model years shown was average fuel economy the lowest?
What was the average fuel economy for that year?

94. During which of the model years shown was average fuel economy the highest?
What was the average fuel economy for that year?

95. Of the following line segments, which has the greatest slope: from 2002 to 2003, from 2006 to 2007, or from 2008 to 2009?

96. Which line segment has a slope of 0?

Solve.

97. Find x so that the pitch of the roof is $\dfrac{1}{3}$.

18 feet

98. Find x so that the pitch of the roof is $\dfrac{2}{5}$.

4 feet

99. Approximately 2207 heart transplants were performed in the United States in 2007. In 2010, the number of heart transplants in the United States rose to 2333. (*Source:* Organ Procurement and Transplantation Network)

a. Write two ordered pairs of the form (year, number of heart transplants).

b. Find the slope of the line between the two points.

c. Write a sentence explaining the meaning of the slope as a rate of change.

100. The average price of an acre of U.S. farmland was $1210 in 2002. In 2008, the price of an acre rose to $2350. (*Source:* National Agricultural Statistics Services)

a. Write two ordered pairs of the form (year, price of an acre).

b. Find the slope of the line through the two points.

c. Write a sentence explaining the meaning of the slope as a rate of change.

101. Show that a triangle with vertices at the points $(1, 1)$, $(-4, 4)$, and $(-3, 0)$ is a right triangle.

102. Show that the quadrilateral with vertices $(1, 3)$, $(2, 1)$, $(-4, 0)$, and $(-3, -2)$ is a parallelogram.

Find the slope of the line through the given points.

103. $(2.1, 6.7)$ and $(-8.3, 9.3)$

104. $(-3.8, 1.2)$ and $(-2.2, 4.5)$

105. $(2.3, 0.2)$ and $(7.9, 5.1)$

106. $(14.3, -10.1)$ and $(9.8, -2.9)$

107. The graph of $y = -\frac{1}{3}x + 2$ has a slope of $-\frac{1}{3}$. The graph of $y = -2x + 2$ has a slope of -2. The graph of $y = -4x + 2$ has a slope of -4. Graph all three equations on a single coordinate system. As the absolute value of the slope becomes larger, how does the steepness of the line change?

108. The graph of $y = \frac{1}{2}x$ has a slope of $\frac{1}{2}$. The graph of $y = 3x$ has a slope of 3. The graph of $y = 5x$ has a slope of 5. Graph all three equations on a single coordinate system. As slope becomes larger, how does the steepness of the line change?

Integrated Review SUMMARY ON SLOPE & GRAPHING LINEAR EQUATIONS

Sections 3.1–3.4

Find the slope of each line.

1.

2.

3.

4.

Graph each linear equation.

5. $y = -2x$

6. $x + y = 3$

7. $x = -1$

8. $y = 4$

9. $x - 2y = 6$

10. $y = 3x + 2$

11. $5x + 3y = 15$

12. $2x - 4y = 8$

Determine whether the lines through the points are parallel, perpendicular, or neither.

13. $y = -\dfrac{1}{5}x + \dfrac{1}{3}$

$3x = -15y$

14. $x - y = \dfrac{1}{2}$

$3x - y = \dfrac{1}{2}$

15. In the years 2000 through 2009 the number of bridges on public roads (in thousands) in the United States can be modeled by the linear equation $y = 1.7x + 587$ where x is years after 2000 and y is number of bridges (in thousands). (*Source:* U.S. Dept. of Transportation)

    a. Find the y-intercept of this line.

    b. Write a sentence explaining the meaning of this intercept.

    c. Find the slope of this line.

    d. Write a sentence explaining the meaning of the slope as a rate of change.

16. Online advertising is a means of promoting products and services using the Internet. The revenue (in billions of dollars) for online advertising for the years 2003 through 2010 is given by $y = 3.3x - 3.1$, where x is the number of years after 2000.

    a. Use this equation to complete the ordered pair $(9, \quad)$.

    b. Write a sentence explaining the meaning of the answer to part (a).

3.5 | Equations of Lines

OBJECTIVES

1 Use the Slope-Intercept Form to Graph a Linear Equation. ▶

2 Use the Slope-Intercept Form to Write an Equation of a Line. ▶

3 Use the Point-Slope Form to Find an Equation of a Line Given Its Slope and a Point of the Line. ▶

4 Use the Point-Slope Form to Find an Equation of a Line Given Two Points of the Line. ▶

5 Find Equations of Vertical and Horizontal Lines. ▶

6 Use the Point-Slope Form to Solve Problems. ▶

Recall that the form $y = mx + b$ is appropriately called the *slope-intercept form* of a linear equation.

slope y-intercept is $(0, b)$

Slope-Intercept Form

When a linear equation in two variables is written in **slope-intercept form,**

$$y = mx + b$$

slope $(0, b)$, y-intercept

then m is the slope of the line and $(0, b)$ is the y-intercept of the line.

OBJECTIVE

1   Using the Slope-Intercept Form to Graph an Equation ▶

We can use the slope-intercept form of the equation of a line to graph a linear equation.

EXAMPLE 1 Use the slope-intercept form to graph the equation

$$y = \frac{3}{5}x - 2$$

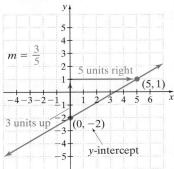

Solution Since the equation $y = \frac{3}{5}x - 2$ is written in slope-intercept form $y = mx + b$, the slope of its graph is $\frac{3}{5}$ and the y-intercept is $(0, -2)$. To graph this equation, we begin by plotting the point $(0, -2)$. From this point, we can find another point of the graph by using the slope $\frac{3}{5}$ and recalling that slope is $\frac{\text{rise}}{\text{run}}$. We start at the y-intercept and move 3 units up since the numerator of the slope is 3; then we move 5 units to the right since the denominator of the slope is 5. We stop at the point $(5, 1)$. The line through $(0, -2)$ and $(5, 1)$ is the graph of $y = \frac{3}{5}x - 2$. ☐

PRACTICE 1 Graph $y = \frac{2}{3}x - 5$.

EXAMPLE 2 Use the slope-intercept form to graph the equation $4x + y = 1$.

Solution First we write the given equation in slope-intercept form.

$$4x + y = 1$$
$$y = -4x + 1$$

The graph of this equation will have slope -4 and y-intercept $(0, 1)$. To graph this line, we first plot the point $(0, 1)$. To find another point of the graph, we use the slope -4, which can be written as $\frac{-4}{1}$ $\left(\frac{4}{-1}\text{ could also be used}\right)$. We start at the point $(0, 1)$ and move 4 units down (since the numerator of the slope is -4) and then 1 unit to the right (since the denominator of the slope is 1).

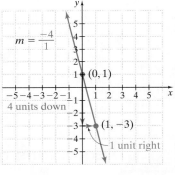

We arrive at the point $(1, -3)$. The line through $(0, 1)$ and $(1, -3)$ is the graph of $4x + y = 1$. ☐

PRACTICE 2 Use the slope-intercept form to graph the equation $3x - y = 2$.

▶ **Helpful Hint**
In Example 2, if we interpret the slope of -4 as $\frac{4}{-1}$, we arrive at $(-1, 5)$ for a second point. Notice that this point is also on the line.

OBJECTIVE
2 Using the Slope-Intercept Form to Write an Equation ▶

The slope-intercept form can also be used to write the equation of a line when we know its slope and y-intercept.

EXAMPLE 3 Find an equation of the line with y-intercept $(0, -3)$ and slope of $\frac{1}{4}$.

Solution We are given the slope and the y-intercept. We let $m = \frac{1}{4}$ and $b = -3$ and write the equation in slope-intercept form, $y = mx + b$.

$$y = mx + b$$
$$y = \frac{1}{4}x + (-3) \quad \text{Let } m = \frac{1}{4} \text{ and } b = -3.$$
$$y = \frac{1}{4}x - 3 \quad \text{Simplify.}$$ ☐

PRACTICE
3   Find an equation of the line with y-intercept $(0, 7)$ and slope of $\frac{1}{2}$.

OBJECTIVE
3   **Writing an Equation Given Slope and a Point**

Thus far, we have seen that we can write an equation of a line if we know its slope and y-intercept. We can also write an equation of a line if we know its slope and any point on the line. To see how we do this, let m represent slope and (x_1, y_1) represent the point on the line. Then if (x, y) is any other point of the line, we have that

$$\frac{y - y_1}{x - x_1} = m$$

$$y - y_1 = m(x - x_1) \quad \text{Multiply both sides by } (x - x_1).$$

$\uparrow$
slope

This is the *point-slope form* of the equation of a line.

Point-Slope Form of the Equation of a Line

The **point-slope form** of the equation of a line is

$$y - y_1 = m(x - x_1)$$

$\qquad\qquad$ slope $\qquad$ (x_1, y_1) point on the line

where m is the slope of the line and (x_1, y_1) is a point on the line.

EXAMPLE 4   Find an equation of the line with slope -2 that passes through $(-1, 5)$. Write the equation in slope-intercept form, $y = mx + b$, and in standard form, $Ax + By = C$.

Solution   Since the slope and a point on the line are given, we use point-slope form $y - y_1 = m(x - x_1)$ to write the equation. Let $m = -2$ and $(-1, 5) = (x_1, y_1)$.

$$y - y_1 = m(x - x_1)$$
$$y - 5 = -2[x - (-1)] \quad \text{Let } m = -2 \text{ and } (x_1, y_1) = (-1, 5).$$
$$y - 5 = -2(x + 1) \qquad \text{Simplify.}$$
$$y - 5 = -2x - 2 \qquad \text{Use the distributive property.}$$

To write the equation in slope-intercept form, $y = mx + b$, we simply solve the equation for y. To do this, we add 5 to both sides.

$$y - 5 = -2x - 2$$
$$y = -2x + 3 \quad \text{Slope-intercept form.}$$
$$2x + y = 3 \qquad \text{Add } 2x \text{ to both sides and we have standard form.} \quad \square$$

PRACTICE
4   Find an equation of the line passing through $(2, 3)$ with slope 4. Write the equation in standard form: $Ax + By = C$.

OBJECTIVE
4   **Writing an Equation Given Two Points**

We can also find an equation of a line when we are given any two points of the line.

EXAMPLE 5 Find an equation of the line through $(2, 5)$ and $(-3, 4)$. Write the equation in standard form.

Solution First, use the two given points to find the slope of the line.

$$m = \frac{4 - 5}{-3 - 2} = \frac{-1}{-5} = \frac{1}{5}$$

Next we use the slope $\frac{1}{5}$ and either one of the given points to write the equation in point-slope form. We use $(2, 5)$. Let $x_1 = 2$, $y_1 = 5$, and $m = \frac{1}{5}$.

$$y - y_1 = m(x - x_1) \qquad \text{Use point-slope form.}$$

$$y - 5 = \frac{1}{5}(x - 2) \qquad \text{Let } x_1 = 2, y_1 = 5, \text{ and } m = \frac{1}{5}.$$

$$5(y - 5) = 5 \cdot \frac{1}{5}(x - 2) \qquad \text{Multiply both sides by 5 to clear fractions.}$$

$$5y - 25 = x - 2 \qquad \text{Use the distributive property and simplify.}$$

$$-x + 5y - 25 = -2 \qquad \text{Subtract } x \text{ from both sides.}$$

$$-x + 5y = 23 \qquad \text{Add 25 to both sides.} \qquad \square$$

PRACTICE
5 Find an equation of the line through $(-1, 6)$ and $(3, 1)$. Write the equation in standard form.

▶ **Helpful Hint**
Multiply both sides of the equation $-x + 5y = 23$ by -1, and it becomes $x - 5y = -23$. Both $-x + 5y = 23$ and $x - 5y = -23$ are in standard form, and they are equations of the same line.

OBJECTIVE
5 **Finding Equations of Vertical and Horizontal Lines**
Recall from Section 3.3 that:

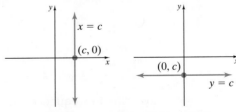

Vertical Line   Horizontal Line

EXAMPLE 6 Find an equation of the vertical line through $(-1, 5)$.

Solution The equation of a vertical line can be written in the form $x = c$, so an equation for a vertical line passing through $(-1, 5)$ is $x = -1$.

$\square$

PRACTICE
6 Find an equation of the vertical line through $(3, -2)$.

△ **EXAMPLE 7**   Find an equation of the line parallel to the line $y = 5$ and passing through $(-2, -3)$.

Solution   Since the graph of $y = 5$ is a horizontal line, any line parallel to it is also horizontal. The equation of a horizontal line can be written in the form $y = c$. An equation for the horizontal line passing through

$$(-2, -3) \text{ is } y = -3.$$

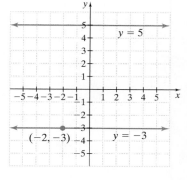

PRACTICE
7   Find an equation of the line parallel to the line $y = -2$ and passing through $(4, 3)$.

OBJECTIVE
6   Using the Point-Slope Form to Solve Problems

Problems occurring in many fields can be modeled by linear equations in two variables. The next example is from the field of marketing and shows how consumer demand of a product depends on the price of the product.

EXAMPLE 8   **Predicting the Sales of T-Shirts**

A web-based T-shirt company has learned that by pricing a clearance-sale T-shirt at $6, sales will reach 2000 T-shirts per day. Raising the price to $8 will cause the sales to fall to 1500 T-shirts per day.

a. Assume that the relationship between sales price and number of T-shirts sold is linear and write an equation describing this relationship. Write the equation in slope-intercept form.

b. Predict the daily sales of T-shirts if the price is $7.50.

Solution

a. First, use the given information and write two ordered pairs. Ordered pairs will be in the form (sales price, number sold) so that our ordered pairs are $(6, 2000)$ and $(8, 1500)$. Use the point-slope form to write an equation. To do so, we find the slope of the line that contains these points.

$$m = \frac{2000 - 1500}{6 - 8} = \frac{500}{-2} = -250$$

Next, use the slope and either one of the points to write the equation in point-slope form. We use $(6, 2000)$.

$$y - y_1 = m(x - x_1) \qquad \text{Use point-slope form.}$$
$$y - 2000 = -250(x - 6) \qquad \text{Let } x_1 = 6, y_1 = 2000, \text{ and } m = -250.$$
$$y - 2000 = -250x + 1500 \qquad \text{Use the distributive property.}$$
$$y = -250x + 3500 \qquad \text{Write in slope-intercept form.}$$

b. To predict the sales if the price is $7.50, we find y when $x = 7.50$.

$$y = -250x + 3500$$
$$y = -250(7.50) + 3500 \qquad \text{Let } x = 7.50.$$
$$y = -1875 + 3500$$
$$y = 1625$$

If the price is $7.50, sales will reach 1625 T-shirts per day.

PRACTICE

8   The new *Camelot* condos were selling at a rate of 30 per month when they were priced at $150,000 each. Lowering the price to $120,000 caused the sales to rise to 50 condos per month.

a. Assume that the relationship between number of condos sold and price is linear, and write an equation describing this relationship. Write the equation in slope-intercept form.

b. How should the condos be priced if the developer wishes to sell 60 condos per month?

The preceding example may also be solved by using ordered pairs of the form (number sold, sales price).

Forms of Linear Equations

$Ax + By = C$	**Standard form** of a linear equation. A and B are not both 0.
$y = mx + b$	**Slope-intercept form** of a linear equation. The slope is m and the y-intercept is $(0, b)$.
$y - y_1 = m(x - x_1)$	**Point-slope form** of a linear equation. The slope is m and (x_1, y_1) is a point on the line.
$y = c$	**Horizontal line** The slope is 0 and the y-intercept is $(0, c)$.
$x = c$	**Vertical line** The slope is undefined and the x-intercept is $(c, 0)$.

Parallel and Perpendicular Lines

Nonvertical parallel lines have the same slope.

The product of the slopes of two nonvertical perpendicular lines is -1.

Graphing Calculator Explorations

A grapher is a very useful tool for discovering patterns. To discover the change in the graph of a linear equation caused by a change in slope, try the following. Use a standard window and graph a linear equation in the form $y = mx + b$. Recall that the graph of such an equation will have slope m and y-intercept b.

First, graph $y = x + 3$. To do so, press the $\boxed{Y =}$ key and enter $Y_1 = x + 3$. Notice that this graph has slope 1 and that the y-intercept is 3. Next, on the same set of axes, graph $y = 2x + 3$ and $y = 3x + 3$ by pressing $\boxed{Y =}$ and entering $Y_2 = 2x + 3$ and $Y_3 = 3x + 3$.

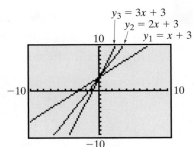

Notice the difference in the graph of each equation as the slope changes from 1 to 2 to 3. How would the graph of $y = 5x + 3$ appear? To see the change in the graph caused by a change in negative slope, try graphing $y = -x + 3$, $y = -2x + 3$, and $y = -3x + 3$ on the same set of axes.

Use a grapher to graph the following equations. For each exercise, graph the first equation and use its graph to predict the appearance of the other equations. Then graph the other equations on the same set of axes and check your prediction.

1. $y = x$; $y = 6x$, $y = -6x$ **2.** $y = -x$; $y = -5x$, $y = -10x$

3. $y = \dfrac{1}{2}x + 2$; $y = \dfrac{3}{4}x + 2$, $y = x + 2$ **4.** $y = x + 1$; $y = \dfrac{5}{4}x + 1$, $y = \dfrac{5}{2}x + 1$

5. $y = -7x + 5$; $y = 7x + 5$ **6.** $y = 3x - 1$; $y = -3x - 1$

Vocabulary, Readiness & Video Check

Use the choices below to fill in each blank. Some choices may be used more than once and some not at all.

b	(y_1, x_1)	point-slope	vertical	standard
m	(x_1, y_1)	slope-intercept	horizontal	

1. The form $y = mx + b$ is called _____ form. When a linear equation in two variables is written in this form, _____ is the slope of its graph and (0, _____) is its y-intercept.

2. The form $y - y_1 = m(x - x_1)$ is called _____ form. When a linear equation in two variables is written in this form, _____ is the slope of its graph and _____ is a point on the graph.

Martin-Gay Interactive Videos

See Video 3.5

Watch the section lecture video and answer the following questions.

OBJECTIVE 1

3. We can use the slope-intercept form to graph a line. Complete these statements based on ▣ Example 1. Start by graphing the _____.

Find another point by applying the slope to this point—rewrite the slope as a _____ if necessary.

OBJECTIVE 2

4. In ▣ Example 3, what is the y-intercept?

OBJECTIVE 3

5. In ▣ Example 4 we use the point-slope form to find the equation of a line given the slope and a point. How do we then write this equation in standard form?

OBJECTIVE 4

6. The lecture before ▣ Example 5 discusses how to find the equation of a line given two points. Is there any circumstance when you might want to use the slope-intercept form to find the equation of a line given two points? If so, when?

OBJECTIVE 5

7. Solve ▣ Examples 6 and 7 again, this time using the point $(-2, -3)$ in each exercise.

OBJECTIVE 6

8. From ▣ Example 8, we are told to use ordered pairs of the form (time, speed). Explain why it is important to keep track of how you define your ordered pairs and/or define your variables.

3.5 Exercise Set · MyMathLab®

Use the slope-intercept form to graph each equation.
See Examples 1 and 2.

1. $y = 2x + 1$

2. $y = -4x - 1$

3. $y = \frac{2}{3}x + 5$

4. $y = \frac{1}{4}x - 3$

5. $y = -5x$

6. $y = -6x$

7. $4x + y = 6$

8. $-3x + y = 2$

9. $4x - 7y = -14$

10. $3x - 4y = 4$

11. $x = \frac{5}{4}y$

12. $x = \frac{3}{2}y$

Write an equation of the line with each given slope, m, and y-intercept, (0, b). See Example 3.

13. $m = 5, b = 3$

14. $m = -3, b = -3$

15. $m = -4, b = -\frac{1}{6}$

16. $m = 2, b = \frac{3}{4}$

17. $m = \frac{2}{3}, b = 0$

18. $m = -\frac{4}{5}, b = 0$

19. $m = 0, b = -8$

20. $m = 0, b = -2$

21. $m = -\frac{1}{5}, b = \frac{1}{9}$

22. $m = \frac{1}{2}, b = -\frac{1}{3}$

Find an equation of each line with the given slope that passes through the given point. Write the equation in the form $Ax + By = C$. See Example 4.

23. $m = 6; \quad (2, 2)$

24. $m = 4; \quad (1, 3)$

25. $m = -8; \quad (-1, -5)$

26. $m = -2; \quad (-11, -12)$

27. $m = \frac{3}{2}; \quad (5, -6)$

28. $m = \frac{2}{3}; \quad (-8, 9)$

29. $m = -\frac{1}{2}; \quad (-3, 0)$

30. $m = -\frac{1}{5}; \quad (4, 0)$

Find an equation of the line passing through each pair of points. Write the equation in the form $Ax + By = C$. See Example 5.

31. $(3, 2)$ and $(5, 6)$

32. $(6, 2)$ and $(8, 8)$

33. $(-1, 3)$ and $(-2, -5)$

34. $(-4, 0)$ and $(6, -1)$

35. $(2, 3)$ and $(-1, -1)$

36. $(7, 10)$ and $(-1, -1)$

37. $(0, 0)$ and $\left(-\frac{1}{8}, \frac{1}{13}\right)$

38. $(0, 0)$ and $\left(-\frac{1}{2}, \frac{1}{3}\right)$

Find an equation of each line. See Example 6.

39. Vertical line through $(0, 2)$

40. Horizontal line through $(1, 4)$

41. Horizontal line through $(-1, 3)$

42. Vertical line through $(-1, 3)$

43. Vertical line through $\left(-\frac{7}{3}, -\frac{2}{5}\right)$

44. Horizontal line through $\left(\frac{2}{7}, 0\right)$

Find an equation of each line. See Example 7.

45. Parallel to $y = 5$, through $(1, 2)$

46. Perpendicular to $y = 5$, through $(1, 2)$

47. Perpendicular to $x = -3$, through $(-2, 5)$

48. Parallel to $y = -4$, through $(0, -3)$

49. Parallel to $x = 0$, through $(6, -8)$

50. Perpendicular to $x = 7$, through $(-5, 0)$

MIXED PRACTICE

See Examples 1 through 7. Find an equation of each line described. Write each equation in slope-intercept form (solved for y), when possible.

51. With slope $-\frac{1}{2}$, through $\left(0, \frac{5}{3}\right)$

52. With slope $\frac{5}{7}$, through $(0, -3)$

53. Through $(10, 7)$ and $(7, 10)$

54. Through $(5, -6)$ and $(-6, 5)$

55. With undefined slope, through $\left(-\frac{3}{4}, 1\right)$

56. With slope 0, through $(6.7, 12.1)$

57. Slope 1, through $(-7, 9)$

58. Slope 5, through $(6, -8)$

59. Slope -5, y-intercept $(0, 7)$

60. Slope -2; y-intercept $(0, -4)$

61. Through $(6, 7)$, parallel to the x-axis

62. Through $(1, -5)$, parallel to the y-axis

63. Through $(2, 3)$ and $(0, 0)$

64. Through $(4, 7)$ and $(0, 0)$

65. Through $(-2, -3)$, perpendicular to the y-axis

66. Through $(0, 12)$, perpendicular to the x-axis

67. Slope $-\frac{4}{7}$, through $(-1, -2)$

68. Slope $-\frac{3}{5}$, through $(4, 4)$

Solve. Assume each exercise describes a linear relationship. Write the equations in slope-intercept form. See Example 8.

69. A rock is dropped from the top of a 400-foot cliff. After 1 second, the rock is traveling 32 feet per second. After 3 seconds, the rock is traveling 96 feet per second.

400 feet

a. Assume that the relationship between time and speed is linear and write an equation describing this relationship. Use ordered pairs of the form (time, speed).

b. Use this equation to determine the speed of the rock 4 seconds after it was dropped.

70. A Hawaiian fruit company is studying the sales of a pineapple sauce to see if this product is to be continued. At the end of its first year, profits on this product amounted to $30,000. At the end of the fourth year, profits were $66,000.

a. Assume that the relationship between years on the market and profit is linear and write an equation describing this relationship. Use ordered pairs of the form (years on the market, profit).

b. Use this equation to predict the profit at the end of 7 years.

71. Sales of hybrid (gas-electric) vehicles have been decreasing for the past few years. In 2007, 356 thousand new gasoline-electric hybrid vehicles were sold in the United States. In 2009, only were 290 thousand were sold. (*Source:* U.S. Energy Information Administration)

a. Write an equation describing the relationship between time and number of registered gasoline-electric hybrid vehicles sold. Use ordered pairs of the form (years past 2007, number of hybrids sold).

b. Use this equation to predict the number of gasoline-electric hybrids sold in the year 2015.

72. In 2011, there were 960 thousand eating establishments in the United States. In 2006, there were 935 thousand eating establishments. (*Source:* National Restaurant Association)

a. Write an equation describing the relationship between time and number of eating establishments. Use ordered pairs of the form (years past 2006, number of eating establishments in thousands).

b. Use this equation to predict the number of eating establishments in 2018.

73. In 2006, the U.S. population per square mile of land area was 85. In 2011, the person per square mile population was 88.

a. Write an equation describing the relationship between year and persons per square mile. Use ordered pairs of the form (years past 2006, persons per square mile).

b. Use this equation to predict the person per square mile population in 2020.

74. In 2005, there were a total of 150 thousand apparel and accessory stores. In 2009, there were a total of 157 thousand apparel and accessory stores. (*Source:* U.S. Bureau of the Census. *County Business Patterns*)

a. Write an equation describing this relationship. Use ordered pairs of the form (years past 2005, numbers of stores in thousands).

b. Use this equation to predict the number of apparel and accessory stores in 2015.

75. It has been said that newspapers are disappearing, replaced by various electronic media. In 2001, newspaper circulation (number of copies it distributed in a day) was about 60 million. In 2009, this circulation dropped to 46 million. (*Source:* Newspaper Asso. of America)

a. Write an equation describing the relationship between time and circulation. Use ordered pairs of the form (years past 2001, number of newspapers circulated).

b. Use this equation to predict the newspaper circulation in 2017.

76. A certain chain of book stores is slowly closing down stores. Suppose that in 2006 there were 3991 stores and in 2010 there were 3200 stores.

a. Write an equation describing the relationship between time and number of store locations. Use ordered pairs of the form (years past 2006, number of stores).

b. Use this equation to predict the number of stores in 2018.

77. The Pool Fun Company has learned that, by pricing a newly released Fun Noodle at $3, sales will reach 10,000 Fun Noodles per day during the summer. Raising the price to $5 will cause sales to fall to 8000 Fun Noodles per day.

a. Assume that the relationship between price and number of Fun Noodles sold is linear and write an equation describing this relationship. Use ordered pairs of the form (price, number sold).

b. Predict the daily sales of Fun Noodles if the price is $3.50.

78. The value of a building bought in 2000 may be depreciated (or decreased) as time passes for income tax purposes. Seven years after the building was bought, this value was \$225,000 and 12 years after it was bought, this value was \$195,000.

   a. If the relationship between number of years past 2000 and the depreciated value of the building is linear, write an equation describing this relationship. Use ordered pairs of the form (years past 2000, value of building).

   b. Use this equation to estimate the depreciated value of the building in 2018.

REVIEW AND PREVIEW

Find the value of $x^2 - 3x + 1$ for each given value of x. See Section 1.7.

79. 2   **80.** 5   **81.** -1 **82.** -3

For each graph, determine whether any x-values correspond to two or more y-values. See Section 3.1.

83.

84.

85.

86.

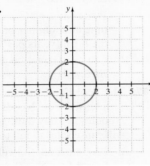

CONCEPT EXTENSIONS

For Exercises 87 through 90, identify the form that the linear equation in two variables is written in. For Exercises 91 and 92, identify the appearance of the graph of the equation.

87. $y - 7 = 4(x + 3)$; _____ form

88. $5x - 9y = 11$; _____ form

89. $y = \dfrac{3}{4}x - \dfrac{1}{3}$; _____ form

90. $y + 2 = \dfrac{-1}{3}(x - 2)$; _____ form

91. $y = \dfrac{1}{2}$; _____ line   **92.** $x = -17$; _____ line

93. Given the equation of a nonvertical line, explain how to find the slope without finding two points on the line.

94. Given two points on a nonvertical line, explain how to use the point-slope form to find the equation of the line.

△ **95.** Write an equation in standard form of the line that contains the point $(-1, 2)$ and is
   a. parallel to the line $y = 3x - 1$.
   b. perpendicular to the line $y = 3x - 1$.

△ **96.** Write an equation in standard form of the line that contains the point $(4, 0)$ and is
   a. parallel to the line $y = -2x + 3$.
   b. perpendicular to the line $y = -2x + 3$.

△ **97.** Write an equation in standard form of the line that contains the point $(3, -5)$ and is
   a. parallel to the line $3x + 2y = 7$.
   b. perpendicular to the line $3x + 2y = 7$.

△ **98.** Write an equation in standard form of the line that contains the point $(-2, 4)$ and is
   a. parallel to the line $x + 3y = 6$.
   b. perpendicular to the line $x + 3y = 6$.

3.6 | Functions

OBJECTIVES

1 Identify Relations, Domains, and Ranges.

2 Identify Functions.

3 Use the Vertical Line Test.

4 Use Function Notation.

OBJECTIVE

1 Identifying Relations, Domains, and Ranges

In previous sections, we have discussed the relationships between two quantities. For example, the relationship between the length of the side of a square x and its area y is described by the equation $y = x^2$. Ordered pairs can be used to write down solutions of this equation. For example, $(2, 4)$ is a solution of $y = x^2$, and this notation tells us that the x-value 2 is related to the y-value 4 for this equation. In other words, when the length of the side of a square is 2 units, its area is 4 square units.

Examples of Relationships Between Two Quantities

Area of Square: $y = x^2$	Equation of Line: $y = x + 2$	U.S. Online Advertising Revenue

U.S. Online Advertising Revenue

Some Ordered Pairs		Some Ordered Pairs		Ordered Pairs	
x	y	x	y	Year	Billions of Dollars
2	4	−3	−1	2010	25.8
5	25	0	2	2011	28.5
7	49	2	4	2012	32.6
12	144	9	11	2013	36
				2014	40.5

(*Source:* GRABstats.com; some years are projected)

A set of ordered pairs is called a **relation.** The set of all x-coordinates is called the **domain** of a relation, and the set of all y-coordinates is called the **range** of a relation. Equations such as $y = x^2$ are also called relations since equations in two variables define a set of ordered pair solutions.

EXAMPLE 1   Find the domain and the range of the relation $\{(0, 2), (3, 3), (-1, 0), (3, -2)\}$.

Solution   The domain is the set of all x-values or $\{-1, 0, 3\}$, and the range is the set of all y-values, or $\{-2, 0, 2, 3\}$.   □

PRACTICE
1   Find the domain and the range of the relation $\{(1, 3), (5, 0), (0, -2), (5, 4)\}$.

OBJECTIVE
2   Identifying Functions
Some relations are also functions.

Function

A function is a set of ordered pairs that assigns to each x-value exactly one y-value.

In other words, a function cannot have two ordered pairs with the same x-coordinate but different y-coordinates.

EXAMPLE 2   Determine whether each relation is also a function.

a. $\{(-1, 1), (2, 3), (7, 3), (8, 6)\}$ **b.** $\{(0, -2), (1, 5), (0, 3), (7, 7)\}$

Solution

a. Although the ordered pairs $(2, 3)$ and $(7, 3)$ have the same y-value, each x-value is assigned to only one y-value, so this set of ordered pairs is a function.

b. The x-value 0 is assigned to two y-values, -2 and 3, so this set of ordered pairs is not a function.   □

2 Determine whether each relation is also a function.

a. $\{(4, 1), (3, -2), (8, 5), (-5, 3)\}$ **b.** $\{(1, 2), (-4, 3), (0, 8), (1, 4)\}$

Relations and functions can be described by a graph of their ordered pairs.

EXAMPLE 3 Determine whether each graph is the graph of a function.

a.

b.
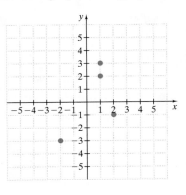

Solution

a. This is the graph of the relation $\{(-4, -2), (-2, -1), (-1, -1), (1, 2)\}$. Each x-coordinate has exactly one y-coordinate, so this is the graph of a function.

b. This is the graph of the relation $\{(-2, -3), (1, 2), (1, 3), (2, -1)\}$. The x-coordinate 1 is paired with two y-coordinates, 2 and 3, so this is not the graph of a function.

3 Determine whether each graph is the graph of a function.

a.

b.

3 Using the Vertical Line Test

The graph in Example 3(b) was not the graph of a function because the x-coordinate 1 was paired with two y-coordinates, 2 and 3. Notice that when an x-coordinate is paired with more than one y-coordinate, a vertical line can be drawn that will intersect the graph at more than one point. We can use this fact to determine whether a relation is also a function. We call this the **vertical line test.**

> **Vertical Line Test**
>
> If a vertical line can be drawn so that it intersects a graph more than once, the graph is not the graph of a function.

This vertical line test works for all types of graphs on the rectangular coordinate system.

EXAMPLE 4   Use the vertical line test to determine whether each graph is the graph of a function.

a.   **b.**   **c.**   **d.**

Solution

a. This graph is the graph of a function since no vertical line will intersect this graph more than once.

b. This graph is also the graph of a function; no vertical line will intersect it more than once.

c. This graph is not the graph of a function. Vertical lines can be drawn that intersect the graph in two points. An example of one is shown.

Not a function

d. This graph is not the graph of a function. A vertical line can be drawn that intersects this line at every point.   ☐

PRACTICE
4   Use the vertical line test to determine whether each graph is the graph of a function.

a.   **b.**   **c.**   **d.**

Recall that the graph of a linear equation is a line, and a line that is not vertical will pass the vertical line test. **Thus, all linear equations are functions except those of the form $x = c$, which are vertical lines.**

EXAMPLE 5   Decide whether the equation describes a function.

a. $y = x$ **b.** $y = 2x + 1$ **c.** $y = 5$ **d.** $x = -1$

Solution   **a, b,** and **c** are functions because their graphs are nonvertical lines. **d** is not a function because its graph is a vertical line.   ☐

PRACTICE
5   Decide whether the equation describes a function.

a. $y = 2x$ **b.** $y = -3x - 1$ **c.** $y = 8$ **d.** $x = 2$

Examples of functions can often be found in magazines, newspapers, books, and other printed material in the form of tables or graphs such as that in Example 6.

EXAMPLE 6 The graph shows the sunrise time for Indianapolis, Indiana, for the year. Use this graph to answer the questions.

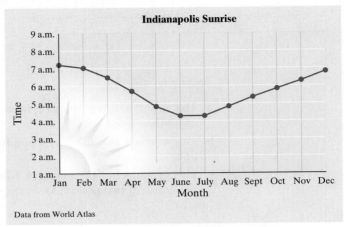

Data from World Atlas

a. Approximate the time of sunrise on February 1.

b. Approximately when does the sun rise at 5 a.m.?

c. Is this the graph of a function?

Solution

a. To approximate the time of sunrise on February 1, we find the mark on the horizontal axis that corresponds to February 1. From this mark, we move vertically upward until the graph is reached. From that point on the graph, we move horizontally to the left until the vertical axis is reached. The vertical axis there reads 7 a.m.

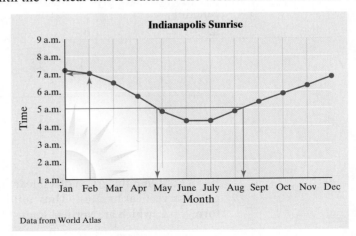

Data from World Atlas

b. To approximate when the sun rises at 5 a.m., we find 5 a.m. on the time axis and move horizontally to the right. Notice that we will reach the graph twice, corresponding to two dates for which the sun rises at 5 a.m. We follow both points on the graph vertically downward until the horizontal axis is reached. The sun rises at 5 a.m. at approximately the end of the month of April and the middle of the month of August.

c. The graph is the graph of a function since it passes the vertical line test. In other words, for every day of the year in Indianapolis, there is exactly one sunrise time. □

PRACTICE
6   The graph shows the average monthly temperature for Chicago, Illinois, for the year. Use this graph to answer the questions.

* (1 is Jan.; 12 is Dec.)

a. Approximate the average monthly temperature for June.

b. For what month is the average monthly temperature 26°?

c. Is this the graph of a function?

OBJECTIVE

4   **Using Function Notation**

The graph of the linear equation $y = 2x + 1$ passes the vertical line test, so we say that $y = 2x + 1$ is a function. In other words, $y = 2x + 1$ gives us a rule for writing ordered pairs where every x-coordinate is paired with one and only one y-coordinate.

The variable y is a function of the variable x. For each value of x, there is only one value of y. Thus, we say the variable x is the **independent variable** because any value in the domain can be assigned to x. The variable y is the **dependent variable** because its value depends on x.

We often use letters such as f, g, and h to name functions. For example, the symbol $f(x)$ means *function of x* and is read "f of x." This notation is called **function notation.** The equation $y = 2x + 1$ can be written as $f(x) = 2x + 1$ using function notation, and these equations mean the same thing. In other words, $y = f(x)$.

The notation $f(1)$ means to replace x with 1 and find the resulting y or function value. Since

$$f(x) = 2x + 1$$

then

$$f(1) = 2(1) + 1$$
$$= 3$$

This means that, when $x = 1$, y or $f(x) = 3$, and we have the ordered pair $(1, 3)$. Now let's find $f(2)$, $f(0)$, and $f(-1)$.

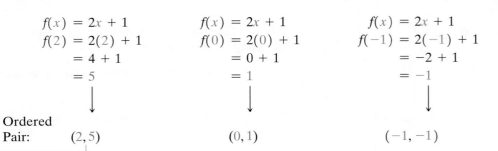

$$f(x) = 2x + 1$$
$$f(2) = 2(2) + 1$$
$$= 4 + 1$$
$$= 5$$

$$f(x) = 2x + 1$$
$$f(0) = 2(0) + 1$$
$$= 0 + 1$$
$$= 1$$

$$f(x) = 2x + 1$$
$$f(-1) = 2(-1) + 1$$
$$= -2 + 1$$
$$= -1$$

Ordered
Pair: $(2, 5)$ $(0, 1)$ $(-1, -1)$

> ▶ **Helpful Hint**
> Note that, for example, if $f(2) = 5$, the corresponding ordered pair is $(2, 5)$.

> ▶ **Helpful Hint**
> Note that $f(x)$ is a special symbol in mathematics used to denote a function. The symbol $f(x)$ is read "f of x." It does **not** mean $f \cdot x$ (f times x).

EXAMPLE 7   Given $g(x) = x^2 - 3$, find the following. Then write the corresponding ordered pairs generated.

a. $g(2)$ **b.** $g(-2)$ **c.** $g(0)$

Solution

a. $g(x) = x^2 - 3$
$g(2) = 2^2 - 3$
$= 4 - 3$
$= 1$

b. $g(x) = x^2 - 3$
$g(-2) = (-2)^2 - 3$
$= 4 - 3$
$= 1$

c. $g(x) = x^2 - 3$
$g(0) = 0^2 - 3$
$= 0 - 3$
$= -3$

Ordered	$g(2) = 1$ gives	$g(-2) = 1$ gives	$g(0) = -3$ gives
Pairs:	$(2, 1)$	$(-2, 1)$	$(0, -3)$

PRACTICE
7   Given $h(x) = x^2 + 5$, find the following. Then write the corresponding ordered pairs generated.

a. $h(2)$ **b.** $h(-5)$ **c.** $h(0)$

We now practice finding the domain and the range of a function. The domains of our functions will be the set of all possible real numbers that x can be replaced by. The range is the set of corresponding y-values.

EXAMPLE 8   Find the domain of each function.

a. $g(x) = \dfrac{1}{x}$ **b.** $f(x) = 2x + 1$

Solution

a. Recall that we cannot divide by 0, so the domain of $g(x)$ is the set of all real numbers except 0. In interval notation, we can write $(-\infty, 0) \cup (0, \infty)$.

b. In this function, x can be any real number. The domain of $f(x)$ is the set of all real numbers, or $(-\infty, \infty)$ in interval notation.

PRACTICE
8   Find the domain of each function.

a. $h(x) = 6x + 3$ **b.** $f(x) = \dfrac{1}{x^2}$

✓CONCEPT CHECK
Suppose that the value of *f* is −7 when the function is evaluated at 2. Write this situation in function notation.

EXAMPLE 9   Find the domain and the range of each function graphed. Use interval notation.

a.

b.

Solution

a.

b.

PRACTICE
9   Find the domain and the range of each function graphed. Use interval notation.

a.

b.

Answer to Concept Check:
$f(2) = -7$

Vocabulary, Readiness & Video Check

Use the choices below to fill in each blank. Some choices may not be used.

$x = c$	horizontal	domain	relation	$(7, 3)$
$y = c$	vertical	range	function	$(3, 7)$

1. A set of ordered pairs is called a(n) _____.
2. A set of ordered pairs that assigns to each x-value exactly one y-value is called a(n) _____.
3. The set of all y-coordinates of a relation is called the _____.
4. The set of all x-coordinates of a relation is called the _____.
5. All linear equations are functions except those whose graphs are _____ lines.
6. All linear equations are functions except those whose equations are of the form _____.

Martin-Gay Interactive Videos

See Video 3.6

Watch the section lecture video and answer the following questions.

OBJECTIVE 1
7. In the lecture before ▣ Example 1, relations are discussed. Why can an equation in two variables define a relation?

OBJECTIVE 2
8. Based on ▣ Examples 2 and 3, can a set of ordered pairs with no repeated x-values, but with repeated y-values, be a function? For example: $\{(0, 4), (-3, 4), (2, 4)\}$.

OBJECTIVE 3
9. After reviewing ▣ Example 8, explain why the vertical line test works.

OBJECTIVE 4
10. Using ▣ Example 10, write the three function values found and their corresponding ordered pairs. For example, $f(0) = 2$ corresponds to $(0, 2)$.

3.6 Exercise Set

MyMathLab®

Find the domain and the range of each relation. See Example 1.

1. $\{(2, 4), (0, 0), (-7, 10), (10, -7)\}$
2. $\{(3, -6), (1, 4), (-2, -2)\}$
▶ 3. $\{(0, -2), (1, -2), (5, -2)\}$
4. $\{(5, 0), (5, -3), (5, 4), (5, 3)\}$

Determine whether each relation is also a function. See Example 2.

▶ 5. $\{(1, 1), (2, 2), (-3, -3), (0, 0)\}$
6. $\{(11, 6), (-1, -2), (0, 0), (3, -2)\}$
▶ 7. $\{(-1, 0), (-1, 6), (-1, 8)\}$
8. $\{(1, 2), (3, 2), (1, 4)\}$

MIXED PRACTICE

Determine whether each graph is the graph of a function. See Examples 3 and 4.

▶ 9.

10.

11.

12.

13.

14.

15.

16.

Decide whether the equation describes a function. See Example 5.

17. $y = x + 1$

18. $y = x - 1$

19. $y - x = 7$

20. $2x - 3y = 9$

21. $y = 6$

22. $x = 3$

23. $x = -2$

24. $y = -9$

25. $x = y^2$

26. $y = x^2 - 3$

The graph shows the sunset times for Seward, Alaska. Use this graph to answer Exercises 27 through 32. See Example 6.

27. Approximate the time of sunset on June 1.

28. Approximate the time of sunset on November 1.

29. Approximate when the sunset is at 3 p.m.

30. Approximate when the sunset is at 9 p.m.

31. Is this graph the graph of a function? Why or why not?

32. Do you think a graph of sunset times for any location will always be a function? Why or why not?

This graph shows the U.S. hourly minimum wage for each year shown. Use this graph to answer Exercises 33 through 38. See Example 6.

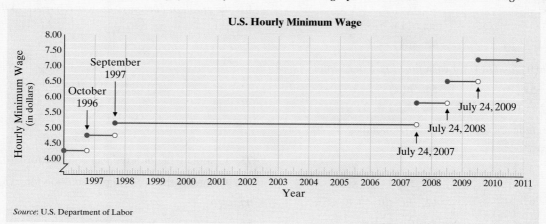

Source: U.S. Department of Labor

33. Approximate the minimum wage before October 1996.

34. Approximate the minimum wage in 2006.

35. Approximate the year when the minimum wage increased to over $7.00 per hour.

36. According to the graph, what hourly wage was in effect for the greatest number of years?

37. Is this graph the graph of a function? Why or why not?

38. Do you think that a similar graph of your hourly wage on January 1 of every year (whether you are working or not) will be the graph of a function? Why or why not?

This graph shows the cost of mailing a large envelope through the U.S. Postal Service by weight. (Note: These costs will increase.) Use this graph to answer Exercises 39 through 44. See Example 6.

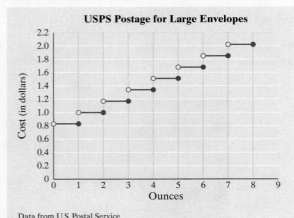

USPS Postage for Large Envelopes

Data from U.S. Postal Service

39. Approximate the postage to mail a large envelope weighing more than 4 ounces but not more than 5 ounces.

40. Approximate the postage to mail a large envelope weighing more than 7 ounces but not more than 8 ounces.

41. Give the weight of a large envelope that costs $1 to mail.

42. If you have $1.25, what is the weight of the largest envelope you can mail for that amount of money?

43. Is this graph a function? Why or why not?

44. Do you think that a similar graph of postage to mail a first-class letter will be the graph of a function? Why or why not?

Find $f(-2), f(0),$ and $f(3)$ for each function. See Example 7.

45. $f(x) = 2x - 5$
46. $f(x) = 3 - 7x$
47. $f(x) = x^2 + 2$
48. $f(x) = x^2 - 4$
49. $f(x) = 3x$
50. $f(x) = -3x$
51. $f(x) = |x|$
52. $f(x) = |2 - x|$

Find $h(-1), h(0),$ and $h(4)$ for each function. See Example 7.

53. $h(x) = -5x$
54. $h(x) = -3x$
55. $h(x) = 2x^2 + 3$
56. $h(x) = 3x^2$

For each given function value, write a corresponding ordered pair.

57. $f(3) = 6$
58. $f(7) = -2$
59. $g(0) = -\dfrac{1}{2}$
60. $g(0) = -\dfrac{7}{8}$
61. $h(-2) = 9$
62. $h(-10) = 1$

Find the domain of each function. See Example 8.

63. $f(x) = 3x - 7$
64. $g(x) = 5 - 2x$
65. $h(x) = \dfrac{1}{x + 5}$
66. $f(x) = \dfrac{1}{x - 6}$
67. $g(x) = |x + 1|$
68. $h(x) = |2x|$

Find the domain and the range of each relation graphed. See Example 9.

69.

70.

71.

72.

73.

74.

Use the graph of f below to answer Exercises 75 through 80.

75. Complete the ordered pair solution for f. $(0, \quad)$

76. Complete the ordered pair solution for f. $(3, \quad)$

77. $f(0) = $ _____?

78. $f(3) = $ _____?

79. If $f(x) = 0$, find the value(s) of x.

80. If $f(x) = -1$, find the value(s) of x.

REVIEW AND PREVIEW

Find the coordinates of the point of intersection. See Section 3.1.

81.

82.

83.

84.

CONCEPT EXTENSIONS

Solve. See the Concept Check in this section.

85. If a function f is evaluated at -5, the value of the function is 12. Write this situation using function notation.

86. Suppose $(9, 20)$ is an ordered pair solution for the function g. Write this situation using function notation.

The graph of the function, f, is below. Use this graph to answer Exercises 87 through 90.

87. Write the coordinates of the lowest point of the graph.

88. Write the answer to Exercise 87 in function notation.

89. An x-intercept of this graph is $(5, 0)$. Write this using function notation.

90. Write the other x-intercept of this graph (see Exercise 89) using function notation.

91. Forensic scientists use the function
$$H(x) = 2.59x + 47.24$$

to estimate the height of a woman in centimeters given the length x of her femur bone.

a. Estimate the height of a woman whose femur measures 46 centimeters.

b. Estimate the height of a woman whose femur measures 39 centimeters.

92. The dosage in milligrams D of Ivermectin, a heartworm preventive for a dog who weighs x pounds, is given by the function

$$D(x) = \frac{136}{25}x$$

a. Find the proper dosage for a dog that weighs 35 pounds.

b. Find the proper dosage for a dog that weighs 70 pounds.

93. In your own words, define **(a)** function; **(b)** domain; **(c)** range.

94. Explain the vertical line test and how it is used.

95. Since $y = x + 7$ is a function, rewrite the equation using function notation.

96. Since $y = 3$ is a function, rewrite this equation using function notation.

See the example below for Exercises 97 through 100.

Example

If $f(x) = x^2 + 2x + 1$, find $f(\pi)$.

Solution:

$$f(x) = x^2 + 2x + 1$$
$$f(\pi) = \pi^2 + 2\pi + 1$$

Given the following functions, find the indicated values.

97. $f(x) = 2x + 7$
  a. $f(2)$ **b.** $f(a)$

98. $g(x) = -3x + 12$
  a. $g(s)$ **b.** $g(r)$

99. $h(x) = x^2 + 7$
  a. $h(3)$ **b.** $h(a)$

100. $f(x) = x^2 - 12$
  a. $f(12)$ **b.** $f(a)$

Chapter 3 Vocabulary Check

Fill in each blank with one of the words listed below.

relation	function	domain	range	standard	slope-intercept
y-axis	x-axis	solution	linear	slope	point-slope
x-intercept	y-intercept	y	x		

1. An ordered pair is a(n) _____ of an equation in two variables if replacing the variables by the coordinates of the ordered pair results in a true statement.
2. The vertical number line in the rectangular coordinate system is called the _____.
3. A(n) _____ equation can be written in the form $Ax + By = C$.
4. A(n) _____ is a point of the graph where the graph crosses the x-axis.
5. The form $Ax + By = C$ is called _____ form.
6. A(n) _____ is a point of the graph where the graph crosses the y-axis.
7. The equation $y = 7x - 5$ is written in _____ form.
8. The equation $y + 1 = 7(x - 2)$ is written in _____ form.
9. To find an x-intercept of a graph, let _____ = 0.
10. The horizontal number line in the rectangular coordinate system is called the _____.
11. To find a y-intercept of a graph, let _____ = 0.
12. The _____ of a line measures the steepness or tilt of a line.
13. A set of ordered pairs that assigns to each x-value exactly one y-value is called a(n) _____.
14. The set of all x-coordinates of a relation is called the _____ of the relation.
15. The set of all y-coordinates of a relation is called the _____ of the relation.
16. A set of ordered pairs is called a(n) _____.

Chapter 3 Highlights

DEFINITIONS AND CONCEPTS	EXAMPLES

Section 3.1   Reading Graphs and the Rectangular Coordinate System

The **rectangular coordinate system** consists of a plane and a vertical and a horizontal number line intersecting at their 0 coordinates. The vertical number line is called the **y-axis** and the horizontal number line is called the **x-axis**. The point of intersection of the axes is called the **origin.**

To **plot** or **graph** an ordered pair means to find its corresponding point on a rectangular coordinate system.

To plot or graph an ordered pair such as $(3, -2)$, start at the origin. Move 3 units to the right and, from there, 2 units down.

To plot or graph $(-3, 4)$ start at the origin. Move 3 units to the left and, from there, 4 units up.

DEFINITIONS AND CONCEPTS	EXAMPLES

Section 3.1   Reading Graphs and the Rectangular Coordinate System (continued)

An ordered pair is a **solution** of an equation in two variables if replacing the variables by the coordinates of the ordered pair results in a true statement.	Determine whether $(-1, 5)$ is a solution of $2x + 3y = 13$. $$2x + 3y = 13$$ $$2(-1) + 3 \cdot 5 = 13 \quad \text{Let } x = -1, y = 5$$ $$-2 + 15 = 13$$ $$13 = 13 \quad \text{True}$$
If one coordinate of an ordered pair solution is known, the other value can be determined by substitution.	Complete the ordered pair solution $(0, \quad)$ for the equation $x - 6y = 12$. $$x - 6y = 12$$ $$0 - 6y = 12 \quad \text{Let } x = 0.$$ $$\frac{-6y}{-6} = \frac{12}{-6} \quad \text{Divide by } -6.$$ $$y = -2$$ The ordered pair solution is $(0, -2)$.

Section 3.2   Graphing Linear Equations

A **linear equation in two variables** is an equation that can be written in the form $Ax + By = C$ where A and B are not both 0. The form $Ax + By = C$ is called **standard form**.	***Linear Equations*** $$3x + 2y = -6 \qquad x = -5$$ $$y = 3 \qquad y = -x + 10$$ $x + y = 10$ is in standard form.
To graph a linear equation in two variables, find three ordered pair solutions. Plot the solution points and draw the line connecting the points.	Graph $x - 2y = 5$. <table><tr><th>x</th><th>y</th></tr><tr><td>5</td><td>0</td></tr><tr><td>1</td><td>-2</td></tr><tr><td>-1</td><td>-3</td></tr></table>

Section 3.3   Intercepts

An **intercept** of a graph is a point where the graph intersects an axis. If a graph intersects the x-axis at a, then $(a, 0)$ is the **x-intercept**. If a graph intersects the y-axis at b, then $(0, b)$ is the **y-intercept**.	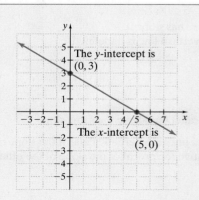

(*continued*)

DEFINITIONS AND CONCEPTS	EXAMPLES

Section 3.3   Intercepts (continued)

To find the x-intercept, let $y = 0$ and solve for x.

To find the y-intercept, let $x = 0$ and solve for y.

Graph $2x - 5y = -10$ by finding intercepts.

$$\text{If } y = 0, \text{ then} \qquad \text{If } x = 0, \text{ then}$$

$$2x - 5 \cdot 0 = -10 \qquad 2 \cdot 0 - 5y = -10$$

$$2x = -10 \qquad -5y = -10$$

$$\frac{2x}{2} = \frac{-10}{2} \qquad \frac{-5y}{-5} = \frac{-10}{-5}$$

$$x = -5 \qquad y = 2$$

The x-intercept is $(-5, 0)$. The y-intercept is $(0, 2)$.

The graph of $x = c$ is a vertical line with x-intercept $(c, 0)$.

The graph of $y = c$ is a horizontal line with y-intercept $(0, c)$.

Section 3.4   Slope and Rate of Change

The **slope m** of the line through points (x_1, y_1) and (x_2, y_2) is given by

$$m = \frac{y_2 - y_1}{x_2 - x_1} \qquad \text{as long as } x_2 \neq x_1$$

A horizontal line has slope 0.
The slope of a vertical line is undefined.

The slope of the line through points $(-1, 6)$ and $(-5, 8)$ is

$$m = \frac{y_2 - y_1}{x_2 - x_1} = \frac{8 - 6}{-5 - (-1)} = \frac{2}{-4} = -\frac{1}{2}$$

The slope of the line $y = -5$ is 0.
The line $x = 3$ has undefined slope.

Nonvertical parallel lines have the same slope.

Two nonvertical lines are perpendicular if the slope of one is the negative reciprocal of the slope of the other.

DEFINITIONS AND CONCEPTS	EXAMPLES

Section 3.5   Equations of Lines

Slope-Intercept Form

$$y = mx + b$$

m is the slope of the line.
$(0, b)$ is the y-intercept.

Find the slope and the y-intercept of the line whose equation is $2x + 3y = 6$.

Solve for y:

$$2x + 3y = 6$$
$$3y = -2x + 6 \quad \text{Subtract } 2x.$$
$$y = -\frac{2}{3}x + 2 \quad \text{Divide by 3.}$$

The slope of the line is $-\frac{2}{3}$ and the y-intercept is $(0, 2)$.

Find an equation of the line with slope 3 and y-intercept $(0, -1)$.

The equation is $y = 3x - 1$.

Point-Slope Form

$$y - y_1 = m(x - x_1)$$

m is the slope.
(x_1, y_1) is a point on the line.

Find an equation of the line with slope $\frac{3}{4}$ that contains the point $(-1, 5)$.

$$y - 5 = \frac{3}{4}[x - (-1)]$$
$$4(y - 5) = 3(x + 1) \quad \text{Multiply by 4.}$$
$$4y - 20 = 3x + 3 \quad \text{Distribute.}$$
$$-3x + 4y = 23 \quad \text{Subtract } 3x \text{ and add 20.}$$

Section 3.6   Functions

A set of ordered pairs is a **relation.** The set of all x-coordinates is called the **domain** of the relation, and the set of all y-coordinates is called the **range** of the relation.

The domain of the relation $\{(0, 5), (2, 5), (4, 5), (5, -2)\}$ is $\{0, 2, 4, 5\}$. The range is $\{-2, 5\}$.

A **function** is a set of ordered pairs that assigns to each x-value exactly one y-value.

Which are graphs of functions?

Vertical Line Test

If a vertical line can be drawn so that it intersects a graph more than once, the graph is not the graph of a function.

This graph is not the graph of a function.

This graph is the graph of a function.

The symbol $f(x)$ means **function of x.** This notation is called **function** notation.

If $f(x) = 2x^2 + 6x - 1$, find $f(3)$.

$$f(3) = 2(3)^2 + 6 \cdot 3 - 1$$
$$= 2 \cdot 9 + 18 - 1$$
$$= 18 + 18 - 1$$
$$= 35$$

Chapter 3 Review

(3.1) *Plot the following ordered pairs on a Cartesian coordinate system.*

1. $(-7, 0)$ **2.** $\left(0, 4\frac{4}{5}\right)$

3. $(-2, -5)$ **4.** $(1, -3)$

5. $(0.7, 0.7)$ **6.** $(-6, 4)$

7. A local office supply store uses quantity pricing. The table shows the price per box of #10 security envelopes for different numbers of envelopes in a box purchased.

Price per Box of Envelopes (in dollars)	Number of Envelopes in Box
5.00	50
8.50	100
20.00	250
27.00	500

   a. Write each paired data as an ordered pair of the form (price per box of envelopes, number of envelopes in box).

   b. Create a scatter diagram of the paired data. Be sure to label the axes appropriately.

8. The table shows the annual overnight stays in national parks. (Data from National Park Service)

Year	Overnight Stays in National Parks (in millions)
2005	13.8
2006	13.6
2007	14.1
2008	13.9
2009	14.6
2010	14.6

   a. Write each paired data as an ordered pair of the form (year, number of overnight stays).

   b. Create a scatter diagram of the paired data. Be sure to label the axes properly.

Determine whether each ordered pair is a solution of the given equation.

9. $7x - 8y = 56$; $(0, 56), (8, 0)$

10. $-2x + 5y = 10$; $(-5, 0), (1, 1)$

11. $x = 13$; $(13, 5), (13, 13)$

12. $y = 2$; $(7, 2), (2, 7)$

Complete the ordered pairs so that each is a solution of the given equation.

13. $-2 + y = 6x$; $(7, \ \ )$ **14.** $y = 3x + 5$; $\left(\ \ , -8 \right)$

Complete the table of values for each given equation; then plot the ordered pairs. Use a single coordinate system for each exercise.

15. $9 = -3x + 4y$

x	y
	0
	3
9	

16. $x = 2y$

x	y
	0
	5
	-5

The cost in dollars of producing x compact disc holders is given by $y = 5x + 2000$. Use this equation for Exercises 17 and 18.

17. Complete the following table.

x	y
1	
100	
1000	

18. Find the number of compact disc holders that can be produced for $6430.

(3.2) *Graph each linear equation.*

19. $x - y = 1$ **20.** $x + y = 6$

21. $x - 3y = 12$ **22.** $5x - y = -8$

23. $x = 3y$ **24.** $y = -2x$

25. $2x - 3y = 6$ **26.** $4x - 3y = 12$

(3.3) *Identify the intercepts.*

27.

28.

29.

30.

Graph each linear equation by finding its intercepts.

31. $x - 3y = 12$

32. $-4x + y = 8$

33. $y = -3$

34. $x = 5$

35. $y = -3x$

36. $x = 5y$

37. $x - 2 = 0$

38. $y + 6 = 0$

(3.4) *Find the slope of each line.*

39.

40.

In Exercises 41 through 44, match each line with its slope.

a.

b.

c.

d.

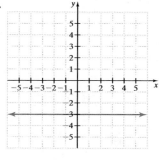

41. $m = 0$

42. $m = -1$

43. undefined slope

44. $m = 3$

Find the slope of the line that goes through the given points.

45. $(2, 5)$ and $(6, 8)$

46. $(4, 7)$ and $(1, 2)$

47. $(1, 3)$ and $(-2, -9)$

48. $(-4, 1)$ and $(3, -6)$

Find the slope of each line.

49. $y = 3x + 7$

50. $x - 2y = 4$

51. $y = -2$

52. $x = 0$

Determine whether each pair of lines is parallel, perpendicular, or neither.

53. $x - y = -6$
$\quad x + y = 3$

54. $3x + y = 7$
$\quad -3x - y = 10$

55. $y = 4x + \dfrac{1}{2}$
$\quad 4x + 2y = 1$

56. $x = 4$
$\quad y = -2$

Find the slope of each line and write the slope as a rate of change. Don't forget to attach the proper units.

57. The graph below approximates the number of U.S. college students (in thousands) earning an associate's degree for each year x.

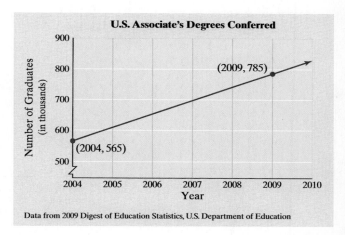

58. The graph below approximates the number of kidney transplants y in the United States for year x.

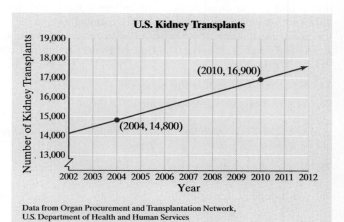

(3.5) Determine the slope and the y-intercept of the graph of each equation.

59. $3x + y = 7$

60. $x - 6y = -1$

61. $y = 2$

62. $x = -5$

Use the slope-intercept form to graph each equation.

63. $y = 3x - 1$

64. $y = -3x$

65. $5x - 3y = 15$

66. $-x + 2y = 8$

Write an equation of each line in slope-intercept form.

67. slope -5; y-intercept $\left(0, \frac{1}{2}\right)$

68. slope $\frac{2}{3}$; y-intercept $(0, 6)$

Match each equation with its graph.

69. $y = -4x$

70. $y = 2x$

71. $y = 2x - 1$

72. $y = -2x + 1$

a.

b.

c.

d.

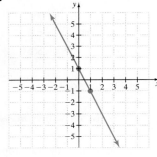

College is getting more expensive every year. The average cost for tuition and fees at a public two-year college y from 1995 through 2011 can be approximated by the linear equation $y = 56x + 1859$, where x is the number of years after 1995. Use this information for Exercises 73 and 74. (Source: The College Board: Trends in College Pricing 2010)

73. Find the y-intercept of this equation.

74. What does the y-intercept mean?

Write an equation of each line. Write each equation in standard form, $Ax + By = C$, or $x = c$ or $y = c$ form.

75. With slope -3, through $(0, -5)$

76. With slope $\frac{1}{2}$, through $\left(0, -\frac{7}{2}\right)$

77. With slope 0, through $(-2, -3)$

78. With 0 slope, through the origin

79. With slope -6, through $(2, -1)$

80. With slope 12, through $\left(\frac{1}{2}, 5\right)$

81. Through $(0, 6)$ and $(6, 0)$

82. Through $(0, -4)$ and $(-8, 0)$

83. Vertical line, through $(5, 7)$

84. Horizontal line, through $(-6, 8)$

85. Through $(6, 0)$, perpendicular to $y = 8$

86. Through $(10, 12)$, perpendicular to $x = -2$

(3.6) Determine whether each of the following are functions.

87. $\{(7, 1), (7, 5), (2, 6)\}$

88. $\{(0, -1), (5, -1), (2, 2)\}$

89. $7x - 6y = 1$

90. $y = 7$

91. $x = 2$

92. $y = x^3$

93.

94.

Given the following functions, find the indicated function values.

95. Given $f(x) = -2x + 6$, find

    a. $f(0)$ **b.** $f(-2)$ **c.** $f\left(\frac{1}{2}\right)$

96. Given $h(x) = -5 - 3x$, find

    a. $h(2)$ **b.** $h(-3)$ **c.** $h(0)$

97. Given $g(x) = x^2 + 12x$, find

    a. $g(3)$ **b.** $g(-5)$ **c.** $g(0)$

98. Given $h(x) = 6 - |x|$, find

    a. $h(-1)$ **b.** $h(1)$ **c.** $h(-4)$

Find the domain of each function.

99. $f(x) = 2x + 7$

100. $g(x) = \dfrac{7}{x - 2}$

Find the domain and the range of each function graphed.

101.

102.

103.

104.

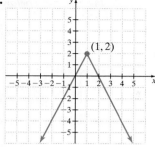

(1, 2)

Find the slope of each line.

117.

118.

MIXED REVIEW

Complete the table of values for each given equation.

105. $2x - 5y = 9$

x	y
	1
2	
	−3

106. $x = -3y$

x	y
0	
	1
6	

Find the intercepts for each equation.

107. $2x - 3y = 6$

108. $-5x + y = 10$

Graph each linear equation.

109. $x - 5y = 10$

110. $x + y = 4$

111. $y = -4x$

112. $2x + 3y = -6$

113. $x = 3$

114. $y = -2$

Find the slope of the line that passes through each pair of points.

115. $(3, -5)$ and $(-4, 2)$

116. $(1, 3)$ and $(-6, -8)$

Determine the slope and y-intercept of the graph of each equation.

119. $-2x + 3y = -15$

120. $6x + y - 2 = 0$

Write an equation of the line with the given slope that passes through the given point. Write the equation in the form $Ax + By = C$.

121. $m = -5; (3, -7)$

122. $m = 3; (0, 6)$

Write an equation of the line passing through each pair of points. Write the equation in the form $Ax + By = C$.

123. $(-3, 9)$ and $(-2, 5)$

124. $(3, 1)$ and $(5, -9)$

Yogurt is an ever more popular food item. In 2002, American Dairy affiliates produced 2134 million pounds of yogurt. In 2009, this number rose to 3800 million pounds of yogurt. Use this information for Exercises 125 and 126.

125. Assume that the relationship between time and yogurt produced is linear and write an equation describing this relationship. Use ordered pairs of the form (years past 2002, millions of pounds of yogurt produced).

126. Use this equation to predict yogurt production in the year 2014.

 Chapter 3 **Test**   MyMathLab®   Test Prep VIDEOS   ▶ You Tube™

Graph the following.

▶ **1.** $y = \frac{1}{2}x$

▶ **2.** $2x + y = 8$

▶ **3.** $5x - 7y = 10$

▶ **4.** $y = -1$

▶ **5.** $x - 3 = 0$

For Exercises 6 through 10, find the slopes of the lines.

▶ **6.**

▶ **7.**

▶ **8.** Through $(6, -5)$ and $(-1, 2)$

▶ **9.** $-3x + y = 5$

▶ **10.** $x = 6$

▶ **11.** Determine the slope and the y-intercept of the graph of $7x - 3y = 2$.

▶ **12.** Determine whether the graphs of $y = 2x - 6$ and $-4x = 2y$ are parallel lines, perpendicular lines, or neither.

Find equations of the following lines. Write the equation in standard form.

▶ **13.** With slope of $-\dfrac{1}{4}$, through $(2, 2)$

▶ **14.** Through the origin and $(6, -7)$

▶ **15.** Through $(2, -5)$ and $(1, 3)$

▶ **16.** Through $(-5, -1)$ and parallel to $x = 7$

▶ **17.** With slope $\dfrac{1}{8}$ and y-intercept $(0, 12)$

Determine whether each graph is the graph of a function.

▶ **18.**   ▶ **19.**

Given the following functions, find the indicated function values.

▶ **20.** $h(x) = x^3 - x$

    a. $h(-1)$ **b.** $h(0)$ **c.** $h(4)$

▶ **21.** Find the domain of $y = \dfrac{1}{x + 1}$.

For Exercises 22 and 23,

    a. *Identify the x- and y-intercepts.*

    b. *Find the domain and the range of each function graphed.*

▶ **22.**   ▶ **23.**

▶ **24.** If $f(7) = 20$, write the corresponding ordered pair.

Use the bar graph below to answer Exercises 25 and 26.

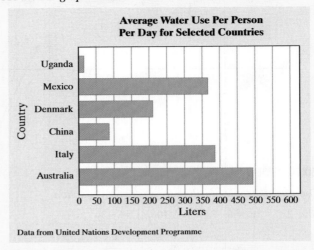

Average Water Use Per Person Per Day for Selected Countries

Data from United Nations Development Programme

▶ **25.** Estimate the average water use per person per day in Denmark.

▶ **26.** Estimate the average water use per person per day in Australia.

Use this graph to answer Exercises 27 through 29.

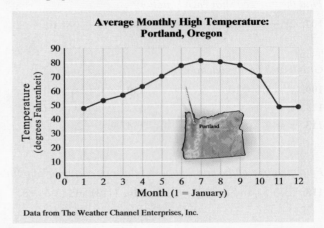

Average Monthly High Temperature: Portland, Oregon

Data from The Weather Channel Enterprises, Inc.

▶ **27.** During what month is the average high temperature the greatest?

▶ **28.** Approximate the average high temperature for the month of April.

▶ **29.** During what month(s) is the average high temperature below 60°F?

▶ **30.** The table gives the number of basic cable TV subscribers (in millions) for the years shown. (Data from National Cable and Telecommunications Association)

Year	Basic Cable TV Subscribers (in millions)
2003	66.0
2004	65.4
2005	65.4
2006	65.6
2007	64.9
2008	63.7
2009	62.1

a. Write this data as a set of ordered pairs of the form (year, number of basic cable TV subscribers in millions).

b. Create a scatter diagram of the data. Be sure to label the axes properly.

▶ **31.** This graph approximates the number of movie ticket sales y (in millions) for the year x.

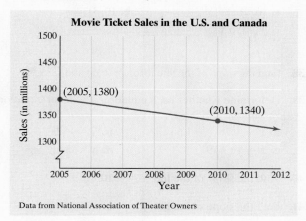

Data from National Association of Theater Owners

a. Find the slope of the line and write the slope as a rate of change. Don't forget to attach the proper units.

b. Write two ordered pairs of the form (years past 2005, number of tickets sold in millions).

c. Use the two ordered pairs from part (b) to write a linear equation. Write the equation in slope-intercept form.

d. Use the equation from part (c) to predict the number of movie tickets sold in 2015.

Chapter 3 Cumulative Review

1. Insert $<$, $>$, or $=$ in the space between each pair of numbers to make each statement true.

   a. 2   3   **b.** 7   4   **c.** 72   27

2. Write the fraction $\dfrac{56}{64}$ in lowest terms.

3. Multiply $\dfrac{2}{15}$ and $\dfrac{5}{13}$. Simplify the product if possible.

4. Add: $\dfrac{10}{3} + \dfrac{5}{21}$

5. Simplify $\dfrac{3 + |4 - 3| + 2^2}{6 - 3}$.

6. Simplify $16 - 3 \cdot 3 + 2^4$.

7. Add.

   a. $-8 + (-11)$ **b.** $-5 + 35$

   c. $0.6 + (-1.1)$ **d.** $-\dfrac{7}{10} + \left(-\dfrac{1}{10}\right)$

   e. $11.4 + (-4.7)$ **f.** $-\dfrac{3}{8} + \dfrac{2}{5}$

8. Simplify $|9 + (-20)| + |-10|$.

9. Simplify each expression.

   a. $-14 - 8 + 10 - (-6)$

   b. $1.6 - (-10.3) + (-5.6)$

10. Simplify $-9 - (3 - 8)$.

11. If $x = -2$ and $y = -4$, evaluate each expression.

   a. $5x - y$ **b.** $x^4 - y^2$

   c. $\dfrac{3x}{2y}$

12. Is -20 a solution of $\dfrac{x}{-10} = 2$?

13. Simplify each expression.

   a. $10 + (x + 12)$

   b. $-3(7x)$

14. Simplify $(12 + x) - (4x - 7)$.

15. Identify the numerical coefficient in each term.

   a. $-3y$ **b.** $22z^4$

   c. y **d.** $-x$

   e. $\dfrac{x}{7}$

16. Multiply $-5(x - 7)$.

17. Solve $x - 7 = 10$ for x.

18. Solve $5(3 + z) - (8z + 9) = -4$.

19. Solve $\dfrac{5}{2}x = 15$.

20. Solve $\dfrac{x}{4} - 1 = -7$.

21. If x is the first of three consecutive integers, express the sum of the three integers in terms of x. Simplify if possible.

22. Solve $\dfrac{x}{3} - 2 = \dfrac{x}{3}$.

23. Solve $\dfrac{2(a + 3)}{3} = 6a + 2$.

24. Solve $x + 2y = 6$ for y.

25. The 112th Congress began on January 3, 2011, and had a total of 435 Democratic and Republican representatives. There were 49 fewer Democratic representatives than Republican. Find the number of representatives from each party. (*Source*: Wikipedia .com).

26. Solve $5(x + 4) \geq 4(2x + 3)$. Write the solution set in interval notation.

27. Charles Pecot can afford enough fencing to enclose a rectangular garden with a perimeter of 140 feet. If the width of his garden must be 30 feet, find the length.

28. Solve $-3 < 4x - 1 \leq 2$. Write the solution set in interval notation.

29. Solve $y = mx + b$ for x.

30. Complete the table for $y = -5x$.

x	y
0	
−1	
	−10

31. A chemist working on his doctoral degree at Massachusetts Institute of Technology needs 12 liters of a 50% acid solution for a lab experiment. The stockroom has only 40% and 70% solutions. How much of each solution should be mixed together to form 12 liters of a 50% solution?

32. Graph: $y = -3x + 5$

33. Graph $x \geq -1$. Then write the solutions in interval notation.

34. Find the x- and y-intercepts of $2x + 4y = -8$.

35. Solve $-1 \leq 2x - 3 < 5$. Graph the solution set and write it in interval notation.

36. Graph $x = 2$ on a rectangular coordinate system.

37. Determine whether each ordered pair is a solution of the equation $x - 2y = 6$.
  a. $(6, 0)$ **b.** $(0, 3)$
  c. $\left(1, -\dfrac{5}{2}\right)$

38. Find the slope of the line through $(0, 5)$ and $(-5, 4)$.

39. Determine whether each equation is a linear equation in two variables.
  a. $x - 1.5y = -1.6$ **b.** $y = -2x$
  c. $x + y^2 = 9$ **d.** $x = 5$

40. Find the slope of the line $x = -10$.

41. Find the slope of the line $y = -1$.

42. Find the slope and y-intercept of the line whose equation is $2x - 5y = 10$.

43. Find an equation of the line with y-intercept $(0, -3)$ and slope of $\dfrac{1}{4}$.

44. Write an equation of the line through $(2, 3)$ and $(0, 0)$. Write the equation in standard form.

CHAPTER 4

Solving Systems of Linear Equations

According to the Bureau of Labor Statistics, workers age 55 years and over are projected to have the greatest increase in the labor force during the years 2008 to 2018. These workers are anticipated to increase from 18.1% to 23.9% of the labor force during this period. Workers age 25 to 34 years are projected to increase also, but not at the same rate. In Section 4.3, Exercise 73, we will predict when these two age groups will have the same percent of the labor force.

In Chapter 3, we graphed equations containing two variables. Equations like these are often needed to represent relationships between two different values. There are also many real-life opportunities to compare and contrast two such equations, called a system of equations. This chapter presents linear systems and ways we solve these systems and apply them to real-life situations.

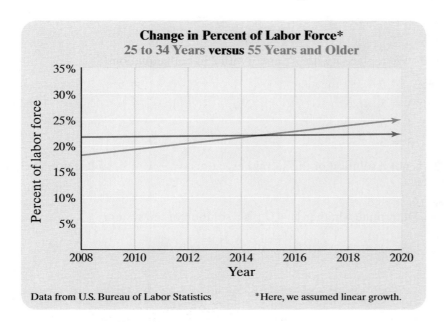

Change in Percent of Labor Force*
25 to 34 Years **versus** 55 Years and Older

Data from U.S. Bureau of Labor Statistics   *Here, we assumed linear growth.

4.1 │ Solving Systems of Linear Equations by Graphing

OBJECTIVES

1 Determine if an Ordered Pair Is a Solution of a System of Equations in Two Variables.

2 Solve a System of Linear Equations by Graphing.

3 Without Graphing, Determine the Number of Solutions of a System.

A **system of linear equations** consists of two or more linear equations. In this section, we focus on solving systems of linear equations containing two equations in two variables. Examples of such linear systems are

$$\begin{cases} 3x - 3y = 0 \\ x = 2y \end{cases} \quad \begin{cases} x - y = 0 \\ 2x + y = 10 \end{cases} \quad \begin{cases} y = 7x - 1 \\ y = 4 \end{cases}$$

OBJECTIVE

1   Deciding Whether an Ordered Pair Is a Solution

A **solution** of a system of two equations in two variables is an ordered pair of numbers that is a solution of both equations in the system.

EXAMPLE 1   Determine whether $(12, 6)$ is a solution of the system

$$\begin{cases} 2x - 3y = 6 \\ x = 2y \end{cases}$$

Solution   To determine whether $(12, 6)$ is a solution of the system, we replace x with 12 and y with 6 in both equations.

$$2x - 3y = 6 \quad \text{First equation} \qquad\qquad x = 2y \quad \text{Second equation}$$
$$2(12) - 3(6) \stackrel{?}{=} 6 \quad \text{Let } x = 12 \text{ and } y = 6. \qquad 12 \stackrel{?}{=} 2(6) \quad \text{Let } x = 12 \text{ and } y = 6.$$
$$24 - 18 \stackrel{?}{=} 6 \quad \text{Simplify.} \qquad\qquad\qquad 12 = 12 \quad \text{True}$$
$$6 = 6 \quad \text{True}$$

Since $(12, 6)$ is a solution of both equations, it is a solution of the system.   □

PRACTICE

1   Determine whether $(4, 12)$ is a solution of the system.

$$\begin{cases} 4x - y = 2 \\ y = 3x \end{cases}$$

EXAMPLE 2   Determine whether $(-1, 2)$ is a solution of the system

$$\begin{cases} x + 2y = 3 \\ 4x - y = 6 \end{cases}$$

Solution   We replace x with -1 and y with 2 in both equations.

$$x + 2y = 3 \quad \text{First equation} \qquad\qquad 4x - y = 6 \quad \text{Second equation}$$
$$-1 + 2(2) \stackrel{?}{=} 3 \quad \text{Let } x = -1 \text{ and } y = 2. \qquad 4(-1) - 2 \stackrel{?}{=} 6 \quad \text{Let } x = -1 \text{ and } y = 2.$$
$$-1 + 4 \stackrel{?}{=} 3 \quad \text{Simplify.} \qquad\qquad\qquad -4 - 2 \stackrel{?}{=} 6 \quad \text{Simplify.}$$
$$3 = 3 \quad \text{True} \qquad\qquad\qquad\qquad -6 = 6 \quad \text{False}$$

$(-1, 2)$ is not a solution of the second equation, $4x - y = 6$, so it is not a solution of the system.   □

PRACTICE

2   Determine whether $(-4, 1)$ is a solution of the system.

$$\begin{cases} x - 3y = -7 \\ 2x + 9y = 1 \end{cases}$$

OBJECTIVE

2   Solving Systems of Equations by Graphing

Since a solution of a system of two equations in two variables is a solution common to both equations, it is also a point common to the graphs of both equations. Let's practice finding solutions of both equations in a system—that is, solutions of a system—by graphing and identifying points of intersection.

EXAMPLE 3   Solve the system of equations by graphing.

$$\begin{cases} -x + 3y = 10 \\ x + y = 2 \end{cases}$$

Solution   On a single set of axes, graph each linear equation.

$-x + 3y = 10$

x	y
0	$\frac{10}{3}$
−4	2
2	4

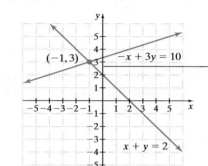

> ▶ Helpful Hint
> The point of intersection gives the solution of the system.

$x + y = 2$

x	y
0	2
2	0
1	1

The two lines appear to intersect at the point $(-1, 3)$. To check, we replace x with -1 and y with 3 in both equations.

$-x + 3y = 10$	First equation		$x + y = 2$	Second equation
$-(-1) + 3(3) \overset{?}{=} 10$	Let $x = -1$ and $y = 3$.		$-1 + 3 \overset{?}{=} 2$	Let $x = -1$ and $y = 3$.
$1 + 9 \overset{?}{=} 10$	Simplify.		$2 = 2$	True
$10 = 10$	True			

$(-1, 3)$ checks, so it is the solution of the system and the solution set is $\{(-1, 3)\}$. (Note: For single ordered-pair solutions, we shall list the ordered pair only.)   □

PRACTICE

3   Solve the system of equations by graphing:

$$\begin{cases} x - y = 3 \\ x + 2y = 18 \end{cases}$$

> ▶ Helpful Hint
> Neatly drawn graphs can help when you are estimating the solution of a system of linear equations by graphing.
>   In the example above, notice that the two lines intersected in a point. This means that the system has 1 solution.

EXAMPLE 4 Solve the system of equations by graphing.

$$\begin{cases} 2x + 3y = -2 \\ x = 2 \end{cases}$$

Solution We graph each linear equation on a single set of axes.

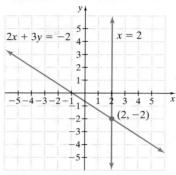

The two lines appear to intersect at the point $(2, -2)$. To determine whether $(2, -2)$ is the solution, we replace x with 2 and y with -2 in both equations.

$2x + 3y = -2$	First equation	$x = 2$	Second equation
$2(2) + 3(-2) \stackrel{?}{=} -2$	Let $x = 2$ and $y = -2$.	$2 \stackrel{?}{=} 2$	Let $x = 2$.
$4 + (-6) \stackrel{?}{=} -2$	Simplify.	$2 = 2$	True
$-2 = -2$	True		

Since a true statement results in both equations, $(2, -2)$ is the solution of the system. □

PRACTICE
4 Solve the system of equations by graphing.

$$\begin{cases} -4x + 3y = -3 \\ y = -5 \end{cases}$$

A system of equations that has at least one solution as in Examples 3 and 4 is said to be a **consistent system.** A system that has no solution is said to be an **inconsistent system.**

EXAMPLE 5 Solve the following system of equations by graphing.

$$\begin{cases} 2x + y = 7 \\ 2y = -4x \end{cases}$$

Solution Graph the two lines in the system.

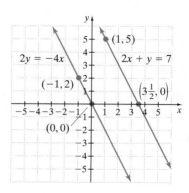

The lines **appear** to be parallel. To confirm this, write both equations in slope-intercept form by solving each equation for y.

$2x + y = 7$	First equation	$2y = -4x$	Second equation
$y = -2x + 7$	Subtract $2x$ from both sides.	$\dfrac{2y}{2} = \dfrac{-4x}{2}$	Divide both sides by 2.
		$y = -2x$	

Recall that when an equation is written in slope-intercept form, the coefficient of x is the slope. Since both equations have the same slope, -2, but different y-intercepts, the lines are parallel and have no points in common. Thus, there is no solution of the system and the system is inconsistent. To indicate this, we can say the system has no solution or the solution set is $\{\ \}$ or $\varnothing$.   □

PRACTICE
5   Solve the system of equations by graphing.

$$\begin{cases} 3y = 9x \\ 6x - 2y = 12 \end{cases}$$

In Examples 3, 4, and 5, the graphs of the two linear equations of each system are different. When this happens, we call these equations **independent equations.** If the graphs of the two equations in a system are identical, we call the equations **dependent equations.**

EXAMPLE 6   Solve the system of equations by graphing.

$$\begin{cases} x - y = 3 \\ -x + y = -3 \end{cases}$$

Solution   Graph each line.

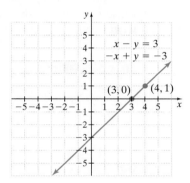

These graphs **appear** to be identical. To confirm this, write each equation in slope-intercept form.

$x - y = 3$ First equation $-x + y = -3$ Second equation

$-y = -x + 3$ Subtract x from both sides. $\boldsymbol{y = x - 3}$ Add x to both sides.

$\dfrac{-y}{-1} = \dfrac{-x}{-1} + \dfrac{3}{-1}$ Divide both sides by -1.

$\boldsymbol{y = x - 3}$

The equations are identical and so must be their graphs. The lines have an infinite number of points in common. Thus, there is an infinite number of solutions of the system and this is a consistent system. The equations are dependent equations. Here, we can say that there are an infinite number of solutions or the solution set is $\{(x, y)\,|\,x - y = 3\}$ or equivalently $\{(x, y)\,|\,-x + y = -3\}$ since the equations describe identical ordered pairs. The second set is read "the set of all ordered pairs (x, y) such that $-x + y = -3$.   □

PRACTICE
6   Solve the system of equations by graphing.

$$\begin{cases} x - y = 4 \\ -2x + 2y = -8 \end{cases}$$

As we have seen, three different situations can occur when graphing the two lines associated with the two equations in a linear system:

One point of intersection: one solution   Parallel lines: no solution   Same line: infinite number of solutions

Consistent system
(at least one solution)
Independent equations
(graphs of equations differ)

Inconsistent system
(no solution)
Independent equations
(graphs of equations differ)

Consistent system
(at least one solution)
Dependent equations
(graphs of equations identical)

OBJECTIVE

3 **Finding the Number of Solutions of a System without Graphing** ▶

You may have suspected by now that graphing alone is not an accurate way to solve a system of linear equations. For example, a solution of $\left(\frac{1}{2}, \frac{2}{9}\right)$ is unlikely to be read correctly from a graph. The next two sections present two accurate methods of solving these systems. In the meantime, we can decide how many solutions a system has by writing each equation in the slope-intercept form.

EXAMPLE 7   Without graphing, determine the number of solutions of the system.

$$\begin{cases} \dfrac{1}{2}x - y = 2 \\ x = 2y + 5 \end{cases}$$

Solution   First write each equation in slope-intercept form.

$\dfrac{1}{2}x - y = 2$ First equation

$\quad \dfrac{1}{2}x = y + 2$ Add y to both sides.

$\dfrac{1}{2}x - 2 = y$ Subtract 2 from both sides.

$x = 2y + 5$ Second equation

$x - 5 = 2y$ Subtract 5 from both sides.

$\dfrac{x}{2} - \dfrac{5}{2} = \dfrac{2y}{2}$ Divide both sides by 2.

$\dfrac{1}{2}x - \dfrac{5}{2} = y$ Simplify.

The slope of each line is $\dfrac{1}{2}$, but they have different y-intercepts. This tells us that the lines representing these equations are parallel. Since the lines are parallel, the system has no solution and is inconsistent. □

PRACTICE

7 Without graphing, determine the number of solutions of the system.

$$\begin{cases} 5x + 4y = 6 \\ x - y = 3 \end{cases}$$

EXAMPLE 8   Without graphing, determine the number of solutions of the system.

$$\begin{cases} 3x - y = 4 \\ x + 2y = 8 \end{cases}$$

Solution Once again, the slope-intercept form helps determine how many solutions this system has.

$3x - y = 4$	First equation	$x + 2y = 8$	Second equation
$3x = y + 4$	Add y to both sides.	$x = -2y + 8$	Subtract $2y$ from both sides.
$3x - 4 = y$	Subtract 4 from both sides.	$x - 8 = -2y$	Subtract 8 from both sides.
		$\dfrac{x}{-2} - \dfrac{8}{-2} = \dfrac{-2y}{-2}$	Divide both sides by -2.
		$-\dfrac{1}{2}x + 4 = y$	Simplify.

The slope of the second line is $-\dfrac{1}{2}$, whereas the slope of the first line is 3. Since the slopes are not equal, the two lines are neither parallel nor identical and must intersect. Therefore, this system has one solution and is consistent. ☐

PRACTICE
8 Without graphing, determine the number of solutions of the system.

$$\begin{cases} -\dfrac{2}{3}x + y = 6 \\ 3y = 2x + 5 \end{cases}$$

Graphing Calculator Explorations

A graphing calculator may be used to approximate solutions of systems of equations. For example, to approximate the solution of the system

$$\begin{cases} y = -3.14x - 1.35 \\ y = 4.88x + 5.25, \end{cases}$$

first graph each equation on the same set of axes. Then use the intersect feature of your calculator to approximate the point of intersection.

The approximate point of intersection is $(-0.82, 1.23)$.

Solve each system of equations. Approximate the solutions to two decimal places.

1. $\begin{cases} y = -2.68x + 1.21 \\ y = 5.22x - 1.68 \end{cases}$
2. $\begin{cases} y = 4.25x + 3.89 \\ y = -1.88x + 3.21 \end{cases}$
3. $\begin{cases} 4.3x - 2.9y = 5.6 \\ 8.1x + 7.6y = -14.1 \end{cases}$
4. $\begin{cases} -3.6x - 8.6y = 10 \\ -4.5x + 9.6y = -7.7 \end{cases}$

Vocabulary, Readiness & Video Check

Fill in each blank with one of the words or phrases listed below.

system of linear equations	solution	consistent
dependent	inconsistent	independent

1. In a system of linear equations in two variables, if the graphs of the equations are the same, the equations are _____ equations.

2. Two or more linear equations are called a(n) _____.

3. A system of equations that has at least one solution is called a(n) _____ system.

4. A(n) _____ of a system of two equations in two variables is an ordered pair of numbers that is a solution of both equations in the system.

5. A system of equations that has no solution is called a(n) _____ system.

6. In a system of linear equations in two variables, if the graphs of the equations are different, the equations are _____ equations.

Martin-Gay Interactive Videos

See Video 4.1

Watch the section lecture video and answer the following questions.

OBJECTIVE 1

7. In Example 1, the first ordered pair is a solution of the first equation of the system. Why is this not enough to determine whether the first ordered pair is a solution of the system?

OBJECTIVE 2

8. From Examples 2 and 3, why is finding the solution of a system of equations from a graph considered "guessing" and this proposed solution checked algebraically?

OBJECTIVE 3

9. From Examples 5–7, explain how the slope-intercept form tells us how many solutions a system of equations has.

4.1 Exercise Set   MyMathLab®

Each rectangular coordinate system shows the graph of the equations in a system of equations. Use each graph to determine the number of solutions for each associated system. If the system has only one solution, give its coordinates.

1.

2.

3.

4.

Determine whether each ordered pair is a solution of the system of linear equations. See Examples 1 and 2.

5. $\begin{cases} x + y = 8 \\ 3x + 2y = 21 \end{cases}$
   a. $(2, 4)$
   b. $(5, 3)$

6. $\begin{cases} 2x + y = 5 \\ x + 3y = 5 \end{cases}$
   a. $(5, 0)$
   b. $(2, 1)$

7. $\begin{cases} 3x - y = 5 \\ x + 2y = 11 \end{cases}$
   a. $(3, 4)$
   b. $(0, -5)$

8. $\begin{cases} 2x - 3y = 8 \\ x - 2y = 6 \end{cases}$
   a. $(-2, -4)$
   b. $(7, 2)$

9. $\begin{cases} 2y = 4x + 6 \\ 2x - y = -3 \end{cases}$
   a. $(-3, -3)$
   b. $(0, 3)$

10. $\begin{cases} x + 5y = -4 \\ -2x = 10y + 8 \end{cases}$
   a. $(-4, 0)$
   b. $(6, -2)$

11. $\begin{cases} -2 = x - 7y \\ 6x - y = 13 \end{cases}$
   a. $(-2, 0)$
   b. $\left(\dfrac{1}{2}, \dfrac{5}{14}\right)$

12. $\begin{cases} 4x = 1 - y \\ x - 3y = -8 \end{cases}$
   a. $(0, 1)$
   b. $\left(\dfrac{1}{6}, \dfrac{1}{3}\right)$

MIXED PRACTICE

Solve each system of linear equations by graphing. See Examples 3 through 6.

13. $\begin{cases} x + y = 4 \\ x - y = 2 \end{cases}$

14. $\begin{cases} x + y = 3 \\ x - y = 5 \end{cases}$

15. $\begin{cases} x + y = 6 \\ -x + y = -6 \end{cases}$

16. $\begin{cases} x + y = 1 \\ -x + y = -3 \end{cases}$

17. $\begin{cases} y = 2x \\ 3x - y = -2 \end{cases}$

18. $\begin{cases} y = -3x \\ 2x - y = -5 \end{cases}$

19. $\begin{cases} y = x + 1 \\ y = 2x - 1 \end{cases}$

20. $\begin{cases} y = 3x - 4 \\ y = x + 2 \end{cases}$

21. $\begin{cases} 2x + y = 0 \\ 3x + y = 1 \end{cases}$

22. $\begin{cases} 2x + y = 1 \\ 3x + y = 0 \end{cases}$

23. $\begin{cases} y = -x - 1 \\ y = 2x + 5 \end{cases}$

24. $\begin{cases} y = x - 1 \\ y = -3x - 5 \end{cases}$

25. $\begin{cases} x + y = 5 \\ x + y = 6 \end{cases}$

26. $\begin{cases} x - y = 4 \\ x - y = 1 \end{cases}$

27. $\begin{cases} 2x - y = 6 \\ y = 2 \end{cases}$

28. $\begin{cases} x + y = 5 \\ x = 4 \end{cases}$

29. $\begin{cases} x - 2y = 2 \\ 3x + 2y = -2 \end{cases}$

30. $\begin{cases} x + 3y = 7 \\ 2x - 3y = -4 \end{cases}$

31. $\begin{cases} 2x + y = 4 \\ 6x = -3y + 6 \end{cases}$

32. $\begin{cases} y + 2x = 3 \\ 4x = 2 - 2y \end{cases}$

33. $\begin{cases} y - 3x = -2 \\ 6x - 2y = 4 \end{cases}$

34. $\begin{cases} x - 2y = -6 \\ -2x + 4y = 12 \end{cases}$

35. $\begin{cases} x = 3 \\ y = -1 \end{cases}$

36. $\begin{cases} x = -5 \\ y = 3 \end{cases}$

37. $\begin{cases} y = x - 2 \\ y = 2x + 3 \end{cases}$

38. $\begin{cases} y = x + 5 \\ y = -2x - 4 \end{cases}$

39. $\begin{cases} 2x - 3y = -2 \\ -3x + 5y = 5 \end{cases}$

40. $\begin{cases} 4x - y = 7 \\ 2x - 3y = -9 \end{cases}$

41. $\begin{cases} 6x - y = 4 \\ \dfrac{1}{2}y = -2 + 3x \end{cases}$ **42.** $\begin{cases} 3x - y = 6 \\ \dfrac{1}{3}y = -2 + x \end{cases}$

Without graphing, decide.

a. Are the graphs of the equations identical lines, parallel lines, or lines intersecting at a single point?

b. How many solutions does the system have? See Examples 7 and 8.

43. $\begin{cases} 4x + y = 24 \\ x + 2y = 2 \end{cases}$ **44.** $\begin{cases} 3x + y = 1 \\ 3x + 2y = 6 \end{cases}$

45. $\begin{cases} 2x + y = 0 \\ 2y = 6 - 4x \end{cases}$ **46.** $\begin{cases} 3x + y = 0 \\ 2y = -6x \end{cases}$

47. $\begin{cases} 6x - y = 4 \\ \dfrac{1}{2}y = -2 + 3x \end{cases}$ **48.** $\begin{cases} 3x - y = 2 \\ \dfrac{1}{3}y = -2 + 3x \end{cases}$

49. $\begin{cases} x = 5 \\ y = -2 \end{cases}$ **50.** $\begin{cases} y = 3 \\ x = -4 \end{cases}$

51. $\begin{cases} 3y - 2x = 3 \\ x + 2y = 9 \end{cases}$ **52.** $\begin{cases} 2y = x + 2 \\ y + 2x = 3 \end{cases}$

53. $\begin{cases} 6y + 4x = 6 \\ 3y - 3 = -2x \end{cases}$ **54.** $\begin{cases} 8y + 6x = 4 \\ 4y - 2 = 3x \end{cases}$

55. $\begin{cases} x + y = 4 \\ x + y = 3 \end{cases}$ **56.** $\begin{cases} 2x + y = 0 \\ y = -2x + 1 \end{cases}$

REVIEW AND PREVIEW

Solve each equation. See Section 2.3.

57. $5(x - 3) + 3x = 1$

58. $-2x + 3(x + 6) = 17$

59. $4\left(\dfrac{y + 1}{2}\right) + 3y = 0$

60. $-y + 12\left(\dfrac{y - 1}{4}\right) = 3$

61. $8a - 2(3a - 1) = 6$

62. $3z - (4z - 2) = 9$

CONCEPT EXTENSIONS

63. Draw a graph of two linear equations whose associated system has the solution $(-1, 4)$.

64. Draw a graph of two linear equations whose associated system has the solution $(3, -2)$.

65. Draw a graph of two linear equations whose associated system has no solution.

66. Draw a graph of two linear equations whose associated system has an infinite number of solutions.

67. The ordered pair $(-2, 3)$ is a solution of all three independent equations:

$$x + y = 1$$
$$2x - y = -7$$
$$x + 3y = 7$$

Describe the graph of all three equations on the same axes.

68. Explain how to use a graph to determine the number of solutions of a system.

The double-line graph below shows the number of pounds of fishery products from U.S. domestic catch and from imports. Use this graph to answer Exercises 69 and 70.

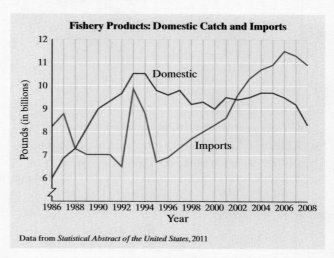

Data from *Statistical Abstract of the United States,* 2011

69. Between what pairs of years did the number of pounds of imported fishery products equal the number of pounds of domestic catch?

70. For what year(s) was the number of pounds of imported fishery products less than the number of pounds of domestic catch?

The double-line graph below shows the average attendance per game for the years shown for the Minnesota Twins and the Texas Rangers baseball teams. Use this for Exercises 71 and 72.

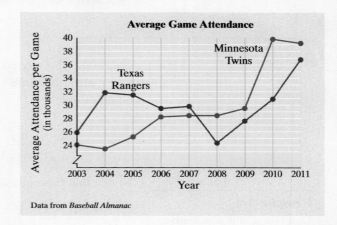

Data from *Baseball Almanac*

71. In what year(s) was the average attendance per game for the Texas Rangers greater than the average attendance per game for the Minnesota Twins?

72. In what year was the average attendance per game for the Texas Rangers closest to the average attendance per game for the Minnesota Twins, 2006 or 2009?

73. Construct a system of two linear equations that has $(1, 3)$ as a solution.

74. Construct a system of two linear equations that has $(0, 7)$ as a solution.

75. Below are tables of values for two linear equations.
a. Find a solution of the corresponding system.
b. Graph several ordered pairs from each table and sketch the two lines.

x	y
1	3
2	5
3	7
4	9
5	11

x	y
1	6
2	7
3	8
4	9
5	10

c. Does your graph confirm the solution from part (a)?

76. Tables of values for two linear equations are shown.

a. Find a solution of the corresponding system.
b. Graph several ordered pairs from each table and sketch the two lines.

x	y
−3	5
−1	1
0	−1
1	−3
2	−5

x	y
−3	7
−1	1
0	−2
1	−5
2	−8

c. Does your graph confirm the solution from part (a)?

77. Explain how writing each equation in a linear system in slope-intercept form helps determine the number of solutions of a system.

78. Is it possible for a system of two linear equations in two variables to be inconsistent but with dependent equations? Why or why not?

4.2 Solving Systems of Linear Equations by Substitution

OBJECTIVE

1 Use the Substitution Method to Solve a System of Linear Equations.

OBJECTIVE

1 Using the Substitution Method ▶

As we stated in the preceding section, graphing alone is not an accurate way to solve a system of linear equations. In this section, we discuss a second, more accurate method for solving systems of equations. This method is called the **substitution method** and is introduced in the next example.

EXAMPLE 1 Solve the system:

$$\begin{cases} 2x + y = 10 & \text{First equation} \\ x = y + 2 & \text{Second equation} \end{cases}$$

Solution The second equation in this system is $x = y + 2$. This tells us that x and $y + 2$ have the same value. This means that we may substitute $y + 2$ for x in the first equation.

$$2x + y = 10 \quad \text{First equation}$$

$$2(y + 2) + y = 10 \quad \text{Substitute } y + 2 \text{ for } x \text{ since } x = y + 2.$$

Notice that this equation now has one variable, y. Let's now solve this equation for y.

▶ **Helpful Hint**
Don't forget the distributive property.

$$2(y + 2) + y = 10$$
$$2y + 4 + y = 10 \quad \text{Use the distributive property.}$$
$$3y + 4 = 10 \quad \text{Combine like terms.}$$
$$3y = 6 \quad \text{Subtract 4 from both sides.}$$
$$y = 2 \quad \text{Divide both sides by 3.}$$

Now we know that the y-value of the ordered pair solution of the system is 2. To find the corresponding x-value, we replace y with 2 in the equation $x = y + 2$ and solve for x.

$$x = y + 2$$
$$x = 2 + 2 \quad \text{Let } y = 2.$$
$$x = 4$$

The solution of the system is the ordered pair $(4, 2)$. Since an ordered pair solution must satisfy both linear equations in the system, we could have chosen the equation $2x + y = 10$ to find the corresponding x-value. The resulting x-value is the same.

Check: We check to see that $(4, 2)$ satisfies both equations of the original system.

First Equation	*Second Equation*

$$2x + y = 10 \qquad\qquad x = y + 2$$
$$2(4) + 2 \overset{?}{=} 10 \qquad\qquad 4 \overset{?}{=} 2 + 2 \quad \text{Let } x = 4 \text{ and } y = 2.$$
$$10 = 10 \quad \text{True} \qquad\qquad 4 = 4 \qquad \text{True}$$

The solution of the system is $(4, 2)$.

A graph of the two equations shows the two lines intersecting at the point $(4, 2)$.

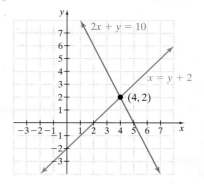

PRACTICE

1   Solve the system:

$$\begin{cases} 2x - y = 9 \\ x = y + 1 \end{cases}$$

EXAMPLE 2   Solve the system:

$$\begin{cases} 5x - y = -2 \\ y = 3x \end{cases}$$

Solution   The second equation is solved for y in terms of x. We substitute $3x$ for y in the first equation.

$$5x - y = -2 \quad \text{First equation}$$
$$5x - (3x) = -2 \quad \text{Substitute } 3x \text{ for } y.$$

Now we solve for x.

$$5x - 3x = -2$$
$$2x = -2 \quad \text{Combine like terms.}$$
$$x = -1 \quad \text{Divide both sides by 2.}$$

The x-value of the ordered pair solution is -1. To find the corresponding y-value, we replace x with -1 in the second equation, $y = 3x$.

$$y = 3x \qquad \text{Second equation}$$
$$y = 3(-1) \quad \text{Let } x = -1.$$
$$y = -3$$

Check to see that the solution of the system is $(-1, -3)$.

(Continued on next page)

PRACTICE
2   Solve the system:

$$\begin{cases} 7x - y = -15 \\ y = 2x \end{cases}$$

To solve a system of equations by substitution, we first need an equation solved for one of its variables, as in Examples 1 and 2. If neither equation in a system is solved for x or y, this will be our first step.

EXAMPLE 3   Solve the system:

$$\begin{cases} x + 2y = 7 \\ 2x + 2y = 13 \end{cases}$$

Solution   We choose one of the equations and solve for x or y. We will solve the first equation for x by subtracting $2y$ from both sides.

$$x + 2y = 7 \qquad \text{First equation}$$
$$x = 7 - 2y \quad \text{Subtract } 2y \text{ from both sides.}$$

Since $x = 7 - 2y$, we now substitute $7 - 2y$ for x in the second equation and solve for y.

$$2x + 2y = 13 \qquad \text{Second equation}$$
$$2(7 - 2y) + 2y = 13 \qquad \text{Let } x = 7 - 2y.$$
$$14 - 4y + 2y = 13 \qquad \text{Use the distributive property.}$$
$$14 - 2y = 13 \qquad \text{Simplify.}$$
$$-2y = -1 \qquad \text{Subtract 14 from both sides.}$$
$$y = \frac{1}{2} \qquad \text{Divide both sides by } -2.$$

> **Helpful Hint**
> Don't forget to insert parentheses when substituting $7 - 2y$ for x.

To find x, we let $y = \frac{1}{2}$ in the equation $x = 7 - 2y$.

$$x = 7 - 2y$$
$$x = 7 - 2\left(\frac{1}{2}\right) \quad \text{Let } y = \frac{1}{2}.$$
$$x = 7 - 1$$
$$x = 6$$

> **Helpful Hint**
> To find x, any equation in two variables equivalent to the original equations of the system may be used. We used this equation since it is solved for x.

The solution is $\left(6, \frac{1}{2}\right)$. Check the solution in both equations of the original system. □

PRACTICE
3   Solve the system: $\begin{cases} x + 3y = 6 \\ 2x + 3y = 10 \end{cases}$

The following steps may be used to solve a system of equations by the substitution method.

Solving a System of Two Linear Equations by the Substitution Method

Step 1.   Solve one of the equations for one of its variables.

Step 2.   Substitute the expression for the variable found in Step 1 into the other equation.

Step 3.   Solve the equation from Step 2 to find the value of one variable.

Step 4.   Substitute the value found in Step 3 in any equation containing both variables to find the value of the other variable.

Step 5.   Check the proposed solution in the original system.

✓CONCEPT CHECK

As you solve the system $\begin{cases} 2x + y = -5 \\ x - y = 5 \end{cases}$ you find that $y = -5$. Is this the solution of the system?

EXAMPLE 4   Solve the system:

$$\begin{cases} 7x - 3y = -14 \\ -3x + y = 6 \end{cases}$$

Solution   To avoid introducing fractions, we will solve the second equation for y.

$$-3x + y = 6 \qquad \text{Second equation}$$
$$y = 3x + 6$$

Next, substitute $3x + 6$ for y in the first equation.

$$7x - 3y = -14 \quad \text{First equation}$$
$$7x - 3(\overbrace{3x + 6}) = -14 \quad \text{Let } y = 3x + 6.$$
$$7x - 9x - 18 = -14 \quad \text{Use the distributive property.}$$
$$-2x - 18 = -14 \quad \text{Simplify.}$$
$$-2x = 4 \quad \text{Add 18 to both sides.}$$
$$x = -2 \quad \text{Divide both sides by } -2.$$

To find the corresponding y-value, substitute -2 for x in the equation $y = 3x + 6$. Then $y = 3(-2) + 6$ or $y = 0$. The solution of the system is $(-2, 0)$. Check this solution in both equations of the system.   □

PRACTICE

4   Solve the system:

$$\begin{cases} 5x + 3y = -9 \\ -2x + y = 8 \end{cases}$$

▶ **Helpful Hint**

When solving a system of equations by the substitution method, begin by solving an equation for one of its variables. If possible, solve for a variable that has a coefficient of 1 or -1. This way, we avoid working with time-consuming fractions.

✓CONCEPT CHECK

To avoid fractions, which of the equations below would you use to solve for x?
a. $3x - 4y = 15$ **b.** $14 - 3y = 8x$ **c.** $7y + x = 12$

Answers to Concept Check:
1. No, the solution will be an ordered pair.
2. c

EXAMPLE 5   Solve the system:

$$\begin{cases} \dfrac{1}{2}x - y = 3 \\ x = 6 + 2y \end{cases}$$

(Continued on next page)

Solution The second equation is already solved for x in terms of y. Thus we substitute $6 + 2y$ for x in the first equation and solve for y.

$$\frac{1}{2}x - y = 3 \quad \text{First equation}$$

$$\frac{1}{2}\overbrace{(6 + 2y)} - y = 3 \quad \text{Let } x = 6 + 2y.$$

$$3 + y - y = 3 \quad \text{Use the distributive property.}$$

$$3 = 3 \quad \text{Simplify.}$$

Arriving at a true statement such as $3 = 3$ indicates that the two linear equations in the original system are equivalent. This means that their graphs are identical and there is an infinite number of solutions of the system. Any solution of one equation is also a solution of the other. For the solution, we can write "infinite number of solutions" or, in set notation, $\left\{(x, y) \mid \frac{1}{2}x - y = 3\right\}$ or $\{(x, y) \mid x = 6 + 2y\}$.

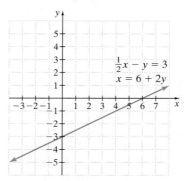

PRACTICE
5 Solve the system:

$$\begin{cases} \dfrac{1}{4}x - y = 2 \\ x = 4y + 8 \end{cases}$$

EXAMPLE 6 Use substitution to solve the system.

$$\begin{cases} 6x + 12y = 5 \\ -4x - 8y = 0 \end{cases}$$

Solution Choose the second equation and solve for y.

$$-4x - 8y = 0 \qquad \text{Second equation}$$

$$-8y = 4x \qquad \text{Add } 4x \text{ to both sides.}$$

$$\frac{-8y}{-8} = \frac{4x}{-8} \qquad \text{Divide both sides by } -8.$$

$$y = -\frac{1}{2}x \qquad \text{Simplify.}$$

Now replace y with $-\frac{1}{2}x$ in the first equation.

$$6x + 12y = 5 \qquad \text{First equation}$$

$$6x + 12\left(-\frac{1}{2}x\right) = 5 \qquad \text{Let } y = -\frac{1}{2}x.$$

$$6x + (-6x) = 5 \qquad \text{Simplify.}$$

$$0 = 5 \qquad \text{Combine like terms.}$$

The false statement $0 = 5$ indicates that this system has no solution and is inconsistent. The graph of the linear equations in the system is a pair of parallel lines. For the solution, we can write "no solution" or, in set notation, write $\{\ \}$ or $\varnothing$.

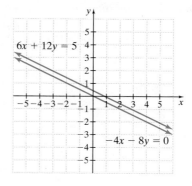

Answers to Concept Check:
a. parallel lines
b. intersect at one point
c. identical graphs

PRACTICE
6   Use substitution to solve the system.

$$\begin{cases} 4x - 3y = 12 \\ -8x + 6y = -30 \end{cases}$$

✓ **CONCEPT CHECK**
Describe how the graphs of the equations in a system appear if the system has
a. no solution
b. one solution
c. an infinite number of solutions

Vocabulary, Readiness & Video Check

Give the solution of each system. If the system has no solution or an infinite number of solutions, say so. If the system has one solution, find it.

1. $\begin{cases} y = 4x \\ -3x + y = 1 \end{cases}$
When solving, you obtain $x = 1$

2. $\begin{cases} 4x - y = 17 \\ -8x + 2y = 0 \end{cases}$
When solving, you obtain $0 = 34$

3. $\begin{cases} 4x - y = 17 \\ -8x + 2y = -34 \end{cases}$
When solving, you obtain $0 = 0$

4. $\begin{cases} 5x + 2y = 25 \\ x = y + 5 \end{cases}$
When solving, you obtain $y = 0$

5. $\begin{cases} x + y = 0 \\ 7x - 7y = 0 \end{cases}$
When solving, you obtain $x = 0$

6. $\begin{cases} y = -2x + 5 \\ 4x + 2y = 10 \end{cases}$
When solving, you obtain $0 = 0$

Martin-Gay Interactive Videos

See Video 4.2

Watch the section lecture video and answer the following question.

OBJECTIVE 1

7. The systems in Examples 2–4 all need one of their equations solved for a variable as a first step. What important part of the substitution method is emphasized in each example?

4.2 Exercise Set

MyMathLab®

Solve each system of equations by the substitution method. See Examples 1 and 2.

1. $\begin{cases} x + y = 3 \\ x = 2y \end{cases}$ **2.** $\begin{cases} x + y = 20 \\ x = 3y \end{cases}$

3. $\begin{cases} x + y = 6 \\ y = -3x \end{cases}$ **4.** $\begin{cases} x + y = 6 \\ y = -4x \end{cases}$

5. $\begin{cases} y = 3x + 1 \\ 4y - 8x = 12 \end{cases}$ **6.** $\begin{cases} y = 2x + 3 \\ 5y - 7x = 18 \end{cases}$

7. $\begin{cases} y = 2x + 9 \\ y = 7x + 10 \end{cases}$ **8.** $\begin{cases} y = 5x - 3 \\ y = 8x + 4 \end{cases}$

MIXED PRACTICE

Solve each system of equations by the substitution method. See Examples 1 through 6.

9. $\begin{cases} 3x - 4y = 10 \\ y = x - 3 \end{cases}$ **10.** $\begin{cases} 4x - 3y = 10 \\ y = x - 5 \end{cases}$

11. $\begin{cases} x + 2y = 6 \\ 2x + 3y = 8 \end{cases}$ **12.** $\begin{cases} x + 3y = -5 \\ 2x + 2y = 6 \end{cases}$

13. $\begin{cases} 3x + 2y = 16 \\ x = 3y - 2 \end{cases}$ **14.** $\begin{cases} 2x + 3y = 18 \\ x = 2y - 5 \end{cases}$

15. $\begin{cases} 2x - 5y = 1 \\ 3x + y = -7 \end{cases}$ **16.** $\begin{cases} 3y - x = 6 \\ 4x + 12y = 0 \end{cases}$

17. $\begin{cases} 4x + 2y = 5 \\ -2x = y + 4 \end{cases}$ **18.** $\begin{cases} 2y = x + 2 \\ 6x - 12y = 0 \end{cases}$

19. $\begin{cases} 4x + y = 11 \\ 2x + 5y = 1 \end{cases}$ **20.** $\begin{cases} 3x + y = -14 \\ 4x + 3y = -22 \end{cases}$

21. $\begin{cases} x + 2y + 5 = -4 + 5y - x \\ 2x + x = y + 4 \end{cases}$
(*Hint:* First simplify each equation.)

22. $\begin{cases} 5x + 4y - 2 = -6 + 7y - 3x \\ 3x + 4x = y + 3 \end{cases}$
(*Hint:* See Exercise 21.)

23. $\begin{cases} 6x - 3y = 5 \\ x + 2y = 0 \end{cases}$ **24.** $\begin{cases} 10x - 5y = -21 \\ x + 3y = 0 \end{cases}$

25. $\begin{cases} 3x - y = 1 \\ 2x - 3y = 10 \end{cases}$ **26.** $\begin{cases} 2x - y = -7 \\ 4x - 3y = -11 \end{cases}$

27. $\begin{cases} -x + 2y = 10 \\ -2x + 3y = 18 \end{cases}$ **28.** $\begin{cases} -x + 3y = 18 \\ -3x + 2y = 19 \end{cases}$

29. $\begin{cases} 5x + 10y = 20 \\ 2x + 6y = 10 \end{cases}$ **30.** $\begin{cases} 6x + 3y = 12 \\ 9x + 6y = 15 \end{cases}$

31. $\begin{cases} 3x + 6y = 9 \\ 4x + 8y = 16 \end{cases}$ **32.** $\begin{cases} 2x + 4y = 6 \\ 5x + 10y = 16 \end{cases}$

33. $\begin{cases} \dfrac{1}{3}x - y = 2 \\ x - 3y = 6 \end{cases}$ **34.** $\begin{cases} \dfrac{1}{4}x - 2y = 1 \\ x - 8y = 4 \end{cases}$

35. $\begin{cases} x = \dfrac{3}{4}y - 1 \\ 8x - 5y = -6 \end{cases}$ **36.** $\begin{cases} x = \dfrac{5}{6}y - 2 \\ 12x - 5y = -9 \end{cases}$

Solve each system by the substitution method. First, simplify each equation by combining like terms.

37. $\begin{cases} -5y + 6y = 3x + 2(x - 5) - 3x + 5 \\ 4(x + y) - x + y = -12 \end{cases}$

38. $\begin{cases} 5x + 2y - 4x - 2y = 2(2y + 6) - 7 \\ 3(2x - y) - 4x = 1 + 9 \end{cases}$

REVIEW AND PREVIEW

Write equivalent equations by multiplying both sides of the given equation by the given nonzero number. See Section 2.2.

39. $3x + 2y = 6$ by -2

40. $-x + y = 10$ by 5

41. $-4x + y = 3$ by 3

42. $5a - 7b = -4$ by -4

Add the expressions by combining any like terms. See Section 2.1.

43. $\begin{array}{r} 3n + 6m \\ \underline{2n - 6m} \end{array}$ **44.** $\begin{array}{r} -2x + 5y \\ \underline{2x + 11y} \end{array}$ **45.** $\begin{array}{r} -5a - 7b \\ \underline{5a - 8b} \end{array}$ **46.** $\begin{array}{r} 9q + p \\ \underline{-9q - p} \end{array}$

CONCEPT EXTENSIONS

47. Explain how to identify a system with no solution when using the substitution method.

48. Occasionally, when using the substitution method, we obtain the equation $0 = 0$. Explain how this result indicates that the graphs of the equations in the system are identical.

Solve. See a Concept Check in this section.

49. As you solve the system $\begin{cases} 3x - y = -6 \\ -3x + 2y = 7 \end{cases}$, you find that $y = 1$. Is this the solution to the system?

50. As you solve the system $\begin{cases} x = 5y \\ y = 2x \end{cases}$, you find that $x = 0$ and $y = 0$. What is the solution to this system?

51. To avoid fractions, which of the equations below would you use if solving for y? Explain why.

   a. $\dfrac{1}{2}x - 4y = \dfrac{3}{4}$ **b.** $8x - 5y = 13$

   c. $7x - y = 19$

52. Give the number of solutions for a system if the graphs of the equations in the system are

   a. lines intersecting in one point

   b. parallel lines

   c. same line

53. The number of men and women receiving bachelor's degrees each year has been steadily increasing. For the years 1970 through the projection of 2014, the number of men receiving degrees (in thousands) is given by the equation $y = 3.9x + 443$, and for women, the equation is $y = 14.2x + 314$ where x is the number of years after 1970. (*Source:* National Center for Education Statistics)

a. Use the substitution method to solve this system of equations. (Round your final results to the nearest whole numbers.)

b. Explain the meaning of your answer to part (a).

c. Sketch a graph of the system of equations. Write a sentence describing the trends for men and women receiving bachelor's degrees.

54. The number of Adult Contemporary Music radio stations in the United States from 2000 to 2009 is given by the equation $y = -11x + 734$, where x is the number of years after 2000. The number of Spanish radio stations is given by $y = 31x + 542$ for the same time period. (*Source:* M Street Corporation)

a. Use the substitution method to solve this system of equations. (Round your numbers to the nearest tenth.)

b. Explain the meaning of your answer to part (a).

c. Sketch a graph of the system of equations. Write a sentence describing the trends in the popularity of these two types of music formats.

Solve each system by substitution. When necessary, round answers to the nearest hundredth.

55. $\begin{cases} y = 5.1x + 14.56 \\ y = -2x - 3.9 \end{cases}$

56. $\begin{cases} y = 3.1x - 16.35 \\ y = -9.7x + 28.45 \end{cases}$

57. $\begin{cases} 3x + 2y = 14.05 \\ 5x + y = 18.5 \end{cases}$

58. $\begin{cases} x + y = -15.2 \\ -2x + 5y = -19.3 \end{cases}$

4.3 Solving Systems of Linear Equations by Addition

OBJECTIVE

1 Use the Addition Method to Solve a System of Linear Equations.

OBJECTIVE

1 Using the Addition Method

We have seen that substitution is an accurate way to solve a linear system. Another method for solving a system of equations accurately is the **addition** or **elimination method.** The addition method is based on the addition property of equality: adding equal quantities to both sides of an equation does not change the solution of the equation. In symbols,

$$\text{if } A = B \text{ and } C = D \text{, then } A + C = B + D.$$

EXAMPLE 1 Solve the system:

$$\begin{cases} x + y = 7 \\ x - y = 5 \end{cases}$$

Solution Since the left side of each equation is equal to the right side, we add equal quantities by adding the left sides of the equations together and the right sides of the equations together. This adding eliminates the variable y and gives us an equation in one variable, x. We can then solve for x.

> **Helpful Hint**
> Notice in Example 1 that our goal when solving a system of equations by the addition method is to eliminate a variable when adding the equations.

$$\begin{array}{ll} x + y = 7 & \text{First equation} \\ \underline{x - y = 5} & \text{Second equation} \\ 2x \quad\;\; = 12 & \text{Add the equations.} \\ x = 6 & \text{Divide both sides by 2.} \end{array}$$

The x-value of the solution is 6. To find the corresponding y-value, let $x = 6$ in either equation of the system. We will use the first equation.

$$\begin{array}{ll} x + y = 7 & \text{First equation} \\ 6 + y = 7 & \text{Let } x = 6. \\ y = 7 - 6 & \text{Solve for } y. \\ y = 1 & \text{Simplify.} \end{array}$$

(Continued on next page)

Check: The solution is $(6, 1)$. Check this in both equations.

First Equation	*Second Equation*
$x + y = 7$	$x - y = 5$
$6 + 1 \overset{?}{=} 7$	$6 - 1 \overset{?}{=} 5$ Let $x = 6$ and $y = 1$.
$7 = 7$ True	$5 = 5$ True

Thus, the solution of the system is $(6, 1)$ and the graphs of the two equations intersect at the point $(6, 1)$ as shown next.

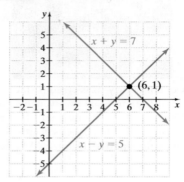

PRACTICE
1   Solve the system: $\begin{cases} x - y = 2 \\ x + y = 8 \end{cases}$

EXAMPLE 2   Solve the system: $\begin{cases} -2x + y = 2 \\ -x + 3y = -4 \end{cases}$

Solution   If we simply add the two equations, the result is still an equation in two variables. However, remember from Example 1 that our goal is to eliminate one of the variables. Notice what happens if we multiply *both sides* of the first equation by -3, which we are allowed to do by the multiplication property of equality. The system

$$\begin{cases} -3(-2x + y) = -3(2) \\ -x + 3y = -4 \end{cases} \quad \text{simplifies to} \quad \begin{cases} 6x - 3y = -6 \\ -x + 3y = -4 \end{cases}$$

Now add the resulting equations and the y-variable is eliminated.

$$\begin{aligned} 6x - 3y &= -6 \\ \underline{-x + 3y} &= \underline{-4} \\ 5x &= -10 \quad \text{Add.} \\ x &= -2 \quad \text{Divide both sides by 5.} \end{aligned}$$

To find the corresponding y-value, let $x = -2$ in any of the preceding equations containing both variables. We use the first equation of the original system.

$$\begin{aligned} -2x + y &= 2 \quad \text{First equation} \\ -2(-2) + y &= 2 \quad \text{Let } x = -2. \\ 4 + y &= 2 \\ y &= -2 \quad \text{Subtract 4 from both sides.} \end{aligned}$$

The solution is $(-2, -2)$. Check this ordered pair in both equations of the original system.

PRACTICE
2   Solve the system: $\begin{cases} x - 2y = 11 \\ 3x - y = 13 \end{cases}$

▶ **Helpful Hint**
When finding the second value of an ordered pair solution, any equation equivalent to one of the original equations in the system may be used.

In Example 2, the decision to multiply the first equation by -3 was no accident. **To eliminate a variable** when adding two equations, **the coefficient of the variable in one equation must be the opposite of its coefficient in the other equation.**

> ▶ **Helpful Hint**
> Be sure to multiply *both sides* of an equation by a chosen number when solving by the addition method. A common mistake is to multiply only the side containing the variables.

EXAMPLE 3   Solve the system: $\begin{cases} 2x - y = 7 \\ 8x - 4y = 1 \end{cases}$

Solution   Multiply both sides of the first equation by -4 and the resulting coefficient of x is -8, the opposite of 8, the coefficient of x in the second equation. The system becomes

> ▶ **Helpful Hint**
> Don't forget to multiply **both** sides by -4.

$$\begin{cases} -4(2x - y) = -4(7) \\ 8x - 4y = 1 \end{cases} \text{ simplifies to } \begin{cases} -8x + 4y = -28 \\ 8x - 4y = 1 \end{cases}$$

Now add the resulting equations.

$$\begin{array}{r} -8x + 4y = -28 \\ \underline{8x - 4y = 1} \quad \text{Add the equations.} \\ 0 = -27 \quad \text{False} \end{array}$$

When we add the equations, both variables are eliminated and we have $0 = -27$, a false statement. This means that the system has no solution. The graphs of these equations are parallel lines. For the solution, we can write "no solution" or, in set notation, { } or ∅.

PRACTICE 3   Solve the system: $\begin{cases} x - 3y = 5 \\ 2x - 6y = -3 \end{cases}$

EXAMPLE 4   Solve the system: $\begin{cases} 3x - 2y = 2 \\ -9x + 6y = -6 \end{cases}$

Solution   First we multiply both sides of the first equation by 3, then we add the resulting equations.

$$\begin{cases} 3(3x - 2y) = 3(2) \\ -9x + 6y = -6 \end{cases} \text{ simplifies to } \begin{array}{r} 9x - 6y = 6 \\ \underline{-9x + 6y = -6} \quad \text{Add the equations.} \\ 0 = 0 \quad \text{True} \end{array}$$

Both variables are eliminated and we have $0 = 0$, a true statement. Whenever you eliminate a variable and get the equation $0 = 0$, the system has an infinite number of solutions. The graphs of these equations are identical. The solution is "infinite number of solutions" or, in set notation, $\{(x, y) \mid 3x - 2y = 2\}$ or $\{(x, y) \mid -9x + 6y = -6\}$

PRACTICE 4   Solve the system: $\begin{cases} 4x - 3y = 5 \\ -8x + 6y = -10 \end{cases}$

Answer to Concept Check: **b**

✓**CONCEPT CHECK**

Suppose you are solving the system

$$\begin{cases} 3x + 8y = -5 \\ 2x - 4y = 3 \end{cases}$$

You decide to use the addition method and begin by multiplying both sides of the first equation by -2. In which of the following was the multiplication performed correctly? Explain.

a. $-6x - 16y = -5$ **b.** $-6x - 16y = 10$

EXAMPLE 5 Solve the system: $\begin{cases} 3x + 4y = 13 \\ 5x - 9y = 6 \end{cases}$

Solution We can eliminate the variable y by multiplying the first equation by 9 and the second equation by 4.

$\begin{cases} 9(3x + 4y) = 9(13) \\ 4(5x - 9y) = 4(6) \end{cases}$ simplifies to $\begin{cases} 27x + 36y = 117 \\ \underline{20x - 36y = 24} \end{cases}$

$$47x = 141 \quad \text{Add the equations.}$$
$$x = 3 \quad \text{Divide both sides by 47.}$$

To find the corresponding y-value, we let $x = 3$ in any equation in this example containing two variables. Doing so in any of these equations will give $y = 1$. The solution to this system is $(3, 1)$. Check to see that $(3, 1)$ satisfies each equation in the original system. □

PRACTICE 5 Solve the system: $\begin{cases} 4x + 3y = 14 \\ 3x - 2y = 2 \end{cases}$

If we had decided to eliminate x instead of y in Example 5, the first equation could have been multiplied by 5 and the second by -3. Try solving the original system this way to check that the solution is $(3, 1)$.

The following steps summarize how to solve a system of linear equations by the addition method.

> **Solving a System of Two Linear Equations by the Addition Method**
>
> **Step 1.** Rewrite each equation in standard form $Ax + By = C$.
> **Step 2.** If necessary, multiply one or both equations by a nonzero number so that the coefficients of a chosen variable in the system are opposites.
> **Step 3.** Add the equations.
> **Step 4.** Find the value of one variable by solving the resulting equation from Step 3.
> **Step 5.** Find the value of the second variable by substituting the value found in Step 4 into either of the original equations.
> **Step 6.** Check the proposed solution in the original system.

✓**CONCEPT CHECK**
Suppose you are solving the system
$$\begin{cases} -4x + 7y = 6 \\ x + 2y = 5 \end{cases}$$
by the addition method.
a. What step(s) should you take if you wish to eliminate x when adding the equations?
b. What step(s) should you take if you wish to eliminate y when adding the equations?

EXAMPLE 6 Solve the system: $\begin{cases} -x - \dfrac{y}{2} = \dfrac{5}{2} \\ \dfrac{x}{6} - \dfrac{y}{2} = 0 \end{cases}$

Answers to Concept Check:
a. multiply the second equation by 4
b. possible answer: multiply the first equation by -2 and the second equation by 7

Solution: We begin by clearing each equation of fractions. To do so, we multiply both sides of the first equation by the LCD, 2, and both sides of the second equation by the LCD, 6. Then the system

$$\begin{cases} 2\left(-x - \dfrac{y}{2}\right) = 2\left(\dfrac{5}{2}\right) \\ 6\left(\dfrac{x}{6} - \dfrac{y}{2}\right) = 6(0) \end{cases} \quad \text{simplifies to} \quad \begin{cases} -2x - y = 5 \\ x - 3y = 0 \end{cases}$$

We can now eliminate the variable x by multiplying the second equation by 2.

$$\begin{cases} -2x - y = 5 \\ 2(x - 3y) = 2(0) \end{cases} \quad \text{simplifies to} \quad \begin{cases} -2x - y = 5 \\ \underline{2x - 6y = 0} \end{cases}$$

$$-7y = 5 \qquad \text{Add the equations.}$$

$$y = -\frac{5}{7} \qquad \text{Solve for } y.$$

To find x, we could replace y with $-\dfrac{5}{7}$ in one of the equations with two variables.

Instead, let's go back to the simplified system and multiply by appropriate factors to eliminate the variable y and solve for x. To do this, we multiply the first equation by -3. Then the system

$$\begin{cases} -3(-2x - y) = -3(5) \\ x - 3y = 0 \end{cases} \quad \text{simplifies to} \quad \begin{cases} 6x + 3y = -15 \\ \underline{x - 3y = 0} \end{cases}$$

$$7x = -15 \qquad \text{Add the equations.}$$

$$x = -\frac{15}{7} \qquad \text{Solve for } x.$$

Check the ordered pair $\left(-\dfrac{15}{7}, -\dfrac{5}{7}\right)$ in both equations of the original system. The solution is $\left(-\dfrac{15}{7}, -\dfrac{5}{7}\right)$. $\qquad\square$

PRACTICE
6   Solve the system: $\begin{cases} -2x + \dfrac{3y}{2} = 5 \\ -\dfrac{x}{2} - \dfrac{y}{4} = \dfrac{1}{2} \end{cases}$

Vocabulary, Readiness & Video Check

Given the system $\begin{cases} 3x - 2y = -9 \\ x + 5y = 14 \end{cases}$ *read each row (Step 1, Step 2, and Result). Then answer whether the result is true or false.*

	Step 1	Step 2	Result	True or False?
1.	Multiply 2nd equation through by -3.	Add the resulting equation to the 1st equation.	The y's are eliminated.	
2.	Multiply 2nd equation through by -3.	Add the resulting equation to the 1st equation.	The x's are eliminated.	
3.	Multiply 1st equation by 5 and 2nd equation by 2.	Add the two new equations.	The y's are eliminated.	
4.	Multiply 1st equation by 5 and 2nd equation by -2.	Add the two new equations.	The y's are eliminated.	

Martin-Gay Interactive Videos

See Video 4.3

Watch the section lecture video and answer the following question.

OBJECTIVE 1

5. For the addition/elimination methods, sometimes you need to multiply an equation through by a nonzero number so that the coefficients of a variable are opposites, as is shown in ▭ Example 2. What property allows us to do this? What important reminder is made at this step?

4.3 Exercise Set

MyMathLab

Solve each system of equations by the addition method. See Example 1.

1. $\begin{cases} 3x + y = 5 \\ 6x - y = 4 \end{cases}$

2. $\begin{cases} 4x + y = 13 \\ 2x - y = 5 \end{cases}$

3. $\begin{cases} x - 2y = 8 \\ -x + 5y = -17 \end{cases}$

4. $\begin{cases} x - 2y = -11 \\ -x + 5y = 23 \end{cases}$

Solve each system of equations by the addition method. If a system contains fractions or decimals, you may want to clear each equation of fractions or decimals first. See Examples 2 through 6.

5. $\begin{cases} 3x + y = -11 \\ 6x - 2y = -2 \end{cases}$

6. $\begin{cases} 4x + y = -13 \\ 6x - 3y = -15 \end{cases}$

7. $\begin{cases} 3x + 2y = 11 \\ 5x - 2y = 29 \end{cases}$

8. $\begin{cases} 4x + 2y = 2 \\ 3x - 2y = 12 \end{cases}$

9. $\begin{cases} x + 5y = 18 \\ 3x + 2y = -11 \end{cases}$

10. $\begin{cases} x + 4y = 14 \\ 5x + 3y = 2 \end{cases}$

11. $\begin{cases} x + y = 6 \\ x - y = 6 \end{cases}$

12. $\begin{cases} x - y = 1 \\ -x + 2y = 0 \end{cases}$

13. $\begin{cases} 2x + 3y = 0 \\ 4x + 6y = 3 \end{cases}$

14. $\begin{cases} 3x + y = 4 \\ 9x + 3y = 6 \end{cases}$

15. $\begin{cases} -x + 5y = -1 \\ 3x - 15y = 3 \end{cases}$

16. $\begin{cases} 2x + y = 6 \\ 4x + 2y = 12 \end{cases}$

17. $\begin{cases} 3x - 2y = 7 \\ 5x + 4y = 8 \end{cases}$

18. $\begin{cases} 6x - 5y = 25 \\ 4x + 15y = 13 \end{cases}$

19. $\begin{cases} 8x = -11y - 16 \\ 2x + 3y = -4 \end{cases}$

20. $\begin{cases} 10x + 3y = -12 \\ 5x = -4y - 16 \end{cases}$

21. $\begin{cases} 4x - 3y = 7 \\ 7x + 5y = 2 \end{cases}$

22. $\begin{cases} -2x + 3y = 10 \\ 3x + 4y = 2 \end{cases}$

23. $\begin{cases} 4x - 6y = 8 \\ 6x - 9y = 16 \end{cases}$

24. $\begin{cases} 9x - 3y = 12 \\ 12x - 4y = 18 \end{cases}$

25. $\begin{cases} 2x - 5y = 4 \\ 3x - 2y = 4 \end{cases}$

26. $\begin{cases} 6x - 5y = 7 \\ 4x - 6y = 7 \end{cases}$

27. $\begin{cases} \dfrac{x}{3} + \dfrac{y}{6} = 1 \\ \dfrac{x}{2} - \dfrac{y}{4} = 0 \end{cases}$

28. $\begin{cases} \dfrac{x}{2} + \dfrac{y}{8} = 3 \\ x - \dfrac{y}{4} = 0 \end{cases}$

29. $\begin{cases} \dfrac{10}{3}x + 4y = -4 \\ 5x + 6y = -6 \end{cases}$

30. $\begin{cases} \dfrac{3}{2}x + 4y = 1 \\ 9x + 24y = 6 \end{cases}$

31. $\begin{cases} x - \dfrac{y}{3} = -1 \\ -\dfrac{x}{2} + \dfrac{y}{8} = \dfrac{1}{4} \end{cases}$

32. $\begin{cases} 2x - \dfrac{3y}{4} = -3 \\ x + \dfrac{y}{9} = \dfrac{13}{3} \end{cases}$

33. $\begin{cases} -4(x + 2) = 3y \\ 2x - 2y = 3 \end{cases}$

34. $\begin{cases} -9(x + 3) = 8y \\ 3x - 3y = 8 \end{cases}$

35. $\begin{cases} \dfrac{x}{3} - y = 2 \\ -\dfrac{x}{2} + \dfrac{3y}{2} = -3 \end{cases}$

36. $\begin{cases} \dfrac{x}{2} + \dfrac{y}{4} = 1 \\ -\dfrac{x}{4} - \dfrac{y}{8} = 1 \end{cases}$

37. $\begin{cases} \dfrac{3}{5}x - y = -\dfrac{4}{5} \\ 3x + \dfrac{y}{2} = -\dfrac{9}{5} \end{cases}$

38. $\begin{cases} 3x + \dfrac{7}{2}y = \dfrac{3}{4} \\ -\dfrac{x}{2} + \dfrac{5}{3}y = -\dfrac{5}{4} \end{cases}$

39. $\begin{cases} 3.5x + 2.5y = 17 \\ -1.5x - 7.5y = -33 \end{cases}$

40. $\begin{cases} -2.5x - 6.5y = 47 \\ 0.5x - 4.5y = 37 \end{cases}$

41. $\begin{cases} 0.02x + 0.04y = 0.09 \\ -0.1x + 0.3y = 0.8 \end{cases}$

42. $\begin{cases} 0.04x - 0.05y = 0.105 \\ 0.2x - 0.6y = 1.05 \end{cases}$

MIXED PRACTICE

Solve each system by either the addition method or the substitution method.

43. $\begin{cases} 2x - 3y = -11 \\ y = 4x - 3 \end{cases}$

44. $\begin{cases} 4x - 5y = 6 \\ y = 3x - 10 \end{cases}$

45. $\begin{cases} x + 2y = 1 \\ 3x + 4y = -1 \end{cases}$

46. $\begin{cases} x + 3y = 5 \\ 5x + 6y = -2 \end{cases}$

47. $\begin{cases} 2y = x + 6 \\ 3x - 2y = -6 \end{cases}$

48. $\begin{cases} 3y = x + 14 \\ 2x - 3y = -16 \end{cases}$

49. $\begin{cases} y = 2x - 3 \\ y = 5x - 18 \end{cases}$

50. $\begin{cases} y = 6x - 5 \\ y = 4x - 11 \end{cases}$

51. $\begin{cases} x + \dfrac{1}{6}y = \dfrac{1}{2} \\ 3x + 2y = 3 \end{cases}$

52. $\begin{cases} x + \dfrac{1}{3}y = \dfrac{5}{12} \\ 8x + 3y = 4 \end{cases}$

53. $\begin{cases} \dfrac{x+2}{2} = \dfrac{y+11}{3} \\ \dfrac{x}{2} = \dfrac{2y+16}{6} \end{cases}$

54. $\begin{cases} \dfrac{2x+5}{2} = \dfrac{4y+14}{4} \\ \dfrac{x}{3} = \dfrac{2y+2}{6} \end{cases}$

55. $\begin{cases} 2x + 3y = 14 \\ 3x - 4y = -69.1 \end{cases}$

56. $\begin{cases} 5x - 2y = -19.8 \\ -3x + 5y = -3.7 \end{cases}$

REVIEW AND PREVIEW

Translating *Rewrite the following sentences using mathematical symbols. Do not solve the equations. See Sections 2.3 and 2.4.*

57. Twice a number, added to 6, is 3 less than the number.

58. The sum of three consecutive integers is 66.

59. Three times a number, subtracted from 20, is 2.

60. Twice the sum of 8 and a number is the difference of the number and 20.

61. The product of 4 and the sum of a number and 6 is twice the number.

62. If the quotient of twice a number and 7 is subtracted from the reciprocal of the number, the result is 2.

CONCEPT EXTENSIONS

Solve. See a Concept Check in this section.

63. To solve this system by the addition method and eliminate the variable y,

$$\begin{cases} 4x + 2y = -7 \\ 3x - y = -12 \end{cases}$$

by what value would you multiply the second equation? What do you get when you complete the multiplication?

64. Given the system of linear equations $\begin{cases} 3x - y = -8 \\ 5x + 3y = 2 \end{cases}$, use the addition method and

   a. Solve the system by eliminating x.

   b. Solve the system by eliminating y.

65. Suppose you are solving the system $\begin{cases} 3x + 8y = -5 \\ 2x - 4y = 3 \end{cases}$.

   You decide to use the addition method by multiplying both sides of the second equation by 2. In which of the following was the multiplication performed correctly? Explain.

   a. $4x - 8y = 3$

   b. $4x - 8y = 6$

66. Suppose you are solving the system $\begin{cases} -2x - y = 0 \\ -2x + 3y = 6 \end{cases}$.

   You decide to use the addition method by multiplying both sides of the first equation by 3, then adding the resulting equation to the second equation. Which of the following is the correct sum? Explain.

   a. $-8x = 6$

   b. $-8x = 9$

67. When solving a system of equations by the addition method, how do we know when the system has no solution?

68. Explain why the addition method might be preferred over the substitution method for solving the system $\begin{cases} 2x - 3y = 5 \\ 5x + 2y = 6 \end{cases}$.

69. Use the system of linear equations below to answer the questions.

$$\begin{cases} x + y = 5 \\ 3x + 3y = b \end{cases}$$

   a. Find the value of b so that the system has an infinite number of solutions.

   b. Find a value of b so that there are no solutions to the system.

70. Use the system of linear equations below to answer the questions.

$$\begin{cases} x + y = 4 \\ 2x + by = 8 \end{cases}$$

   a. Find the value of b so that the system has an infinite number of solutions.

   b. Find a value of b so that the system has a single solution.

Solve each system by the addition method.

71. $\begin{cases} 1.2x + 3.4y = 27.6 \\ 7.2x - 1.7y = -46.56 \end{cases}$

72. $\begin{cases} 5.1x - 2.4y = 3.15 \\ -15.3x + 1.2y = 27.75 \end{cases}$

73. Two age groups predicted to increase in percent of the workforce are those age 25–34 and those age 55 and older. The percent of workers age 25–34 predicted for 2008 through 2018 can be approximated by $0.05x - y = -21.6$. The percent of workers age 55 and older for the same years can be approximated by $0.58x - y = -18.1$. For both equations, x is the number of years since 2008 and y is the percent of the workforce. (*Source:* Bureau of Labor Statistics)

   a. Use the addition method to solve the system:

$$\begin{cases} 0.05x - y = -21.6 \\ 0.58x - y = -18.1 \end{cases}$$

   (Round answer to the nearest whole.)

   b. Use your result from part (a) and estimate the year in which both percents will be the same.

   c. Use your results from part (a) and part (b) to estimate the percent of workers age 25–34 and those age 55 and older.

74. Two occupations predicted to greatly increase in the number of jobs are pharmacy technicians and network system analysts. The number of pharmacy technician jobs predicted for 2006 through 2016 can be approximated by $9.1x - y = -295$. The number of network system analyst jobs predicted for 2006 through 2016 can be approximated by $14x - y = -262$. For both equations, x is the number of years since 2006, and y is the number of jobs in the thousands. (*Source:* Bureau of Labor Statistics)

a. Use the addition method to solve this system of equations.

$$\begin{cases} 9.1x - y = -295 \\ 14x - y = -262 \end{cases}$$

(Eliminate y first and solve for x. Round this result to the nearest whole.)

b. Interpret your solution from part (a).

c. Using the year in your answer to part (b), estimate the number of pharmacy technician jobs and network system analyst jobs in that year.

Integrated Review) SOLVING SYSTEMS OF EQUATIONS

Sections 4.1–4.3
Solve each system by either the addition method or the substitution method.

1. $\begin{cases} 2x - 3y = -11 \\ y = 4x - 3 \end{cases}$

2. $\begin{cases} 4x - 5y = 6 \\ y = 3x - 10 \end{cases}$

3. $\begin{cases} x + y = 3 \\ x - y = 7 \end{cases}$

4. $\begin{cases} x - y = 20 \\ x + y = -8 \end{cases}$

5. $\begin{cases} x + 2y = 1 \\ 3x + 4y = -1 \end{cases}$

6. $\begin{cases} x + 3y = 5 \\ 5x + 6y = -2 \end{cases}$

7. $\begin{cases} y = x + 3 \\ 3x - 2y = -6 \end{cases}$

8. $\begin{cases} y = -2x \\ 2x - 3y = -16 \end{cases}$

9. $\begin{cases} y = 2x - 3 \\ y = 5x - 18 \end{cases}$

10. $\begin{cases} y = 6x - 5 \\ y = 4x - 11 \end{cases}$

11. $\begin{cases} x + \dfrac{1}{6}y = \dfrac{1}{2} \\ 3x + 2y = 3 \end{cases}$

12. $\begin{cases} x + \dfrac{1}{3}y = \dfrac{5}{12} \\ 8x + 3y = 4 \end{cases}$

13. $\begin{cases} x - 5y = 1 \\ -2x + 10y = 3 \end{cases}$

14. $\begin{cases} -x + 2y = 3 \\ 3x - 6y = -9 \end{cases}$

15. $\begin{cases} 0.2x - 0.3y = -0.95 \\ 0.4x + 0.1y = 0.55 \end{cases}$

16. $\begin{cases} 0.08x - 0.04y = -0.11 \\ 0.02x - 0.06y = -0.09 \end{cases}$

17. $\begin{cases} x = 3y - 7 \\ 2x - 6y = -14 \end{cases}$

18. $\begin{cases} y = \dfrac{x}{2} - 3 \\ 2x - 4y = 0 \end{cases}$

19. $\begin{cases} 2x + 5y = -1 \\ 3x - 4y = 33 \end{cases}$

20. $\begin{cases} 7x - 3y = 2 \\ 6x + 5y = -21 \end{cases}$

21. Which method, substitution or addition, would you prefer to use to solve the system below? Explain your reasoning.

$$\begin{cases} 3x + 2y = -2 \\ y = -2x \end{cases}$$

22. Which method, substitution or addition, would you prefer to use to solve the system below? Explain your reasoning.

$$\begin{cases} 3x - 2y = -3 \\ 6x + 2y = 12 \end{cases}$$

4.5 | Systems of Linear Equations and Problem Solving

OBJECTIVES

1 Solve Problems That Can Be Modeled by a System of Two Linear Equations. ▶

2 Solve Problems with Cost and Revenue Functions. ▶

3 Solve Problems That Can Be Modeled by a System of Three Linear Equations. ▶

OBJECTIVE

1 **Solving Problems Modeled by Systems of Two Equations**

Thus far, we have solved problems by writing one-variable equations and solving for the variable. Some of these problems can be solved, perhaps more easily, by writing a system of equations, as illustrated in this section.

EXAMPLE 1 **Predicting Equal Consumption of Red Meat and Poultry**

America's consumption of red meat has decreased most years since 2000, while consumption of poultry has increased. The function $y = -0.56x + 113.6$ approximates the annual pounds of red meat consumed per capita, where x is the number of years since 2000. The function $y = 0.76x + 68.57$ approximates the annual pounds of poultry consumed per capita, where x is also the number of years since 2000. If this trend continues, determine the year when the annual consumption of red meat and poultry will be equal. (*Source:* USDA: Economic Research Service)

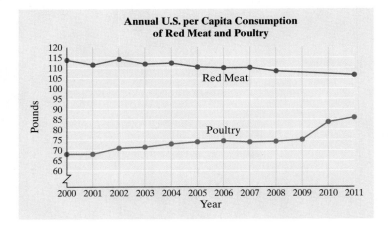

Solution:

1. UNDERSTAND. Read and reread the problem and guess a year. Let's guess the year 2020. This year is 20 years since 2000, so $x = 20$. Now let $x = 20$ in each given function.

$$\text{Red meat: } y = -0.56x + 113.6 = -0.56(20) + 113.6 = 102.4 \text{ pounds}$$
$$\text{Poultry: } \quad y = \quad 0.76x + 68.57 = \quad 0.76(20) + 68.57 = 83.77 \text{ pounds}$$

Since the projected pounds in 2020 for red meat and poultry are not the same, we guessed incorrectly, but we do have a better understanding of the problem. We know that the year will be later than 2020.

2. TRANSLATE. We are already given the system of equations.

3. SOLVE. We want to know the year x in which pounds y are the same, so we solve the system:

$$\begin{cases} y = -0.56x + 113.6 \\ y = 0.76x + 68.57 \end{cases}$$

Since both equations are solved for y, one way to solve is to use the substitution method.

$$y = 0.76x + 68.57 \qquad \text{Second equation}$$

$$-0.56x + 113.6 = 0.76x + 68.57 \qquad \text{Let } y = -0.56x + 113.6$$

$$-1.32x = -45.03$$

$$x = \frac{-45.03}{-1.32} \approx 34.11$$

4. INTERPRET. Since we are only asked to find the year, we need only solve for x.

Check: To check, see whether $x \approx 34.11$ gives approximately the same number of pounds of red meat and poultry.

Red meat: $y = -0.56x + 113.6 = -0.56(34.11) + 113.6 \approx 94.4984\,\text{pounds}$

Poultry: $y = 0.76x + 68.57 = 0.76(34.11) + 68.57 \approx 94.4936\,\text{pounds}$

Since we rounded the number of years, the numbers of pounds do differ slightly. They differ only by 0.0048, so we can assume we solved correctly.

State: The consumption of red meat and poultry will be the same about 34.11 years after 2000, or 2034.11. Thus, in the year 2034, we predict the consumption will be the same.   □

PRACTICE

1   Read Example 1. If we use the years 2005, 2006, 2007, and 2008 only to write functions approximating the consumption of red meat and poultry, we have the following:

Red Meat: $y = -0.54x + 110.6$

Poultry: $y = -0.36x + 74.1$

where x is the number of years since 2005 and y is pounds per year consumed.

a. Assuming this trend continues, predict the year when consumption of red meat and poultry will be the same. Round to the nearest year.

b. Does your answer differ from the answer to Example 1? Why or why not?

For Example 1, the equations in the system were given to us. Let's now practice writing our own system of equations that we will use to solve an application.

Many of the applications solved earlier using one-variable equations can also be solved using two equations in **two** variables. We use the same problem-solving steps that have been used throughout this text. The only difference is that two variables are assigned to represent the two unknown quantities and that the stated problem is translated into **two** equations.

Problem-Solving Steps

Step 1. UNDERSTAND the problem. During this step, become comfortable with the problem. Some ways of doing this are to

Read and reread the problem.

Choose two variables to represent the two unknowns.

Construct a drawing if possible.

Propose a solution and check. Pay careful attention to how you check your proposed solution. This will help when writing equations to model the problem.

Step 2. TRANSLATE the problem into two equations.

Step 3. SOLVE the system of equations.

Step 4. INTERPRET the results: **Check** the proposed solution in the stated problem and **state** your conclusion.

EXAMPLE 2 **Finding Unknown Numbers**

Find two numbers whose sum is 37 and whose difference is 21.

Solution

1. UNDERSTAND. Read and reread the problem. Suppose that one number is 20. If their sum is 37, the other number is 17 because $20 + 17 = 37$. Is their difference 21? No; $20 - 17 = 3$. Our proposed solution is incorrect, but we now have a better understanding of the problem.

   Since we are looking for two numbers, we let

   x = first number

   y = second number

2. TRANSLATE. Since we have assigned two variables to this problem, we translate our problem into two equations.

   In words: | two numbers whose sum | is | 37

   Translate: $x + y$ $=$ 37

   In words: | two numbers whose difference | is | 21

   Translate: $x - y$ $=$ 21

3. SOLVE. Now we solve the system

$$\begin{cases} x + y = 37 \\ x - y = 21 \end{cases}$$

Notice that the coefficients of the variable y are opposites. Let's then solve by the addition method and begin by adding the equations.

$$\begin{array}{r} x + y = 37 \\ \underline{x - y = 21} \\ 2x = 58 \end{array}$$ Add the equations.

$$x = \frac{58}{2} = 29$$ Divide both sides by 2.

Now we let $x = 29$ in the first equation to find y.

$$x + y = 37 \quad \text{First equation}$$
$$29 + y = 37$$
$$y = 8 \quad \text{Subtract 29 from both sides.}$$

4. INTERPRET. The solution of the system is $(29, 8)$.

Check: Notice that the sum of 29 and 8 is $29 + 8 = 37$, the required sum. Their difference is $29 - 8 = 21$, the required difference.

State: The numbers are 29 and 8.   □

PRACTICE

2   Find two numbers whose sum is 30 and whose difference is 6.

.... ■

EXAMPLE 3   **Finding Unknown Numbers**

A first number is 4 less than a second number. Four times the first number is 6 more than twice the second. Find the numbers.

Solution

1. UNDERSTAND. Read and reread the problem and guess a solution. If a first number is 10 and this is 4 less than a second number, the second number is 14. Four times the first number is $4(10)$, or 40. This is not equal to 6 more than twice the second number, which is $2(14) + 6$ or 34. Although we guessed incorrectly, we now have a better understanding of the problem.

Since we are looking for two numbers, we will let

$$x = \text{first number}$$
$$y = \text{second number}$$

2. TRANSLATE. Since we have assigned two variables to this problem, we will translate the given facts into two equations. For the first statement we have

In words:	the first number	is	4 less than the second number
	↓	↓	↓
Translate:	x	$=$	$y - 4$

Next we translate the second statement into an equation.

In words:	four times the first number	is	6 more than twice the second number
	↓	↓	↓
Translate:	$4x$	$=$	$2y + 6$

3. SOLVE. Here we solve the system

$$\begin{cases} x = y - 4 \\ 4x = 2y + 6 \end{cases}$$

Since the first equation expresses x in terms of y, we will use substitution. We substitute $y - 4$ for x in the second equation and solve for y.

$$4x = 2y + 6 \quad \text{Second equation}$$
$$4(y - 4) = 2y + 6$$
$$4y - 16 = 2y + 6 \quad \text{Let } x = y - 4.$$
$$2y = 22$$
$$y = 11$$

(Continued on next page)

Now we replace y with 11 in the equation $x = y - 4$ and solve for x. Then $x = y - 4$ becomes $x = 11 - 4 = 7$. The ordered pair solution of the system is $(7, 11)$.

4. INTERPRET. Since the solution of the system is $(7, 11)$, then the first number we are looking for is 7 and the second number is 11.

Check: Notice that 7 *is* 4 less than 11, and 4 times 7 *is* 6 more than twice 11. The proposed numbers, 7 and 11, are correct.

State: The numbers are 7 and 11. □

PRACTICE

3 A first number is 5 more than a second number. Twice the first number is 2 less than 3 times the second number. Find the numbers.

EXAMPLE 4 **Solving a Problem about Prices**

The Cirque du Soleil show Varekai is performing locally. Matinee admission for 4 adults and 2 children is $374, while admission for 2 adults and 3 children is $285.

a. What is the price of an adult's ticket?

b. What is the price of a child's ticket?

c. Suppose that a special rate of $1000 is offered for groups of 20 persons. Should a group of 4 adults and 16 children use the group rate? Why or why not?

Solution

1. UNDERSTAND. Read and reread the problem and guess a solution. Let's suppose that the price of an adult's ticket is $50 and the price of a child's ticket is $40. To check our proposed solution, let's see if admission for 4 adults and 2 children is $374. Admission for 4 adults is 4($50) or $200 and admission for 2 children is 2($40) or $80. This gives a total admission of $200 + $80 = $280, not the required $374. Again, though, we have accomplished the purpose of this process: We have a better understanding of the problem. To continue, we let

A = the price of an adult's ticket and

C = the price of a child's ticket

2. TRANSLATE. We translate the problem into two equations using both variables.

In words:	admission for 4 adults	and	admission for 2 children	is	$374
	↓	↓	↓	↓	↓
Translate:	$4A$	$+$	$2C$	$=$	374

In words:	admission for 2 adults	and	admission for 3 children	is	$285
	↓	↓	↓	↓	↓
Translate:	$2A$	$+$	$3C$	$=$	285

3. SOLVE. We solve the system.

$$\begin{cases} 4A + 2C = 374 \\ 2A + 3C = 285 \end{cases}$$

Since both equations are written in standard form, we solve by the addition method. First we multiply the second equation by -2 so that when we add the equations, we eliminate the variable A. Then the system

$$\begin{cases} 4A + 2C = 374 \\ -2(2A + 3C) = -2(285) \end{cases}$$ simplifies to $\begin{cases} 4A + 2C = 374 \\ -4A - 6C = -570 \end{cases}$

Add the equations.

$$\begin{array}{r} -4C = -196 \\ C = 49 \text{ or } \$49, \text{ the} \\ \text{children's} \\ \text{ticket price.} \end{array}$$

To find A, we replace C with 49 in the first equation.

$4A + 2C = 374$ First equation

$4A + 2(49) = 374$ Let $C = 49$

$4A + 98 = 374$

$4A = 276$

$A = 69$ or $\$69$, the adult's ticket price

4. INTERPRET.

Check: Notice that 4 adults and 2 children will pay

$4(\$69) + 2(\$49) = \$276 + \$98 = \$374$, the required amount. Also, the price for 2 adults and 3 children is $2(\$69) + 3(\$49) = \$138 + \$147 = \$285$, the required amount.

State: Answer the three original questions.

a. Since $A = 69$, the price of an adult's ticket is $69.

b. Since $C = 49$, the price of a child's ticket is $49.

c. The regular admission price for 4 adults and 16 children is

$4(\$69) + 16(\$49) = \$276 + \$784$

$= \$1060$

This is $60 more than the special group rate of $1000, so they should request the group rate.   □

PRACTICE

4   It is considered a premium game when the Red Sox or the Yankees come to Texas to play the Rangers. Admission for one of these games for three adults and three children under 14 is $75, while admission for two adults and four children is $62. (*Source:* MLB.com, Texas Rangers)

a. What is the price of an adult admission at Ameriquest Park?

b. What is the price of a child's admission?

c. Suppose that a special rate of $200 is offered for groups of 20 persons. Should a group of 5 adults and 15 children use the group rate? Why or why not?

EXAMPLE 5 **Finding the Rate of Speed**

Two cars leave Indianapolis, one traveling east and the other west. After 3 hours, they are 297 miles apart. If one car is traveling 5 mph faster than the other, what is the speed of each?

Solution

1. UNDERSTAND. Read and reread the problem. Let's guess a solution and use the formula $d = rt$ (distance = rate · time) to check. Suppose that one car is traveling at a rate of 55 miles per hour. This means that the other car is traveling at a rate of 50 miles per hour since we are told that one car is traveling 5 mph faster than the other. To find the distance apart after 3 hours, we will first find the distance traveled by each car. One car's distance is rate · time = 55(3) = 165 miles. The other car's distance is rate · time = 50(3) = 150 miles. Since one car is traveling east and the other west, their distance apart is the sum of their distances, or 165 miles + 150 miles = 315 miles. Although this distance apart is not the required distance of 297 miles, we now have a better understanding of the problem.

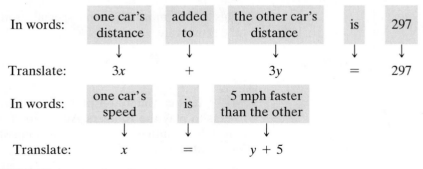

Let's model the problem with a system of equations. We will let

$$x = \text{speed of one car}$$
$$y = \text{speed of the other car}$$

We summarize the information on the following chart. Both cars have traveled 3 hours. Since distance = rate · time, their distances are $3x$ and $3y$ miles, respectively.

	Rate •	*Time* =	*Distance*
One Car	x	3	$3x$
Other Car	y	3	$3y$

2. TRANSLATE. We can now translate the stated conditions into two equations.

In words: one car's distance   added to   the other car's distance   is   297

Translate: $3x$ $+$ $3y$ $=$ 297

In words: one car's speed   is   5 mph faster than the other

Translate: x $=$ $y + 5$

3. SOLVE. Here we solve the system

$$\begin{cases} 3x + 3y = 297 \\ x = y + 5 \end{cases}$$

Again, the substitution method is appropriate. We replace x with $y + 5$ in the first equation and solve for y.

$$3x + 3y = 297 \quad \text{First equation}$$

$$3(y + 5) + 3y = 297 \quad \text{Let } x = y + 5.$$
$$3y + 15 + 3y = 297$$
$$6y = 282$$
$$y = 47$$

To find x, we replace y with 47 in the equation $x = y + 5$. Then $x = 47 + 5 = 52$. The ordered pair solution of the system is $(52, 47)$.

4. INTERPRET. The solution $(52, 47)$ means that the cars are traveling at 52 mph and 47 mph, respectively.

Check: Notice that one car is traveling 5 mph faster than the other. Also, if one car travels 52 mph for 3 hours, the distance is $3(52) = 156$ miles. The other car traveling for 3 hours at 47 mph travels a distance of $3(47) = 141$ miles. The sum of the distances $156 + 141$ is 297 miles, the required distance.

State: The cars are traveling at 52 mph and 47 mph.   □

> ▶ **Helpful Hint**
> Don't forget to attach units if appropriate.

PRACTICE

5   In 2007, the French train TGV V150 became the fastest conventional rail train in the world. It broke the 1990 record of the next fastest conventional rail train, the French TGV Atlantique. Assume the V150 and the Atlantique left the same station in Paris, with one heading west and one heading east. After 2 hours, they were 2150 kilometers apart. If the V150 is 75 kph faster than the Atlantique, what is the speed of each?

EXAMPLE 6   **Mixing Solutions**

Lynn Pike, a pharmacist, needs 70 liters of a 50% alcohol solution. She has available a 30% alcohol solution and an 80% alcohol solution. How many liters of each solution should she mix to obtain 70 liters of a 50% alcohol solution?

Solution

1. UNDERSTAND. Read and reread the problem. Next, guess the solution. Suppose that we need 20 liters of the 30% solution. Then we need $70 - 20 = 50$ liters of the 80% solution. To see if this gives us 70 liters of a 50% alcohol solution, let's find the amount of pure alcohol in each solution.

number of liters	×	alcohol strength	=	amount of pure alcohol
20 liters	×	0.30	=	6 liters
50 liters	×	0.80	=	40 liters
70 liters	×	0.50	=	35 liters

Since 6 liters + 40 liters = 46 liters and not 35 liters, our guess is incorrect, but we have gained some insight as to how to model and check this problem.

We will let

$$x = \text{amount of 30\% solution, in liters}$$
$$y = \text{amount of 80\% solution, in liters}$$

(Continued on next page)

and use a table to organize the given data.

	Number of Liters	Alcohol Strength	Amount of Pure Alcohol
30% Solution	x	30%	$0.30x$
80% Solution	y	80%	$0.80y$
50% Solution Needed	70	50%	$(0.50)(70)$

2. TRANSLATE. We translate the stated conditions into two equations.

In words: amount of 30% solution   +   amount of 80% solution   =   70

Translate: x + y =   70

In words: amount of pure alcohol in 30% solution   +   amount of pure alcohol in 80% solution   =   amount of pure alcohol in 50% solution

Translate: $0.30x$ + $0.80y$ = $(0.50)(70)$

3. SOLVE. Here we solve the system

$$\begin{cases} x + y = 70 \\ 0.30x + 0.80y = (0.50)(70) \end{cases}$$

To solve this system, we use the elimination method. We multiply both sides of the first equation by -3 and both sides of the second equation by 10. Then

Now we replace y with 28 in the equation $x + y = 70$ and find that $x + 28 = 70$, or $x = 42$.
The ordered pair solution of the system is $(42, 28)$.

4. INTERPRET.

Check: Check the solution in the same way that we checked our guess.

State: The pharmacist needs to mix 42 liters of 30% solution and 28 liters of 80% solution to obtain 70 liters of 50% solution. □

PRACTICE

6   Keith Robinson is a chemistry teacher who needs 1 liter of a solution of 5% hydrochloric acid to carry out an experiment. If he only has a stock solution of 99% hydrochloric acid, how much water (0% acid) and how much stock solution (99%) of HCL must he mix to get 1 liter of 5% solution? Round answers to the nearest hundredth of a liter.

> ✓CONCEPT CHECK
> Suppose you mix an amount of 25% acid solution with an amount of 60% acid solution. You then calculate the acid strength of the resulting acid mixture. For which of the following results should you suspect an error in your calculation? Why?
> **a.** 14%   **b.** 32%   **c.** 55%

OBJECTIVE
2   Solving Problems with Cost and Revenue Functions

Recall that businesses are often computing cost and revenue functions or equations to predict sales, to determine whether prices need to be adjusted, and to see whether the company is making or losing money. Recall also that the value at which revenue equals cost is called the break-even point. When revenue is less than cost, the company is losing money; when revenue is greater than cost, the company is making money.

EXAMPLE 7   Finding a Break-Even Point

A manufacturing company recently purchased $3000 worth of new equipment to offer new personalized stationery to its customers. The cost of producing a package of personalized stationery is $3.00, and it is sold for $5.50. Find the number of packages that must be sold for the company to break even.

Solution

1. UNDERSTAND. Read and reread the problem. Notice that the cost to the company will include a one-time cost of $3000 for the equipment and then $3.00 per package produced. The revenue will be $5.50 per package sold.

To model this problem, we will let

$$x = \text{number of packages of personalized stationery}$$
$$C(x) = \text{total cost of producing } x \text{ packages of stationery}$$
$$R(x) = \text{total revenue from selling } x \text{ packages of stationery}$$

2. TRANSLATE. The revenue equation is

In words:	revenue for selling x packages of stationery	=	price per package	·	number of packages
	↓		↓		↓
Translate:	$R(x)$	=	5.5	·	x

The cost equation is

In words:	cost for producing x packages of stationery	=	cost per package	·	number of packages	+	cost for equipment
	↓		↓		↓		↓
Translate:	$C(x)$	=	3	·	x	+	3000

Since the break-even point is when $R(x) = C(x)$, we solve the equation

$$5.5x = 3x + 3000$$

(Continued on next page)

3. SOLVE.

$$5.5x = 3x + 3000$$

$$2.5x = 3000 \qquad \text{Subtract } 3x \text{ from both sides.}$$

$$x = 1200 \qquad \text{Divide both sides by 2.5.}$$

4. INTERPRET.

Check: To see whether the break-even point occurs when 1200 packages are produced and sold, see if revenue equals cost when $x = 1200$. When $x = 1200$, $R(x) = 5.5x = 5.5(1200) = 6600$ and $C(x) = 3x + 3000 = 3(1200) + 3000 = 6600$. Since $R(1200) = C(1200) = 6600$, the break-even point is 1200.

State: The company must sell 1200 packages of stationery to break even. The graph of this system is shown.

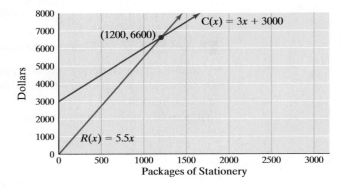

PRACTICE

7 An online-only electronics firm recently purchased $3000 worth of new equipment to create shock-proof packaging for its products. The cost of producing one shock-proof package is $2.50, and the firm charges the customer $4.50 for the packaging. Find the number of packages that must be sold for the company to break even.

OBJECTIVE

3 Solving Problems Modeled by Systems of Three Equations

To introduce problem solving by writing a system of three linear equations in three variables, we solve a problem about triangles.

 EXAMPLE 8 Finding Angle Measures

The measure of the largest angle of a triangle is 80° more than the measure of the smallest angle, and the measure of the remaining angle is 10° more than the measure of the smallest angle. Find the measure of each angle.

Solution

1. UNDERSTAND. Read and reread the problem. Recall that the sum of the measures of the angles of a triangle is 180°. Then guess a solution. If the smallest angle measures 20°, the measure of the largest angle is 80° more, or 20° + 80° = 100°. The measure of the remaining angle is 10° more than the measure of the smallest angle, or 20° + 10° = 30°. The sum of these three angles is 20° + 100° + 30° = 150°, not the required 180°. We now know that the measure of the smallest angle is greater than 20°.

To model this problem, we will let

x = degree measure of the smallest angle

y = degree measure of the largest angle

z = degree measure of the remaining angle

2. TRANSLATE. We translate the given information into three equations.

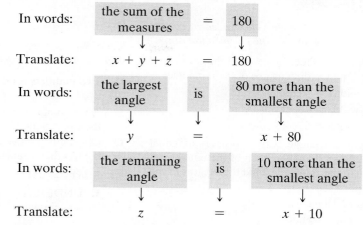

In words: | the sum of the measures | = | 180 |

Translate: $x + y + z$ = 180

In words: | the largest angle | is | 80 more than the smallest angle |

Translate: y = $x + 80$

In words: | the remaining angle | is | 10 more than the smallest angle |

Translate: z = $x + 10$

3. SOLVE. We solve the system

$$\begin{cases} x + y + z = 180 \\ y = x + 80 \\ z = x + 10 \end{cases}$$

Since y and z are both expressed in terms of x, we will solve using the substitution method. We substitute $y = x + 80$ and $z = x + 10$ in the first equation. Then

$$x + y + z = 180$$

$x + (x + 80) + (x + 10) = 180$ First equation

$3x + 90 = 180$ Let $y = x + 80$ and $z = x + 10$.

$3x = 90$

$x = 30$

Then $y = x + 80 = 30 + 80 = 110$, and $z = x + 10 = 30 + 10 = 40$. The ordered triple solution is $(30, 110, 40)$.

4. INTERPRET.

Check: Notice that $30° + 40° + 110° = 180°$. Also, the measure of the largest angle, $110°$, is $80°$ more than the measure of the smallest angle, $30°$. The measure of the remaining angle, $40°$, is $10°$ more than the measure of the smallest angle, $30°$.   □

PRACTICE

8   The measure of the largest angle of a triangle is $40°$ more than the measure of the smallest angle, and the measure of the remaining angle is $20°$ more than the measure of the smallest angle. Find the measure of each angle.

Vocabulary, Readiness & Video Check

Martin-Gay Interactive Videos

See Video 4.5

Watch the section lecture video and answer the following questions.

OBJECTIVE 1

1. In ▭ Example 1 and the lecture before, the problem-solving steps for solving applications are mentioned. What is the difference here from when we've used these steps in the past?

OBJECTIVE 2

2. Based on ▭ Example 6, explain the meaning of a break-even point. How do you find the break-even point algebraically?

OBJECTIVE 3

3. In ▭ Example 7, why is the ordered triple not the final stated solution to the application?

4.5 Exercise Set MyMathLab®

Without actually solving each problem, choose each correct solution by deciding which choice satisfies the given conditions.

△ **1.** The length of a rectangle is 3 feet longer than the width. The perimeter is 30 feet. Find the dimensions of the rectangle.

   a. length = 8 feet; width = 5 feet
   b. length = 8 feet; width = 7 feet
   c. length = 9 feet; width = 6 feet

△ **2.** An isosceles triangle, a triangle with two sides of equal length, has a perimeter of 20 inches. Each of the equal sides is one inch longer than the third side. Find the lengths of the three sides.

   a. 6 inches, 6 inches, and 7 inches
   b. 7 inches, 7 inches, and 6 inches
   c. 6 inches, 7 inches, and 8 inches

3. Two computer disks and three notebooks cost $17. However, five computer disks and four notebooks cost $32. Find the price of each.

   a. notebook = $4; computer disk = $3
   b. notebook = $3; computer disk = $4
   c. notebook = $5; computer disk = $2

4. Two music CDs and four music cassette tapes cost a total of $40. However, three music CDs and five cassette tapes cost $55. Find the price of each.

   a. CD = $12; cassette = $4
   b. CD = $15; cassette = $2
   c. CD = $10; cassette = $5

5. Kesha has a total of 100 coins, all of which are either dimes or quarters. The total value of the coins is $13.00. Find the number of each type of coin.

   a. 80 dimes; 20 quarters   **b.** 20 dimes; 44 quarters
   c. 60 dimes; 40 quarters

6. Samuel has 28 gallons of saline solution available in two large containers at his pharmacy. One container holds three times as much as the other container. Find the capacity of each container.

   a. 15 gallons; 5 gallons   **b.** 20 gallons; 8 gallons
   c. 21 gallons; 7 gallons

TRANSLATING

Write a system of equations in x and y describing each situation. Do not solve the system. See Example 2.

7. A smaller number and a larger number add up to 15 and have a difference of 7. (Let x be the larger number.)

8. The total of two numbers is 16. The first number plus 2 more than 3 times the second equals 18. (Let x be the first number.)

9. Keiko has a total of $6500, which she has invested in two accounts. The larger account is $800 greater than the smaller account. (Let x be the amount of money in the larger account.)

10. Dominique has four times as much money in his savings account as in his checking account. The total amount is $2300. (Let x be the amount of money in his checking account.)

MIXED PRACTICE

Solve. See Examples 1 through 6. For Exercises 13 and 14, the solutions have been started for you.

11. Two numbers total 83 and have a difference of 17. Find the two numbers.

12. The sum of two numbers is 76 and their difference is 52. Find the two numbers.

13. One number is two more than a second number. Twice the first is 4 less than 3 times the second. Find the numbers.

Start the solution:

1. UNDERSTAND the problem. Since we are looking for two numbers, let

$$x = \text{one number}$$
$$y = \text{second number}$$

2. TRANSLATE. Since we have assigned two variables, we will translate the facts into two equations. (Fill in the blanks.)

First equation:

Second equation:

Finish with:

3. SOLVE the system and

4. INTERPRET the results.

14. Three times one number minus a second is 8, and the sum of the numbers is 12. Find the numbers.

Start the solution:

1. UNDERSTAND the problem. Since we are looking for two numbers, let

$$x = \text{one number}$$
$$y = \text{second number}$$

2. TRANSLATE. Since we have assigned two variables, we will translate the facts into two equations. (Fill in the blanks.)

First equation:

Second equation:

In words:	The sum of the numbers	is	12
	↓	↓	↓
Translate:	x + ___ ___		12

Finish with:

3. SOLVE the system and

4. INTERPRET the results.

15. A first number plus twice a second number is 8. Twice the first number, plus the second, totals 25. Find the numbers.

16. One number is 4 more than twice the second number. Their total is 25. Find the numbers.

17. Miguel Cabrera of the Detroit Tigers led Major League Baseball in runs batted in for the 2010 regular season. Alex Rodriguez of the New York Yankees, who came in second to Cabrera, had 1 fewer run batted in for the 2010 regular season. Together, these two players brought home 251 runs during the 2010 regular season. How many runs batted in did each player account for? (*Source:* Major League Baseball)

18. The highest scorer during the WNBA 2010 regular season was Cappie Pondexter of the New York Liberty. Over the season, Pondexter scored 13 more points than the second-highest scorer, Angel McCoughtry of the Atlanta Dream. Together, Pondexter and McCoughtry scored 1445 points during the 2010 regular season. How many points did each player score over the course of the season? (*Source:* Women's National Basketball Association)

19. Ann Marie Jones has been pricing Amtrak train fares for a group trip to New York. Three adults and four children must pay $159. Two adults and three children must pay $112. Find the price of an adult's ticket and find the price of a child's ticket.

20. Last month, Jerry Papa purchased two DVDs and five CDs at Wall-to-Wall Sound for $65. This month, he bought four DVDs and three CDs for $81. Find the price of each DVD and find the price of each CD.

21. Johnston and Betsy Waring have a jar containing 80 coins, all of which are either quarters or nickels. The total value of the coins is $14.60. How many of each type of coin do they have?

22. Sarah and Keith Robinson purchased 40 stamps, a mixture of 44¢ and 20¢ stamps. Find the number of each type of stamp if they spent $16.40.

23. Norman and Suzanne Scarpulla own 35 shares of McDonald's stock and 69 shares of The Ohio Art Company stock (makers of Etch A Sketch and other toys). On a particular day in 2011, their stock portfolio consisting of these two stocks was worth $2814. The McDonald's stock was $70 more per share than The Ohio Art Company stock. What was the price of each stock on that day? (*Source:* Yahoo finance)

24. Saralee Rose has investments in Google and Nintendo stock. During a particular day in 2011, Google stock was at $540 per share, and Nintendo stock was at $30 per share. Saralee's portfolio made up of these two stocks was worth $20,610 at that time. If Saralee owns 16 more shares of Google stock than she owns of Nintendo stock, how many shares of each type of stock does she own?

25. Twice last month, Judy Carter rented a car from Enterprise in Fresno, California, and traveled around the Southwest on business. Enterprise rents this car for a daily fee plus an additional charge per mile driven. Judy recalls that her first trip lasted 4 days, she drove 450 miles, and the rental cost her $240.50. On her second business trip, she drove the same model of car a distance of 200 miles in 3 days and paid $146.00 for the rental. Find the daily fee and the mileage charge.

26. Joan Gundersen rented the same car model twice from Hertz, which rents this car model for a daily fee plus an additional charge per mile driven. Joan recalls that the car rented for 5 days and driven for 300 miles cost her $178, while the same model car rented for 4 days and driven for 500 miles cost $197. Find the daily fee and find the mileage charge.

27. Pratap Puri rowed 18 miles down the Delaware River in 2 hours, but the return trip took him $4\frac{1}{2}$ hours. Find the rate Pratap can row in still water and find the rate of the current.

Let x = rate Pratap can row in still water and
y = rate of the current

	d	$=$	r	$\cdot$	t
Downstream			$x + y$		
Upstream			$x - y$		

28. The Jonathan Schultz family took a canoe 10 miles down the Allegheny River in $1\frac{1}{4}$ hours. After lunch, it took them 4 hours to return. Find the rate of the current.

Let x = rate the family can row in still water and
y = rate of the current

	d	$=$	r	$\cdot$	t
Downstream			$x + y$		
Upstream			$x - y$		

29. Dave and Sandy Hartranft are frequent flyers with Delta Airlines. They often fly from Philadelphia to Chicago, a distance of 780 miles. On one particular trip, they fly into the wind, and the flight takes 2 hours. The return trip, with the wind behind them, only takes $1\frac{1}{2}$ hours. If the wind speed is the same on each trip, find the speed of the wind and find the speed of the plane in still air.

30. With a strong wind behind it, a United Airlines jet flies 2400 miles from Los Angeles to Orlando in $4\frac{3}{4}$ hours. The return trip takes 6 hours because the plane flies into the wind. If the wind speed is the same on each trip, find the speed of the plane in still air and find the wind speed to the nearest tenth of a mile per hour.

31. Kevin Briley began a 114-mile bicycle trip to build up stamina for a triathlete competition. Unfortunately, his bicycle chain broke, so he finished the trip walking. The whole trip took 6 hours. If Kevin walks at a rate of 4 miles per hour and rides at 24 miles per hour, find the amount of time he spent on the bicycle.

32. In Canada, eastbound and westbound trains travel along the same track, with sidings to pull onto to avoid accidents. Two trains are now 150 miles apart, with the westbound train traveling twice as fast as the eastbound train. A warning must be issued to pull one train onto a siding or else the trains will crash in $1\frac{1}{4}$ hours. Find the speed of the eastbound train and the speed of the westbound train.

33. Doreen Schmidt is a chemist with Gemco Pharmaceutical. She needs to prepare 12 liters of a 9% hydrochloric acid solution. Find the amount of a 4% solution and the amount of a 12% solution she should mix to get this solution.

Concentration Rate	Liters of Solution	Liters of Pure Acid
0.04	x	0.04x
0.12	y	?
0.09	12	?

34. Elise Everly is preparing 15 liters of a 25% saline solution. Elise has two other saline solutions, with strengths of 40% and 10%. Find the amount of 40% solution and the amount of 10% solution she should mix to get 15 liters of a 25% solution.

Concentration Rate	Liters of Solution	Liters of Pure Salt
0.40	x	0.40x
0.10	y	?
0.25	15	?

35. Wayne Osby blends coffee for a local coffee café. He needs to prepare 200 pounds of blended coffee beans selling for $3.95 per pound. He intends to do this by blending together a high-quality bean costing $4.95 per pound and a cheaper bean costing $2.65 per pound. To the nearest pound, find how much high-quality coffee bean and how much cheaper coffee bean he should blend.

36. Macadamia nuts cost an astounding $16.50 per pound, but research by an independent firm says that mixed nuts sell better if macadamias are included. The standard mix costs $9.25 per pound. Find how many pounds of macadamias and how many pounds of the standard mix should be combined to produce 40 pounds that will cost $10 per pound. Find the amounts to the nearest tenth of a pound.

37. Recall that two angles are complementary if the sum of their measures is 90°. Find the measures of two complementary angles if one angle is twice the other.

38. Recall that two angles are supplementary if the sum of their measures is 180°. Find the measures of two supplementary angles if one angle is 20° more than four times the other.

39. Find the measures of two complementary angles if one angle is 10° more than three times the other.

40. Find the measures of two supplementary angles if one angle is 18° more than twice the other.

41. Kathi and Robert Hawn had a pottery stand at the annual Skippack Craft Fair. They sold some of their pottery at the original price of $9.50 each but later decreased the price of each by $2. If they sold all 90 pieces and took in $721, find how many they sold at the original price and how many they sold at the reduced price.

42. A charity fund-raiser consisted of a spaghetti supper where a total of 387 people were fed. They charged $6.80 for adults and half price for children. If they took in $2444.60, find how many adults and how many children attended the supper.

43. The Santa Fe National Historic Trail is approximately 1200 miles between Old Franklin, Missouri, and Santa Fe, New Mexico. Suppose that a group of hikers start from each town and walk the trail toward each other. They meet after a total hiking time of 240 hours. If one group travels $\frac{1}{2}$ mile per hour slower than the other group, find the rate of each group. (*Source:* National Park Service)

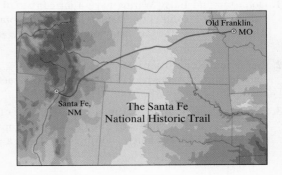

44. California 1 South is a historic highway that stretches 123 miles along the coast from Monterey to Morro Bay. Suppose that two antique cars start driving this highway, one from each town. They meet after 3 hours. Find the rate of each car if one car travels 1 mile per hour faster than the other car. (*Source:* National Geographic)

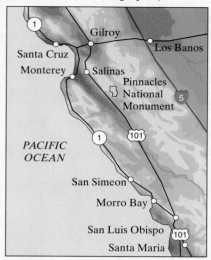

45. A 30% solution of fertilizer is to be mixed with a 60% solution of fertilizer to get 150 gallons of a 50% solution. How many gallons of the 30% solution and 60% solution should be mixed?

46. A 10% acid solution is to be mixed with a 50% acid solution to get 120 ounces of a 20% acid solution. How many ounces of the 10% solution and 50% solution should be mixed?

47. Traffic signs are regulated by the *Manual on Uniform Traffic Control Devices* (MUTCD). According to this manual, if the sign below is placed on a freeway, its perimeter must be 144 inches. Also, its length is 12 inches longer than its width. Find the dimensions of this sign.

48. According to the MUTCD (see Exercise 47), this sign must have a perimeter of 60 inches. Also, its length must be 6 inches longer than its width. Find the dimensions of this sign.

49. In the United States, the percent of adult blogging has changed within the various age ranges. From 2007 to 2009, the function $y = -4.5x + 24$ can be used to estimate the percent of adults under 30 who blogged, and the function $y = 2x + 7$ can be used to estimate the percent of adults over 30 who blogged. For both functions, x is the number of years after 2007. (*Source:* Pew Internet & American Life Project)

a. If this trend continued, estimate the year in which the percent of adults under 30 and the percent of adults over 30 who blogged was the same.

b. Use these equations to predict the percent of adults under 30 who blog and the percent of adults over 30 who blog for the current year.

50. The rate of fatalities per 100 million vehicle-miles has been decreasing for both automobiles and light trucks (pickups, sport-utility vehicles, and minivans). For the years 2001 through 2009, the function $y = -0.06x + 1.7$ can be used to estimate the rate of fatalities per 100 million vehicle-miles for automobiles during this period, and the function $y = -0.08x + 2.1$ can be used to estimate the rate of fatalities per 100 million vehicle-miles for light trucks during this period. For both functions, x is the number of years since 2000. (*Source:* Bureau of Statistics, U.S. Department of Transportation)

a. If this trend continues, predict the year in which the fatality rate for automobiles equals the fatality rate for light trucks.

b. Use these equations to predict the fatality rate per million vehicle-miles for automobiles and light trucks for the current year.

51. The annual U.S. per capita consumption of cheddar cheese has remained about the same since the millennium, while the consumption of mozzarella cheese has increased. For the years 2000–2010, the function $y = 0.06x + 9.7$ approximates the annual U.S. per capita consumption of cheddar cheese in pounds, and the function $y = 0.21x + 9.3$ approximates the annual U.S. per capita consumption of mozzarella cheese in pounds. For both functions, x is the number of years after 2000.

a. Explain how the given function verifies that the consumption of cheddar cheese has remained the same, while the given function verifies that the consumption of mozzarella cheese has increased.

b. Based on this information, determine the year in which the pounds of cheddar cheese consumed equaled the pounds of mozzarella cheese consumed. (*Source:* Based on data from the U.S. Department of Agriculture)

52. Two of the major job categories defined by the U.S. Department of Labor are manufacturing jobs and jobs in the service sector. Jobs in the manufacturing sector have decreased nearly every year since the 1960s. During the same time period, service sector jobs have been steadily increasing. For the years from 1988 through 2009, the function $y = -0.225x + 16.1$ approximates the percent of jobs in the U.S. economy that are manufacturing jobs, while the function $y = 0.45x + 21.7$ approximates the percent of jobs that are service sector jobs. (*Source:* Based on data from the U.S. Department of Labor)

a. Explain how the decrease in manufacturing jobs can be verified by the given function, and the increase of service sector jobs can be verified by the given function.

b. Based on this information, determine the year when the percent of manufacturing jobs and the percent of service sector jobs were the same.

△ **53.** In the figure, line *l* and line *m* are parallel lines cut by transversal *t*. Find the values of x and y.

△ **54.** Find the values of x and y in the following isosceles triangle.

Given the cost function $C(x)$ and the revenue function $R(x)$, find the number of units x that must be sold to break even. See Example 7.

55. $C(x) = 30x + 10,000 \ R(x) = 46x$

56. $C(x) = 12x + 15,000 \ R(x) = 32x$

57. $C(x) = 1.2x + 1500 \ R(x) = 1.7x$

58. $C(x) = 0.8x + 900 \ R(x) = 2x$

59. $C(x) = 75x + 160,000 \ R(x) = 200x$

60. $C(x) = 105x + 70,000 \ R(x) = 245x$

▶ **61.** The planning department of Abstract Office Supplies has been asked to determine whether the company should introduce a new computer desk next year. The department estimates that $6000 of new manufacturing equipment will need to be purchased and that the cost of constructing each desk

will be $200. The department also estimates that the revenue from each desk will be $450.

a. Determine the revenue function $R(x)$ from the sale of x desks.

b. Determine the cost function $C(x)$ for manufacturing x desks.

c. Find the break-even point.

62. Baskets, Inc., is planning to introduce a new woven basket. The company estimates that $500 worth of new equipment will be needed to manufacture this new type of basket and that it will cost $15 per basket to manufacture. The company also estimates that the revenue from each basket will be $31.

a. Determine the revenue function $R(x)$ from the sale of x baskets.

b. Determine the cost function $C(x)$ for manufacturing x baskets.

c. Find the break-even point. Round up to the nearest whole basket.

Solve. See Example 8.

63. Rabbits in a lab are to be kept on a strict daily diet that includes 30 grams of protein, 16 grams of fat, and 24 grams of carbohydrates. The scientist has only three food mixes available with the following grams of nutrients per unit.

	Protein	*Fat*	*Carbohydrate*
Mix A	4	6	3
Mix B	6	1	2
Mix C	4	1	12

Find how many units of each mix are needed daily to meet each rabbit's dietary need.

64. Gerry Gundersen mixes different solutions with concentrations of 25%, 40%, and 50% to get 200 liters of a 32% solution. If he uses twice as much of the 25% solution as of the 40% solution, find how many liters of each kind he uses.

65. The perimeter of a quadrilateral (four-sided polygon) is 29 inches. The longest side is twice as long as the shortest side. The other two sides are equally long and are 2 inches longer than the shortest side. Find the lengths of all four sides.

66. The measure of the largest angle of a triangle is 90° more than the measure of the smallest angle, and the measure of the remaining angle is 30° more than the measure of the smallest angle. Find the measure of each angle.

67. The sum of three numbers is 40. The first number is five more than the second number. It is also twice the third. Find the numbers.

68. The sum of the digits of a three-digit number is 15. The tens-place digit is twice the hundreds-place digit, and the ones-place digit is 1 less than the hundreds-place digit. Find the three-digit number.

69. During the 2010–2011 regular NBA season, the top-scoring player was Kevin Durant of the Oklahoma City Thunder. Durant scored a total of 2161 points during the regular season. The number of free throws (each worth one point) he made was 14 more than four times the number of three-point field goals he made. The number of two-point field goals that Durant made was 28 less than the number of free throws he made. How many free throws, two-point field goals, and three-point field goals did Kevin Durant make during the 2010–2011 NBA season? (*Source*: National Basketball Association)

70. For 2010, the WNBA's top scorer was Diana Taurasi of the Phoenix Mercury. She scored a total of 745 points during the regular season. The number of two-point field goals Taurasi made was 36 fewer than two times the number of three-point field goals she made. The number of free throws (each worth one point) she made was 61 more than the number of two-point field goals she made. Find how many free throws, two-point field goals, and three-point field goals Diana Taurasi made during the 2010 regular season. (*Source*: Women's National Basketball Association)

71. Find the values of x, y, and z in the following triangle.

72. The sum of the measures of the angles of a quadrilateral is 360°. Find the values of x, y, and z in the following quadrilateral.

REVIEW AND PREVIEW

Solve each linear inequality. Write your solution in interval notation. See Section 2.8.

73. $-3x < -9$

74. $2x - 7 \leq 5x + 11$

75. $4(2x - 1) \geq 0$

76. $\frac{2}{3}x < \frac{1}{3}$

CONCEPT EXTENSIONS

Solve. See the Concept Check in this section.

77. Suppose you mix an amount of candy costing $0.49 a pound with candy costing $0.65 a pound. Which of the following costs per pound could result?

   a. $0.58   **b.** $0.72   **c.** $0.29

78. Suppose you mix a 50% acid solution with pure acid (100%). Which of the following acid strengths are possible for the resulting acid mixture?

   a. 25%   **b.** 150%   **c.** 62%   **d.** 90%

79. Dale and Sharon Mahnke have decided to fence off a garden plot behind their house, using their house as the "fence" along one side of the garden. The length (which runs parallel to the house) is 3 feet less than twice the width. Find the dimensions if 33 feet of fencing is used along the three sides requiring it.

80. Judy McElroy plans to erect 152 feet of fencing around her rectangular horse pasture. A river bank serves as one side length of the rectangle. If each width is 4 feet longer than half the length, find the dimensions.

81. Find the values of a, b, and c such that the equation $y = ax^2 + bx + c$ has ordered pair solutions $(1, 6)$, $(-1, -2)$, and $(0, -1)$. To do so, substitute each ordered pair solution into the equation. Each time, the result is an equation in three unknowns: $a, b,$ and c. Then solve the resulting system of three linear equations in three unknowns, $a, b,$ and c.

82. Find the values of $a, b,$ and c such that the equation $y = ax^2 + bx + c$ has ordered pair solutions $(1, 2), (2, 3),$ and $(-1, 6)$. (*Hint:* See Exercise 81.)

83. Data (x, y) for the total number (in thousands) of college-bound students who took the ACT assessment in the year x are approximately $(3, 927), (11, 1179),$ and $(19, 1495),$ where $x = 3$ represents 1993 and $x = 11$ represents 2001. Find the values $a, b,$ and c such that the equation $y = ax^2 + bx + c$ models these data. According to your model, how many students will take the ACT in 2015? (*Source:* ACT, Inc.)

84. Monthly normal rainfall data (x, y) for Portland, Oregon, are $(4, 2.47), (7, 0.58), (8, 1.07),$ where x represents time in

months (with $x = 1$ representing January) and y represents rainfall in inches. Find the values of $a, b,$ and c rounded to 2 decimal places such that the equation $y = ax^2 + bx + c$ models this data. According to your model, how much rain should Portland expect during September? (*Source:* National Climatic Data Center)

The function $f(x) = -8.6x + 275$ represents the U.S. average number of monthly calls (sent or received) per wireless subscriber and the function $f(x) = 204.9x - 1217$ represents the average number of text messages (sent or received) per wireless subscriber. For both functions, x is the number of years since 2000, and these functions are good for the years 2006–2010.

85. Solve the system formed by these functions. Round each coordinate to the nearest whole number.

86. Use your answer to Exercise 85 to predict the year in which the monthly calls and text messages are/were the same.

Chapter 4 Vocabulary Check

Fill in each blank with one of the words or phrases listed below.

system of linear equations   solution   consistent   independent

dependent   inconsistent   substitution   addition

1. In a system of linear equations in two variables, if the graphs of the equations are the same, the equations are _____ equations.
2. Two or more linear equations are called a(n) _____.
3. A system of equations that has at least one solution is called a(n) _____ system.
4. A(n) _____ of a system of two equations in two variables is an ordered pair of numbers that is a solution of both equations in the system.
5. Two algebraic methods for solving systems of equations are _____ and _____.
6. A system of equations that has no solution is called a(n) _____ system.
7. In a system of linear equations in two variables, if the graphs of the equations are different, the equations are _____ equations.

Chapter 4 Highlights

DEFINITIONS AND CONCEPTS	EXAMPLES
Section 4.1 Solving Systems of Linear Equations by Graphing	
A **solution** of a system of two equations in two variables is an ordered pair of numbers that is a solution of both equations in the system.	Determine whether $(-1, 3)$ is a solution of the system: $$\begin{cases} 2x - y = -5 \\ x = 3y - 10 \end{cases}$$ Replace x with -1 and y with 3 in both equations. $$2x - y = -5 \qquad x = 3y - 10$$ $$2(-1) - 3 \stackrel{?}{=} -5 \qquad -1 \stackrel{?}{=} 3 \cdot 3 - 10$$ $$-5 = -5 \text{ True} \qquad -1 = -1 \text{ True}$$ $(-1, 3)$ is a solution of the system.

(continued)

DEFINITIONS AND CONCEPTS	**EXAMPLES**

Section 4.1 Solving Systems of Linear Equations by Graphing (continued)

Graphically, a solution of a system is a point common to the graphs of both equations.

Solve by graphing. $\begin{cases} 3x - 2y = -3 \\ x + y = 4 \end{cases}$

A system of equations with at least one solution is a **consistent system.** A system that has no solution is an **inconsistent system.**

If the graphs of two linear equations are identical, the equations are **dependent.** If their graphs are different, the equations are **independent.**

Consistent and independent   Consistent and dependent   Inconsistent and independent

Section 4.2 Solving Systems of Linear Equations by Substitution

To solve a system of linear equations by the substitution method:

Step 1. Solve one equation for a variable.

Step 2. Substitute the expression for the variable into the other equation.

Step 3. Solve the equation from Step 2 to find the value of one variable.

Step 4. Substitute the value from Step 3 in either original equation to find the value of the other variable.

Step 5. Check the solution in both equations.

Solve by substitution.

$$\begin{cases} 3x + 2y = 1 \\ x = y - 3 \end{cases}$$

Substitute $y - 3$ for x in the first equation.

$$3x + 2y = 1$$
$$3(y - 3) + 2y = 1$$
$$3y - 9 + 2y = 1$$
$$5y = 10$$
$$y = 2 \quad \text{Divide by 5.}$$

To find x, substitute 2 for y in $x = y - 3$ so that $x = 2 - 3$ or -1. The solution $(-1, 2)$ checks.

Section 4.3 Solving Systems of Linear Equations by Addition

To solve a system of linear equations by the addition method:

Step 1. Rewrite each equation in standard form $Ax + By = C$.

Step 2. Multiply one or both equations by a nonzero number so that the coefficients of a variable are opposites.

Step 3. Add the equations.

Step 4. Find the value of one variable by solving the resulting equation.

Step 5. Substitute the value from Step 4 into either original equation to find the value of the other variable.

Step 6. Check the solution in both equations.

Solve by addition.

$$\begin{cases} x - 2y = 8 \\ 3x + y = -4 \end{cases}$$

Multiply both sides of the first equation by -3.

$$\begin{cases} -3x + 6y = -24 \\ \underline{3x + y = -4} \end{cases}$$
$$7y = -28 \quad \text{Add.}$$
$$y = -4 \quad \text{Divide by 7.}$$

To find x, let $y = -4$ in an original equation.

$$x - 2(-4) = 8 \quad \text{First equation}$$
$$x + 8 = 8$$
$$x = 0$$

The solution $(0, -4)$ checks.

(continued)

DEFINITIONS AND CONCEPTS	EXAMPLES

Section 4.3 Solving Systems of Linear Equations by Addition (continued)

If solving a system of linear equations by substitution or addition yields a true statement such as $-2 = -2$, then the graphs of the equations in the system are identical and there is an infinite number of solutions of the system.

Solve: $\begin{cases} 2x - 6y = -2 \\ x = 3y - 1 \end{cases}$

Substitute $3y - 1$ for x in the first equation.

$$2(3y - 1) - 6y = -2$$
$$6y - 2 - 6y = -2$$
$$-2 = -2 \quad \text{True}$$

The system has an infinite number of solutions. In set notation, we write $\{(x, y)\,|\,2x - 6y = -2\}$ or $\{(x, y)\,|\,x = 3y - 1\}$.

DEFINITIONS AND CONCEPTS	**EXAMPLES**
	Section 4.5 Systems of Linear Equations and Problem Solving

Problem-solving steps

1. UNDERSTAND. Read and reread the problem.

Two angles are supplementary if their sum is 180°.

The larger of two supplementary angles is three times the smaller, decreased by twelve. Find the measure of each angle. Let

$$x = \text{measure of smaller angle}$$
$$y = \text{measure of larger angle}$$

2. TRANSLATE.

In words:

the sum of supplementary angles	is	180°
↓	↓	↓

Translate: $x + y$ $=$ 180

In words:

larger angle	is	3 times smaller	decreased by	12
↓	↓	↓	↓	↓

Translate: y $=$ $3x$ $-$ 12

3. SOLVE.

Solve the system:

$$\begin{cases} x + y = 180 \\ y = 3x - 12 \end{cases}$$

Use the substitution method and replace y with $3x - 12$ in the first equation.

$$x + y = 180$$
$$x + (3x - 12) = 180$$
$$4x = 192$$
$$x = 48$$

Since $y = 3x - 12$, then $y = 3 \cdot 48 - 12$ or 132.

4. INTERPRET.

The solution checks. The smaller angle measures 48° and the larger angle measures 132°.

Chapter 4 **Review**

(4.1) *Determine whether any of the following ordered pairs satisfy the system of linear equations.*

1. $\begin{cases} 2x - 3y = 12 \\ 3x + 4y = 1 \end{cases}$

    a. $(12, 4)$ **b.** $(3, -2)$ **c.** $(-3, 6)$

2. $\begin{cases} 4x + y = 0 \\ -8x - 5y = 9 \end{cases}$

    a. $\left(\dfrac{3}{4}, -3 \right)$ **b.** $(-2, 8)$ **c.** $\left(\dfrac{1}{2}, -2 \right)$

3. $\begin{cases} 5x - 6y = 18 \\ 2y - x = -4 \end{cases}$

    a. $(-6, -8)$ **b.** $\left(3, \dfrac{5}{2} \right)$ **c.** $\left(3, -\dfrac{1}{2} \right)$

4. $\begin{cases} 2x + 3y = 1 \\ 3y - x = 4 \end{cases}$

    a. $(2, 2)$ **b.** $(-1, 1)$ **c.** $(2, -1)$

Solve each system of equations by graphing.

5. $\begin{cases} x + y = 5 \\ x - y = 1 \end{cases}$ **6.** $\begin{cases} x + y = 3 \\ x - y = -1 \end{cases}$

7. $\begin{cases} x = 5 \\ y = -1 \end{cases}$ **8.** $\begin{cases} x = -3 \\ y = 2 \end{cases}$

9. $\begin{cases} 2x + y = 5 \\ x = -3y \end{cases}$ **10.** $\begin{cases} 3x + y = -2 \\ y = -5x \end{cases}$

11. $\begin{cases} y = 3x \\ -6x + 2y = 6 \end{cases}$ **12.** $\begin{cases} x - 2y = 2 \\ -2x + 4y = -4 \end{cases}$

(4.2) Solve each system of equations by the substitution method.

13. $\begin{cases} y = 2x + 6 \\ 3x - 2y = -11 \end{cases}$ **14.** $\begin{cases} y = 3x - 7 \\ 2x - 3y = 7 \end{cases}$

15. $\begin{cases} x + 3y = -3 \\ 2x + y = 4 \end{cases}$ **16.** $\begin{cases} 3x + y = 11 \\ x + 2y = 12 \end{cases}$

17. $\begin{cases} 4y = 2x + 6 \\ x - 2y = -3 \end{cases}$ **18.** $\begin{cases} 9x = 6y + 3 \\ 6x - 4y = 2 \end{cases}$

19. $\begin{cases} x + y = 6 \\ y = -x - 4 \end{cases}$ **20.** $\begin{cases} -3x + y = 6 \\ y = 3x + 2 \end{cases}$

(4.3) Solve each system of equations by the addition method.

21. $\begin{cases} 2x + 3y = -6 \\ x - 3y = -12 \end{cases}$ **22.** $\begin{cases} 4x + y = 15 \\ -4x + 3y = -19 \end{cases}$

23. $\begin{cases} 2x - 3y = -15 \\ x + 4y = 31 \end{cases}$ **24.** $\begin{cases} x - 5y = -22 \\ 4x + 3y = 4 \end{cases}$

25. $\begin{cases} 2x - 6y = -1 \\ -x + 3y = \dfrac{1}{2} \end{cases}$ **26.** $\begin{cases} 0.6x - 0.3y = -1.5 \\ 0.04x - 0.02y = -0.1 \end{cases}$

27. $\begin{cases} \dfrac{3}{4}x + \dfrac{2}{3}y = 2 \\ x + \dfrac{y}{3} = 6 \end{cases}$ **28.** $\begin{cases} 10x + 2y = 0 \\ 3x + 5y = 33 \end{cases}$

(4.4) Solve each system of equations in three variables.

29. $\begin{cases} x \quad\;\; + z = 4 \\ 2x - y \quad\;\; = 4 \\ x + y - z = 0 \end{cases}$

30. $\begin{cases} 2x + 5y \quad\;\; = 4 \\ x - 5y + z = -1 \\ 4x \quad\quad - z = 11 \end{cases}$

31. $\begin{cases} 4y + 2z = 5 \\ 2x + 8y \quad\;\; = 5 \\ 6x + \quad\;\; 4z = 1 \end{cases}$

32. $\begin{cases} 5x + 7y \quad\;\; = 9 \\ 14y - z = 28 \\ 4x \quad\quad + 2z = -4 \end{cases}$

33. $\begin{cases} 3x - 2y + 2z = 5 \\ -x + 6y + z = 4 \\ 3x + 14y + 7z = 20 \end{cases}$

34. $\begin{cases} x + 2y + 3z = 11 \\ y + 2z = 3 \\ 2x \quad\quad + 2z = 10 \end{cases}$

35. $\begin{cases} 7x - 3y + 2z = 0 \\ 4x - 4y - z = 2 \\ 5x + 2y + 3z = 1 \end{cases}$

36. $\begin{cases} x - 3y - 5z = -5 \\ 4x - 2y + 3z = 13 \\ 5x + 3y + 4z = 22 \end{cases}$

(4.5) Solve each problem by writing and solving a system of linear equations.

37. The sum of two numbers is 16. Three times the larger number decreased by the smaller number is 72. Find the two numbers.

38. The Forrest Theater can seat a total of 360 people. They take in $15,150 when every seat is sold. If orchestra section tickets cost $45 and balcony tickets cost $35, find the number of seats in the orchestra section and the number of seats in the balcony.

39. A riverboat can head 340 miles upriver in 19 hours, but the return trip takes only 14 hours. Find the current of the river and find the speed of the riverboat in still water to the nearest tenth of a mile.

	d	$=$	r	$\cdot$	t
Upriver	340		$x - y$		19
Downriver	340		$x + y$		14

40. Find the amount of a 6% acid solution and the amount of a 14% acid solution Pat Mayfield should combine to prepare 50 cc (cubic centimeters) of a 12% solution.

41. A deli charges $3.80 for a breakfast of three eggs and four strips of bacon. The charge is $2.75 for two eggs and three strips of bacon. Find the cost of each egg and the cost of each strip of bacon.

42. An exercise enthusiast alternates between jogging and walking. He traveled 15 miles during the past 3 hours. He jogs at a rate of 7.5 miles per hour and walks at a rate of 4 miles per hour. Find how much time, to the nearest hundredth of an hour, he actually spent jogging and how much time he spent walking.

43. Chris Kringler has $2.77 in her coin jar—all in pennies, nickels, and dimes. If she has 53 coins in all and four more nickels than dimes, find how many of each type of coin she has.

44. An employee at See's Candy Store needs a special mixture of candy. She has creme-filled chocolates that sell for $3.00 per pound, chocolate-covered nuts that sell for $2.70 per pound, and chocolate-covered raisins that sell for $2.25 per pound. She wants to have twice as many raisins as nuts in the mixture. Find how many pounds of each she should use to make 45 pounds worth $2.80 per pound.

45. The perimeter of an isosceles (two sides equal) triangle is 73 centimeters. If the unequal side is 7 centimeters longer than the two equal sides, find the lengths of the three sides.

46. The sum of three numbers is 295. One number is five more than a second and twice the third. Find the numbers.

MIXED REVIEW

Solve each system of equations by graphing.

47. $\begin{cases} x - 2y = 1 \\ 2x + 3y = -12 \end{cases}$

48. $\begin{cases} 3x - y = -4 \\ 6x - 2y = -8 \end{cases}$

Solve each system of equations.

49. $\begin{cases} x + 4y = 11 \\ 5x - 9y = -3 \end{cases}$

50. $\begin{cases} x + 9y = 16 \\ 3x - 8y = 13 \end{cases}$

51. $\begin{cases} y = -2x \\ 4x + 7y = -15 \end{cases}$

52. $\begin{cases} 3y = 2x + 15 \\ -2x + 3y = 21 \end{cases}$

53. $\begin{cases} 3x - y = 4 \\ 4y = 12x - 16 \end{cases}$

54. $\begin{cases} x + y = 19 \\ x - y = -3 \end{cases}$

55. $\begin{cases} x - 3y = -11 \\ 4x + 5y = -10 \end{cases}$

56. $\begin{cases} -x - 15y = 44 \\ 2x + 3y = 20 \end{cases}$

57. $\begin{cases} x - 3y + 2z = 0 \\ 9y - z = 22 \\ 5x + 3z = 10 \end{cases}$

58. $\begin{cases} x - 4y = 4 \\ \dfrac{1}{8}x - \dfrac{1}{2}y = 3 \end{cases}$

Solve each problem by writing and solving a system of linear equations.

59. The sum of two numbers is 12. Three times the smaller number increased by the larger number is 20. Find the numbers.

60. The difference of two numbers is -18. Twice the smaller decreased by the larger is -23. Find the two numbers.

61. Emma Hodges has a jar containing 65 coins, all of which are either nickels or dimes. The total value of the coins is $5.30. How many of each type does she have?

62. Sarah and Owen Hebert purchased 26 stamps, a mixture of 17¢ and 20¢ stamps. Find the number of each type of stamp if they spent $4.93.

63. The perimeter of a triangle is 126 units. The length of one side is twice the length of the shortest side. The length of the third side is fourteen more than the length of the shortest side. Find the length of the sides of the triangles.

Chapter 4 Test   MyMathLab®   Test Prep VIDEOS   YouTube™

Answer each question true or false.

▶ **1.** A system of two linear equations in two variables can have exactly two solutions.

▶ **2.** Although (1, 4) is not a solution of $x + 2y = 6$, it can still be a solution of the system $\begin{cases} x + 2y = 6 \\ x + y = 5 \end{cases}$.

▶ **3.** If the two equations in a system of linear equations are added and the result is $3 = 0$, the system has no solution.

▶ **4.** If the two equations in a system of linear equations are added and the result is $3x = 0$, the system has no solution.

Is the ordered pair a solution of the given linear system?

▶ **5.** $\begin{cases} 2x - 3y = 5 \\ 6x + y = 1 \end{cases}$; $(1, -1)$

▶ **6.** $\begin{cases} 4x - 3y = 24 \\ 4x + 5y = -8 \end{cases}$; $(3, -4)$

▶ **7.** Use graphing to find the solutions of the system $\begin{cases} y - x = 6 \\ y + 2x = -6 \end{cases}$

▶ **8.** Use the substitution method to solve the system $\begin{cases} 3x - 2y = -14 \\ x + 3y = -1 \end{cases}$

▶ **9.** Use the substitution method to solve the system $\begin{cases} \dfrac{1}{2}x + 2y = -\dfrac{15}{4} \\ 4x = -y \end{cases}$

▶ **10.** Use the addition method to solve the system $\begin{cases} 3x + 5y = 2 \\ 2x - 3y = 14 \end{cases}$

▶ **11.** Use the addition method to solve the system $\begin{cases} 4x - 6y = 7 \\ -2x + 3y = 0 \end{cases}$

Solve each system using the substitution method or the addition method.

▶ **12.** $\begin{cases} 3x + y = 7 \\ 4x + 3y = 1 \end{cases}$

▶ **13.** $\begin{cases} 3(2x + y) = 4x + 20 \\ x - 2y = 3 \end{cases}$

▶ **14.** $\begin{cases} \dfrac{x - 3}{2} = \dfrac{2 - y}{4} \\ \dfrac{7 - 2x}{3} = \dfrac{y}{2} \end{cases}$

Solve each problem by writing and using a system of linear equations.

▶ **15.** Two numbers have a sum of 124 and a difference of 32. Find the numbers.

▶ **16.** Find the amount of a 12% saline solution a lab assistant should add to 80 cc (cubic centimeters) of a 22% saline solution to have a 16% solution.

▶ **17.** Texas and Missouri are the states with the most farms. Texas has 140 thousand more farms than Missouri and the total number of farms for these two states is 356 thousand. Find the number of farms for each state.

▶ **18.** Two hikers start at opposite ends of the St. Tammany Trail and walk toward each other. The trail is 36 miles long and they meet in 4 hours. If one hiker is twice as fast as the other, find both hiking speeds.

▶ **19.** $\begin{cases} 2x - 3y & = 4 \\ 3y + 2z = 2 \\ x \quad - z = -5 \end{cases}$

▶ **20.** $\begin{cases} 3x - 2y - z = -1 \\ 2x - 2y \quad = 4 \\ 2x \quad - 2z = -12 \end{cases}$

▶ **21.** The measure of the largest angle of a triangle is three less than 5 times the measure of the smallest angle. The measure of the remaining angle is 1 less than twice the measure of the smallest angle. Find the measure of each angle.

Chapter 4 Cumulative Review

1. Insert $<, >,$ or $=$ in the appropriate space between the paired numbers to make each statement true.

   a. $-1 \quad 0$ **b.** $7 \quad \dfrac{14}{2}$ **c.** $-5 \quad -6$

2. Evaluate.

   a. 5^2 **b.** 2^5

3. Name the property or properties illustrated by each true statement.

   a. $3 \cdot y = y \cdot 3$
   b. $(x + 7) + 9 = x + (7 + 9)$
   c. $(b + 0) + 3 = b + 3$
   d. $0.2 \cdot (z \cdot 5) = 0.2 \cdot (5 \cdot z)$
   e. $-2 \cdot \left(-\dfrac{1}{2}\right) = 1$
   f. $-2 + 2 = 0$
   g. $-6 \cdot (y \cdot 2) = (-6 \cdot 2) \cdot y$

4. Evaluate $y^2 - 3x$ for $x = 8$ and $y = 5$.

5. Write the phrase as an algebraic expression, then simplify if possible: Subtract $4x - 2$ from $2x - 3$.

6. Simplify: $7 - 12 + (-5) - 2 + (-2)$

7. Solve: $7 = -5(2a - 1) - (-11a + 6)$.

8. Evaluate $2y^2 - x^2$ for $x = -7$ and $y = -3$.

9. Solve: $\dfrac{5}{2}x = 15$

10. Simplify: $0.4y - 6.7 + y - 0.3 - 2.6y$

11. Solve: $\dfrac{x}{2} - 1 = \dfrac{2}{3}x - 3$

12. Solve: $7(x - 2) - 6(x + 1) = 20$

13. Twice the sum of a number and 4 is the same as four times the number, decreased by 12. Find the number.

14. Solve: $5(y - 5) = 5y + 10$

15. Solve $y = mx + b$ for x.

16. Five times the sum of a number and -1 is the same as 6 times the number. Find the number.

17. Solve $-2x \le -4$. Write the solution set in interval notation.

18. Solve $P = a + b + c$ for b.

19. Graph $x = -2y$ by plotting intercepts.

20. Solve $3x + 7 \ge x - 9$. Write the solution set in interval notation.

21. Find the slope of the line through $(-1, 5)$ and $(2, -3)$.

22. Complete the table of values for $x - 3y = 3$

x	y
	-1
3	
	2

23. Find the slope and y-intercept of the line whose equation is $y = \dfrac{3}{4}x + 6$.

24. Find the slope of a line parallel to the line passing through $(-1, 3)$ and $(2, -8)$.

25. Find the slope and the y-intercept of the line whose equation is $3x - 4y = 4$.

26. Find the slope and y-intercept of the line whose equation is $y = 7x$.

27. Find an equation of the line passing through $(-1, 5)$ with slope -2. Write the equation in slope-intercept form, $y = mx + b$, and in standard form, $Ax + By = C$.

28. Determine whether the lines are parallel, perpendicular, or neither.
$$y = 4x - 5$$
$$-4x + y = 7$$

29. Find an equation of the vertical line through $(-1, 5)$.

30. Write an equation of the line with slope -5, through $(-2, 3)$.

31. Find the domain and the range of the relation $\{(0, 2), (3, 3), (-1, 0), (3, -2)\}$.

32. If $f(x) = 5x^2 - 6$, find $f(0)$ and $f(-2)$.

33. Determine whether each relation is also a function.
a. $\{(-1, 1), (2, 3), (7, 3), (8, 6)\}$

b. $\{(0, -2), (1, 5), (0, 3), (7, 7)\}$

34. Determine whether each graph is also the graph of a function.
a.   **b.**   **c.**

   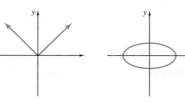

35. Determine the number of solutions of the system.
$$\begin{cases} 3x - y = 4 \\ x + 2y = 8 \end{cases}$$

36. Determine whether each ordered pair is a solution of the given system.
$$\begin{cases} 2x - y = 6 \\ 3x + 2y = -5 \end{cases}$$

a. $(1, -4)$ **b.** $(0, 6)$ **c.** $(3, 0)$

Solve each system.

37. $\begin{cases} x + 2y = 7 \\ 2x + 2y = 13 \end{cases}$

38. $\begin{cases} 3x - 4y = 10 \\ \quad\quad y = 2x \end{cases}$

39. $\begin{cases} x + y = 7 \\ x - y = 5 \end{cases}$

40. $\begin{cases} x = 5y - 3 \\ x = 8y + 4 \end{cases}$

41. Solve the system.
$$\begin{cases} 3x - y + z = -15 \\ x + 2y - z = 1 \\ 2x + 3y - 2z = 0 \end{cases}$$

42. Solve the system.
$$\begin{cases} x - 2y + z = 0 \\ 3x - y - 2z = -15 \\ 2x - 3y + 3z = 7 \end{cases}$$

43. A first number is 4 less than a second number. Four times the first number is 6 more than twice the second. Find the numbers.

44. Find two numbers whose sum is 37 and whose difference is 21.

CHAPTER 5

Exponents and Polynomials

Recall from Chapter 1 that an exponent is a shorthand notation for repeated factors. This chapter explores additional concepts about exponents and exponential expressions. An especially useful type of exponential expression is a polynomial. Polynomials model many real-world phenomena. In this chapter, we focus on polynomials and operations on polynomials.

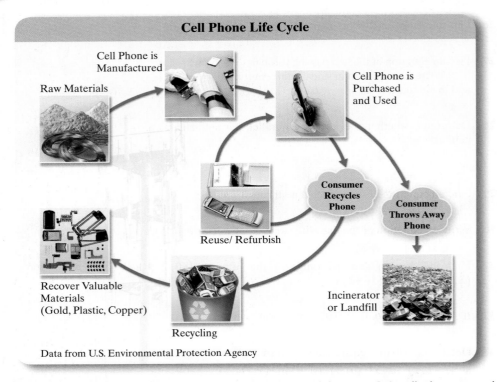

Cell Phone Life Cycle

Cell Phone is Manufactured

Raw Materials

Cell Phone is Purchased and Used

Consumer Recycles Phone

Consumer Throws Away Phone

Reuse/ Refurbish

Recover Valuable Materials (Gold, Plastic, Copper)

Recycling

Incinerator or Landfill

Data from U.S. Environmental Protection Agency

According to a recent survey, the average American adult owns 2.4 cell phones, and over 56% of those surveyed still have their old cell phones. In fact, it is estimated that 130 million cell phones will be retired this year. With new cell phone models having new features and increased technologies, this number of retired cell phones will probably only increase. The good news is that the number of cell phones being recycled is increasing. Below is a graph showing the growth of cell phones recycled by the largest recycler. In Exercises 99 and 100 of Section 5.2, you will explore some information about recycling cell phones.

Cell Phones Recycled by Largest Recycler

Cell Phones Collected (in millions) vs. Year

Data from ReCellular, Inc. (www.recellular.com)

5.1 | Exponents

OBJECTIVES

1. Evaluate Exponential Expressions.
2. Use the Product Rule for Exponents.
3. Use the Power Rule for Exponents.
4. Use the Power Rules for Products and Quotients.
5. Use the Quotient Rule for Exponents, and Define a Number Raised to the 0 Power.
6. Decide Which Rule(s) to Use to Simplify an Expression.

OBJECTIVE

1 Evaluating Exponential Expressions

As we reviewed in Section 1.4, an exponent is a shorthand notation for repeated factors. For example, $2 \cdot 2 \cdot 2 \cdot 2 \cdot 2$ can be written as 2^5. The expression 2^5 is called an **exponential expression.** It is also called the fifth **power** of 2, or we say that 2 is **raised** to the fifth power.

$$5^6 = \underbrace{5 \cdot 5 \cdot 5 \cdot 5 \cdot 5 \cdot 5}_{\text{6 factors; each factor is } 5} \quad \text{and} \quad (-3)^4 = \underbrace{(-3) \cdot (-3) \cdot (-3) \cdot (-3)}_{\text{4 factors; each factor is } -3}$$

The **base** of an exponential expression is the repeated factor. The **exponent** is the number of times that the base is used as a factor.

$$5^6 \overset{\text{exponent}}{\underset{\text{base}}{}} \qquad (-3)^4 \overset{\text{exponent}}{\underset{\text{base}}{}}$$

EXAMPLE 1 Evaluate each expression.

a. 2^3 **b.** 3^1 **c.** $(-4)^2$ **d.** -4^2 **e.** $\left(\dfrac{1}{2}\right)^4$ **f.** $(0.5)^3$ **g.** $4 \cdot 3^2$

Solution

a. $2^3 = 2 \cdot 2 \cdot 2 = 8$

b. To raise 3 to the first power means to use 3 as a factor only once. Therefore, $3^1 = 3$. Also, when no exponent is shown, the exponent is assumed to be 1.

c. $(-4)^2 = (-4)(-4) = 16$ **d.** $-4^2 = -(4 \cdot 4) = -16$

e. $\left(\dfrac{1}{2}\right)^4 = \dfrac{1}{2} \cdot \dfrac{1}{2} \cdot \dfrac{1}{2} \cdot \dfrac{1}{2} = \dfrac{1}{16}$ **f.** $(0.5)^3 = (0.5)(0.5)(0.5) = 0.125$

g. $4 \cdot 3^2 = 4 \cdot 9 = 36$

PRACTICE

1 Evaluate each expression.

a. 3^3 **b.** 4^1 **c.** $(-8)^2$ **d.** -8^2

e. $\left(\dfrac{3}{4}\right)^3$ **f.** $(0.3)^4$ **g.** $3 \cdot 5^2$

Notice how similar -4^2 is to $(-4)^2$ in the example above. The difference between the two is the parentheses. In $(-4)^2$, the parentheses tell us that the base, or repeated factor, is -4. In -4^2, only 4 is the base.

> ▶ **Helpful Hint**
>
> Be careful when identifying the base of an exponential expression. Pay close attention to the use of parentheses.
>
> $(-3)^2$ $\qquad$ -3^2 $\qquad$ $2 \cdot 3^2$
> The base is -3. $\qquad$ The base is 3. $\qquad$ The base is 3.
> $(-3)^2 = (-3)(-3) = 9$ $\quad$ $-3^2 = -(3 \cdot 3) = -9$ $\quad$ $2 \cdot 3^2 = 2 \cdot 3 \cdot 3 = 18$

An exponent has the same meaning whether the base is a number or a variable. If x is a real number and n is a positive integer, then x^n is the product of n factors, each of which is x.

$$x^n = \underbrace{x \cdot x \cdot x \cdot x \cdot x \cdot \ldots \cdot x}_{n \text{ factors of } x}$$

EXAMPLE 2 Evaluate each expression for the given value of x.

a. $2x^3$; x is 5   **b.** $\dfrac{9}{x^2}$; x is -3

Solution   **a.** If x is 5, $2x^3 = 2 \cdot (5)^3$ **b.** If x is -3, $\dfrac{9}{x^2} = \dfrac{9}{(-3)^2}$

$$= 2 \cdot (5 \cdot 5 \cdot 5)$$
$$= 2 \cdot 125$$
$$= 250$$

$$= \dfrac{9}{(-3)(-3)}$$
$$= \dfrac{9}{9}$$
$$= 1 \qquad \square$$

PRACTICE
2   Evaluate each expression for the given value of x.

a. $3x^4$; x is 3   **b.** $\dfrac{6}{x^2}$; x is -4

OBJECTIVE
2 Using the Product Rule

Exponential expressions can be multiplied, divided, added, subtracted, and themselves raised to powers. By our definition of an exponent,

$$5^4 \cdot 5^3 = \underbrace{(5 \cdot 5 \cdot 5 \cdot 5)}_{4 \text{ factors of } 5} \cdot \underbrace{(5 \cdot 5 \cdot 5)}_{3 \text{ factors of } 5}$$

$$= \underbrace{5 \cdot 5 \cdot 5 \cdot 5 \cdot 5 \cdot 5 \cdot 5}_{7 \text{ factors of } 5}$$

$$= 5^7$$

Also,

$$x^2 \cdot x^3 = (x \cdot x) \cdot (x \cdot x \cdot x)$$
$$= x \cdot x \cdot x \cdot x \cdot x$$
$$= x^5$$

In both cases, notice that the result is exactly the same if the exponents are added.

$$5^4 \cdot 5^3 = 5^{4+3} = 5^7 \qquad \text{and} \qquad x^2 \cdot x^3 = x^{2+3} = x^5$$

This suggests the following rule.

Product Rule for Exponents

If m and n are positive integers and a is a real number, then

$$a^m \cdot a^n = a^{m+n} \; \leftarrow \text{Add exponents.}$$
$$\phantom{a^m \cdot a^n = a^{m+n}} \text{Keep common base.}$$

For example, $3^5 \cdot 3^7 = 3^{5+7} = 3^{12} \; \leftarrow$ Add exponents.
$\phantom{For example, 3^5 \cdot 3^7 = 3^{5+7}}$ Keep common base.

▶ **Helpful Hint**

Don't forget that

$$3^5 \cdot 3^7 \neq 9^{12} \; \leftarrow \text{Add exponents.}$$
$$\phantom{3^5 \cdot 3^7 \neq 9^{12}} \text{Common base } not \text{ kept.}$$

$$3^5 \cdot 3^7 = \underbrace{3 \cdot 3 \cdot 3 \cdot 3 \cdot 3}_{5 \text{ factors of } 3} \cdot \underbrace{3 \cdot 3 \cdot 3 \cdot 3 \cdot 3 \cdot 3 \cdot 3}_{7 \text{ factors of } 3}$$

$$= 3^{12} \quad 12 \text{ factors of } 3, not \text{ } 9$$

In other words, to multiply two exponential expressions with the **same base,** we keep the base and add the exponents. We call this **simplifying** the exponential expression.

EXAMPLE 3   Use the product rule to simplify.

a. $4^2 \cdot 4^5$ **b.** $x^4 \cdot x^6$ **c.** $y^3 \cdot y$ ▶ **d.** $y^3 \cdot y^2 \cdot y^7$ ▶ **e.** $(-5)^7 \cdot (-5)^8$ **f.** $a^2 \cdot b^2$

Solution

a. $4^2 \cdot 4^5 = 4^{2+5} = 4^7$ ⟵ Add exponents.
   — **Keep** common base.

b. $x^4 \cdot x^6 = x^{4+6} = x^{10}$

c. $y^3 \cdot y = y^3 \cdot y^1$
   $= y^{3+1}$
   $= y^4$

> ▶ **Helpful Hint**
> Don't forget that if no exponent is written, it is assumed to be 1.

d. $y^3 \cdot y^2 \cdot y^7 = y^{3+2+7} = y^{12}$

e. $(-5)^7 \cdot (-5)^8 = (-5)^{7+8} = (-5)^{15}$

f. $a^2 \cdot b^2$ Cannot be simplified because a and b are different bases.   □

PRACTICE
3   Use the product rule to simplify.

a. $3^4 \cdot 3^6$ **b.** $y^3 \cdot y^2$

c. $z \cdot z^4$ **d.** $x^3 \cdot x^2 \cdot x^6$

e. $(-2)^5 \cdot (-2)^3$ **f.** $b^3 \cdot t^5$

✓**CONCEPT CHECK**
Where possible, use the product rule to simplify the expression.
   a. $z^2 \cdot z^{14}$ **b.** $x^2 \cdot y^{14}$ **c.** $9^8 \cdot 9^3$ **d.** $9^8 \cdot 2^7$

EXAMPLE 4   Use the product rule to simplify $(2x^2)(-3x^5)$.

Solution   Recall that $2x^2$ means $2 \cdot x^2$ and $-3x^5$ means $-3 \cdot x^5$.

$(2x^2)(-3x^5) = 2 \cdot x^2 \cdot -3 \cdot x^5$ Remove parentheses.
$= 2 \cdot -3 \cdot x^2 \cdot x^5$ Group factors with common bases.
$= -6x^7$ Simplify.   □

PRACTICE
4   Use the product rule to simplify $(-5y^3)(-3y^4)$.

EXAMPLE 5   Simplify.

a. $(x^2y)(x^3y^2)$ **b.** $(-a^7b^4)(3ab^9)$

Solution

a. $(x^2y)(x^3y^2) = (x^2 \cdot x^3) \cdot (y^1 \cdot y^2)$ Group like bases and write y as y^1.
   $= x^5 \cdot y^3$ or x^5y^3 Multiply.

b. $(-a^7b^4)(3ab^9) = (-1 \cdot 3) \cdot (a^7 \cdot a^1) \cdot (b^4 \cdot b^9)$
   $= -3a^8b^{13}$ □

PRACTICE
5   Simplify.

a. $(y^7z^3)(y^5z)$ **b.** $(-m^4n^4)(7mn^{10})$

> ▶ **Helpful Hint**
>
> These examples will remind you of the difference between adding and multiplying terms.
>
> **Addition**
>
> $$5x^3 + 3x^3 = (5+3)x^3 = 8x^3 \quad \text{By the distributive property.}$$
> $$7x + 4x^2 = 7x + 4x^2 \qquad\qquad \text{Cannot be combined.}$$
>
> **Multiplication**
>
> $$(5x^3)(3x^3) = 5 \cdot 3 \cdot x^3 \cdot x^3 = 15x^{3+3} = 15x^6 \quad \text{By the product rule.}$$
> $$(7x)(4x^2) = 7 \cdot 4 \cdot x \cdot x^2 = 28x^{1+2} = 28x^3 \quad \text{By the product rule.}$$

OBJECTIVE

3   Using the Power Rule ▶

Exponential expressions can themselves be raised to powers. Let's try to discover a rule that simplifies an expression like $(x^2)^3$. By definition,

$$(x^2)^3 = \underbrace{(x^2)(x^2)(x^2)}_{3 \text{ factors of } x^2}$$

which can be simplified by the product rule for exponents.

$$(x^2)^3 = (x^2)(x^2)(x^2) = x^{2+2+2} = x^6$$

Notice that the result is exactly the same if we multiply the exponents.

$$(x^2)^3 = x^{2 \cdot 3} = x^6$$

The following property states this result.

Power Rule for Exponents

If m and n are positive integers and a is a real number, then

$$(a^m)^n = a^{mn} \leftarrow \text{Multiply exponents.}$$

Keep common base.

For example, $(7^2)^5 = 7^{2 \cdot 5} = 7^{10} \leftarrow$ Multiply exponents.

Keep common base.

To raise a power to a power, keep the base and multiply the exponents.

EXAMPLE 6   Use the power rule to simplify.

a. $(y^8)^2$ **b.** $(8^4)^5$ ▶ **c.** $[(-5)^3]^7$

Solution

a. $(y^8)^2 = y^{8 \cdot 2} = y^{16}$ **b.** $(8^4)^5 = 8^{4 \cdot 5} = 8^{20}$ **c.** $[(-5)^3]^7 = (-5)^{21}$ □

PRACTICE

6   Use the power rule to simplify.

a. $(z^3)^7$ **b.** $(4^9)^2$ **c.** $[(-2)^3]^5$

> ▶ **Helpful Hint**
>
> Take a moment to make sure that you understand when to apply the product rule and when to apply the power rule.
>
> | *Product Rule* → *Add Exponents* | *Power Rule* → *Multiply Exponents* |
> | --- | --- |
> | $x^5 \cdot x^7 = x^{5+7} = x^{12}$ | $(x^5)^7 = x^{5 \cdot 7} = x^{35}$ |
> | $y^6 \cdot y^2 = y^{6+2} = y^8$ | $(y^6)^2 = y^{6 \cdot 2} = y^{12}$ |

OBJECTIVE

4 Using the Power Rules for Products and Quotients

When the base of an exponential expression is a product, the definition of x^n still applies. To simplify $(xy)^3$, for example,

$$(xy)^3 = (xy)(xy)(xy) \qquad (xy)^3 \text{ means 3 factors of } (xy).$$
$$= x \cdot x \cdot x \cdot y \cdot y \cdot y \qquad \text{Group factors with common bases.}$$
$$= x^3 y^3 \qquad \text{Simplify.}$$

Notice that to simplify the expression $(xy)^3$, we raise each factor within the parentheses to a power of 3.

$$(xy)^3 = x^3 y^3$$

In general, we have the following rule.

Power of a Product Rule

If n is a positive integer and a and b are real numbers, then

$$(ab)^n = a^n b^n$$

For example, $(3x)^5 = 3^5 x^5$.

In other words, to raise a product to a power, we raise each factor to the power.

EXAMPLE 7 Simplify each expression.

a. $(st)^4$ **b.** $(2a)^3$ **c.** $\left(\dfrac{1}{3}mn^3\right)^2$ **d.** $(-5x^2y^3z)^2$

Solution

a. $(st)^4 = s^4 \cdot t^4 = s^4 t^4$ Use the power of a product rule.

b. $(2a)^3 = 2^3 \cdot a^3 = 8a^3$ Use the power of a product rule.

c. $\left(\dfrac{1}{3}mn^3\right)^2 = \left(\dfrac{1}{3}\right)^2 \cdot (m)^2 \cdot (n^3)^2 = \dfrac{1}{9}m^2 n^6$ Use the power of a product rule.

d. $(-5x^2y^3z)^2 = (-5)^2 \cdot (x^2)^2 \cdot (y^3)^2 \cdot (z^1)^2$ Use the power of a product rule.

$\qquad\qquad\qquad = 25x^4 y^6 z^2$ Use the power rule for exponents.   □

PRACTICE

7 Simplify each expression.

a. $(pr)^5$ **b.** $(6b)^2$ **c.** $\left(\dfrac{1}{4}x^2 y\right)^3$ **d.** $(-3a^3 b^4 c)^4$

Let's see what happens when we raise a quotient to a power. To simplify $\left(\dfrac{x}{y}\right)^3$, for example,

$$\left(\dfrac{x}{y}\right)^3 = \left(\dfrac{x}{y}\right)\left(\dfrac{x}{y}\right)\left(\dfrac{x}{y}\right) \qquad \left(\dfrac{x}{y}\right)^3 \text{ means 3 factors of } \left(\dfrac{x}{y}\right)$$

$$= \dfrac{x \cdot x \cdot x}{y \cdot y \cdot y} \qquad \text{Multiply fractions.}$$

$$= \dfrac{x^3}{y^3} \qquad \text{Simplify.}$$

Notice that to simplify the expression $\left(\dfrac{x}{y}\right)^3$, we raise both the numerator and the denominator to a power of 3.

$$\left(\dfrac{x}{y}\right)^3 = \dfrac{x^3}{y^3}$$

In general, we have the following.

> **Power of a Quotient Rule**
>
> If n is a positive integer and a and c are real numbers, then
>
> $$\left(\frac{a}{c}\right)^n = \frac{a^n}{c^n}, \quad c \neq 0$$

For example, $\left(\dfrac{y}{7}\right)^4 = \dfrac{y^4}{7^4}$.

In other words, to raise a quotient to a power, we raise both the numerator and the denominator to the power.

EXAMPLE 8   Simplify each expression.

a. $\left(\dfrac{m}{n}\right)^7$ **b.** $\left(\dfrac{x^3}{3y^5}\right)^4$

Solution

a. $\left(\dfrac{m}{n}\right)^7 = \dfrac{m^7}{n^7}, n \neq 0$ Use the power of a quotient rule.

b. $\left(\dfrac{x^3}{3y^5}\right)^4 = \dfrac{(x^3)^4}{3^4 \cdot (y^5)^4}, y \neq 0$ Use the power of a product or quotient rule.

$\qquad\qquad = \dfrac{x^{12}}{81y^{20}}$ Use the power rule for exponents.   □

PRACTICE
8   Simplify each expression.

a. $\left(\dfrac{x}{y^2}\right)^5$ **b.** $\left(\dfrac{2a^4}{b^3}\right)^5$

OBJECTIVE
5   Using the Quotient Rule and Defining the Zero Exponent

Another pattern for simplifying exponential expressions involves quotients.

To simplify an expression like $\dfrac{x^5}{x^3}$, in which the numerator and the denominator have a common base, we can apply the fundamental principle of fractions and divide the numerator and the denominator by the common base factors. Assume for the remainder of this section that denominators are not 0.

$$\frac{x^5}{x^3} = \frac{x \cdot x \cdot x \cdot x \cdot x}{x \cdot x \cdot x}$$
$$= \frac{x \cdot x \cdot x \cdot x \cdot x}{x \cdot x \cdot x}$$
$$= x \cdot x$$
$$= x^2$$

Notice that the result is exactly the same if we subtract exponents of the common bases.

$$\frac{x^5}{x^3} = x^{5-3} = x^2$$

The quotient rule for exponents states this result in a general way.

> **Quotient Rule for Exponents**
>
> If m and n are positive integers and a is a real number, then
>
> $$\frac{a^m}{a^n} = a^{m-n}$$
>
> as long as a is not 0.

For example, $\dfrac{x^6}{x^2} = x^{6-2} = x^4$.

In other words, to divide one exponential expression by another with a common base, keep the base and subtract exponents.

EXAMPLE 9   Simplify each quotient.

a. $\dfrac{x^5}{x^2}$ b. $\dfrac{4^7}{4^3}$ c. $\dfrac{(-3)^5}{(-3)^2}$ d. $\dfrac{s^2}{t^3}$ e. $\dfrac{2x^5y^2}{xy}$

Solution

a. $\dfrac{x^5}{x^2} = x^{5-2} = x^3$ Use the quotient rule.

b. $\dfrac{4^7}{4^3} = 4^{7-3} = 4^4 = 256$ Use the quotient rule.

c. $\dfrac{(-3)^5}{(-3)^2} = (-3)^3 = -27$ Use the quotient rule.

d. $\dfrac{s^2}{t^3}$ Cannot be simplified because s and t are different bases.

e. Begin by grouping common bases.

$$\frac{2x^5y^2}{xy} = 2 \cdot \frac{x^5}{x^1} \cdot \frac{y^2}{y^1}$$
$$= 2 \cdot (x^{5-1}) \cdot (y^{2-1}) \quad \text{Use the quotient rule.}$$
$$= 2x^4y^1 \quad \text{or} \quad 2x^4y$$

PRACTICE
9   Simplify each quotient.

a. $\dfrac{z^8}{z^4}$ b. $\dfrac{(-5)^5}{(-5)^3}$ c. $\dfrac{8^8}{8^6}$ d. $\dfrac{q^5}{t^2}$ e. $\dfrac{6x^3y^7}{xy^5}$

✓CONCEPT CHECK

Suppose you are simplifying each expression. Tell whether you would *add* the exponents, *subtract* the exponents, *multiply* the exponents, *divide* the exponents, or *none of these*.

a. $(x^{63})^{21}$ b. $\dfrac{y^{15}}{y^3}$ c. $z^{16} + z^8$ d. $w^{45} \cdot w^9$

Let's now give meaning to an expression such as x^0. To do so, we will simplify $\dfrac{x^3}{x^3}$ in two ways and compare the results.

$$\frac{x^3}{x^3} = x^{3-3} = x^0 \quad \text{Apply the quotient rule.}$$

$$\frac{x^3}{x^3} = \frac{x \cdot x \cdot x}{x \cdot x \cdot x} = 1 \quad \text{Apply the fundamental principle for fractions.}$$

Answers to Concept Check:
a. multiply   b. subtract
c. none of these   d. add

Since $\dfrac{x^3}{x^3} = x^0$ and $\dfrac{x^3}{x^3} = 1$, we define that $x^0 = 1$ as long as x is not 0.

> **Zero Exponent**
> $a^0 = 1$, as long as a is not 0.

In other words, any base raised to the 0 power is 1 as long as the base is not 0.

EXAMPLE 10 Simplify each expression.

a. 3^0 **b.** $(5x^3y^2)^0$ **c.** $(-5)^0$ **d.** -5^0 **e.** $\left(\dfrac{3}{100}\right)^0$ **f.** $4x^0$

Solution

a. $3^0 = 1$

b. Assume that neither x nor y is zero.

$$(5x^3y^2)^0 = 1$$

c. $(-5)^0 = 1$

d. $-5^0 = -1 \cdot 5^0 = -1 \cdot 1 = -1$

e. $\left(\dfrac{3}{100}\right)^0 = 1$

f. $4x^0 = 4 \cdot x^0 = 4 \cdot 1 = 4$

PRACTICE
10 Simplify the following expressions.

a. -3^0 **b.** $(-3)^0$ **c.** 8^0 **d.** $(0.2)^0$
e. $(7a^2y^4)^0$ **f.** $7y^0$

OBJECTIVE
6 Deciding Which Rule to Use ▶

Let's practice deciding which rule(s) to use to simplify. We will continue this discussion with more examples in Section 5.5.

EXAMPLE 11 Simplify each expression.

a. $x^7 \cdot x^4$ **b.** $\left(\dfrac{t}{2}\right)^4$ **c.** $(9y^5)^2$

Solution

a. Here, we have a product, so we use the product rule to simplify.
$$x^7 \cdot x^4 = x^{7+4} = x^{11}$$

b. This is a quotient raised to a power, so we use the power of a quotient rule.
$$\left(\dfrac{t}{2}\right)^4 = \dfrac{t^4}{2^4} = \dfrac{t^4}{16}$$

c. This is a product raised to a power, so we use the power of a product rule.
$$(9y^5)^2 = 9^2(y^5)^2 = 81y^{10}$$

PRACTICE
11

a. $\left(\dfrac{z}{12}\right)^2$ **b.** $(4x^6)^3$ **c.** $y^{10} \cdot y^3$

EXAMPLE 12   Simplify each expression.

a. $4^2 - 4^0$ **b.** $(x^0)^3 + (2^0)^5$ **c.** $\left(\dfrac{3y^7}{6x^5}\right)^2$ **d.** $\dfrac{(2a^3b^4)^3}{-8a^9b^2}$

Solution

a. $4^2 - 4^0 = 16 - 1 = 15$ Remember that $4^0 = 1$.

b. $(x^0)^3 + (2^0)^5 = 1^3 + 1^5 = 1 + 1 = 2$

c. $\left(\dfrac{3y^7}{6x^5}\right)^2 = \dfrac{3^2(y^7)^2}{6^2(x^5)^2} = \dfrac{9 \cdot y^{14}}{36 \cdot x^{10}} = \dfrac{y^{14}}{4x^{10}}$

d. $\dfrac{(2a^3b^4)^3}{-8a^9b^2} = \dfrac{2^3(a^3)^3(b^4)^3}{-8a^9b^2} = \dfrac{8a^9b^{12}}{-8a^9b^2} = -1 \cdot (a^{9-9}) \cdot (b^{12-2})$

$= -1 \cdot a^0 \cdot b^{10} = -1 \cdot 1 \cdot b^{10} = -b^{10}$ □

PRACTICE
12   Simplify each expression.

a. $8^2 - 8^0$ **b.** $(z^0)^6 + (4^0)^5$ **c.** $\left(\dfrac{5x^3}{15y^4}\right)^2$ **d.** $\dfrac{(2z^8x^5)^4}{-16z^2x^{20}}$

Vocabulary, Readiness & Video Check

Use the choices below to fill in each blank. Some choices may be used more than once.

0	base	add
1	exponent	multiply

1. Repeated multiplication of the same factor can be written using a(n) _____.

2. In 5^2, the 2 is called the _____ and the 5 is called the _____.

3. To simplify $x^2 \cdot x^7$, keep the base and _____ the exponents.

4. To simplify $(x^3)^6$, keep the base and _____ the exponents.

5. The understood exponent on the term y is _____.

6. If $x^\square = 1$, the exponent is _____.

Martin-Gay Interactive Videos

See Video 5.1

Watch the section lecture video and answer the following questions.

OBJECTIVE 1
7. ▭ Examples 3 and 4 illustrate how to find the base of an exponential expression both with and without parentheses. Explain how identifying the base of ▭ Example 7 is similar to identifying the base of ▭ Example 4.

OBJECTIVE 2
8. Why were the commutative and associative properties applied in ▭ Example 12? Were these properties used in another example?

OBJECTIVE 3
9. What point is made at the end of ▭ Example 15?

OBJECTIVE 4
10. Although it's not especially emphasized in ▭ Example 20, what is helpful to remind yourself about the −2 in the problem?

OBJECTIVE 5
11. In ▭ Example 24, which exponent rule is used to show that any non-zero base raised to zero is 1?

OBJECTIVE 6
12. When simplifying an exponential expression that's a fraction, will you always use the quotient rule? Refer to ▭ Example 30 for this objective to support your answer.

5.1 Exercise Set

MyMathLab®

For each of the following expressions, state the exponent shown and its corresponding base.

1. 3^2

2. $(-3)^6$

3. -4^2

4. $5 \cdot 3^4$

5. $5x^2$

6. $(5x)^2$

Evaluate each expression. See Example 1.

7. 7^2

8. -3^2

9. $(-5)^1$

10. $(-3)^2$

11. -2^4

12. -4^3

13. $(-2)^4$

14. $(-4)^3$

15. $(0.1)^5$

16. $(0.2)^5$

17. $\left(\dfrac{1}{3}\right)^4$

18. $\left(-\dfrac{1}{9}\right)^2$

19. $7 \cdot 2^5$

20. $9 \cdot 1^7$

21. $-2 \cdot 5^3$

22. $-4 \cdot 3^3$

Evaluate each expression given the replacement values for x. See Example 2.

23. $x^2; x = -2$

24. $x^3; x = -2$

25. $5x^3; x = 3$

26. $4x^2; x = -1$

27. $2xy^2; x = 3$ and $y = 5$

28. $-4x^2y^3; x = 2$ and $y = -1$

29. $\dfrac{2z^4}{5}; z = -2$

30. $\dfrac{10}{3y^3}; y = 5$

Use the product rule to simplify each expression. Write the results using exponents. See Examples 3 through 5.

31. $x^2 \cdot x^5$

32. $y^2 \cdot y$

33. $(-3)^3 \cdot (-3)^9$

34. $(-5)^7 \cdot (-5)^6$

35. $(5y^4)(3y)$

36. $(-2z^3)(-2z^2)$

37. $(x^9y)(x^{10}y^5)$

38. $(a^2b)(a^{13}b^{17})$

39. $(-8mn^6)(9m^2n^2)$

40. $(-7a^3b^3)(7a^{19}b)$

41. $(4z^{10})(-6z^7)(z^3)$

42. $(12x^5)(-x^6)(x^4)$

43. The rectangle below has width $4x^2$ feet and length $5x^3$ feet. Find its area as an expression in x. $(A = l \cdot w)$

$4x^2$ feet

$5x^3$ feet

44. The parallelogram below has base length $9y^7$ meters and height $2y^{10}$ meters. Find its area as an expression in y. $(A = b \cdot h)$

$2y^{10}$ meters

$9y^7$ meters

MIXED PRACTICE

Use the power rule and the power of a product or quotient rule to simplify each expression. See Examples 6 through 8.

45. $(x^9)^4$

46. $(y^7)^5$

47. $(pq)^8$

48. $(ab)^6$

49. $(2a^5)^3$

50. $(4x^6)^2$

51. $(x^2y^3)^5$

52. $(a^4b)^7$

53. $(-7a^2b^5c)^2$

54. $(-3x^7yz^2)^3$

55. $\left(\dfrac{r}{s}\right)^9$

56. $\left(\dfrac{q}{t}\right)^{11}$

57. $\left(\dfrac{mp}{n}\right)^5$

58. $\left(\dfrac{xy}{7}\right)^2$

59. $\left(\dfrac{-2xz}{y^5}\right)^2$

60. $\left(\dfrac{xy^4}{-3z^3}\right)^3$

61. The square shown has sides of length $8z^5$ decimeters. Find its area. $(A = s^2)$

$8z^5$
decimeters

62. Given the circle below with radius $5y$ centimeters, find its area. Do not approximate π. $(A = \pi r^2)$

$5y$ cm

63. The vault below is in the shape of a cube. If each side is $3y^4$ feet, find its volume. $(V = s^3)$

$3y^4$ feet

$3y^4$ feet

$3y^4$ feet

64. The silo shown is in the shape of a cylinder. If its radius is $4x$ meters and its height is $5x^3$ meters, find its volume. Do not approximate π. $(V = \pi r^2h)$

$4x$ meters

$5x^3$
meters

Use the quotient rule and simplify each expression. See Example 9.

65. $\dfrac{x^3}{x}$

66. $\dfrac{y^{10}}{y^9}$

67. $\dfrac{(-4)^6}{(-4)^3}$

68. $\dfrac{(-6)^{13}}{(-6)^{11}}$

69. $\dfrac{p^7 q^{20}}{pq^{15}}$

70. $\dfrac{x^8 y^6}{xy^5}$

71. $\dfrac{7x^2 y^6}{14x^2 y^3}$

72. $\dfrac{9a^4 b^7}{27ab^2}$

Simplify each expression. See Example 10.

73. 7^0

74. 23^0

75. $(2x)^0$

76. $(4y)^0$

77. $-7x^0$

78. $-2x^0$

79. $5^0 + y^0$

80. $-3^0 + 4^0$

MIXED PRACTICE

Simplify each expression. See Examples 1 through 12.

81. -9^2

82. $(-9)^2$

83. $\left(\dfrac{1}{4}\right)^3$

84. $\left(\dfrac{2}{3}\right)^3$

85. $b^4 b^2$

86. $y^4 y$

87. $a^2 a^3 a^4$

88. $x^2 x^{15} x^9$

89. $(2x^3)(-8x^4)$

90. $(3y^4)(-5y)$

91. $(a^7 b^{12})(a^4 b^8)$

92. $(y^2 z^2)(y^{15} z^{13})$

93. $(-2mn^6)(-13m^8 n)$

94. $(-3s^5 t)(-7st^{10})$

95. $(z^4)^{10}$

96. $(t^5)^{11}$

97. $(4ab)^3$

98. $(2ab)^4$

99. $(-6xyz^3)^2$

100. $(-3xy^2 a^3)^3$

101. $\dfrac{3x^5}{x^4}$

102. $\dfrac{5x^9}{x^3}$

103. $(9xy)^2$

104. $(2ab)^5$

105. $2^3 + 2^0$

106. $7^2 - 7^0$

107. $\left(\dfrac{3y^5}{6x^4}\right)^3$

108. $\left(\dfrac{2ab}{6yz}\right)^4$

109. $\dfrac{2x^3 y^2 z}{xyz}$

110. $\dfrac{x^{12} y^{13}}{x^5 y^7}$

111. $(5^0)^3 + (y^0)^7$

112. $(9^0)^4 + (z^0)^5$

113. $\left(\dfrac{5x^9}{10y^{11}}\right)^2$

114. $\left(\dfrac{3a^4}{9b^5}\right)^2$

115. $\dfrac{(2a^5 b^3)^4}{-16a^{20} b^7}$

116. $\dfrac{(2x^6 y^2)^5}{-32x^{20} y^{10}}$

REVIEW AND PREVIEW

Simplify each expression by combining any like terms. Use the distributive property to remove any parentheses. See Section 2.1.

117. $y - 10 + y$

118. $-6z + 20 - 3z$

119. $7x + 2 - 8x - 6$

120. $10y - 14 - y - 14$

121. $2(x - 5) + 3(5 - x)$

122. $-3(w + 7) + 5(w + 1)$

CONCEPT EXTENSIONS

Solve. See the Concept Checks in this section. For Exercises 123 through 126, match the expression with the operation needed to simplify each. A letter may be used more than once and a letter may not be used at all.

123. $(x^{14})^{23}$

124. $x^{14} \cdot x^{23}$

125. $x^{14} + x^{23}$

126. $\dfrac{x^{35}}{x^{17}}$

   a. Add the exponents
   b. Subtract the exponents
   c. Multiply the exponents
   d. Divide the exponents
   e. None of these

Fill in the boxes so that each statement is true. (More than one answer is possible for each exercise.)

127. $x^{\square} \cdot x^{\square} = x^{12}$

128. $(x^{\square})^{\square} = x^{20}$

129. $\dfrac{y^{\square}}{y^{\square}} = y^7$

130. $(y^{\square})^{\square} \cdot (y^{\square})^{\square} = y^{30}$

△ **131.** The formula $V = x^3$ can be used to find the volume V of a cube with side length x. Find the volume of a cube with side length 7 meters. (Volume is measured in cubic units.)

△ **132.** The formula $S = 6x^2$ can be used to find the surface area S of a cube with side length x. Find the surface area of a cube with side length 5 meters. (Surface area is measured in square units.)

△ **133.** To find the amount of water that a swimming pool in the shape of a cube can hold, do we use the formula for volume of the cube or surface area of the cube? (See Exercises 131 and 132.)

△ **134.** To find the amount of material needed to cover an ottoman in the shape of a cube, do we use the formula for volume of the cube or surface area of the cube? (See Exercises 131 and 132.)

135. Explain why $(-5)^4 = 625$, while $-5^4 = -625$.

136. Explain why $5 \cdot 4^2 = 80$, while $(5 \cdot 4)^2 = 400$.

137. In your own words, explain why $5^0 = 1$.

138. In your own words, explain when $(-3)^n$ is positive and when it is negative.

Simplify each expression. Assume that variables represent positive integers.

139. $x^{5a} x^{4a}$

140. $b^{9a} b^{4a}$

141. $(a^b)^5$

142. $(2a^{4b})^4$

143. $\dfrac{x^{9a}}{x^{4a}}$

144. $\dfrac{y^{15b}}{y^{6b}}$

Solve. Round money amounts to 2 decimal places.

145. Suppose you borrow money for 6 months. If the interest is compounded monthly, the formula $A = P\left(1 + \dfrac{r}{12}\right)^6$ gives the total amount A to be repaid at the end of 6 months. For a loan of $P = \$1000$ and interest rate of 9% ($r = 0.09$), how much money is needed to pay off the loan?

146. Suppose you borrow money for 3 years. If the interest is compounded quarterly, the formula $A = P\left(1 + \dfrac{r}{4}\right)^{12}$ gives the total amount A to be repaid at the end of 3 years. For a loan of $\$10,000$ and interest rate of 8% ($r = 0.08$), how much money is needed to pay off the loan in 3 years?

5.2 | Polynomial Functions and Adding and Subtracting Polynomials

OBJECTIVES

1 Define Polynomial, Monomial, Binomial, Trinomial, and Degree.

2 Define Polynomial Functions.

3 Simplify a Polynomial by Combining Like Terms.

4 Add and Subtract Polynomials.

OBJECTIVE

1 Defining Polynomial, Monomial, Binomial, Trinomial, and Degree

In this section, we introduce a special algebraic expression called a polynomial. Let's first review some definitions presented in Section 2.1.

Recall that a **term** is a number or the product of a number and variables raised to powers. The terms of the expression $4x^2 + 3x$ are $4x^2$ and $3x$.

The terms of the expression $9x^4 - 7x - 1$ are $9x^4$, $-7x$, and -1.

Expression	Terms
$4x^2 + 3x$	$4x^2, 3x$
$9x^4 - 7x - 1$	$9x^4, -7x, -1$
$7y^3$	$7y^3$
5	5

The **numerical coefficient** of a term, or simply the **coefficient**, is the numerical factor of each term. If no numerical factor appears in the term, then the coefficient is understood to be 1. If the term is a number only, it is called a **constant term** or simply a **constant.**

Term	Coefficient
x^5	1
$3x^2$	3
$-4x$	-4
$-x^2y$	-1
3 (constant)	3

Now we are ready to define a polynomial.

Polynomial

A **polynomial in x** is a finite sum of terms of the form ax^n, where a is a real number and n is a whole number.

For example,

$$x^5 - 3x^3 + 2x^2 - 5x + 1$$

is a polynomial. Notice that this polynomial is written in **descending powers** of x because the powers of x decrease from left to right. (Recall that the term 1 can be thought of as $1x^0$.)

On the other hand,

$$x^{-5} + 2x - 3$$

is **not** a polynomial because it contains an exponent, -5, that is not a whole number. (We study negative exponents in Section 5.5 of this chapter.)

Some polynomials are given special names.

Types of Polynomials

A **monomial** is a polynomial with exactly one term.

A **binomial** is a polynomial with exactly two terms.

A **trinomial** is a polynomial with exactly three terms.

The following are examples of monomials, binomials, and trinomials. Each of these examples is also a polynomial.

POLYNOMIALS

Monomials	*Binomials*	*Trinomials*	*More than Three Terms*
ax^2	$x + y$	$x^2 + 4xy + y^2$	$5x^3 - 6x^2 + 3x - 6$
$-3z$	$3p + 2$	$x^5 + 7x^2 - x$	$-y^5 + y^4 - 3y^3 - y^2 + y$
4	$4x^2 - 7$	$-q^4 + q^3 - 2q$	$x^6 + x^4 - x^3 + 1$

Each term of a polynomial has a **degree.**

> **Degree of a Term**
>
> The degree of a term is the sum of the exponents on the variables contained in the term.

EXAMPLE 1   Find the degree of each term.

a. $3x^2$ **b.** -2^3x^5 **c.** y **d.** $12x^2yz^3$ **e.** 5

Solution

a. The exponent on x is 2, so the degree of the term is 2.

b. The exponent on x is 5, so the degree of the term is 5. (Recall that the degree is the sum of the exponents on only the *variables*.)

c. The degree of y, or y^1, is 1.

d. The degree is the sum of the exponents on the variables, or $2 + 1 + 3 = 6$.

e. The degree of 5, which can be written as $5x^0$, is 0.   ☐

PRACTICE

1   Find the degree of each term.

a. $5y^3$ **b.** $10\,xy$ **c.** z **d.** $-3a^2b^5c$ **e.** 8

From the preceding, we can say that **the degree of a constant is 0.**
   Each polynomial also has a degree.

> **Degree of a Polynomial**
>
> The degree of a polynomial is the greatest degree of any term of the polynomial.

EXAMPLE 2   Find the degree of each polynomial and tell whether the polynomial is a monomial, binomial, trinomial, or none of these.

▶ **a.** $-2t^2 + 3t + 6$ **b.** $15x - 10$ **c.** $7x + 3x^3 + 2x^2 - 1$

Solution

a. The degree of the trinomial $-2t^2 + 3t + 6$ is 2, the greatest degree of any of its terms.

b. The degree of the binomial $15x - 10$ or $15x^1 - 10$ is 1.

c. The degree of the polynomial $7x + 3x^3 + 2x^2 - 1$ is 3.   ☐

PRACTICE

2   Find the degree of each polynomial and tell whether the polynomial is a monomial, binomial, trinomial, or none of these.

a. $5b^2 - 3b + 7$ **b.** $7t + 3$

c. $5x^2 + 3x - 6x^3 + 4$

EXAMPLE 3 Complete the table for the polynomial

$$7x^2y - 6xy + x^2 - 3y + 7$$

Use the table to give the degree of the polynomial.

Solution

Term	Numerical Coefficient	Degree of Term
$7x^2y$	7	3
$-6xy$	-6	2
x^2	1	2
$-3y$	-3	1
7	7	0

The degree of the polynomial is 3. ←

PRACTICE
3 Complete the table for the polynomial $-3x^3y^2 + 4xy^2 - y^2 + 3x - 2$.

Term	Numerical Coefficient	Degree of Term
$-3x^3y^2$		
$4xy^2$		
$-y^2$		
$3x$		
-2		

OBJECTIVE
2   Defining Polynomial Functions

At times, it is convenient to use function notation to represent polynomials. For example, we may write $P(x)$ to represent the polynomial $3x^2 - 2x - 5$. In symbols, this is

$$P(x) = 3x^2 - 2x - 5$$

This function is called a **polynomial function** because the expression $3x^2 - 2x - 5$ is a polynomial.

> ▶ **Helpful Hint**
> Recall that the symbol $P(x)$ **does not mean** P times x. It is a special symbol used to denote a function.

EXAMPLE 4 If $P(x) = 3x^2 - 2x - 5$, find the following.

a. $P(1)$ **b.** $P(-2)$

Solution

a. Substitute 1 for x in $P(x) = 3x^2 - 2x - 5$ and simplify.

$$P(x) = 3x^2 - 2x - 5$$
$$P(1) = 3(1)^2 - 2(1) - 5 = -4$$

b. Substitute -2 for x in $P(x) = 3x^2 - 2x - 5$ and simplify.

$$P(x) = 3x^2 - 2x - 5$$
$$P(-2) = 3(-2)^2 - 2(-2) - 5 = 11$$

☐

PRACTICE

4   If $P(x) = -2x^2 - x + 7$, find

a. $P(1)$ **b.** $P(-4)$

Many real-world phenomena are modeled by polynomial functions. If the polynomial function model is given, we can often find the solution of a problem by evaluating the function at a certain value.

EXAMPLE 5   **Finding the Height of a Dropped Object**

The Swiss Re Building, in London, is a unique building. Londoners often refer to it as the "pickle building." The building is 592.1 feet tall. An object is dropped from the highest point of this building. Neglecting air resistance, the height in feet of the object above ground at time t seconds is given by the polynomial function $P(t) = -16t^2 + 592.1$. Find the height of the object when $t = 1$ second, and when $t = 6$ seconds.

Solution   To find each height, we find $P(1)$ and $P(6)$.

$$P(t) = -16t^2 + 592.1$$
$$P(1) = -16(1)^2 + 592.1 \quad \text{Replace } t \text{ with } 1.$$
$$P(1) = -16 + 592.1$$
$$P(1) = 576.1$$

The height of the object at 1 second is 576.1 feet.

$$P(t) = -16t^2 + 592.1$$
$$P(6) = -16(6)^2 + 592.1 \quad \text{Replace } t \text{ with } 6.$$
$$P(6) = -576 + 592.1$$
$$P(6) = 16.1$$

$t = 1$

576.1 ft

592.1 ft

$t = 6$

16.1 ft

The height of the object at 6 seconds is 16.1 feet.

☐

PRACTICE

5   The cliff divers of Acapulco dive 130 feet into La Quebrada several times a day for the entertainment of the tourists. If a tourist is standing near the diving platform and drops his camera off the cliff, the height of the camera above the water at time t seconds is given by the polynomial function $P(t) = -16t^2 + 130$. Find the height of the camera when $t = 1$ second and when $t = 2$ seconds.

OBJECTIVE

3   **Simplifying Polynomials by Combining Like Terms**

Polynomials with like terms can be simplified by combining the like terms. Recall that like terms are terms that contain exactly the same variables raised to exactly the same powers.

Like Terms	Unlike Terms
$5x^2, -7x^2$	$3x, 3y$
$y, 2y$	$-2x^2, -5x$
$\frac{1}{2}a^2b, -a^2b$	$6st^2, 4s^2t$

Only like terms can be combined. We combine like terms by applying the distributive property.

EXAMPLE 6 Simplify each polynomial by combining any like terms.

a. $-3x + 7x$ **b.** $x + 3x^2$

c. $9x^3 + x^3$ **d.** $11x^2 + 5 + 2x^2 - 7$

e. $\dfrac{2}{5}x^4 + \dfrac{2}{3}x^3 - x^2 + \dfrac{1}{10}x^4 - \dfrac{1}{6}x^3$

Solution

a. $-3x + 7x = (-3 + 7)x = 4x$

b. $x + 3x^2$ These terms cannot be combined because x and $3x^2$ are not like terms.

c. $9x^3 + x^3 = 9x^3 + 1x^3 = 10x^3$

d. $11x^2 + 5 + 2x^2 - 7 = 11x^2 + 2x^2 + 5 - 7$

$\qquad\qquad\qquad\qquad\quad = 13x^2 - 2$ Combine like terms.

e. $\dfrac{2}{5}x^4 + \dfrac{2}{3}x^3 - x^2 + \dfrac{1}{10}x^4 - \dfrac{1}{6}x^3$

$$= \left(\dfrac{2}{5} + \dfrac{1}{10}\right)x^4 + \left(\dfrac{2}{3} - \dfrac{1}{6}\right)x^3 - x^2$$

$$= \left(\dfrac{4}{10} + \dfrac{1}{10}\right)x^4 + \left(\dfrac{4}{6} - \dfrac{1}{6}\right)x^3 - x^2$$

$$= \dfrac{5}{10}x^4 + \dfrac{3}{6}x^3 - x^2$$

$$= \dfrac{1}{2}x^4 + \dfrac{1}{2}x^3 - x^2$$

PRACTICE
6 Simplify each polynomial by combining any like terms.

a. $-4y + 2y$ **b.** $z + 5z^3$ **c.** $15x^3 - x^3$

d. $7a^2 - 5 - 3a^2 - 7$ **e.** $\dfrac{3}{8}x^3 - x^2 + \dfrac{5}{6}x^4 + \dfrac{1}{12}x^3 - \dfrac{1}{2}x^4$

✓**CONCEPT CHECK**

When combining like terms in the expression $5x - 8x^2 - 8x$, which of the following is the proper result?

a. $-11x^2$ **b.** $-8x^2 - 3x$ **c.** $-11x$ **d.** $-11x^4$

EXAMPLE 7 Combine like terms to simplify.

$$-9x^2 + 3xy - 5y^2 + 7yx$$

Solution

$$-9x^2 + 3xy - 5y^2 + 7yx = -9x^2 + (3 + 7)xy - 5y^2$$
$$= -9x^2 + 10xy - 5y^2$$

▶ **Helpful Hint**

This term can be written as $7yx$ or $7xy$.

PRACTICE
7 Combine like terms to simplify: $9xy - 3x^2 - 4yx + 5y^2$.

Answer to Concept Check:
b

EXAMPLE 8 Write a polynomial that describes the total area of the squares and rectangles shown on page 323. Then simplify the polynomial.

Solution

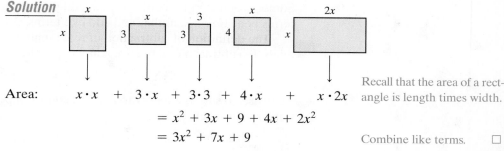

Area: $x \cdot x$ + $3 \cdot x$ + $3 \cdot 3$ + $4 \cdot x$ + $x \cdot 2x$ Recall that the area of a rectangle is length times width.

$$= x^2 + 3x + 9 + 4x + 2x^2$$
$$= 3x^2 + 7x + 9 \qquad \text{Combine like terms.} \quad \square$$

PRACTICE
8   Write a polynomial that describes the total area of the squares and rectangles shown below. Then simplify the polynomial.

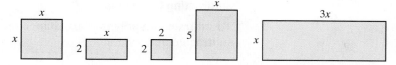

OBJECTIVE
4   Adding and Subtracting Polynomials
We now practice adding and subtracting polynomials.

> **Adding Polynomials**
>
> To add polynomials, combine all like terms.

EXAMPLE 9   Add.

a. $(7x^3y - xy^3 + 11) + (6x^3y - 4)$ **b.** $(3a^3 - b + 2a - 5) + (a + b + 5)$

Solution

a. To add, remove the parentheses and group like terms.

$$(7x^3y - xy^3 + 11) + (6x^3y - 4)$$
$$= 7x^3y - xy^3 + 11 + 6x^3y - 4$$
$$= 7x^3y + 6x^3y - xy^3 + 11 - 4 \qquad \text{Group like terms.}$$
$$= 13x^3y - xy^3 + 7 \qquad \text{Combine like terms.}$$

b. $(3a^3 - b + 2a - 5) + (a + b + 5)$
$$= 3a^3 - b + 2a - 5 + a + b + 5$$
$$= 3a^3 - b + b + 2a + a - 5 + 5 \qquad \text{Group like terms.}$$
$$= 3a^3 + 3a \qquad \text{Combine like terms.} \quad \square$$

PRACTICE
9   Add.

a. $(4y^2 + x - 3y - 7) + (x + y^2 - 2)$
b. $(-8a^2b - ab^2 + 10) + (-2ab^2 - 10)$

EXAMPLE 10   Add $(11x^3 - 12x^2 + x - 3)$ and $(x^3 - 10x + 5)$.

Solution

$$(11x^3 - 12x^2 + x - 3) + (x^3 - 10x + 5)$$
$$= 11x^3 + x^3 - 12x^2 + x - 10x - 3 + 5 \qquad \text{Group like terms.}$$
$$= 12x^3 - 12x^2 - 9x + 2 \qquad \text{Combine like terms.} \quad \square$$

PRACTICE
10   Add $(3x^2 - 9x + 11)$ and $(-3x^2 + 7x^3 + 3x - 4)$

Sometimes it is more convenient to add polynomials vertically. To do this, line up like terms beneath one another and add like terms.

The definition of subtraction of real numbers can be extended to apply to polynomials. To subtract a number, we add its opposite.

$$a - b = a + (-b)$$

Likewise, to subtract a polynomial, we add its opposite. In other words, if P and Q are polynomials, then

$$P - Q = P + (-Q)$$

The polynomial $-Q$ is the **opposite,** or **additive inverse,** of the polynomial Q. We can find $-Q$ by writing the opposite of each term of Q.

> **Subtracting Polynomials**
>
> To subtract two polynomials, change the signs of the terms of the polynomial being subtracted and then add.

✓CONCEPT CHECK

Which polynomial is the opposite of $16x^3 - 5x + 7$?

a. $-16x^3 - 5x + 7$ b. $-16x^3 + 5x - 7$ c. $16x^3 + 5x + 7$ d. $-16x^3 + 5x + 7$

EXAMPLE 11 Subtract: $(2x^3 + 8x^2 - 6x) - (2x^3 - x^2 + 1)$.

Solution First, change the sign of each term of the second polynomial and then add.

> **Helpful Hint**
> Notice the sign of each term is changed.

$$(2x^3 + 8x^2 - 6x) - (2x^3 - x^2 + 1) = (2x^3 + 8x^2 - 6x) + (-2x^3 + x^2 - 1)$$
$$= 2x^3 - 2x^3 + 8x^2 + x^2 - 6x - 1$$
$$= 9x^2 - 6x - 1 \quad \text{Combine like terms.} \quad \square$$

PRACTICE 11 Subtract: $(3x^3 - 5x^2 + 4x) - (x^3 - x^2 + 6)$.

EXAMPLE 12 Subtract $(5z - 7)$ from the sum of $(8z + 11)$ and $(9z - 2)$.

Solution Notice that $(5z - 7)$ is to be subtracted **from** a sum. The translation is

$$[(8z + 11) + (9z - 2)] - (5z - 7)$$
$$= 8z + 11 + 9z - 2 - 5z + 7 \quad \text{Remove grouping symbols.}$$
$$= 8z + 9z - 5z + 11 - 2 + 7 \quad \text{Group like terms.}$$
$$= 12z + 16 \quad \text{Combine like terms.} \quad \square$$

PRACTICE 12 Subtract $(3x + 5)$ from the sum of $(8x - 11)$ and $(2x + 5)$.

EXAMPLE 13 Add or subtract as indicated.

a. $(3x^2 - 6xy + 5y^2) + (-2x^2 + 8xy - y^2)$
b. $(9a^2b^2 + 6ab - 3ab^2) - (5b^2a + 2ab - 3 - 9b^2)$

Solution

a. $(3x^2 - 6xy + 5y^2) + (-2x^2 + 8xy - y^2)$
$$= 3x^2 - 6xy + 5y^2 - 2x^2 + 8xy - y^2$$
$$= x^2 + 2xy + 4y^2 \quad \text{Combine like terms.}$$

b. $(9a^2b^2 + 6ab - 3ab^2) - (5b^2a + 2ab - 3 - 9b^2)$ Change the sign of each term of
$= 9a^2b^2 + 6ab - 3ab^2 - 5b^2a - 2ab + 3 + 9b^2$ the polynomial being subtracted.
$= 9a^2b^2 + 4ab - 8ab^2 + 3 + 9b^2$ Combine like terms.   □

PRACTICE
13   Add or subtract as indicated.

a. $(3a^2 - 4ab + 7b^2) + (-8a^2 + 3ab - b^2)$
b. $(5x^2y^2 - 6xy - 4xy^2) - (2x^2y^2 + 4xy - 5 + 6y^2)$

✓**CONCEPT CHECK**
If possible, simplify each expression by performing the indicated operation.
  a. $2y + y$ **b.** $2y \cdot y$ **c.** $-2y - y$ **d.** $(-2y)(-y)$ **e.** $2x + y$

To add or subtract polynomials vertically, just remember to line up like terms. For example, perform the subtraction $(10x^3y^2 - 7x^2y^2) - (4x^3y^2 - 3x^2y^2 + 2y^2)$ vertically.
Add the opposite of the second polynomial.

$$10x^3y^2 - 7x^2y^2$$
$$\underline{-(4x^3y^2 - 3x^2y^2 + 2y^2)}$$ is equivalent to

$$10x^3y^2 - 7x^2y^2$$
$$\underline{-4x^3y^2 + 3x^2y^2 - 2y^2}$$
$$6x^3y^2 - 4x^2y^2 - 2y^2$$

✓**CONCEPT CHECK**
Why is the following subtraction incorrect?

$$(7z - 5) - (3z - 4)$$
$$= 7z - 5 - 3z - 4$$
$$= 4z - 9$$

Polynomial functions, like polynomials, can be added, subtracted, multiplied, and divided. For example, if

$$P(x) = x^2 + x + 1$$

then

$$2P(x) = 2(x^2 + x + 1) = 2x^2 + 2x + 2$$ Use the distributive property.

Also, if $Q(x) = 5x^2 - 1$, then $P(x) + Q(x) = (x^2 + x + 1) + (5x^2 - 1)$
$$= 6x^2 + x.$$

A useful business and economics application of subtracting polynomial functions is finding the profit function $P(x)$ when given a revenue function $R(x)$ and a cost function $C(x)$. In business, it is true that

$$\text{profit} = \text{revenue} - \text{cost, or}$$
$$P(x) = R(x) - C(x)$$

For example, if the revenue function is $R(x) = 7x$ and the cost function is $C(x) = 2x + 5000$, then the profit function is

$$P(x) = R(x) - C(x)$$

or

$$P(x) = 7x - (2x + 5000)$$ Substitute $R(x) = 7x$
$$P(x) = 5x - 5000$$ and $C(x) = 2x + 5000$.

Answers to Concept Check:
a. $3y$ **b.** $2y^2$ **c.** $-3y$ **d.** $2y^2$
e. cannot be simplified; With parentheses removed, the expression should be
$7z - 5 - 3z + 4 = 4z - 1$

Graphing Calculator Explorations

A graphing calculator may be used to visualize addition and subtraction of polynomials in one variable. For example, to visualize the following polynomial subtraction statement

$$(3x^2 - 6x + 9) - (x^2 - 5x + 6) = 2x^2 - x + 3$$

graph both

$$Y_1 = (3x^2 - 6x + 9) - (x^2 - 5x + 6) \quad \text{Left side of equation}$$

and

$$Y_2 = 2x^2 - x + 3 \quad \text{Right side of equation}$$

on the same screen and see that their graphs coincide. (*Note:* If the graphs do not coincide, we can be sure that a mistake has been made in combining polynomials or in calculator keystrokes. If the graphs appear to coincide, we cannot be sure that our work is correct. This is because it is possible for the graphs to differ so slightly that we do not notice it.)

The graphs of Y_1 and Y_2 are shown. The graphs appear to coincide, so the subtraction statement

$$(3x^2 - 6x + 9) - (x^2 - 5x + 6) = 2x^2 - x + 3$$

appears to be correct.

Perform the indicated operations. Then visualize by using the procedure described above.

1. $(2x^2 + 7x + 6) + (x^3 - 6x^2 - 14)$
2. $(-14x^3 - x + 2) + (-x^3 + 3x^2 + 4x)$
3. $(1.8x^2 - 6.8x - 1.7) - (3.9x^2 - 3.6x)$
4. $(-4.8x^2 + 12.5x - 7.8) - (3.1x^2 - 7.8x)$
5. $(1.29x - 5.68) + (7.69x^2 - 2.55x + 10.98)$
6. $(-0.98x^2 - 1.56x + 5.57) + (4.36x - 3.71)$

Vocabulary, Readiness & Video Check

Use the choices below to fill in each blank. Not all choices will be used.

| least | monomial | trinomial | coefficient |
| greatest | binomial | constant | |

1. A _____ is a polynomial with exactly 2 terms.
2. A _____ is a polynomial with exactly one term.
3. A _____ is a polynomial with exactly three terms.
4. The numerical factor of a term is called the _____ .
5. A number term is also called a _____ .
6. The degree of a polynomial is the _____ degree of any term of the polynomial.

Martin-Gay Interactive Videos

See Video 5.2

Watch the section lecture video and answer the following questions.

OBJECTIVE 1

7. For Example 2, why is the degree of each **term** found when the example asks for the degree of the **polynomial** only?

OBJECTIVE 2

8. From Example 3, how do you find the value of a polynomial function $Q(x)$ given a value for x?

OBJECTIVE 3

9. When combining any like terms in a polynomial, as in Examples 4–6, what are we doing to the polynomial?

OBJECTIVE 4

10. From Example 7, when we simply remove parentheses and combine the like terms of two polynomials, what operation do we perform? Is this true of Examples 9–11?

5.2   Exercise Set   MyMathLab®

Find the degree of each of the following polynomials and determine whether it is a monomial, binomial, trinomial, or none of these. See Examples 1 through 3.

1. $x + 2$

2. $-6y + 4$

3. $9m^3 - 5m^2 + 4m - 8$

4. $a + 5a^2 + 3a^3 - 4a^4$

5. $12x^4y - x^2y^2 - 12x^2y^4$

6. $7r^2s^2 + 2rs - 3rs^5$

7. $3 - 5x^8$

8. $5y^7 + 2$

In the second column, write the degree of the polynomial in the first column. See Examples 1 through 3.

	Polynomial	Degree
9.	$3xy^2 - 4$	
10.	$8x^2y^2$	
11.	$5a^2 - 2a + 1$	
12.	$4z^6 + 3z^2$	

If $P(x) = x^2 + x + 1$ and $Q(x) = 5x^2 - 1$, find the following. See Examples 4 and 5.

13. $P(7)$

14. $Q(4)$

15. $Q(-10)$

16. $P(-4)$

17. $P(0)$

18. $Q(0)$

19. $Q\left(\dfrac{1}{4}\right)$

20. $P\left(\dfrac{1}{2}\right)$

The CN Tower in Toronto, Ontario, is 1821 feet tall and is the world's tallest self-supporting structure. An object is dropped from the Skypod of the Tower, which is at 1150 feet. Neglecting air resistance, the height of the object at time t seconds is given by the polynomial function $P(t) = -16t^2 + 1150$. Find the height of the object at the given times.

1150 ft

	Time, t (in seconds)	Height $P(t) = -16t^2 + 1150$
21.	1	
22.	7	
23.	3	
24.	6	

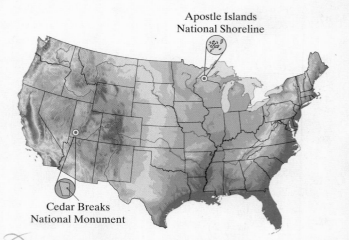

Apostle Islands National Shoreline

Cedar Breaks National Monument

25. The polynomial $P(x) = -7.5x^2 + 93x - 100$ models the yearly number of visitors (in thousands) x years after 2000 at Apostle Islands National Park. Use this polynomial to estimate the number of visitors to the park in 2008 ($P(8)$).

26. The polynomial $P(x) = 8x^2 - 90.6x + 752$ models the yearly number of visitors (in thousands) x years after 2000 at Cedar Breaks National Park. Use this polynomial to estimate the number of visitors to the park in 2007 ($P(7)$).

Simplify each of the following by combining like terms. See Examples 6 and 7.

27. $14x^2 + 9x^2$

28. $18x^3 - 4x^3$

29. $15x^2 - 3x^2 - y$

30. $12k^3 - 9k^3 + 11$

31. $8s - 5s + 4s$

32. $5y + 7y - 6y$

33. $0.1y^2 - 1.2y^2 + 6.7 - 1.9$

34. $7.6y + 3.2y^2 - 8y - 2.5y^2$

35. $\frac{2}{5}x^2 - \frac{1}{3}x^3 + x^2 - \frac{1}{4}x^3 + 6$

36. $\frac{1}{6}x^4 - \frac{1}{7}x^2 + 5 - \frac{1}{2}x^4 - \frac{3}{7}x^2 + \frac{1}{3}$

37. $6a^2 - 4ab + 7b^2 - a^2 - 5ab + 9b^2$

38. $x^2y + xy - y + 10x^2y - 2y + xy$

Perform the indicated operations. See Examples 9 through 13.

39. $(-7x + 5) + (-3x^2 + 7x + 5)$

40. $(3x - 8) + (4x^2 - 3x + 3)$

41. $(2x^2 + 5) - (3x^2 - 9)$

42. $(5x^2 + 4) - (-2y^2 + 4)$

43. $3x - (5x - 9)$

44. $4 - (-y - 4)$

45. $(2x^2 + 3x - 9) - (-4x + 7)$

46. $(-7x^2 + 4x + 7) - (-8x + 2)$

47. $\begin{array}{r} 3t^2 + 4 \\ + 5t^2 - 8 \\ \hline \end{array}$

48. $\begin{array}{r} 7x^3 + 3 \\ + 2x^3 + 1 \\ \hline \end{array}$

49. $\begin{array}{r} 4z^2 - 8z + 3 \\ -(6z^2 + 8z - 3) \\ \hline \end{array}$

50. $\begin{array}{r} 5u^5 - 4u^2 + 3u - 7 \\ -(3u^5 + 6u^2 - 8u + 2) \\ \hline \end{array}$

51. $\begin{array}{r} 5x^3 - 4x^2 + 6x - 2 \\ -(3x^3 - 2x^2 - x - 4) \\ \hline \end{array}$

52. $\begin{array}{r} 7a^2 - 9a + 6 \\ -(11a^2 - 4a + 2) \\ \hline \end{array}$

MIXED PRACTICE

Perform the indicated operations.

53. $(-3y^2 - 4y) + (2y^2 + y - 1)$

54. $(7x^2 + 2x - 9) + (-3x^2 + 5)$

55. $(5x + 8) - (-2x^2 - 6x + 8)$

56. $(-6y^2 + 3y - 4) - (9y^2 - 3y)$

57. $(-8x^4 + 7x) + (-8x^4 + x + 9)$

58. $(6y^5 - 6y^3 + 4) + (-2y^5 - 8y^3 - 7)$

59. $(3x^2 + 5x - 8) + (5x^2 + 9x + 12) - (x^2 - 14)$

60. $(-a^2 + 1) - (a^2 - 3) + (5a^2 - 6a + 7)$

TRANSLATING

Perform each indicated operation.

61. Subtract $4x$ from $(7x - 3)$.

62. Subtract y from $(y^2 - 4y + 1)$.

63. Add $(4x^2 - 6x + 1)$ and $(3x^2 + 2x + 1)$.

64. Add $(-3x^2 - 5x + 2)$ and $(x^2 - 6x + 9)$.

65. Subtract $(19x^2 + 5)$ from $(81x^2 + 10)$.

66. Subtract $(2x + xy)$ from $(3x - 9xy)$.

67. Subtract $(5x + 7)$ from $(7x^2 + 3x + 9)$.

68. Subtract $(5y^2 + 8y + 2)$ from $(7y^2 + 9y - 8)$.

69. Subtract $(2x + 2)$ from the sum of $(8x + 1)$ and $(6x + 3)$.

70. Subtract $(-12x - 3)$ from the sum of $(-5x - 7)$ and $(12x + 3)$.

71. Subtract $(4y^2 - 6y - 3)$ from the sum of $(8y^2 + 7)$ and $(6y + 9)$.

72. Subtract $(4x^2 - 2x + 2)$ from the sum of $(x^2 + 7x + 1)$ and $(7x + 5)$.

Find the area of each figure. Write a polynomial that describes the total area of the rectangles and squares shown in Exercises 73–74. Then simplify the polynomial. See Example 8.

73.

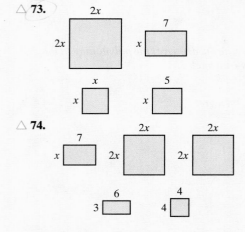

74.

Add or subtract as indicated. See Examples 9 through 13.

75. $(9a + 6b - 5) + (-11a - 7b + 6)$

76. $(3x - 2 + 6y) + (7x - 2 - y)$

77. $(4x^2 + y^2 + 3) - (x^2 + y^2 - 2)$

78. $(7a^2 - 3b^2 + 10) - (-2a^2 + b^2 - 12)$

79. $(x^2 + 2xy - y^2) + (5x^2 - 4xy + 20y^2)$

80. $(a^2 - ab + 4b^2) + (6a^2 + 8ab - b^2)$

81. $(11r^2s + 16rs - 3 - 2r^2s^2) - (3sr^2 + 5 - 9r^2s^2)$

82. $(3x^2y - 6xy + x^2y^2 - 5) - (11x^2y^2 - 1 + 5yx^2)$

Simplify each polynomial by combining like terms.

83. $7.75x + 9.16x^2 - 1.27 - 14.58x^2 - 18.34$

84. $1.85x^2 - 3.76x + 9.25x^2 + 10.76 - 4.21x$

Perform each indicated operation.

85. $[(7.9y^4 - 6.8y^3 + 3.3y) + (6.1y^3 - 5)] - (4.2y^4 + 1.1y - 1)$

86. $[(1.2x^2 - 3x + 9.1) - (7.8x^2 - 3.1 + 8)] + (1.2x - 6)$

REVIEW AND PREVIEW

Multiply. See Section 5.1.

87. $3x(2x)$

88. $-7x(x)$

89. $(12x^3)(-x^5)$

90. $6r^3(7r^{10})$

91. $10x^2(20xy^2)$

92. $-z^2y(11zy)$

CONCEPT EXTENSIONS

Recall that the perimeter of a figure is the sum of the lengths of its sides. For Exercises 93 through 96, find the perimeter of each polynomial.

△ **93.**

△ **94.**

△ **95.**

△ **96.**

△ **97.** A wooden beam is $(4y^2 + 4y + 1)$ meters long. If a piece $(y^2 - 10)$ meters is cut, express the length of the remaining piece of beam as a polynomial in y.

△ **98.** A piece of quarter-round molding is $(13x - 7)$ inches long. If a piece $(2x + 2)$ inches is removed, express the length of the remaining piece of molding as a polynomial in x.

The number of cell phones recycled by the largest recycler x years after 2004 is given by the polynomial function $P(x) = 0.16x^2 + 0.29x + 1.88$ for the years 2004 through 2010. Use this polynomial function for Exercises 99 and 100.

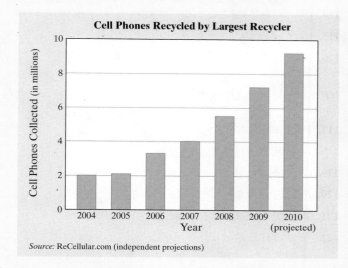

Cell Phones Recycled by Largest Recycler

Source: ReCellular.com (independent projections)

99. Estimate the number of cell phones recycled by this company in 2009.

100. Use the given polynomial function to predict the number of cell phones recycled in 2014.

101. Describe how to find the degree of a term.

102. Describe how to find the degree of a polynomial.

103. Explain why xyz is a monomial while $x + y + z$ is a trinomial.

104. Explain why the degree of the term $5y^3$ is 3 and the degree of the polynomial $2y + y + 2y$ is 1.

Match each expression on the left with its simplification on the right. Not all letters on the right must be used, and a letter may be used more than once.

105. $10y - 6y^2 - y$

106. $5x + 5x$

107. $(5x - 3) + (5x - 3)$

108. $(15x - 3) - (5x - 3)$

a. $3y$

b. $9y - 6y^2$

c. $10x$

d. $25x^2$

e. $10x - 6$

f. none of these

Simplify each expression by performing the indicated operation. Explain how you arrived at each answer. See the third Concept Check in this section.

109. a. $z + 3z$ **b.** $z \cdot 3z$
     c. $-z - 3z$ **d.** $(-z)(-3z)$

110. a. $2y + y$ **b.** $2y \cdot y$
     c. $-2y - y$ **d.** $(-2y)(-y)$

111. a. $m \cdot m \cdot m$ **b.** $m + m + m$
     c. $(-m)(-m)(-m)$ **d.** $-m - m - m$

112. a. $x + x$ **b.** $x \cdot x$
     c. $-x - x$ **d.** $(-x)(-x)$

Perform indicated operations.

113. $(4x^{2a} - 3x^a + 0.5) - (x^{2a} - 5x^a - 0.2)$

114. $(9y^{5a} - 4y^{3a} + 1.5y) - (6y^{5a} - y^{3a} + 4.7y)$

115. $(8x^{2y} - 7x^y + 3) + (-4x^{2y} + 9x^y - 14)$

116. $(14z^{5x} + 3z^{2x} + z) - (2z^{5x} - 10z^{2x} + 3z)$

If $P(x) = 3x + 3$, $Q(x) = 4x^2 - 6x + 3$, and $R(x) = 5x^2 - 7$, find the following.

117. $P(x) + Q(x)$

118. $R(x) + P(x)$

119. $Q(x) - R(x)$

120. $P(x) - Q(x)$

121. $2[Q(x)] - R(x)$

122. $-5[P(x)] - Q(x)$

*If $P(x)$ is the polynomial given, find **a.** $P(a)$, **b.** $P(-x)$, and* **c.** $P(x + h)$.

123. $P(x) = 2x - 3$

124. $P(x) = 8x + 3$

125. $P(x) = 4x$

126. $P(x) = -4x$

Fill in the squares so that each is a true statement.

127. $3x^{\square} + 4x^2 = 7x^{\square}$

128. $9y^7 + 3y^{\square} = 12y^7$

129. $2x^{\square} + 3x^{\square} - 5x^{\square} + 4x^{\square} = 6x^4 - 2x^3$

130. $3y^{\square} + 7y^{\square} - 2y^{\square} - y^{\square} = 10y^5 - 3y^2$

Write a polynomial that describes the surface area of each figure. (Recall that the surface area of a solid is the sum of the areas of the faces or sides of the solid.)

△ **131.**

△ **132.**

 5.3 | **Multiplying Polynomials**

OBJECTIVES

1 Multiply Monomials.

2 Use the Distributive Property to Multiply Polynomials.

3 Multiply Polynomials Vertically.

OBJECTIVE

1   **Multiplying Monomials**

Recall from Section 5.1 that to multiply two monomials such as $(-5x^3)$ and $(-2x^4)$, we use the associative and commutative properties and regroup. Remember, also, that to multiply exponential expressions with a common base, we use the product rule for exponents and add exponents.

$$(-5x^3)(-2x^4) = (-5)(-2)(x^3)(x^4) = 10x^7$$

EXAMPLES   Multiply.

1. $6x \cdot 4x = (6 \cdot 4)(x \cdot x)$ Use the commutative and associative properties.
        $= 24x^2$ Multiply.

2. $-7x^2 \cdot 0.2x^5 = (-7 \cdot 0.2)(x^2 \cdot x^5)$
             $= -1.4x^7$

3. $\left(-\dfrac{1}{3}x^5\right)\left(-\dfrac{2}{9}x\right) = \left(-\dfrac{1}{3} \cdot -\dfrac{2}{9}\right) \cdot (x^5 \cdot x)$

$\qquad\qquad\qquad = \dfrac{2}{27}x^6$

PRACTICES

1–3   Multiply.

1. $5y \cdot 2y$ **2.** $(5z^3) \cdot (-0.4z^5)$ **3.** $\left(-\dfrac{1}{9}b^6\right)\left(-\dfrac{7}{8}b^3\right)$

✔ **CONCEPT CHECK**
Simplify.
  a. $3x \cdot 2x$ **b.** $3x + 2x$

OBJECTIVE

2   Using the Distributive Property to Multiply Polynomials

To multiply polynomials that are not monomials, use the distributive property.

EXAMPLE 4   Use the distributive property to find each product.

a. $5x(2x^3 + 6)$ **b.** $-3x^2(5x^2 + 6x - 1)$

Solution

a. $5x(2x^3 + 6) = 5x(2x^3) + 5x(6)$ Use the distributive property.

$\qquad\qquad\qquad = 10x^4 + 30x$ Multiply.

b. $-3x^2(5x^2 + 6x - 1)$

$\quad = (-3x^2)(5x^2) + (-3x^2)(6x) + (-3x^2)(-1)$ Use the distributive property.

$\quad = -15x^4 - 18x^3 + 3x^2$ Multiply.

PRACTICE

4   Use the distributive property to find each product.

a. $3x(9x^5 + 11)$ **b.** $-6x^3(2x^2 - 9x + 2)$

We also use the distributive property to multiply two binomials. To multiply $(x + 3)$ by $(x + 1)$, distribute the factor $(x + 3)$ first.

$(x + 3)(x + 1) = x(x + 1) + 3(x + 1)$ Distribute $(x + 3)$.

$\qquad\qquad\quad = x(x) + x(1) + 3(x) + 3(1)$ Apply the distributive property a second time.

$\qquad\qquad\quad = x^2 + x + 3x + 3$ Multiply.

$\qquad\qquad\quad = x^2 + 4x + 3$ Combine like terms.

This idea can be expanded so that we can multiply any two polynomials.

To Multiply Two Polynomials

Multiply each term of the first polynomial by each term of the second polynomial and then combine like terms.

Answers to Concept Check:
a. $6x^2$ **b.** $5x$

EXAMPLE 5 Multiply $(3x + 2)(2x - 5)$.

Solution Multiply each term of the first binomial by each term of the second.

$$(3x + 2)(2x - 5) = 3x(2x) + 3x(-5) + 2(2x) + 2(-5)$$
$$= 6x^2 - 15x + 4x - 10 \qquad \text{Multiply.}$$
$$= 6x^2 - 11x - 10 \qquad \text{Combine like terms.} \quad \square$$

PRACTICE
5   Multiply $(5x - 2)(2x + 3)$

EXAMPLE 6 Multiply $(2x - y)^2$.

Solution Recall that $a^2 = a \cdot a$, so $(2x - y)^2 = (2x - y)(2x - y)$. Multiply each term of the first polynomial by each term of the second.

$$(2x - y)(2x - y) = 2x(2x) + 2x(-y) + (-y)(2x) + (-y)(-y)$$
$$= 4x^2 - 2xy - 2xy + y^2 \qquad \text{Multiply.}$$
$$= 4x^2 - 4xy + y^2 \qquad \text{Combine like terms.} \quad \square$$

PRACTICE
6   Multiply $(5x - 3y)^2$

> ✓**CONCEPT CHECK**
> Square where indicated. Simplify if possible.
> **a.** $(4a)^2 + (3b)^2$ **b.** $(4a + 3b)^2$

EXAMPLE 7 Multiply $(t + 2)$ by $(3t^2 - 4t + 2)$.

Solution Multiply each term of the first polynomial by each term of the second.

$$(t + 2)(3t^2 - 4t + 2) = t(3t^2) + t(-4t) + t(2) + 2(3t^2) + 2(-4t) + 2(2)$$
$$= 3t^3 - 4t^2 + 2t + 6t^2 - 8t + 4$$
$$= 3t^3 + 2t^2 - 6t + 4 \quad \text{Combine like terms.} \quad \square$$

PRACTICE
7   Multiply $(y + 4)$ by $(2y^2 - 3y + 5)$

EXAMPLE 8 Multiply $(3a + b)^3$.

Solution Write $(3a + b)^3$ as $(3a + b)(3a + b)(3a + b)$.

$$(3a + b)(3a + b)(3a + b) = (9a^2 + 3ab + 3ab + b^2)(3a + b)$$
$$= (9a^2 + 6ab + b^2)(3a + b)$$
$$= 9a^2(3a + b) + 6ab(3a + b) + b^2(3a + b)$$
$$= 27a^3 + 9a^2b + 18a^2b + 6ab^2 + 3ab^2 + b^3$$
$$= 27a^3 + 27a^2b + 9ab^2 + b^3 \quad \square$$

Answers to Concept Check:
a. $16a^2 + 9b^2$
b. $16a^2 + 24ab + 9b^2$

PRACTICE
8   Multiply $(s + 2t)^3$.

OBJECTIVE

3 Multiplying Polynomials Vertically

Another convenient method for multiplying polynomials is to use a vertical format similar to the format used to multiply real numbers. We demonstrate this method by multiplying $(3y^2 - 4y + 1)$ by $(y + 2)$.

EXAMPLE 9 Multiply $(3y^2 - 4y + 1)(y + 2)$. Use a vertical format.

Solution

▶ **Helpful Hint**
Make sure like terms are lined up.

$$
\begin{array}{r}
3y^2 - 4y + 1 \\
\times \qquad y + 2 \\
\hline
6y^2 - 8y + 2 \\
3y^3 - 4y^2 + \ y \\
\hline
3y^3 + 2y^2 - 7y + 2
\end{array}
$$

1st, Multiply $3y^2 - 4y + 1$ by 2.
2nd, Multiply $3y^2 - 4y + 1$ by y.
Line up like terms.
3rd, Combine like terms.

Thus, $(3y^2 - 4y + 1)(y + 2) = 3y^3 + 2y^2 - 7y + 2$. □

PRACTICE

9 Multiply $(5x^2 - 3x + 5)(x - 4)$.

When multiplying vertically, be careful if a power is missing; you may want to leave space in the partial products and take care that like terms are lined up.

EXAMPLE 10 Multiply $(2x^3 - 3x + 4)(x^2 + 1)$. Use a vertical format.

Solution

$$
\begin{array}{r}
2x^3 - 3x + 4 \\
\times \qquad x^2 + 1 \\
\hline
2x^3 \qquad - 3x + 4 \\
2x^5 - 3x^3 + 4x^2 \\
\hline
2x^5 - \ x^3 + 4x^2 - 3x + 4
\end{array}
$$

Leave space for missing powers of x.
← Line up like terms.
Combine like terms. □

PRACTICE

10 Multiply $(x^3 - 2x^2 + 1)(x^2 + 2)$ using a vertical format.

EXAMPLE 11 Find the product of $(2x^2 - 3x + 4)$ and $(x^2 + 5x - 2)$ using a vertical format.

Solution First, we arrange the polynomials in a vertical format. Then we multiply each term of the second polynomial by each term of the first polynomial.

$$
\begin{array}{r}
2x^2 - \ 3x + 4 \\
\times \qquad x^2 + \ 5x - 2 \\
\hline
-4x^2 + \ 6x - 8 \\
10x^3 - 15x^2 + 20x \\
2x^4 - \ 3x^3 + \ 4x^2 \\
\hline
2x^4 + \ 7x^3 - 15x^2 + 26x - 8
\end{array}
$$

Multiply $2x^2 - 3x + 4$ by -2.
Multiply $2x^2 - 3x + 4$ by $5x$.
Multiply $2x^2 - 3x + 4$ by x^2.
Combine like terms. □

PRACTICE

11 Find the product of $(5x^2 + 2x - 2)$ and $(x^2 - x + 3)$ using a vertical format.

Vocabulary, Readiness & Video Check

Fill in each blank with the correct choice.

1. The expression $5x(3x + 2)$ equals $5x \cdot 3x + 5x \cdot 2$ by the _____ property.
   a. commutative   b. associative   c. distributive

2. The expression $(x + 4)(7x - 1)$ equals $x(7x - 1) + 4(7x - 1)$ by the _____ property.
   a. commutative   b. associative   c. distributive

3. The expression $(5y - 1)^2$ equals _____.
   a. $2(5y - 1)$ b. $(5y - 1)(5y + 1)$ c. $(5y - 1)(5y - 1)$

4. The expression $9x \cdot 3x$ equals _____.
   a. $27x$ b. $27x^2$ c. $12x$ d. $12x^2$

Martin-Gay Interactive Videos

See Video 5.3

Watch the section lecture video and answer the following questions.

OBJECTIVE 1

5. For Example 1, we use the product property to multiply the monomials. Is it possible to add the same two monomials? Why or why not?

OBJECTIVE 2

6. What property and what exponent rule is used in Examples 2–6?

OBJECTIVE 3

7. Would you say the vertical format used in Example 7 also applies the distributive property? Explain.

5.3 Exercise Set   MyMathLab®

Multiply. See Examples 1 through 3.

1. $-4n^3 \cdot 7n^7$
2. $9t^6(-3t^5)$
3. $(-3.1x^3)(4x^9)$
4. $(-5.2x^4)(3x^4)$
5. $\left(-\dfrac{1}{3}y^2\right)\left(\dfrac{2}{5}y\right)$
6. $\left(-\dfrac{3}{4}y^7\right)\left(\dfrac{1}{7}y^4\right)$
7. $(2x)(-3x^2)(4x^5)$
8. $(x)(5x^4)(-6x^7)$

Multiply. See Example 4.

9. $3x(2x + 5)$
10. $2x(6x + 3)$
11. $-2a(a + 4)$
12. $-3a(2a + 7)$
13. $3x(2x^2 - 3x + 4)$
14. $4x(5x^2 - 6x - 10)$
15. $-2a^2(3a^2 - 2a + 3)$
16. $-4b^2(3b^3 - 12b^2 - 6)$
17. $-y(4x^3 - 7x^2y + xy^2 + 3y^3)$
18. $-x(6y^3 - 5xy^2 + x^2y - 5x^3)$
19. $\dfrac{1}{2}x^2(8x^2 - 6x + 1)$
20. $\dfrac{1}{3}y^2(9y^2 - 6y + 1)$

Multiply. See Examples 5 and 6.

21. $(x + 4)(x + 3)$
22. $(x + 2)(x + 9)$
23. $(a + 7)(a - 2)$
24. $(y - 10)(y + 11)$
25. $\left(x + \dfrac{2}{3}\right)\left(x - \dfrac{1}{3}\right)$
26. $\left(x + \dfrac{3}{5}\right)\left(x - \dfrac{2}{5}\right)$
27. $(3x^2 + 1)(4x^2 + 7)$
28. $(5x^2 + 2)(6x^2 + 2)$
29. $(2y - 4)^2$
30. $(6x - 7)^2$
31. $(4x - 3)(3x - 5)$
32. $(8x - 3)(2x - 4)$
33. $(3x^2 + 1)^2$
34. $(x^2 + 4)^2$
35. Perform the indicated operations.
   a. $4y^2(-y^2)$
   b. $4y^2 - y^2$
   c. Explain the difference between the two expressions.
36. Perform the indicated operations.
   a. $9x^2(-10x^2)$
   b. $9x^2 - 10x^2$
   c. Explain the difference between the two expressions.

Multiply. See Example 7.

37. $(x - 2)(x^2 - 3x + 7)$

38. $(x + 3)(x^2 + 5x - 8)$

▶ **39.** $(x + 5)(x^3 - 3x + 4)$

40. $(a + 2)(a^3 - 3a^2 + 7)$

41. $(2a - 3)(5a^2 - 6a + 4)$

42. $(3 + b)(2 - 5b - 3b^2)$

Multiply. See Example 8.

43. $(x + 2)^3$

44. $(y - 1)^3$

45. $(2y - 3)^3$

46. $(3x + 4)^3$

Multiply vertically. See Examples 9 through 11.

47. $(2x - 11)(6x + 1)$

48. $(4x - 7)(5x + 1)$

▶ **49.** $(5x + 1)(2x^2 + 4x - 1)$

50. $(4x - 5)(8x^2 + 2x - 4)$

51. $(x^2 + 5x - 7)(2x^2 - 7x - 9)$

52. $(3x^2 - x + 2)(x^2 + 2x + 1)$

MIXED PRACTICE

Multiply. See Examples 1 through 11.

53. $-1.2y(-7y^6)$

54. $-4.2x(-2x^5)$

55. $-3x(x^2 + 2x - 8)$

56. $-5x(x^2 - 3x + 10)$

57. $(x + 19)(2x + 1)$

58. $(3y + 4)(y + 11)$

59. $\left(x + \dfrac{1}{7}\right)\left(x - \dfrac{3}{7}\right)$

60. $\left(m + \dfrac{2}{9}\right)\left(m - \dfrac{1}{9}\right)$

61. $(3y + 5)^2$

62. $(7y + 2)^2$

63. $(a + 4)(a^2 - 6a + 6)$

64. $(t + 3)(t^2 - 5t + 5)$

REVIEW AND PREVIEW

In this section, we review operations on monomials. Study the box below, then proceed. See Sections 1.8, 5.1, and 5.2. (Continued on next page.)

65. $(2x - 5)^3$

66. $(3y - 1)^3$

67. $(4x + 5)(8x^2 + 2x - 4)$

68. $(5x + 4)(x^2 - x + 4)$

69. $(3x^2 + 2x - 4)(2x^2 - 4x + 3)$

70. $(a^2 + 3a - 2)(2a^2 - 5a - 1)$

Express as the product of polynomials. Then multiply.

△ **71.** Find the area of the rectangle.

$(2x + 5)$ yards

$(2x - 5)$ yards

△ **72.** Find the area of the square field.

$(x + 4)$ feet

△ **73.** Find the area of the triangle.

$\left(\text{Triangle Area} = \dfrac{1}{2} \cdot \text{base} \cdot \text{height}\right)$

$4x$ inches

$(3x - 2)$ inches

△ **74.** Find the volume of the cube.

$(\text{Volume} = \text{length} \cdot \text{width} \cdot \text{height})$

$(y - 1)$ meters

Operations on Monomials	
Multiply	Review the product rule for exponents.
Divide	Review the quotient rule for exponents.
Add or Subtract	Remember, we may only combine like terms.

Perform the operations on the monomials if possible. The first two rows have been completed for you.

Monomials	Add	Subtract	Multiply	Divide
$6x, 3x$	$6x + 3x = 9x$	$6x - 3x = 3x$	$6x \cdot 3x = 18x^2$	$\dfrac{6x}{3x} = 2$
$-12x^2, 2x$	$-12x^2 + 2x$, can't be simplified	$-12x^2 - 2x$, can't be simplified	$-12x^2 \cdot 2x = -24x^3$	$\dfrac{-12x^2}{2x} = -6x$
75. $5a, 15a$				
76. $4y^7, 4y^3$				
77. $-3y^5, 9y^4$				
78. $-14x^2, 2x^2$				

CONCEPT EXTENSIONS

79. Perform each indicated operation. Explain the difference between the two expressions.
   a. $(3x + 5) + (3x + 7)$
   b. $(3x + 5)(3x + 7)$

80. Perform each indicated operation. Explain the difference between the two expressions.
   a. $(8x - 3) - (5x - 2)$
   b. $(8x - 3)(5x - 2)$

MIXED PRACTICE

Perform the indicated operations. See Sections 5.1 and 5.2.

81. $(3x - 1) + (10x - 6)$
82. $(2x - 1) + (10x - 7)$
83. $(3x - 1)(10x - 6)$
84. $(2x - 1)(10x - 7)$
85. $(3x - 1) - (10x - 6)$
86. $(2x - 1) - (10x - 7)$

CONCEPT EXTENSIONS

△ **87.** The area of the larger rectangle on the right is $x(x + 3)$. Find another expression for this area by finding the sum of the areas of the two smaller rectangles.

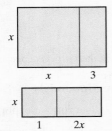

△ **88.** Write an expression for the area of the larger rectangle on the right in two different ways.

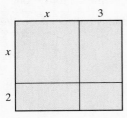

△ **89.** The area of the figure on the right is $(x + 2)(x + 3)$. Find another expression for this area by finding the sum of the areas of the four smaller rectangles.

△ **90.** Write an expression for the area of the figure in two different ways.

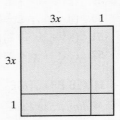

Simplify. See the Concept Checks in this section.

91. $5a + 6a$ **92.** $5a \cdot 6a$

Square where indicated. Simplify if possible.

93. $(5x)^2 + (2y)^2$ **94.** $(5x + 2y)^2$

95. Multiply each of the following polynomials.
   a. $(a + b)(a - b)$
   b. $(2x + 3y)(2x - 3y)$
   c. $(4x + 7)(4x - 7)$
   d. Can you make a general statement about all products of the form $(x + y)(x - y)$?

96. Evaluate each of the following.
   a. $(2 + 3)^2; 2^2 + 3^2$
   b. $(8 + 10)^2; 8^2 + 10^2$
   c. Does $(a + b)^2 = a^2 + b^2$ no matter what the values of a and b are? Why or why not?

△ **97.** Write a polynomial that describes the area of the shaded region. (Find the area of the larger square minus the area of the smaller square.)

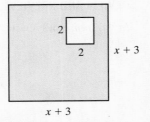

△ **98.** Write a polynomial that describes the area of the shaded region. (See Exercise 97.)

5.4 | Special Products

OBJECTIVES

1 Multiply Two Binomials Using the FOIL Method. ▶

2 Square a Binomial. ▶

3 Multiply the Sum and Difference of Two Terms. ▶

4 Use Special Products to Multiply Binomials. ▶

OBJECTIVE

1   Using the FOIL Method ▶

In this section, we multiply binomials using special products. First, a special order for multiplying binomials called the FOIL order or method is introduced. This method is demonstrated by multiplying $(3x + 1)$ by $(2x + 5)$ as shown below.

The FOIL Method

F stands for the product of the **First** terms. $(3x + 1)(2x + 5)$
$$(3x)(2x) = 6x^2 \quad \textbf{F}$$

O stands for the product of the **Outer** terms. $(3x + 1)(2x + 5)$
$$(3x)(5) = 15x \quad \textbf{O}$$

I stands for the product of the **Inner** terms. $(3x + 1)(2x + 5)$
$$(1)(2x) = 2x \quad \textbf{I}$$

L stands for the product of the **Last** terms. $(3x + 1)(3x + 5)$
$$(1)(5) = 5 \quad \textbf{L}$$

$$\begin{array}{cccc} \text{F} & \text{O} & \text{I} & \text{L} \end{array}$$
$$(3x + 1)(2x + 5) = 6x^2 + 15x + 2x + 5$$
$$= 6x^2 + 17x + 5 \quad \text{Combine like terms.}$$

✓CONCEPT CHECK

Multiply $(3x + 1)(2x + 5)$ using methods from the last section. Show that the product is still $6x^2 + 17x + 5$.

EXAMPLE 1   Multiply $(x - 3)(x + 4)$ by the FOIL method.

Solution

$$\begin{array}{cccc} \text{F} & \text{O} & \text{I} & \text{L} \end{array}$$
$$(x - 3)(x + 4) = (x)(x) + (x)(4) + (-3)(x) + (-3)(4)$$

$$= x^2 + 4x - 3x - 12$$
$$= x^2 + x - 12 \quad \text{Combine like terms.} \qquad \square$$

▶ **Helpful Hint**
Remember that the FOIL order for multiplying can be used only for the product of 2 binomials.

PRACTICE
1   Multiply $(x + 2)(x - 5)$ by the FOIL method.

EXAMPLE 2   Multiply $(5x - 7)(x - 2)$ by the FOIL method.

Solution

$$\begin{array}{cccc} \text{F} & \text{O} & \text{I} & \text{L} \end{array}$$
$$(5x - 7)(x - 2) = 5x(x) + 5x(-2) + (-7)(x) + (-7)(-2)$$

$$= 5x^2 - 10x - 7x + 14$$
$$= 5x^2 - 17x + 14 \quad \text{Combine like terms.} \qquad \square$$

Answer to Concept Check:
Multiply and simplify:
$3x(2x + 5) + 1(2x + 5)$

PRACTICE
2   Multiply $(4x - 9)(x - 1)$ by the FOIL method.

EXAMPLE 3 Multiply $2(y + 6)(2y - 1)$.

Solution $2(y + 6)(2y - 1) = 2(2y^2 - 1y + 12y - 6)$

$\qquad\qquad\qquad\qquad\quad = 2(2y^2 + 11y - 6)$ Simplify inside parentheses.

$\qquad\qquad\qquad\qquad\quad = 4y^2 + 22y - 12$ Now use the distributive property. ☐

PRACTICE
3   Multiply $3(x + 5)(3x - 1)$.

OBJECTIVE
2   **Squaring Binomials** ▶

Now, try squaring a binomial using the FOIL method.

EXAMPLE 4 Multiply $(3y + 1)^2$.

Solution $(3y + 1)^2 = (3y + 1)(3y + 1)$

$\qquad\qquad\qquad\qquad$ F $\qquad$ O $\qquad$ I $\qquad$ L

$\qquad\qquad\qquad = (3y)(3y) + (3y)(1) + 1(3y) + 1(1)$

$\qquad\qquad\qquad = 9y^2 + 3y + 3y + 1$

$\qquad\qquad\qquad = 9y^2 + 6y + 1$ ☐

PRACTICE
4   Multiply $(4x - 1)^2$.

Notice the pattern that appears in Example 4.

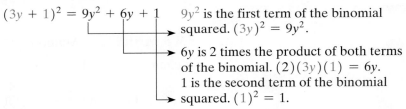

$(3y + 1)^2 = 9y^2 + 6y + 1$ $9y^2$ is the first term of the binomial squared. $(3y)^2 = 9y^2$.

6y is 2 times the product of both terms of the binomial. $(2)(3y)(1) = 6y$.
1 is the second term of the binomial squared. $(1)^2 = 1$.

This pattern leads to the following, which can be used when squaring a binomial. We call these **special products.**

> **Squaring a Binomial**
>
> A binomial squared is equal to the square of the first term plus or minus twice the product of both terms plus the square of the second term.
>
> $$(a + b)^2 = a^2 + 2ab + b^2$$
> $$(a - b)^2 = a^2 - 2ab + b^2$$

This product can be visualized geometrically.

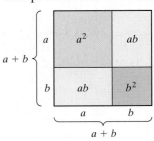

The area of the large square is side · side.

$$\text{Area} = (a + b)(a + b) = (a + b)^2$$

The area of the large square is also the sum of the areas of the smaller rectangles.

$$\text{Area} = a^2 + ab + ab + b^2 = a^2 + 2ab + b^2$$

Thus, $(a + b)^2 = a^2 + 2ab + b^2$.

EXAMPLE 5   Use a special product to square each binomial.

a. $(t + 2)^2$ **b.** $(p - q)^2$ **c.** $(2x + 5)^2$ **d.** $(x^2 - 7y)^2$

Solution

	first term squared	plus or minus	twice the product of the terms	plus	second term squared

a. $(t + 2)^2 \;=\; t^2 \;+\; 2(t)(2) \;+\; 2^2 = t^2 + 4t + 4$

b. $(p - q)^2 \;=\; p^2 \;-\; 2(p)(q) \;+\; q^2 = p^2 - 2pq + q^2$

c. $(2x + 5)^2 \;=\; (2x)^2 \;+\; 2(2x)(5) \;+\; 5^2 = 4x^2 + 20x + 25$

d. $(x^2 - 7y)^2 \;=\; (x^2)^2 \;-\; 2(x^2)(7y) \;+\; (7y^2) = x^4 - 14x^2y + 49y^2 \;\square$

PRACTICE

5   Use a special product to square each binomial.

a. $(b + 3)^2$ **b.** $(x - y)^2$

c. $(3y + 2)^2$ **d.** $(a^2 - 5b)^2$

> ▶ **Helpful Hint**
>
> Notice that
>
> $$(a + b)^2 \neq a^2 + b^2 \quad \text{The middle term } 2ab \text{ is missing.}$$
> $$(a + b)^2 = (a + b)(a + b) = a^2 + 2ab + b^2$$
>
> Likewise,
>
> $$(a - b)^2 \neq a^2 - b^2$$
> $$(a - b)^2 = (a - b)(a - b) = a^2 - 2ab + b^2$$

OBJECTIVE

3   Multiplying the Sum and Difference of Two Terms

Another special product is the product of the sum and difference of the same two terms, such as $(x + y)(x - y)$. Finding this product by the FOIL method, we see a pattern emerge.

$$\overset{\text{F O I L}}{(x + y)(x - y) = x^2 - xy + xy - y^2}$$

$$= x^2 - y^2$$

Notice that the middle two terms subtract out. This is because the **O**uter product is the opposite of the **I**nner product. Only the **difference of squares** remains.

> **Multiplying the Sum and Difference of Two Terms**
>
> The product of the sum and difference of two terms is the square of the first term minus the square of the second term.
>
> $$(a + b)(a - b) = a^2 - b^2$$

EXAMPLE 6 Use a special product to multiply.

a. $4(x + 4)(x - 4)$

b. $(6t + 7)(6t - 7)$

c. $\left(x - \frac{1}{4}\right)\left(x + \frac{1}{4}\right)$

d. $(2p - q)(2p + q)$

e. $(3x^2 - 5y)(3x^2 + 5y)$

Solution

first term squared	minus	second term squared
↓	↓	↙

a. $4(x + 4)(x - 4) = 4(x^2 - 4^2) = 4(x^2 - 16) = 4x^2 - 64$

b. $(6t + 7)(6t - 7) = (6t)^2 - 7^2 = 36t^2 - 49$

c. $\left(x - \frac{1}{4}\right)\left(x + \frac{1}{4}\right) = x^2 - \left(\frac{1}{4}\right)^2 = x^2 - \frac{1}{16}$

d. $(2p - q)(2p + q) = (2p)^2 - q^2 = 4p^2 - q^2$

e. $(3x^2 - 5y)(3x^2 + 5y) = (3x^2)^2 - (5y)^2 = 9x^4 - 25y^2$

PRACTICE
6 Use a special product to multiply.

a. $3(x + 5)(x - 5)$

b. $(4b - 3)(4b + 3)$

c. $\left(x + \frac{2}{3}\right)\left(x - \frac{2}{3}\right)$

d. $(5s + t)(5s - t)$

e. $(2y - 3z^2)(2y + 3z^2)$

✓**CONCEPT CHECK**
Match expression number 1 and number 2 to the equivalent expression or expressions in the list below.
1. $(a + b)^2$ **2.** $(a + b)(a - b)$
  a. $(a + b)(a + b)$ **b.** $a^2 - b^2$ **c.** $a^2 + b^2$ **d.** $a^2 - 2ab + b^2$ **e.** $a^2 + 2ab + b^2$

OBJECTIVE
4 Using Special Products ▶
Let's now practice multiplying polynomials in general. If possible, use a special product.

EXAMPLE 7 Use a special product to multiply, if possible.

a. $(x - 5)(3x + 4)$ **b.** $(7x + 4)^2$ **c.** $(y - 0.6)(y + 0.6)$

d. $\left(y^4 + \frac{2}{5}\right)\left(3y^2 - \frac{1}{5}\right)$ **e.** $(a - 3)(a^2 + 2a - 1)$

Solution

a. $(x - 5)(3x + 4) = 3x^2 + 4x - 15x - 20$ FOIL.
$= 3x^2 - 11x - 20$

b. $(7x + 4)^2 = (7x)^2 + 2(7x)(4) + 4^2$ Squaring a binomial.
$= 49x^2 + 56x + 16$

c. $(y - 0.6)(y + 0.6) = y^2 - (0.6)^2 = y^2 - 0.36$ Multiplying the sum and difference of 2 terms.

d. $\left(y^4 + \frac{2}{5}\right)\left(3y^2 - \frac{1}{5}\right) = 3y^6 - \frac{1}{5}y^4 + \frac{6}{5}y^2 - \frac{2}{25}$ FOIL.

e. I've inserted this product as a reminder that since it is not a binomial times a binomial, the FOIL order may not be used.

$$(a - 3)(a^2 + 2a - 1) = a(a^2 + 2a - 1) - 3(a^2 + 2a - 1)$$
$$= a^3 + 2a^2 - a - 3a^2 - 6a + 3$$
$$= a^3 - a^2 - 7a + 3$$

Multiplying each term of the binomial by each term of the trinomial.

PRACTICE
7 Use a special product to multiply, if possible.

a. $(4x + 3)(x - 6)$

b. $(7b - 2)^2$

c. $(x + 0.4)(x - 0.4)$

d. $\left(x^2 - \dfrac{3}{7}\right)\left(3x^4 + \dfrac{2}{7}\right)$

e. $(x + 1)(x^2 + 5x - 2)$

▶ **Helpful Hint**
- When multiplying two binomials, you may always use the FOIL order or method.
- When multiplying any two polynomials, you may always use the distributive property to find the product.

Vocabulary, Readiness & Video Check

Answer each exercise true or false.

1. $(x + 4)^2 = x^2 + 16$

2. For $(x + 6)(2x - 1)$ the product of the first terms is $2x^2$.

3. $(x + 4)(x - 4) = x^2 + 16$

4. The product $(x - 1)(x^3 + 3x - 1)$ is a polynomial of degree 5.

Martin-Gay Interactive Videos

See Video 5.4

Watch the section lecture video and answer the following questions.

OBJECTIVE 1
5. From ▣ Examples 1–3, for what type of multiplication problem is the FOIL order of multiplication used?

OBJECTIVE 2
6. Name at least one other method you can use to multiply ▣ Example 4.

OBJECTIVE 3
7. From ▣ Example 5, why does multiplying the sum and difference of the same two terms always give you a binomial answer?

OBJECTIVE 4
8. Why was the FOIL method not used for Example 10?

5.4 Exercise Set MyMathLab®

Multiply using the FOIL method. See Examples 1 through 3.

1. $(x + 3)(x + 4)$
2. $(x + 5)(x - 1)$
3. $(x - 5)(x + 10)$
4. $(y - 12)(y + 4)$
5. $(5x - 6)(x + 2)$
6. $(3y - 5)(2y - 7)$
7. $5(y - 6)(4y - 1)$
8. $2(x - 11)(2x - 9)$
9. $(2x + 5)(3x - 1)$
10. $(6x + 2)(x - 2)$

11. $\left(x - \dfrac{1}{3}\right)\left(x + \dfrac{2}{3}\right)$
12. $\left(x - \dfrac{2}{5}\right)\left(x + \dfrac{1}{5}\right)$

Multiply. See Examples 4 and 5.

13. $(x + 2)^2$
14. $(x + 7)^2$
15. $(2x - 1)^2$
16. $(7x - 3)^2$
17. $(3a - 5)^2$
18. $(5a + 2)^2$
19. $(5x + 9)^2$
20. $(6s - 2)^2$

Multiply. See Example 6.

▶ **21.** $(a - 7)(a + 7)$

22. $(b + 3)(b - 3)$

23. $(3x - 1)(3x + 1)$

24. $(4x - 5)(4x + 5)$

25. $\left(3x - \dfrac{1}{2}\right)\left(3x + \dfrac{1}{2}\right)$

26. $\left(10x + \dfrac{2}{7}\right)\left(10x - \dfrac{2}{7}\right)$

▶ **27.** $(9x + y)(9x - y)$

28. $(2x - y)(2x + y)$

29. $(2x + 0.1)(2x - 0.1)$

30. $(5x - 1.3)(5x + 1.3)$

MIXED PRACTICE

Multiply. See Example 7.

31. $(a + 5)(a + 4)$

32. $(a - 5)(a - 7)$

33. $(a + 7)^2$

34. $(b - 2)^2$

35. $(4a + 1)(3a - 1)$

36. $(6a + 7)(6a + 5)$

37. $(x + 2)(x - 2)$

38. $(x - 10)(x + 10)$

▶ **39.** $(3a + 1)^2$

40. $(4a - 2)^2$

41. $(x^2 + y)(4x - y^4)$

42. $(x^3 - 2)(5x + y)$

▶ **43.** $(x + 3)(x^2 - 6x + 1)$

44. $(x - 2)(x^2 - 4x + 2)$

45. $(2a - 3)^2$

46. $(5b - 4x)^2$

47. $(5x - 6z)(5x + 6z)$

48. $(11x - 7y)(11x + 7y)$

49. $(x^5 - 3)(x^5 - 5)$

50. $(a^4 + 5)(a^4 + 6)$

51. $(x + 0.8)(x - 0.8)$

52. $(y - 0.9)(y + 0.9)$

53. $(a^3 + 11)(a^4 - 3)$

54. $(x^5 + 5)(x^2 - 8)$

55. $3(x - 2)^2$

56. $2(3b + 7)^2$

▶ **57.** $(3b + 7)(2b - 5)$

58. $(3y - 13)(y - 3)$

59. $(7p - 8)(7p + 8)$

60. $(3s - 4)(3s + 4)$

▶ **61.** $\left(\dfrac{1}{3}a^2 - 7\right)\left(\dfrac{1}{3}a^2 + 7\right)$

62. $\left(\dfrac{2}{3}a - b^2\right)\left(\dfrac{2}{3}a - b^2\right)$

63. $5x^2(3x^2 - x + 2)$

64. $4x^3(2x^2 + 5x - 1)$

65. $(2r - 3s)(2r + 3s)$

66. $(6r - 2x)(6r + 2x)$

67. $(3x - 7y)^2$

68. $(4s - 2y)^2$

▶ **69.** $(4x + 5)(4x - 5)$

70. $(3x + 5)(3x - 5)$

71. $(8x + 4)^2$

72. $(3x + 2)^2$

73. $\left(a - \dfrac{1}{2}y\right)\left(a + \dfrac{1}{2}y\right)$

74. $\left(\dfrac{a}{2} + 4y\right)\left(\dfrac{a}{2} - 4y\right)$

75. $\left(\dfrac{1}{5}x - y\right)\left(\dfrac{1}{5}x + y\right)$

76. $\left(\dfrac{y}{6} - 8\right)\left(\dfrac{y}{6} + 8\right)$

77. $(a + 1)(3a^2 - a + 1)$

78. $(b + 3)(2b^2 + b - 3)$

Express each as a product of polynomials in x. Then multiply and simplify.

△ **79.** Find the area of the square rug shown if its side is $(2x + 1)$ feet.

$(2x + 1)$ feet

$(2x + 1)$ feet

△ **80.** Find the area of the rectangular canvas if its length is $(3x - 2)$ inches and its width is $(x - 4)$ inches.

$(x - 4)$ inches

$(3x - 2)$ inches

REVIEW AND PREVIEW

Simplify each expression. See Section 5.1.

81. $\dfrac{50b^{10}}{70b^5}$

82. $\dfrac{x^3y^6}{xy^2}$

83. $\dfrac{8a^{17}b^{15}}{-4a^7b^{10}}$

84. $\dfrac{-6a^8y}{3a^4y}$

85. $\dfrac{2x^4y^{12}}{3x^4y^4}$

86. $\dfrac{-48ab^6}{32ab^3}$

Find the slope of each line. See Section 3.4.

87.

88.

89.

90.

CONCEPT EXTENSIONS

Match each expression on the left to the equivalent expression on the right. See the second Concept Check in this section.

91. $(a - b)^2$

92. $(a - b)(a + b)$

93. $(a + b)^2$

94. $(a + b)^2(a - b)^2$

    a. $a^2 - b^2$

    b. $a^2 + b^2$

    c. $a^2 - 2ab + b^2$

    d. $a^2 + 2ab + b^2$

    e. none of these

Fill in the squares so that a true statement forms.

95. $(x^\square + 7)(x^\square + 3) = x^4 + 10x^2 + 21$

96. $(5x^\square - 2)^2 = 25x^6 - 20x^3 + 4$

Find the area of the shaded figure. To do so, subtract the area of the smaller square(s) from the area of the larger geometric figure.

△ **97.**

△ **98.**

△ **99.**

△ **100.**

For Exercises 101 and 102, find the area of the shaded figure.

△ **101.**

△ **102.**

103. In your own words, describe the different methods that can be used to find the product: $(2x - 5)(3x + 1)$.

104. In your own words, describe the different methods that can be used to find the product: $(5x + 1)^2$.

105. Suppose that a classmate asked you why $(2x + 1)^2$ is **not** $(4x^2 + 1)$. Write down your response to this classmate.

106. Suppose that a classmate asked you why $(2x + 1)^2$ **is** $(4x^2 + 4x + 1)$. Write down your response to this classmate.

107. Using your own words, explain how to square a binomial such as $(a + b)^2$.

108. Explain how to find the product of two binomials using the FOIL method.

Find each product. For example,

$$[(a + b) - 2][(a + b) + 2] = (a + b)^2 - 2^2$$
$$= a^2 + 2ab + b^2 - 4$$

109. $[(x + y) - 3][(x + y) + 3]$

110. $[(a + c) - 5][(a + c) + 5]$

111. $[(a - 3) + b][(a - 3) - b]$

112. $[(x - 2) + y][(x - 2) - y]$

Integrated Review EXPONENTS AND OPERATIONS ON POLYNOMIALS

Sections 5.1–5.4
Perform the indicated operations and simplify.

1. $(5x^2)(7x^3)$

2. $(4y^2)(8y^7)$

3. -4^2

4. $(-4)^2$

5. $(x - 5)(2x + 1)$

6. $(3x - 2)(x + 5)$

7. $(x - 5) + (2x + 1)$

8. $(3x - 2) + (x + 5)$

9. $\dfrac{7x^9y^{12}}{x^3y^{10}}$

10. $\dfrac{20a^2b^8}{14a^2b^2}$

11. $(12m^7n^6)^2$

12. $(4y^9z^{10})^3$

13. $3(4y - 3)(4y + 3)$

14. $2(7x - 1)(7x + 1)$

15. $(x^7y^5)^9$

16. $(3^1x^9)^3$

17. $(7x^2 - 2x + 3) - (5x^2 + 9)$

18. $(10x^2 + 7x - 9) - (4x^2 - 6x + 2)$

19. $0.7y^2 - 1.2 + 1.8y^2 - 6y + 1$

20. $7.8x^2 - 6.8x + 3.3 + 0.6x^2 - 9$

21. $(x + 4y)^2$

22. $(y - 9z)^2$

23. $(x + 4y) + (x + 4y)$

24. $(y - 9z) + (y - 9z)$

25. $7x^2 - 6xy + 4(y^2 - xy)$

26. $5a^2 - 3ab + 6(b^2 - a^2)$

27. $(x - 3)(x^2 + 5x - 1)$

28. $(x + 1)(x^2 - 3x - 2)$

29. $(2x^3 - 7)(3x^2 + 10)$

30. $(5x^3 - 1)(4x^4 + 5)$

31. $(2x - 7)(x^2 - 6x + 1)$

32. $(5x - 1)(x^2 + 2x - 3)$

Perform exercises and simplify if possible.

33. $5x^3 + 5y^3$

34. $(5x^3)(5y^3)$

35. $(5x^3)^3$

36. $\dfrac{5x^3}{5y^3}$

37. $x + x$

38. $x \cdot x$

5.5 | Negative Exponents and Scientific Notation

OBJECTIVES

1 Simplify Expressions Containing Negative Exponents.

2 Use All the Rules and Definitions for Exponents to Simplify Exponential Expressions.

3 Write Numbers in Scientific Notation.

4 Convert Numbers from Scientific Notation to Standard Form.

5 Perform Operations on Numbers Written in Scientific Notation.

OBJECTIVE
1 Simplifying Expressions Containing Negative Exponents

Our work with exponential expressions so far has been limited to exponents that are positive integers or 0. Here we expand to give meaning to an expression like x^{-3}.

Suppose that we wish to simplify the expression $\dfrac{x^2}{x^5}$. If we use the quotient rule for exponents, we subtract exponents:

$$\frac{x^2}{x^5} = x^{2-5} = x^{-3}, \quad x \neq 0$$

But what does x^{-3} mean? Let's simplify $\dfrac{x^2}{x^5}$ using the definition of x^n.

$$\frac{x^2}{x^5} = \frac{x \cdot x}{x \cdot x \cdot x \cdot x \cdot x}$$

$$= \frac{x \cdot x}{x \cdot x \cdot x \cdot x \cdot x} \quad \begin{array}{l}\text{Divide numerator and denominator} \\ \text{by common factors by applying the} \\ \text{fundamental principle for fractions.}\end{array}$$

$$= \frac{1}{x^3}$$

If the quotient rule is to hold true for negative exponents, then x^{-3} must equal $\dfrac{1}{x^3}$. From this example, we state the definition for negative exponents.

Negative Exponents

If a is a real number other than 0 and n is an integer, then

$$a^{-n} = \frac{1}{a^n}$$

For example, $x^{-3} = \frac{1}{x^3}$.

In other words, another way to write a^{-n} is to take its reciprocal and change the sign of its exponent.

▶ **EXAMPLE 1**   Simplify by writing each expression with positive exponents only.

a. 3^{-2} **b.** $2x^{-3}$ **c.** $2^{-1} + 4^{-1}$ **d.** $(-2)^{-4}$ **e.** y^{-4}

Solution

a. $3^{-2} = \frac{1}{3^2} = \frac{1}{9}$ Use the definition of negative exponents.

b. $2x^{-3} = 2 \cdot \frac{1}{x^3} = \frac{2}{x^3}$ Use the definition of negative exponents.

c. $2^{-1} + 4^{-1} = \frac{1}{2} + \frac{1}{4} = \frac{2}{4} + \frac{1}{4} = \frac{3}{4}$

d. $(-2)^{-4} = \frac{1}{(-2)^4} = \frac{1}{(-2)(-2)(-2)(-2)} = \frac{1}{16}$

e. $y^{-4} = \frac{1}{y^4}$

> ▶ **Helpful Hint**
> Don't forget that since there are no parentheses, only x is the base for the exponent -3.

PRACTICE
1   Simplify by writing each expression with positive exponents only.

a. 5^{-3} **b.** $3y^{-4}$ **c.** $3^{-1} + 2^{-1}$ **d.** $(-5)^{-2}$ **e.** x^{-5}

> ▶ **Helpful Hint**
> A negative exponent *does not affect* the sign of its base.
> Remember: Another way to write a^{-n} is to take its reciprocal and change the sign of its exponent: $a^{-n} = \frac{1}{a^n}$. For example,
>
> $$x^{-2} = \frac{1}{x^2}, \qquad 2^{-3} = \frac{1}{2^3} \quad \text{or} \quad \frac{1}{8}$$
>
> $$\frac{1}{y^{-4}} = \frac{1}{\frac{1}{y^4}} = y^4, \qquad \frac{1}{5^{-2}} = 5^2 \quad \text{or} \quad 25$$

From the preceding Helpful Hint, we know that $x^{-2} = \frac{1}{x^2}$ and $\frac{1}{y^{-4}} = y^4$. We can use this to include another statement in our definition of negative exponents.

Negative Exponents

If a is a real number other than 0 and n is an integer, then

$$a^{-n} = \frac{1}{a^n} \quad \text{and} \quad \frac{1}{a^{-n}} = a^n$$

EXAMPLE 2 Simplify each expression. Write results using positive exponents only.

a. $\dfrac{1}{x^{-3}}$ **b.** $\dfrac{1}{3^{-4}}$ **c.** $\dfrac{p^{-4}}{q^{-9}}$ **d.** $\dfrac{5^{-3}}{2^{-5}}$

Solution

a. $\dfrac{1}{x^{-3}} = \dfrac{x^3}{1} = x^3$ **b.** $\dfrac{1}{3^{-4}} = \dfrac{3^4}{1} = 81$ **c.** $\dfrac{p^{-4}}{q^{-9}} = \dfrac{q^9}{p^4}$ **d.** $\dfrac{5^{-3}}{2^{-5}} = \dfrac{2^5}{5^3} = \dfrac{32}{125}$ □

PRACTICE
2 Simplify each expression. Write results using positive exponents only.

a. $\dfrac{1}{s^{-5}}$ **b.** $\dfrac{1}{2^{-3}}$ **c.** $\dfrac{x^{-7}}{y^{-5}}$ **d.** $\dfrac{4^{-3}}{3^{-2}}$

EXAMPLE 3 Simplify each expression. Write answers with positive exponents.

a. $\dfrac{y}{y^{-2}}$ **b.** $\dfrac{3}{x^{-4}}$ **c.** $\dfrac{x^{-5}}{x^7}$ **d.** $\left(\dfrac{2}{3}\right)^{-3}$

Solution

a. $\dfrac{y}{y^{-2}} = \dfrac{y^1}{y^{-2}} = y^{1-(-2)} = y^3$ Remember that $\dfrac{a^m}{a^n} = a^{m-n}$.

b. $\dfrac{3}{x^{-4}} = 3 \cdot \dfrac{1}{x^{-4}} = 3 \cdot x^4$ or $3x^4$

c. $\dfrac{x^{-5}}{x^7} = x^{-5-7} = x^{-12} = \dfrac{1}{x^{12}}$

d. $\left(\dfrac{2}{3}\right)^{-3} = \dfrac{2^{-3}}{3^{-3}} = \dfrac{3^3}{2^3} = \dfrac{27}{8}$ □

PRACTICE
3 Simplify each expression. Write answers with positive exponents.

a. $\dfrac{x^{-3}}{x^2}$ **b.** $\dfrac{5}{y^{-7}}$ **c.** $\dfrac{z}{z^{-4}}$ **d.** $\left(\dfrac{5}{9}\right)^{-2}$

OBJECTIVE
2 Simplifying Exponential Expressions

All the previously stated rules for exponents apply for negative exponents also. Here is a summary of the rules and definitions for exponents.

Summary of Exponent Rules

If m and n are integers and a, b, and c are real numbers, then:

Product rule for exponents: $a^m \cdot a^n = a^{m+n}$

Power rule for exponents: $(a^m)^n = a^{m \cdot n}$

Power of a product: $(ab)^n = a^n b^n$

Power of a quotient: $\left(\dfrac{a}{c}\right)^n = \dfrac{a^n}{c^n}, \quad c \neq 0$

Quotient rule for exponents: $\dfrac{a^m}{a^n} = a^{m-n}, \quad a \neq 0$

Zero exponent: $a^0 = 1, \quad a \neq 0$

Negative exponent: $a^{-n} = \dfrac{1}{a^n}, \quad a \neq 0$

EXAMPLE 4   Simplify the following expressions. Write each result using positive exponents only.

a. $(y^{-3}z^6)^{-6}$ **b.** $\dfrac{(2x^3)^4x}{x^7}$ **c.** $\left(\dfrac{3a^2}{b}\right)^{-3}$ **d.** $\dfrac{4^{-1}x^{-3}y}{4^{-3}x^2y^{-6}}$ **e.** $\left(\dfrac{-2x^3y}{xy^{-1}}\right)^3$

**Solution**

a. $(y^{-3}z^6)^{-6} = y^{18} \cdot z^{-36} = \dfrac{y^{18}}{z^{36}}$

b. $\dfrac{(2x^3)^4x}{x^7} = \dfrac{2^4 \cdot x^{12} \cdot x}{x^7} = \dfrac{16 \cdot x^{12+1}}{x^7} = \dfrac{16x^{13}}{x^7} = 16x^{13-7} = 16x^6$ Use the power rule.

c. $\left(\dfrac{3a^2}{b}\right)^{-3} = \dfrac{3^{-3}(a^2)^{-3}}{b^{-3}}$ Raise each factor in the numerator and the denominator to the -3 power.

$= \dfrac{3^{-3}a^{-6}}{b^{-3}}$ Use the power rule.

$= \dfrac{b^3}{3^3a^6}$ Use the negative exponent rule.

$= \dfrac{b^3}{27a^6}$ Write 3^3 as 27.

d. $\dfrac{4^{-1}x^{-3}y}{4^{-3}x^2y^{-6}} = 4^{-1-(-3)}x^{-3-2}y^{1-(-6)} = 4^2x^{-5}y^7 = \dfrac{4^2y^7}{x^5} = \dfrac{16y^7}{x^5}$

e. $\left(\dfrac{-2x^3y}{xy^{-1}}\right)^3 = \dfrac{(-2)^3x^9y^3}{x^3y^{-3}} = \dfrac{-8x^9y^3}{x^3y^{-3}} = -8x^{9-3}y^{3-(-3)} = -8x^6y^6$ ☐

PRACTICE

4   Simplify the following expressions. Write each result using positive exponents only.

a. $(a^4b^{-3})^{-5}$ **b.** $\dfrac{x^2(x^5)^3}{x^7}$ **c.** $\left(\dfrac{5p^8}{q}\right)^{-2}$

d. $\dfrac{6^{-2}x^{-4}y^{-7}}{6^{-3}x^3y^{-9}}$ **e.** $\left(\dfrac{-3x^4y}{x^2y^{-2}}\right)^3$

OBJECTIVE

3   Writing Numbers in Scientific Notation

Both very large and very small numbers frequently occur in many fields of science. For example, the distance between the sun and the dwarf planet Pluto is approximately 5,906,000,000 kilometers, and the mass of a proton is approximately 0.000000000000000000000000165 gram. It can be tedious to write these numbers in this standard decimal notation, so **scientific notation** is used as a convenient shorthand for expressing very large and very small numbers.

proton

Mass of proton is approximately
0.000 000 000 000 000 000 000 001 65 gram

Sun   5,906,000,000   Pluto
kilometers

Scientific Notation

A positive number is written in scientific notation if it is written as the product of a number a, where $1 \le a < 10$, and an integer power r of 10:

$$a \times 10^r$$

The numbers below are written in scientific notation. The $\times$ sign for multiplication is used as part of the notation.

$$2.03 \times 10^2 \qquad 7.362 \times 10^7 \qquad 5.906 \times 10^9 \qquad \text{(Distance between the sun and Pluto)}$$
$$1 \times 10^{-3} \qquad 8.1 \times 10^{-5} \qquad 1.65 \times 10^{-24} \qquad \text{(Mass of a proton)}$$

The following steps are useful when writing numbers in scientific notation.

To Write a Number in Scientific Notation

Step 1. Move the decimal point in the original number to the left or right so that the new number has a value between 1 and 10.

Step 2. Count the number of decimal places the decimal point is moved in Step 1. If the original number is 10 or greater, the count is positive. If the original number is less than 1, the count is negative.

Step 3. Multiply the new number in Step 1 by 10 raised to an exponent equal to the count found in Step 2.

EXAMPLE 5 Write each number in scientific notation.

a. 367,000,000 **b.** 0.000003 **c.** 20,520,000,000 **d.** 0.00085

Solution

a. Step 1. Move the decimal point until the number is between 1 and 10.

367,000,000.
8 places

Step 2. The decimal point is moved 8 places, and the original number is 10 or greater, so the count is positive 8.

Step 3. $367,000,000 = 3.67 \times 10^8$.

b. Step 1. Move the decimal point until the number is between 1 and 10.

0.000003
6 places

Step 2. The decimal point is moved 6 places, and the original number is less than 1, so the count is -6.

Step 3. $0.000003 = 3.0 \times 10^{-6}$

c. $20,520,000,000 = 2.052 \times 10^{10}$

d. $0.00085 = 8.5 \times 10^{-4}$

PRACTICE
5 Write each number in scientific notation.

a. 0.000007 **b.** 20,700,000
c. 0.0043 **d.** 812,000,000

OBJECTIVE
4 Converting Numbers to Standard Form

A number written in scientific notation can be rewritten in standard form. For example, to write 8.63×10^3 in standard form, recall that $10^3 = 1000$.

$$8.63 \times 10^3 = 8.63(1000) = 8630$$

Notice that the exponent on the 10 is positive 3, and we moved the decimal point 3 places to the right.

To write 7.29×10^{-3} in standard form, recall that $10^{-3} = \dfrac{1}{10^3} = \dfrac{1}{1000}$.

$$7.29 \times 10^{-3} = 7.29\left(\frac{1}{1000}\right) = \frac{7.29}{1000} = 0.00729$$

The exponent on the 10 is negative 3, and we moved the decimal to the left 3 places.

In general, **to write a scientific notation number in standard form,** move the decimal point the same number of places as the exponent on 10. If the exponent is positive, move the decimal point to the right; if the exponent is negative, move the decimal point to the left.

EXAMPLE 6 Write each number in standard notation, without exponents.

a. 1.02×10^5 **b.** 7.358×10^{-3} **c.** 8.4×10^7 **d.** 3.007×10^{-5}

Solution

a. Move the decimal point 5 places to the right.

$$1.02 \times 10^5 = 102{,}000.$$

b. Move the decimal point 3 places to the left.

$$7.358 \times 10^{-3} = 0.007358$$

c. $8.4 \times 10^7 = 84{,}000{,}000.$ 7 places to the right

d. $3.007 \times 10^{-5} = 0.00003007$ 5 places to the left

PRACTICE
6 Write each number in standard notation, without exponents.

a. 3.67×10^{-4} **b.** 8.954×10^6
c. 2.009×10^{-5} **d.** 4.054×10^3

✓**CONCEPT CHECK**
Which number in each pair is larger?
a. 7.8×10^3 or 2.1×10^5 **b.** 9.2×10^{-2} or 2.7×10^4 **c.** 5.6×10^{-4} or 6.3×10^{-5}

OBJECTIVE
5 Performing Operations with Scientific Notation

Performing operations on numbers written in scientific notation uses the rules and definitions for exponents.

EXAMPLE 7 Perform each indicated operation. Write each result in standard decimal notation.

a. $(8 \times 10^{-6})(7 \times 10^3)$ **b.** $\dfrac{12 \times 10^2}{6 \times 10^{-3}}$

Solution

a. $(8 \times 10^{-6})(7 \times 10^3) = (8 \cdot 7) \times (10^{-6} \cdot 10^3)$
$$= 56 \times 10^{-3}$$
$$= 0.056$$

b. $\dfrac{12 \times 10^2}{6 \times 10^{-3}} = \dfrac{12}{6} \times 10^{2-(-3)} = 2 \times 10^5 = 200{,}000$

PRACTICE
7 Perform each indicated operation. Write each result in standard decimal notation.

a. $(5 \times 10^{-4})(8 \times 10^6)$ **b.** $\dfrac{64 \times 10^3}{32 \times 10^{-7}}$

Graphing Calculator Explorations

Scientific Notation

To enter a number written in scientific notation on a scientific calculator, locate the scientific notation key, which may be marked $\boxed{EE}$ or $\boxed{EXP}$. To enter 3.1×10^7, press $\boxed{3.1}$ $\boxed{EE}$ $\boxed{7}$. The display should read $\boxed{3.1 \quad 07}$.

Enter each number written in scientific notation on your calculator.

1. 5.31×10^3 **2.** -4.8×10^{14}

3. 6.6×10^{-9} **4.** -9.9811×10^{-2}

Multiply each of the following on your calculator. Notice the form of the result.

5. $3,000,000 \times 5,000,000$ **6.** $230,000 \times 1000$

Multiply each of the following on your calculator. Write the product in scientific notation.

7. $(3.26 \times 10^6)(2.5 \times 10^{13})$ **8.** $(8.76 \times 10^{-4})(1.237 \times 10^9)$

Vocabulary, Readiness & Video Check

Fill in each blank with the correct choice.

1. The expression x^{-3} equals _____.

     a. $-x^3$ **b.** $\dfrac{1}{x^3}$ **c.** $\dfrac{-1}{x^3}$ **d.** $\dfrac{1}{x^{-3}}$

2. The expression 5^{-4} equals _____.

     a. -20 **b.** -625 **c.** $\dfrac{1}{20}$ **d.** $\dfrac{1}{625}$

3. The number 3.021×10^{-3} is written in _____.

     a. standard form   **b.** expanded form

     c. scientific notation

4. The number 0.0261 is written in _____.

     a. standard form   **b.** expanded form

     c. scientific notation

Martin-Gay Interactive Videos

See Video 5.5

Watch the section lecture video and answer the following questions.

OBJECTIVE 1   **5.** What important reminder is made at the end of ▭ Example 1?

OBJECTIVE 2   **6.** Name all the rules and definitions used to simplify ▭ Example 8.

OBJECTIVE 3   **7.** From ▭ Examples 9 and 10, explain how the movement of the decimal point in step 1 suggests the sign of the exponent on the number 10.

OBJECTIVE 4   **8.** From ▭ Example 11, what part of a number written in scientific notation is key in telling you how to write the number in standard form?

OBJECTIVE 5   **9.** For ▭ Example 13, what exponent rules were needed to evaluate?

5.5 Exercise Set

MyMathLab®

Simplify each expression. Write each result using positive exponents only. See Examples 1 through 3.

1. 4^{-3} **2.** 6^{-2} **3.** $(-3)^{-4}$

4. $(-3)^{-5}$ **5.** $7x^{-3}$ **6.** $(7x)^{-3}$

7. $\left(\dfrac{1}{2}\right)^{-5}$ **8.** $\left(\dfrac{1}{8}\right)^{-2}$ **9.** $\left(-\dfrac{1}{4}\right)^{-3}$

10. $\left(-\dfrac{1}{8}\right)^{-2}$ **11.** $3^{-1} + 5^{-1}$ **12.** $4^{-1} + 4^{-2}$

13. $\dfrac{1}{p^{-3}}$ **14.** $\dfrac{1}{q^{-5}}$ **15.** $\dfrac{p^{-5}}{q^{-4}}$

16. $\dfrac{r^{-5}}{s^{-2}}$ **17.** $\dfrac{x^{-2}}{x}$ **18.** $\dfrac{y}{y^{-3}}$

19. $\dfrac{z^{-4}}{z^{-7}}$ **20.** $\dfrac{x^{-4}}{x^{-1}}$ **21.** $3^{-2} + 3^{-1}$

22. $4^{-2} - 4^{-3}$ **23.** $\dfrac{-1}{p^{-4}}$ **24.** $\dfrac{-1}{y^{-6}}$

25. $-2^0 - 3^0$ **26.** $5^0 + (-5)^0$

MIXED PRACTICE

Simplify each expression. Write each result using positive exponents only. See Examples 1 through 4.

27. $\dfrac{x^2 x^5}{x^3}$ **28.** $\dfrac{y^4 y^5}{y^6}$ **29.** $\dfrac{p^2 p}{p^{-1}}$

30. $\dfrac{y^3 y}{y^{-2}}$ **31.** $\dfrac{(m^5)^4 m}{m^{10}}$ **32.** $\dfrac{(x^2)^8 x}{x^9}$

▶ 33. $\dfrac{r}{r^{-3} r^{-2}}$ **34.** $\dfrac{p}{p^{-3} q^{-5}}$ **35.** $(x^5 y^3)^{-3}$

36. $(z^5 x^5)^{-3}$ **37.** $\dfrac{(x^2)^3}{x^{10}}$ **38.** $\dfrac{(y^4)^2}{y^{12}}$

39. $\dfrac{(a^5)^2}{(a^3)^4}$ **40.** $\dfrac{(x^2)^5}{(x^4)^3}$ **41.** $\dfrac{8k^4}{2k}$

42. $\dfrac{27r^4}{3r^6}$ **43.** $\dfrac{-6m^4}{-2m^3}$

44. $\dfrac{15a^4}{-15a^5}$ **45.** $\dfrac{-24a^6 b}{6ab^2}$

46. $\dfrac{-5x^4 y^5}{15x^4 y^2}$ **47.** $(-2x^3 y^{-4})(3x^{-1} y)$

48. $(-5a^4 b^{-7})(-a^{-4} b^3)$ **49.** $(a^{-5} b^2)^{-6}$

50. $(4^{-1} x^5)^{-2}$ **51.** $\left(\dfrac{x^{-2} y^4}{x^3 y^7}\right)^2$

52. $\left(\dfrac{a^5 b}{a^7 b^{-2}}\right)^{-3}$ **53.** $\dfrac{4^2 z^{-3}}{4^3 z^{-5}}$

54. $\dfrac{3^{-1} x^4}{3^3 x^{-7}}$ **55.** $\dfrac{2^{-3} x^{-4}}{2^2 x}$

56. $\dfrac{5^{-1} z^7}{5^{-2} z^9}$ **57.** $\dfrac{7ab^{-4}}{7^{-1} a^{-3} b^2}$

58. $\dfrac{6^{-5} x^{-1} y^2}{6^{-2} x^{-4} y^4}$ **59.** $\left(\dfrac{a^{-5} b}{ab^3}\right)^{-4}$

60. $\left(\dfrac{r^{-2} s^{-3}}{r^{-4} s^{-3}}\right)^{-3}$ **61.** $\dfrac{(xy^3)^5}{(xy)^{-4}}$

62. $\dfrac{(rs)^{-3}}{(r^2 s^3)^2}$ **▶ 63.** $\dfrac{(-2xy^{-3})^{-3}}{(xy^{-1})^{-1}}$

64. $\dfrac{(-3x^2 y^2)^{-2}}{(xyz)^{-2}}$ **65.** $\dfrac{6x^2 y^3}{-7xy^5}$

66. $\dfrac{-8xa^2 b}{-5xa^5 b}$ **67.** $\dfrac{(a^4 b^{-7})^{-5}}{(5a^2 b^{-1})^{-2}}$

68. $\dfrac{(a^6 b^{-2})^4}{(4a^{-3} b^{-3})^3}$

Write each number in scientific notation. See Example 5.

▶ 69. 78,000   **70.** 9,300,000,000

▶ 71. 0.00000167   **72.** 0.00000017

73. 0.00635   **74.** 0.00194

75. 1,160,000   **76.** 700,000

77. More than 2,000,000,000 pencils are manufactured in the United States annually. Write this number in scientific notation. (*Source:* AbsoluteTrivia.com)

78. The temperature at the interior of the Earth is 20,000,000 degrees Celsius. Write 20,000,000 in scientific notation.

79. As of this writing, the world's largest optical telescope is the Gran Telescopio Canaris, located in La Palma, Canary Islands, Spain. The elevation of this telescope is 2400 meters above sea level. Write 2400 in scientific notation.

80. In January 2009, the twin Mars rovers, Spirit and Opportunity, celebrated their fifth anniversary of landing on Mars. These rovers, which were expected to last about 90 days, have defied all expectations and have been transmitting signals back to Earth from as far away as 250,000,000 miles. Write 250,000,000 in scientific notation. (*Source:* NASA)

Write each number in standard notation. See Example 6.

81. 8.673×10^{-10}

82. 9.056×10^{-4}

▶ 83. 3.3×10^{-2}

84. 4.8×10^{-6}

▶ **85.** 2.032×10^4

86. 9.07×10^{10}

87. Each second, the Sun converts 7.0×10^8 tons of hydrogen into helium and energy in the form of gamma rays. Write this number in standard notation. (*Source:* Students for the Exploration and Development of Space)

88. In chemistry, Avogadro's number is the number of atoms in one mole of an element. Avogadro's number is $6.02214199 \times 10^{23}$. Write this number in standard notation. (*Source:* National Institute of Standards and Technology)

89. The distance light travels in 1 year is 9.460×10^{12} kilometers. Write this number in standard notation.

90. The population of the world is 6.95×10^9. Write this number in standard notation. (*Source:* U.S. Bureau of the Census)

MIXED PRACTICE

See Examples 5 and 6. Below are some interesting facts about selected countries' national debts during a certain time period. If a number is written in standard form, write it in scientific notation. If a number is written in scientific notation, write it in standard form. (Data from CIA World Factbook)

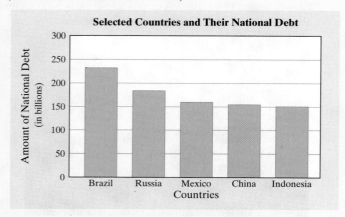

91. The national debt of Russia during a certain time period was $184,000,000,000.

92. The amount by which Russia's debt is greater than Mexico's debt is $24,000,000,000.

93. At a certain time period, China's national debt was 1.55×10^{11}.

94. At a certain time period, the national debt of the United States was 1.1×10^{13}.

95. At a certain time period, the estimated per person share of the United States' national debt was 3.5×10^4.

96. The bar graph shows the national debt of five countries. Estimate the height of the tallest bar and the shortest bar in standard notation. Then write each number in scientific notation.

Evaluate each expression using exponential rules. Write each result in standard notation. See Example 7.

97. $(1.2 \times 10^{-3})(3 \times 10^{-2})$

98. $(2.5 \times 10^6)(2 \times 10^{-6})$

99. $(4 \times 10^{-10})(7 \times 10^{-9})$

100. $(5 \times 10^6)(4 \times 10^{-8})$

101. $\dfrac{8 \times 10^{-1}}{16 \times 10^5}$

102. $\dfrac{25 \times 10^{-4}}{5 \times 10^{-9}}$

▶ **103.** $\dfrac{1.4 \times 10^{-2}}{7 \times 10^{-8}}$

104. $\dfrac{0.4 \times 10^5}{0.2 \times 10^{11}}$

REVIEW AND PREVIEW

Simplify the following. See Section 5.1.

105. $\dfrac{5x^7}{3x^4}$

106. $\dfrac{27y^{14}}{3y^7}$

107. $\dfrac{15z^4y^3}{21zy}$

108. $\dfrac{18a^7b^{17}}{30a^7b}$

Use the distributive property and multiply. See Section 5.3.

109. $\dfrac{1}{y}(5y^2 - 6y + 5)$

110. $\dfrac{2}{x}(3x^5 + x^4 - 2)$

CONCEPT EXTENSIONS

△ **111.** Find the volume of the cube.

$\dfrac{3x^{-2}}{z}$ inches

△ **112.** Find the area of the triangle.

$\dfrac{4}{x}$ m

$\dfrac{5x^{-3}}{7}$ m

Simplify.

113. $(2a^3)^3 a^4 + a^5 a^8$

114. $(2a^3)^3 a^{-3} + a^{11} a^{-5}$

Fill in the boxes so that each statement is true. (More than one answer may be possible for these exercises.)

115. $x^{\square} = \dfrac{1}{x^5}$

116. $7^{\square} = \dfrac{1}{49}$

117. $z^{\square} \cdot z^{\square} = z^{-10}$

118. $(x^{\square})^{\square} = x^{-15}$

119. Which is larger? See the Concept Check in this section.

    a. 9.7×10^{-2} or 1.3×10^1

    b. 8.6×10^5 or 4.4×10^7

    c. 6.1×10^{-2} or 5.6×10^{-4}

120. Determine whether each statement is true or false.

    a. $5^{-1} < 5^{-2}$

    b. $\left(\dfrac{1}{5}\right)^{-1} < \left(\dfrac{1}{5}\right)^{-2}$

    c. $a^{-1} < a^{-2}$ for all nonzero numbers.

121. It was stated earlier that for an integer n,

$$x^{-n} = \frac{1}{x^n}, \quad x \neq 0$$

Explain why x may not equal 0.

122. The quotient rule states that

$$\frac{a^m}{a^n} = a^{m-n}, a \neq 0.$$

Explain why a may not equal 0.

Simplify each expression. Assume that variables represent positive integers.

123. $a^{-4m} \cdot a^{5m}$

124. $(x^{-3s})^3$

125. $(3y^{2z})^3$

126. $a^{4m+1} \cdot a^4$

Simplify each expression. Write each result in standard notation.

127. $(2.63 \times 10^{12})(-1.5 \times 10^{-10})$

128. $(6.785 \times 10^{-4})(4.68 \times 10^{10})$

Light travels at a rate of 1.86×10^5 miles per second. Use this information and the distance formula $d = r \cdot t$ to answer Exercises 129 and 130.

129. If the distance from the moon to Earth is 238,857 miles, find how long it takes the reflected light of the moon to reach Earth. (Round to the nearest tenth of a second.)

130. If the distance from the sun to Earth is 93,000,000 miles, find how long it takes the light of the sun to reach Earth.

5.6 | Dividing Polynomials

OBJECTIVES

1 Divide a Polynomial by a Monomial.

2 Use Long Division to Divide a Polynomial by Another Polynomial.

OBJECTIVE

1   Dividing by a Monomial

Now that we know how to add, subtract, and multiply polynomials, we practice dividing polynomials.

To divide a polynomial by a monomial, recall addition of fractions. Fractions that have a common denominator are added by adding the numerators:

$$\frac{a}{c} + \frac{b}{c} = \frac{a+b}{c}$$

If we read this equation from right to left and let a, b, and c be monomials, $c \neq 0$, we have the following:

Dividing a Polynomial by a Monomial

Divide each term of the polynomial by the monomial.

$$\frac{a+b}{c} = \frac{a}{c} + \frac{b}{c}, \quad c \neq 0$$

Throughout this section, we assume that denominators are not 0.

EXAMPLE 1   Divide $6m^2 + 2m$ by $2m$.

Solution   We begin by writing the quotient in fraction form. Then we divide each term of the polynomial $6m^2 + 2m$ by the monomial $2m$.

$$\frac{6m^2 + 2m}{2m} = \frac{6m^2}{2m} + \frac{2m}{2m}$$

$$= 3m + 1 \qquad \text{Simplify.}$$

Check: We know that if $\frac{6m^2 + 2m}{2m} = 3m + 1$, then $2m \cdot (3m + 1)$ must equal $6m^2 + 2m$. Thus, to check, we multiply.

$$2m(3m + 1) = 2m(3m) + 2m(1) = 6m^2 + 2m$$

The quotient $3m + 1$ checks. ☐

PRACTICE

1   Divide $8t^3 + 4t^2$ by $4t^2$

EXAMPLE 2   Divide $\dfrac{9x^5 - 12x^2 + 3x}{3x^2}$.

Solution

$$\frac{9x^5 - 12x^2 + 3x}{3x^2} = \frac{9x^5}{3x^2} - \frac{12x^2}{3x^2} + \frac{3x}{3x^2} \qquad \text{Divide each term by } 3x^2.$$

$$= 3x^3 - 4 + \frac{1}{x} \qquad \text{Simplify.}$$

Notice that the quotient is not a polynomial because of the term $\dfrac{1}{x}$. This expression is called a rational expression—we will study rational expressions further in Chapter 7. Although the quotient of two polynomials is not always a polynomial, we may still check by multiplying.

Check: $3x^2\left(3x^3 - 4 + \dfrac{1}{x}\right) = 3x^2(3x^3) - 3x^2(4) + 3x^2\left(\dfrac{1}{\dot{x}}\right)$

$$= 9x^5 - 12x^2 + 3x \qquad \qquad \square$$

PRACTICE
2   Divide $\dfrac{16x^6 + 20x^3 - 12x}{4x^2}$.

- ■

EXAMPLE 3   Divide $\dfrac{8x^2y^2 - 16xy + 2x}{4xy}$.

Solution

$$\frac{8x^2y^2 - 16xy + 2x}{4xy} = \frac{8x^2y^2}{4xy} - \frac{16xy}{4xy} + \frac{2x}{4xy} \qquad \text{Divide each term by } 4xy.$$

$$= 2xy - 4 + \frac{1}{2y} \qquad \text{Simplify.}$$

Check: $4xy\left(2xy - 4 + \dfrac{1}{2y}\right) = 4xy(2xy) - 4xy(4) + 4xy\left(\dfrac{1}{2y}\right)$

$$= 8x^2y^2 - 16xy + 2x \qquad \qquad \square$$

PRACTICE
3   Divide $\dfrac{15x^4y^4 - 10xy + y}{5xy}$.

- ■

✓CONCEPT CHECK

In which of the following is $\dfrac{x + 5}{5}$ simplified correctly?

a. $\dfrac{x}{5} + 1$ **b.** x **c.** $x + 1$

OBJECTIVE
2   Using Long Division to Divide by a Polynomial

To divide a polynomial by a polynomial other than a monomial, we use a process known as long division. Polynomial long division is similar to number long division, so we review long division by dividing 13 into 3660.

> ▶ Helpful Hint
> Recall that 3660 is called the dividend.

$$
\begin{array}{r}
281 \\
13\overline{)3660} \\
\end{array}
$$

$\underline{26}\!\downarrow\!\downarrow$ $2\cdot13 = 26$
106 Subtract and bring down the next digit in the dividend.
$\underline{104}\!\downarrow$ $8\cdot13 = 104$
20 Subtract and bring down the next digit in the dividend.
$\underline{13}$ $1\cdot13 = 13$
7 Subtract. There are no more digits to bring down, so the remainder is 7.

The quotient is 281 R 7, which can be written as $281\frac{7}{13}$. $\leftarrow$ remainder $\leftarrow$ divisor

Recall that division can be checked by multiplication. To check a division problem such as this one, we see that

$$13 \cdot 281 + 7 = 3660$$

Now we demonstrate long division of polynomials.

EXAMPLE 4   Divide $x^2 + 7x + 12$ by $x + 3$ using long division.

Solution

To subtract, change the signs of these terms and add.

$$\begin{array}{r} x \\ x+3\overline{)x^2 + 7x + 12} \\ x^2 + 3x \\ \hline 4x + 12 \end{array}$$

How many times does x divide x^2? $\frac{x^2}{x} = x$.
Multiply: $x(x + 3)$.
Subtract and bring down the next term.

Now we repeat this process.

$$\begin{array}{r} x + 4 \\ x+3\overline{)x^2 + 7x + 12} \\ x^2 + 3x \\ \hline 4x + 12 \\ 4x + 12 \\ \hline 0 \end{array}$$

How many times does x divide $4x$? $\frac{4x}{x} = 4$.

To subtract, change the signs of these terms and add.

Multiply: $4(x + 3)$.
Subtract. The remainder is 0.

The quotient is $x + 4$.

Check: We check by multiplying.

divisor · quotient + remainder = dividend

$(x + 3)$ · $(x + 4)$ + 0 = $x^2 + 7x + 12$

The quotient checks.

PRACTICE
4   Divide $x^2 + 5x + 6$ by $x + 2$ using long division.

EXAMPLE 5   Divide $6x^2 + 10x - 5$ by $3x - 1$ using long division.

Solution

$$\begin{array}{r} 2x + 4 \\ 3x-1\overline{)6x^2 + 10x - 5} \\ 6x^2 - 2x \\ \hline 12x - 5 \\ 12x - 4 \\ \hline -1 \end{array}$$

$\frac{6x^2}{3x} = 2x$, so $2x$ is a term of the quotient.
Multiply $2x(3x - 1)$.
Subtract and bring down the next term.
$\frac{12x}{3x} = 4$, multiply $4(3x - 1)$
Subtract. The remainder is -1.

Thus $(6x^2 + 10x - 5)$ divided by $(3x - 1)$ is $(2x + 4)$ with a remainder of -1. This can be written as

$$\frac{6x^2 + 10x - 5}{3x - 1} = 2x + 4 + \frac{-1}{3x - 1} \quad \begin{array}{l} \leftarrow \text{remainder} \\ \leftarrow \text{divisor} \end{array}$$

Check: To check, we multiply $(3x - 1)(2x + 4)$. Then we add the remainder, -1, to this product.

$$(3x - 1)(2x + 4) + (-1) = (6x^2 + 12x - 2x - 4) - 1$$
$$= 6x^2 + 10x - 5$$

The quotient checks.

PRACTICE
5   Divide $4x^2 + 8x - 7$ by $2x + 1$ using long division.

In Example 5, the degree of the divisor, $3x - 1$, is 1 and the degree of the remainder, -1, is 0. The division process is continued until the degree of the remainder polynomial is less than the degree of the divisor polynomial.

Writing the dividend and divisor in a form with descending order of powers and with no missing terms is helpful when dividing polynomials.

EXAMPLE 6 Divide $\dfrac{4x^2 + 7 + 8x^3}{2x + 3}$.

Solution Before we begin the division process, we rewrite

$$4x^2 + 7 + 8x^3 \quad \text{as} \quad 8x^3 + 4x^2 + 0x + 7$$

Notice that we have written the polynomial in descending order and have represented the missing x term by $0x$.

$$
\require{enclose}
\begin{array}{r}
4x^2 - 4x + 6 \\
2x + 3 \enclose{longdiv}{8x^3 + 4x^2 + 0x + 7} \\
\underline{8x^3 \mp 12x^2} \\
-8x^2 + 0x \\
\underline{\pm 8x^2 \mp 12x} \\
12x + 7 \\
\underline{12x \mp 18} \\
-11 \quad \text{Remainder}
\end{array}
$$

Thus, $\dfrac{4x^2 + 7 + 8x^3}{2x + 3} = 4x^2 - 4x + 6 + \dfrac{-11}{2x + 3}$. □

PRACTICE
6 Divide $\dfrac{11x - 3 + 9x^3}{3x + 2}$.

EXAMPLE 7 Divide $\dfrac{2x^4 - x^3 + 3x^2 + x - 1}{x^2 + 1}$.

Solution Before dividing, rewrite the divisor polynomial

$$x^2 + 1 \quad \text{as} \quad x^2 + 0x + 1$$

The $0x$ term represents the missing x^1 term in the divisor.

$$
\require{enclose}
\begin{array}{r}
2x^2 - x + 1 \\
x^2 + 0x + 1 \enclose{longdiv}{2x^4 - x^3 + 3x^2 + x - 1} \\
\underline{2x^4 \mp 0x^3 \mp 2x^2} \\
-x^3 + x^2 + x \\
\underline{\pm x^3 \mp 0x^2 \mp x} \\
x^2 + 2x - 1 \\
\underline{\mp x^2 \mp 0x \mp 1} \\
2x - 2 \quad \text{Remainder}
\end{array}
$$

Thus, $\dfrac{2x^4 - x^3 + 3x^2 + x - 1}{x^2 + 1} = 2x^2 - x + 1 + \dfrac{2x - 2}{x^2 + 1}$. □

PRACTICE
7 Divide $\dfrac{3x^4 - 2x^3 - 3x^2 + x + 4}{x^2 + 2}$.

EXAMPLE 8   Divide $x^3 - 8$ by $x - 2$.

Solution: Notice that the polynomial $x^3 - 8$ is missing an x^2-term and an x-term. We'll represent these terms by inserting $0x^2$ and $0x$.

$$
\begin{array}{r}
x^2 + 2x + 4 \\
x - 2\overline{)x^3 + 0x^2 + 0x - 8} \\
\underline{x^3 - 2x^2} \\
2x^2 + 0x \\
\underline{2x^2 - 4x} \\
4x - 8 \\
\underline{4x - 8} \\
0
\end{array}
$$

Thus, $\dfrac{x^3 - 8}{x - 2} = x^2 + 2x + 4$.

Check: To check, see that $(x^2 + 2x + 4)(x - 2) = x^3 - 8$.   □

PRACTICE
8   Divide $x^3 + 27$ by $x + 3$.

Vocabulary, Readiness & Video Check

Use the choices below to fill in each blank. Choices may be used more than once.

   dividend   divisor   quotient

1. In $6\overline{)18}^{\,3}$, the 18 is the _____, the 3 is the _____ and the 6 is the _____.

2. In $x + 1\overline{)x^2 + 3x + 2}^{\,x + 2}$, the $x + 1$ is the _____, the $x^2 + 3x + 2$ is the _____ and the $x + 2$ is the _____.

Simplify each expression mentally.

3. $\dfrac{a^6}{a^4}$ **4.** $\dfrac{p^8}{p^3}$ **5.** $\dfrac{y^2}{y}$ **6.** $\dfrac{a^3}{a}$

Martin-Gay Interactive Videos

See Video 5.6

Watch the section lecture video and answer the following questions.

OBJECTIVE 1

7. The lecture before ▢ Example 1 begins with adding two fractions with the same denominator. From there, the lecture continues to a method for dividing a polynomial by a monomial. What role does the monomial play in the fraction example?

OBJECTIVE 2

8. In ▢ Example 5, you're told that although you don't have to fill in missing powers in the divisor and the dividend, it really is a good idea to do so. Why?

5.6 Exercise Set

  MyMathLab®

Perform each division. See Examples 1 through 3.

1. $\dfrac{12x^4 + 3x^2}{x}$

2. $\dfrac{15x^2 - 9x^5}{x}$

3. $\dfrac{20x^3 - 30x^2 + 5x + 5}{5}$

4. $\dfrac{8x^3 - 4x^2 + 6x + 2}{2}$

5. $\dfrac{15p^3 + 18p^2}{3p}$

6. $\dfrac{14m^2 - 27m^3}{7m}$

7. $\dfrac{-9x^4 + 18x^5}{6x^5}$

8. $\dfrac{6x^5 + 3x^4}{3x^4}$

9. $\dfrac{-9x^5 + 3x^4 - 12}{3x^3}$

10. $\dfrac{6a^2 - 4a + 12}{-2a^2}$

11. $\dfrac{4x^4 - 6x^3 + 7}{-4x^4}$

12. $\dfrac{-12a^3 + 36a - 15}{3a}$

Find each quotient using long division. See Examples 4 and 5.

13. $\dfrac{x^2 + 4x + 3}{x + 3}$

14. $\dfrac{x^2 + 7x + 10}{x + 5}$

15. $\dfrac{2x^2 + 13x + 15}{x + 5}$

16. $\dfrac{3x^2 + 8x + 4}{x + 2}$

17. $\dfrac{2x^2 - 7x + 3}{x - 4}$

18. $\dfrac{3x^2 - x - 4}{x - 1}$

19. $\dfrac{9a^3 - 3a^2 - 3a + 4}{3a + 2}$

20. $\dfrac{4x^3 + 12x^2 + x - 14}{2x + 3}$

21. $\dfrac{8x^2 + 10x + 1}{2x + 1}$

22. $\dfrac{3x^2 + 17x + 7}{3x + 2}$

23. $\dfrac{2x^3 + 2x^2 - 17x + 8}{x - 2}$

24. $\dfrac{4x^3 + 11x^2 - 8x - 10}{x + 3}$

Find each quotient using long division. Don't forget to write the polynomials in descending order and fill in any missing terms. See Examples 6 through 8.

25. $\dfrac{x^2 - 36}{x - 6}$

26. $\dfrac{a^2 - 49}{a - 7}$

27. $\dfrac{x^3 - 27}{x - 3}$

28. $\dfrac{x^3 + 64}{x + 4}$

29. $\dfrac{1 - 3x^2}{x + 2}$

30. $\dfrac{7 - 5x^2}{x + 3}$

31. $\dfrac{-4b + 4b^2 - 5}{2b - 1}$

32. $\dfrac{-3y + 2y^2 - 15}{2y + 5}$

MIXED PRACTICE

Divide. If the divisor contains 2 or more terms, use long division. See Examples 1 through 8.

33. $\dfrac{a^2b^2 - ab^3}{ab}$

34. $\dfrac{m^3n^2 - mn^4}{mn}$

35. $\dfrac{8x^2 + 6x - 27}{2x - 3}$

36. $\dfrac{18w^2 + 18w - 8}{3w + 4}$

37. $\dfrac{2x^2y + 8x^2y^2 - xy^2}{2xy}$

38. $\dfrac{11x^3y^3 - 33xy + x^2y^2}{11xy}$

39. $\dfrac{2b^3 + 9b^2 + 6b - 4}{b + 4}$

40. $\dfrac{2x^3 + 3x^2 - 3x + 4}{x + 2}$

41. $\dfrac{5x^2 + 28x - 10}{x + 6}$

42. $\dfrac{2x^2 + x - 15}{x + 3}$

43. $\dfrac{10x^3 - 24x^2 - 10x}{10x}$

44. $\dfrac{2x^3 + 12x^2 + 16}{4x^2}$

45. $\dfrac{6x^2 + 17x - 4}{x + 3}$

46. $\dfrac{2x^2 - 9x + 15}{x - 6}$

47. $\dfrac{30x^2 - 17x + 2}{5x - 2}$

48. $\dfrac{4x^2 - 13x - 12}{4x + 3}$

49. $\dfrac{3x^4 - 9x^3 + 12}{-3x}$

50. $\dfrac{8y^6 - 3y^2 - 4y}{4y}$

51. $\dfrac{x^3 + 6x^2 + 18x + 27}{x + 3}$

52. $\dfrac{x^3 - 8x^2 + 32x - 64}{x - 4}$

53. $\dfrac{y^3 + 3y^2 + 4}{y - 2}$

54. $\dfrac{3x^3 + 11x + 12}{x + 4}$

55. $\dfrac{5 - 6x^2}{x - 2}$

56. $\dfrac{3 - 7x^2}{x - 3}$

Divide.

57. $\dfrac{x^5 + x^2}{x^2 + x}$

58. $\dfrac{x^6 - x^4}{x^3 + 1}$

REVIEW AND PREVIEW

Multiply each expression. See Section 5.3.

59. $2a(a^2 + 1)$

60. $-4a(3a^2 - 4)$

61. $2x(x^2 + 7x - 5)$

62. $4y(y^2 - 8y - 4)$

63. $-3xy(xy^2 + 7x^2y + 8)$

64. $-9xy(4xyz + 7xy^2z + 2)$

65. $9ab(ab^2c + 4bc - 8)$

66. $-7sr(6s^2r + 9sr^2 + 9rs + 8)$

CONCEPT EXTENSIONS

67. The perimeter of a square is $(12x^3 + 4x - 16)$ feet. Find the length of its side.

Perimeter is $(12x^3 + 4x - 16)$ feet

68. The volume of the swimming pool shown is $(36x^5 - 12x^3 + 6x^2)$ cubic feet. If its height is $2x$ feet and its width is $3x$ feet, find its length.

3x feet
2x feet

69. In which of the following is $\dfrac{a + 7}{7}$ simplified correctly? See the Concept Check in this section.

a. $a + 1$ **b.** a **c.** $\dfrac{a}{7} + 1$

70. In which of the following is $\dfrac{5x + 15}{5}$ simplified correctly? See the Concept Check in this section.

a. $x + 15$ **b.** $x + 3$ **c.** $x + 1$

71. Explain how to check a polynomial long division result when the remainder is 0.

72. Explain how to check a polynomial long division result when the remainder is not 0.

73. The area of the following parallelogram is $(10x^2 + 31x + 15)$ square meters. If its base is $(5x + 3)$ meters, find its height.

$(5x + 3)$ meters

74. The area of the top of the Ping-Pong table is $(49x^2 + 70x - 200)$ square inches. If its length is $(7x + 20)$ inches, find its width.

$(7x + 20)$ inches

75. $(18x^{10a} - 12x^{8a} + 14x^{5a} - 2x^{3a}) \div 2x^{3a}$

76. $(25y^{11b} + 5y^{6b} - 20y^{3b} + 100y^b) \div 5y^b$

Chapter 5 Vocabulary Check

Fill in each blank with one of the words or phrases listed below.

term	coefficient	monomial	binomial	trinomial
polynomials	degree of a term	distributive	FOIL	degree of a polynomial

1. A _____ is a number or the product of numbers and variables raised to powers.

2. The _____ method may be used when multiplying two binomials.

3. A polynomial with exactly 3 terms is called a _____.

4. The _____ is the greatest degree of any term of the polynomial.

5. A polynomial with exactly 2 terms is called a _____.

6. The _____ of a term is its numerical factor.

7. The _____ is the sum of the exponents on the variables in the term.

8. A polynomial with exactly 1 term is called a _____.

9. Monomials, binomials, and trinomials are all examples of _____.

10. The _____ property is used to multiply $2x(x - 4)$.

Chapter 5 Highlights

DEFINITIONS AND CONCEPTS	EXAMPLES

Section 5.1 Exponents

a^n means the product of n factors, each of which is a.

$$3^2 = 3 \cdot 3 = 9$$
$$(-5)^3 = (-5)(-5)(-5) = -125$$
$$\left(\frac{1}{2}\right)^4 = \frac{1}{2} \cdot \frac{1}{2} \cdot \frac{1}{2} \cdot \frac{1}{2} = \frac{1}{16}$$

If m and n are integers and no denominators are 0,

Product Rule: $a^m \cdot a^n = a^{m+n}$

Power Rule: $(a^m)^n = a^{mn}$

Power of a Product Rule: $(ab)^n = a^n b^n$

Power of a Quotient Rule: $\left(\dfrac{a}{b}\right)^n = \dfrac{a^n}{b^n}$

Quotient Rule: $\dfrac{a^m}{a^n} = a^{m-n}$

Zero Exponent: $a^0 = 1, a \neq 0$.

$$x^2 \cdot x^7 = x^{2+7} = x^9$$
$$(5^3)^8 = 5^{3 \cdot 8} = 5^{24}$$
$$(7y)^4 = 7^4 y^4$$
$$\left(\frac{x}{8}\right)^3 = \frac{x^3}{8^3}$$
$$\frac{x^9}{x^4} = x^{9-4} = x^5$$
$$5^0 = 1, x^0 = 1, x \neq 0$$

Section 5.2 Polynomial Functions and Adding and Subtracting Polynomials

A **term** is a number or the product of numbers and variables raised to powers.

Terms

$-5x, 7a^2 b, \dfrac{1}{4}y^4, 0.2$

The **numerical coefficient** or **coefficient** of a term is its numerical factor.

Term	**Coefficient**
$7x^2$	7
y	1
$-a^2 b$	-1

A **polynomial** is a finite sum of terms in which all variables have exponents that are nonnegative integers and no variables appear in the denominator.

Polynomials

$1.3x^2$ (monomial)

$-\dfrac{1}{3}y + 5$ (binomial)

$6z^2 - 5z + 7$ (trinomial)

A function P is a **polynomial function** if $P(x)$ is a polynomial.

For the polynomial function
$$P(x) = -x^2 + 6x - 12, \text{ find } P(-2)$$
$$P(-2) = -(-2)^2 + 6(-2) - 12 = -28.$$

The **degree of a term** is the sum of the exponents on the variables in the term.

Term	**Degree**
$-5x^3$	3
3 (or $3x^0$)	0
$2a^2 b^2 c$	$2 + 2 + 1 = 5$

The **degree of a polynomial** is the greatest degree of any term of the polynomial.

Polynomial	**Degree**
$5x^2 - 3x + 2$	2
$7y + 8y^2 z^3 - 12$	$2 + 3 = 5$

(continued)

DEFINITIONS AND CONCEPTS	EXAMPLES

Section 5.2 Polynomial Functions and Adding and Subtracting Polynomials (continued)

To add polynomials, add or combine like terms.

Add:
$$(7x^2 - 3x + 2) + (-5x - 6) = 7x^2 - 3x + 2 - 5x - 6$$
$$= 7x^2 - 8x - 4$$

To subtract two polynomials, change the signs of the terms of the second polynomial, then add.

Subtract:
$$(17y^2 - 2y + 1) - (-3y^3 + 5y - 6)$$
$$= (17y^2 - 2y + 1) + (3y^3 - 5y + 6)$$
$$= 17y^2 - 2y + 1 + 3y^3 - 5y + 6$$
$$= 3y^3 + 17y^2 - 7y + 7$$

Section 5.3 Multiplying Polynomials

To multiply two polynomials, multiply each term of one polynomial by each term of the other polynomial, and then combine like terms.

Multiply:

$$(2x + 1)(5x^2 - 6x + 2)$$

$$= 2x(5x^2 - 6x + 2) + 1(5x^2 - 6x + 2)$$
$$= 10x^3 - 12x^2 + 4x + 5x^2 - 6x + 2$$
$$= 10x^3 - 7x^2 - 2x + 2$$

Section 5.4 Special Products

The **FOIL method** may be used when multiplying two binomials.

Multiply: $(5x - 3)(2x + 3)$

$$(5x - 3)(2x + 3) = (5x)(2x) + (5x)(3) + (-3)(2x) + (-3)(3)$$
$$= 10x^2 + 15x - 6x - 9$$
$$= 10x^2 + 9x - 9$$

Squaring a Binomial
$$(a + b)^2 = a^2 + 2ab + b^2$$

$$(a - b)^2 = a^2 - 2ab + b^2$$

Square each binomial.
$$(x + 5)^2 = x^2 + 2(x)(5) + 5^2$$
$$= x^2 + 10x + 25$$
$$(3x - 2y)^2 = (3x)^2 - 2(3x)(2y) + (2y)^2$$
$$= 9x^2 - 12xy + 4y^2$$

Multiplying the Sum and Difference of Two Terms
$$(a + b)(a - b) = a^2 - b^2$$

Multiply:
$$(6y + 5)(6y - 5) = (6y)^2 - 5^2$$
$$= 36y^2 - 25$$

Section 5.5 Negative Exponents and Scientific Notation

If $a \neq 0$ and n is an integer,
$$a^{-n} = \frac{1}{a^n}$$

Rules for exponents are true for positive and negative integers.

$$3^{-2} = \frac{1}{3^2} = \frac{1}{9}; \ 5x^{-2} = \frac{5}{x^2}$$

Simplify: $\left(\dfrac{x^{-2}y}{x^5}\right)^{-2} = \dfrac{x^4y^{-2}}{x^{-10}}$

$$= x^{4-(-10)}y^{-2}$$

$$= \frac{x^{14}}{y^2}$$

DEFINITIONS AND CONCEPTS	EXAMPLES

Section 5.5   Negative Exponents and Scientific Notation (continued)

A positive number is written in scientific notation if it is written as the product of a number a, $1 \leq a < 10$, and an integer power r of 10. $$a \times 10^r$$	Write each number in scientific notation. $$12,000 = 1.2 \times 10^4$$ $$0.00000568 = 5.68 \times 10^{-6}$$

Section 5.6   Dividing Polynomials

To divide a polynomial by a monomial: $$\frac{a+b}{c} = \frac{a}{c} + \frac{b}{c}$$ To divide a polynomial by a polynomial other than a monomial, use long division.	Divide: $$\frac{15x^5 - 10x^3 + 5x^2 - 2x}{5x^2} = \frac{15x^5}{5x^2} - \frac{10x^3}{5x^2} + \frac{5x^2}{5x^2} - \frac{2x}{5x^2}$$ $$= 3x^3 - 2x + 1 - \frac{2}{5x}$$ $$5x - 1 + \frac{-4}{2x+3}$$ $$2x+3\overline{)10x^2 + 13x - 7}$$ $$\underline{10x^2 + 15x}$$ $$-2x - 7$$ $$\underline{+2x + 3}$$ $$-4$$

Chapter 5 Review

(5.1) *State the base and the exponent for each expression.*

1. 7^9

2. $(-5)^4$

3. -5^4

4. x^6

Evaluate each expression.

5. 8^3

6. $(-6)^2$

7. -6^2

8. $-4^3 - 4^0$

9. $(3b)^0$

10. $\dfrac{8b}{8b}$

Simplify each expression.

11. $y^2 \cdot y^7$

12. $x^9 \cdot x^5$

13. $(2x^5)(-3x^6)$

14. $(-5y^3)(4y^4)$

15. $(x^4)^2$

16. $(y^3)^5$

17. $(3y^6)^4$

18. $(2x^3)^3$

19. $\dfrac{x^9}{x^4}$

20. $\dfrac{z^{12}}{z^5}$

21. $\dfrac{a^5b^4}{ab}$

22. $\dfrac{x^4y^6}{xy}$

23. $\dfrac{3x^4y^{10}}{12xy^6}$

24. $\dfrac{2x^7y^8}{8xy^2}$

25. $5a^7(2a^4)^3$

26. $(2x)^2(9x)$

27. $(-5a)^0 + 7^0 + 8^0$

28. $8x^0 + 9^0$

Simplify the given expression and choose the correct result.

29. $\left(\dfrac{3x^4}{4y}\right)^3$

    a. $\dfrac{27x^{64}}{64y^3}$ **b.** $\dfrac{27x^{12}}{64y^3}$ **c.** $\dfrac{9x^{12}}{12y^3}$ **d.** $\dfrac{3x^{12}}{4y^3}$

30. $\left(\dfrac{5a^6}{b^3}\right)^2$

   a. $\dfrac{10a^{12}}{b^6}$ **b.** $\dfrac{25a^{36}}{b^9}$ **c.** $\dfrac{25a^{12}}{b^6}$ **d.** $25a^{12}b^6$

(5.2) Find the degree of each term.

31. $-5x^4y^3$ **32.** $10x^3y^2z$

33. $35a^5bc^2$ **34.** $95xyz$

Find the degree of each polynomial.

35. $y^5 + 7x - 8x^4$

36. $9y^2 + 30y + 25$

37. $-14x^2y - 28x^2y^3 - 42x^2y^2$

38. $6x^2y^2z^2 + 5x^2y^3 - 12xyz$

39. The Glass Bridge Skywalk is suspended 4000 feet over the Colorado River at the very edge of the Grand Canyon. Neglecting air resistance, the height of an object dropped from the Skywalk at time t seconds is given by the polynomial function $P(t) = -16t^2 + 4000$. Find the height of the object at the given times.

t	0 seconds	1 second	3 seconds	5 seconds
$P(t) = -16t^2 + 4000$				

40. The surface area of a box with a square base and a height of 5 units is given by the polynomial function $P(x) = 2x^2 + 20x$. Fill in the table below by evaluating the function for the given values of x.

x	1	3	5.1	10
$P(x) = 2x^2 + 20x$				

Combine like terms in each expression.

41. $6a^2 + 4a + 9a^2$

42. $21x^2 + 3x + x^2 + 6$

43. $4a^2b - 3b^2 - 8q^2 - 10a^2b + 7q^2$

44. $2s^{14} + 3s^{13} + 12s^{12} - s^{10}$

Add or subtract as indicated.

45. $(3x^2 + 2x + 6) + (5x^2 + x)$

46. $(2x^5 + 3x^4 + 4x^3 + 5x^2) + (4x^2 + 7x + 6)$

47. $(-5y^2 + 3) - (2y^2 + 4)$

48. $(3x^2 - 7xy + 7y^2) - (4x^2 - xy + 9y^2)$

TRANSLATING

Perform the indicated operations.

49. Subtract $(3x - y)$ from $(7x - 14y)$.

50. Subtract $(4x^2 + 8x - 7)$ from the sum of $(x^2 + 7x + 9)$ and $(x^2 + 4)$.

If $P(x) = 9x^2 - 7x + 8$, find the following.

51. $P(6)$ **52.** $P(-2)$

53. Find the perimeter of the rectangle.

$(x^2y + 5)$ cm

$(2x^2y - 6x + 1)$ cm

54. With the ownership of computers growing rapidly, the market for new software is also increasing. The revenue for software publishers (in millions of dollars) in the United States from 2001 to 2006 can be represented by the polynomial function $f(x) = 754x^2 - 228x + 80,134$ where x is the number of years since 2001. Use this model to find the revenues from software sales in 2009. (*Source:* Software & Information Industry Association)

(5.3) Multiply each expression.

55. $4(2a + 7)$

56. $9(6a - 3)$

57. $-7x(x^2 + 5)$

58. $-8y(4y^2 - 6)$

59. $(3a^3 - 4a + 1)(-2a)$

60. $(6b^3 - 4b + 2)(7b)$

61. $(2x + 2)(x - 7)$

62. $(2x - 5)(3x + 2)$

63. $(x - 9)^2$

64. $(x - 12)^2$

65. $(4a - 1)(a + 7)$

66. $(6a - 1)(7a + 3)$

67. $(5x + 2)^2$

68. $(3x + 5)^2$

69. $(x + 7)(x^3 + 4x - 5)$

70. $(x + 2)(x^5 + x + 1)$

71. $(x^2 + 2x + 4)(x^2 + 2x - 4)$

72. $(x^3 + 4x + 4)(x^3 + 4x - 4)$

73. $(x + 7)^3$

74. $(2x - 5)^3$

(5.4) Use special products to multiply each of the following.

75. $(x + 7)^2$

76. $(x - 5)^2$

77. $(3x - 7)^2$

78. $(4x + 2)^2$

79. $(5x - 9)^2$

80. $(5x + 1)(5x - 1)$

81. $(7x + 4)(7x - 4)$

82. $(a + 2b)(a - 2b)$

83. $(2x - 6)(2x + 6)$

84. $(4a^2 - 2b)(4a^2 + 2b)$

Express each as a product of polynomials in x. Then multiply and simplify.

△ **85.** Find the area of the square if its side is $(3x - 1)$ meters.

$(3x - 1)$ meters

△ **86.** Find the area of the rectangle.

$(x - 1)$ miles
$(5x + 2)$ miles

(5.5) Simplify each expression.

87. 7^{-2} **88.** -7^{-2} **89.** $2x^{-4}$ **90.** $(2x)^{-4}$

91. $\left(\dfrac{1}{5}\right)^{-3}$ **92.** $\left(\dfrac{-2}{3}\right)^{-2}$

93. $2^0 + 2^{-4}$ **94.** $6^{-1} - 7^{-1}$

Simplify each expression. Write each answer using positive exponents only.

95. $\dfrac{x^5}{x^{-3}}$ **96.** $\dfrac{z^4}{z^{-4}}$

97. $\dfrac{r^{-3}}{r^{-4}}$ **98.** $\dfrac{y^{-2}}{y^{-5}}$

99. $\left(\dfrac{bc^{-2}}{bc^{-3}}\right)^4$ **100.** $\left(\dfrac{x^{-3}y^{-4}}{x^{-2}y^{-5}}\right)^{-3}$

101. $\dfrac{x^{-4}y^{-6}}{x^2y^7}$ **102.** $\dfrac{a^5b^{-5}}{a^{-5}b^5}$

103. $a^{6m}a^{5m}$ **104.** $\dfrac{(x^{5+h})^3}{x^5}$

105. $(3xy^{2z})^3$ **106.** $a^{m+2}a^{m+3}$

Write each number in scientific notation.

107. 0.00027   **108.** 0.8868

109. 80,800,000   **110.** 868,000

111. Google.com is an Internet search engine that handles 91,000,000 searches every day. Write 91,000,000 in scientific notation. (*Source:* Google, Inc.)

112. The approximate diameter of the Milky Way galaxy is 150,000 light years. Write this number in scientific notation. (*Source:* NASA IMAGE/POETRY Education and Public Outreach Program)

150,000 light years

Write each number in standard form.

113. 8.67×10^5 **114.** 3.86×10^{-3}

115. 8.6×10^{-4} **116.** 8.936×10^5

117. The volume of the planet Jupiter is 1.43128×10^{15} cubic kilometers. Write this number in standard notation. (*Source:* National Space Science Data Center)

118. An angstrom is a unit of measure, equal to 1×10^{-10} meter, used for measuring wavelengths or the diameters of atoms. Write this number in standard notation. (*Source:* National Institute of Standards and Technology)

Simplify. Express each result in standard form.

119. $(8 \times 10^4)(2 \times 10^{-7})$ **120.** $\dfrac{8 \times 10^4}{2 \times 10^{-7}}$

(5.6) Divide.

121. $\dfrac{x^2 + 21x + 49}{7x^2}$

122. $\dfrac{5a^3b - 15ab^2 + 20ab}{-5ab}$

123. $(a^2 - a + 4) \div (a - 2)$

124. $(4x^2 + 20x + 7) \div (x + 5)$

125. $\dfrac{a^3 + a^2 + 2a + 6}{a - 2}$

126. $\dfrac{9b^3 - 18b^2 + 8b - 1}{3b - 2}$

127. $\dfrac{4x^4 - 4x^3 + x^2 + 4x - 3}{2x - 1}$

128. $\dfrac{-10x^2 - x^3 - 21x + 18}{x - 6}$

△ **129.** The area of the rectangle below is $(15x^3 - 3x^2 + 60)$ square feet. If its length is $3x^2$ feet, find its width.

Area is $(15x^3 - 3x^2 + 60)$ sq feet

△ **130.** The perimeter of the equilateral triangle below is $(21a^3b^6 + 3a - 3)$ units. Find the length of a side.

Perimeter is
$(21a^3b^6 + 3a - 3)$ units

(5.7) *Use synthetic division to find each quotient.*

131. $(3x^3 + 12x - 4) \div (x - 2)$

132. $(3x^3 + 2x^2 - 4x - 1) \div \left(x + \dfrac{3}{2}\right)$

133. $(x^5 - 1) \div (x + 1)$

134. $(x^3 - 81) \div (x - 3)$

135. $(x^3 - x^2 + 3x^4 - 2) \div (x - 4)$

136. $(3x^4 - 2x^2 + 10) \div (x + 2)$

If $P(x) = 3x^5 - 9x + 7$, use the remainder theorem to find the following.

137. $P(4)$ **138.** $P(-5)$

MIXED REVIEW

Evaluate.

139. $\left(-\dfrac{1}{2}\right)^3$

Simplify each expression. Write each answer using positive exponents only.

140. $(4xy^2)(x^3y^5)$

141. $\dfrac{18x^9}{27x^3}$

142. $\left(\dfrac{3a^4}{b^2}\right)^3$

143. $(2x^{-4}y^3)^{-4}$

144. $\dfrac{a^{-3}b^6}{9^{-1}a^{-5}b^{-2}}$

Perform the indicated operations and simplify.

145. $(6x + 2) + (5x - 7)$

146. $(-y^2 - 4) + (3y^2 - 6)$

147. $(8y^2 - 3y + 1) - (3y^2 + 2)$

148. $(5x^2 + 2x - 6) - (-x - 4)$

149. $4x(7x^2 + 3)$

150. $(2x + 5)(3x - 2)$

151. $(x - 3)(x^2 + 4x - 6)$

152. $(7x - 2)(4x - 9)$

Use special products to multiply.

153. $(5x + 4)^2$

154. $(6x + 3)(6x - 3)$

Divide.

155. $\dfrac{8a^4 - 2a^3 + 4a - 5}{2a^3}$

156. $\dfrac{x^2 + 2x + 10}{x + 5}$

157. $\dfrac{4x^3 + 8x^2 - 11x + 4}{2x - 3}$

Chapter 5 Test MyMathLab® Test Prep VIDEOS You Tube

Evaluate each expression.

▶ **1.** 2^5 ▶ **2.** $(-3)^4$ ▶ **3.** -3^4 ▶ **4.** 4^{-3}

Simplify each exponential expression. Write the result using only positive exponents.

▶ **5.** $(3x^2)(-5x^9)$

▶ **6.** $\dfrac{y^7}{y^2}$

▶ **7.** $\dfrac{r^{-8}}{r^{-3}}$

▶ **8.** $\left(\dfrac{x^2y^3}{x^3y^{-4}}\right)^2$

▶ **9.** $\dfrac{6^2x^{-4}y^{-1}}{6^3x^{-3}y^7}$

Express each number in scientific notation.

▶ **10.** $563{,}000$ ▶ **11.** 0.0000863

Write each number in standard form.

▶ **12.** 1.5×10^{-3} ▶ **13.** 6.23×10^4

▶ **14.** Simplify. Write the answer in standard form.

$$(1.2 \times 10^5)(3 \times 10^{-7})$$

15. a. Complete the table for the polynomial
$4xy^2 + 7xyz + x^3y - 2$.

Term	Numerical Coefficient	Degree of Term
$4xy^2$		
$7xyz$		
x^3y		
-2		

b. What is the degree of the polynomial?

16. Simplify by combining like terms.

$$5x^2 + 4xy - 7x^2 + 11 + 8xy$$

Perform each indicated operation.

17. $(8x^3 + 7x^2 + 4x - 7) + (8x^3 - 7x - 6)$

18. $5x^3 + x^2 + 5x - 2 - (8x^3 - 4x^2 + x - 7)$

19. Subtract $(4x + 2)$ from the sum of $(8x^2 + 7x + 5)$ and $(x^3 - 8)$.

Multiply.

20. $(3x + 7)(x^2 + 5x + 2)$

21. $3x^2(2x^2 - 3x + 7)$

22. $(x + 7)(3x - 5)$

23. $\left(3x - \dfrac{1}{5}\right)\left(3x + \dfrac{1}{5}\right)$

24. $(4x - 2)^2$

25. $(8x + 3)^2$

26. $(x^2 - 9b)(x^2 + 9b)$

Solve.

27. The height of the Bank of China in Hong Kong is 1001 feet. Neglecting air resistance, the height of an object dropped from this building at time t seconds is given by the polynomial function $P(t) = -16t^2 + 1001$. Find the height of the object at the given times below.

t	0 seconds	1 second	3 seconds	5 seconds
$P(t) = -16t^2 + 1001$				

28. Find the area of the top of the table. Express the area as a product, then multiply and simplify.

$(2x - 3)$ inches $(2x + 3)$ inches

Divide.

29. $\dfrac{4x^2 + 24xy - 7x}{8xy}$

30. $(x^2 + 7x + 10) \div (x + 5)$

31. $\dfrac{27x^3 - 8}{3x + 2}$

32. A pebble is hurled upward from the top of the Canada Trust Tower, which is 880 feet tall, with an initial velocity of 96 feet per second. Neglecting air resistance, the height $h(t)$ of the pebble after t seconds is given by the polynomial function

$$h(t) = -16t^2 + 96t + 880$$

a. Find the height of the pebble when $t = 1$.

b. Find the height of the pebble when $t = 5.1$.

33. Use synthetic division to divide $(4x^4 - 3x^3 - x - 1)$ by $(x + 3)$.

34. If $P(x) = 4x^4 + 7x^2 - 2x - 5$, use the remainder theorem to find $P(-2)$.

Chapter 5 Cumulative Review

1. Tell whether each statement is true or false.

a. $8 \geq 8$ **b.** $8 \leq 8$

c. $23 \leq 0$ **d.** $23 \geq 0$

2. Find the absolute value of each number.

a. $|-7.2|$ **b.** $|0|$ **c.** $\left|-\dfrac{1}{2}\right|$

3. Divide. Write all quotients in lowest terms

a. $\dfrac{4}{5} \div \dfrac{5}{16}$ **b.** $\dfrac{7}{10} \div 14$ **c.** $\dfrac{3}{8} \div \dfrac{3}{10}$

4. Multiply. Write products in lowest terms.

a. $\dfrac{3}{4} \cdot \dfrac{7}{21}$ **b.** $\dfrac{1}{2} \cdot 4\dfrac{5}{6}$

5. Evaluate the following:

a. 3^2 **b.** 5^3 **c.** 2^4

d. 7^1 **e.** $\left(\dfrac{3}{7}\right)^2$

6. Evaluate $\dfrac{2x - 7y}{x^2}$ for $x = 5$ and $y = 1$.

7. Add.

a. $-3 + (-7)$ **b.** $-1 + (-20)$

c. $-2 + (-10)$

8. Simplify: $8 + 3(2 \cdot 6 - 1)$

9. Subtract 8 from -4.

10. Is $x = 1$ a solution of $5x^2 + 2 = x - 8$?

11. Find the reciprocal of each number.

a. 22   **b.** $\dfrac{3}{16}$

c. -10 **d.** $-\dfrac{9}{13}$

12. Subtract:

a. $7 - 40$ **b.** $-5 - (-10)$

13. Use an associative property to complete each statement.

    a. $5 + (4 + 6) =$ _____

    b. $(-1 \cdot 2) \cdot 5 =$ _____

14. Simplify: $\dfrac{4(-3) + (-8)}{5 + (-5)}$

15. Simplify each expression.

    a. $10 + (x + 12)$

    b. $-3(7x)$

16. Use the distributive property to write $-2(x + 3y - z)$ without parentheses.

17. Find each product by using the distributive property to remove parentheses.

    a. $5(3x + 2)$

    b. $-2(y + 0.3z - 1)$

    c. $-(9x + y - 2z + 6)$

18. Simplify: $2(6x - 1) - (x - 7)$

19. Solve $x - 7 = 10$ for x.

20. Write the phrase as an algebraic expression: double a number, subtracted from the sum of the number and seven

21. Solve: $\dfrac{5}{2}x = 15$

22. Solve: $2x + \dfrac{1}{8} = x - \dfrac{3}{8}$

23. Twice a number, added to seven, is the same as three subtracted from the number. Find the number.

24. Solve: $10 = 5j - 2$

25. Twice the sum of a number and 4 is the same as four times the number, decreased by 12. Find the number.

26. Solve: $\dfrac{7x + 5}{3} = x + 3$

27. The length of a rectangular road sign is 2 feet less than three times its width. Find the dimensions if the perimeter is 28 feet.

28. Graph $x < 5$ and write in interval notation.

29. Solve $F = \dfrac{9}{5}C + 32$ for C.

30. Find the slope of each line.

    a. $x = -1$

    b. $y = 7$

31. Graph $2 < x \le 4$.

32. Recall that the grade of a road is its slope written as a percent. Find the grade of the road shown.

33. Complete the following ordered pair solutions for the equation $3x + y = 12$.

    a. $(0, \ )$

    b. $(\ , 6)$

    c. $(-1, \ )$

34. Solve the system: $\begin{cases} 3x + 2y = -8 \\ 2x - 6y = -9 \end{cases}$

35. Graph the linear equation $2x + y = 5$.

36. Solve the system: $\begin{cases} x = -3y + 3 \\ 2x + 9y = 5 \end{cases}$

37. Graph $x = 2$.

38. Evaluate.

    a. $(-5)^2$

    b. -5^2

    c. $2 \cdot 5^2$

39. Find the slope of the line $x = 5$.

40. Simplify: $\dfrac{(z^2)^3 \cdot z^7}{z^9}$

41. Subtract: $(2x^3 + 8x^2 - 6x) - (2x^3 - x^2 + 1)$.

42. Subtract $(5y^2 - 6) - (y^2 + 2)$.

43. Use the product rule to simplify $(2x^2)(-3x^5)$.

44. Find the value of $-x^2$ when

    a. $x = 2$

    b. $x = -2$

45. Add $(11x^3 - 12x^2 + x - 3)$ and $(x^3 - 10x + 5)$.

46. Multiply $(10x^2 - 3)(10x^2 + 3)$.

47. Multiply $(2x - y)^2$.

48. Multiply $(10x^2 + 3)^2$.

49. Divide $6m^2 + 2m$ by $2m$.

50. Evaluate.

    a. 5^{-1}

    b. 7^{-2}

Factoring Polynomials

As shown on the circle graph below, games and music are the leading moneymakers in the digital market. Record companies' revenue from digital music channels grew 6% in a recent year to total $4.6 billion in the United States alone. From 2004 to 2010, the digital music market increased 1000%.

In Section 6.1, Exercise 109, we explore digital music downloads further.

Global Digital Revenues

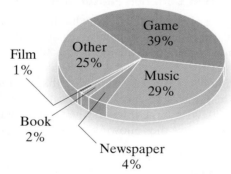

Data from NPD Group; Pollstar; Recording Industry Association of America (RIAA); U.S. Department of Labor; and Tera Consultants

In Chapter 5, you learned how to multiply polynomials. This chapter deals with an operation that is the reverse process of multiplying, called *factoring*. Factoring is an important algebraic skill because this process allows us to write a sum as a product.

At the end of this chapter, we use factoring to help us solve equations other than linear equations, and in Chapter 7, we use factoring to simplify and perform arithmetic operations on rational expressions.

6.1 | The Greatest Common Factor and Factoring by Grouping

OBJECTIVES

1 Find the Greatest Common Factor of a List of Integers.

2 Find the Greatest Common Factor of a List of Terms.

3 Factor Out the Greatest Common Factor from a Polynomial.

4 Factor a Polynomial by Grouping.

In the product $2 \cdot 3 = 6$, the numbers 2 and 3 are called **factors** of 6 and $2 \cdot 3$ is a **factored form** of 6. This is true of polynomials also. Since $(x + 2)(x + 3) = x^2 + 5x + 6$, $(x + 2)$ and $(x + 3)$ are factors of $x^2 + 5x + 6$, and $(x + 2)(x + 3)$ is a factored form of the polynomial.

$$\overbrace{\underset{\uparrow \atop factor}{2} \cdot \underset{\uparrow \atop factor}{3}}^{\text{a factored form of 6}} = \underset{\uparrow \atop product}{6}$$

$$\overbrace{\underset{\uparrow \atop factor}{x^2} \cdot \underset{\uparrow \atop factor}{x^3}}^{\text{a factored form of } x^5} = \underset{\uparrow \atop product}{x^5}$$

$$\overbrace{\underset{\uparrow \atop factor}{(x + 2)} \underset{\uparrow \atop factor}{(x + 3)}}^{\text{a factored form of } x^2 + 5x + 6} = \underset{\uparrow \atop product}{x^2 + 5x + 6}$$

> The process of writing a polynomial as a product is called **factoring** the polynomial.

Do you see that factoring is the reverse process of multiplying?

$$x^2 + 5x + 6 \overset{\text{factoring}}{\underset{\text{multiplying}}{=}} (x + 2)(x + 3)$$

✓**CONCEPT CHECK**

Multiply: $2(x - 4)$

What do you think the result of factoring $2x - 8$ would be? Why?

OBJECTIVE

1 Finding the Greatest Common Factor of a List of Integers

The first step in factoring a polynomial is to see whether the terms of the polynomial have a common factor. If there is one, we can write the polynomial as a product by **factoring out** the common factor. We will usually factor out the **greatest common factor (GCF).**

The GCF of a list of integers is the largest integer that is a factor of all the integers in the list. For example, the GCF of 12 and 20 is 4 because 4 is the largest integer that is a factor of both 12 and 20. With large integers, the GCF may not be found easily by inspection. When this happens, use the following steps.

Finding the GCF of a List of Integers

Step 1. Write each number as a product of prime numbers.

Step 2. Identify the common prime factors.

Step 3. The product of all common prime factors found in Step 2 is the greatest common factor. If there are no common prime factors, the greatest common factor is 1.

Recall from Section 1.3 that a prime number is a whole number other than 1 whose only factors are 1 and itself.

Answers to Concept Check:
$2x - 8$; The result would be $2(x - 4)$ because factoring is the reverse process of multiplying.

EXAMPLE 1   Find the GCF of each list of numbers.

a. 28 and 40   **b.** 55 and 21   **c.** 15, 18, and 66

Solution

a. Write each number as a product of primes.

$$28 = 2 \cdot 2 \cdot 7 = 2^2 \cdot 7$$
$$40 = 2 \cdot 2 \cdot 2 \cdot 5 = 2^3 \cdot 5$$

There are two common factors, each of which is 2, so the GCF is

$$\text{GCF} = 2 \cdot 2 = 4$$

b. $55 = 5 \cdot 11$
$21 = 3 \cdot 7$

There are no common prime factors; thus, the GCF is 1.

c. $15 = 3 \cdot 5$
$18 = 2 \cdot 3 \cdot 3 = 2 \cdot 3^2$
$66 = 2 \cdot 3 \cdot 11$

The only prime factor common to all three numbers is 3, so the GCF is

$$\text{GCF} = 3$$

PRACTICE
1   Find the GCF of each list of numbers.

a. 36 and 42   **b.** 35 and 44   **c.** 12, 16, and 40

OBJECTIVE
2   Finding the Greatest Common Factor of a List of Terms

The greatest common factor of a list of variables raised to powers is found in a similar way. For example, the GCF of x^2, x^3, and x^5 is x^2 because each term contains a factor of x^2 and no higher power of x is a factor of each term.

$$x^2 = x \cdot x$$
$$x^3 = x \cdot x \cdot x$$
$$x^5 = x \cdot x \cdot x \cdot x \cdot x$$

There are two common factors, each of which is x, so the GCF $= x \cdot x$ or x^2.

From this example, we see that **the GCF of a list of common variables raised to powers is the variable raised to the smallest exponent in the list.**

EXAMPLE 2   Find the GCF of each list of terms.

a. x^3, x^7, and x^5 **b.** y, y^4, and y^7

Solution

a. The GCF is x^3, since 3 is the smallest exponent to which x is raised.
b. The GCF is y^1 or y, since 1 is the smallest exponent on y.

PRACTICE
2   Find the GCF of each list of terms.

a. y^7, y^4, and y^6 **b.** x, x^4, and x^2

In general, the **greatest common factor (GCF) of a list of terms** is the product of the GCF of the numerical coefficients and the GCF of the variable factors.

$$20x^2y^2 = 2\cdot2\cdot5\cdot x\cdot x\cdot y\cdot y$$
$$6xy^3 = 2\cdot3\cdot x\cdot y\cdot y\cdot y$$
$$\text{GCF} = 2\cdot x\cdot y\cdot y = 2xy^2$$

> ▶ **Helpful Hint**
>
> Remember that the GCF of a list of terms contains the smallest exponent on each common variable.
>
> The GCF of x^5y^6, x^2y^7, and x^3y^4 is x^2y^4. ⎯⎯ Smallest exponent on x
> ⎯⎯ Smallest exponent on y

EXAMPLE 3   Find the GCF of each list of terms.

a. $6x^2$, $10x^3$, and $-8x$ **b.** $-18y^2$, $-63y^3$, and $27y^4$ **c.** a^3b^2, a^5b, and a^6b^2

Solution

a. $6x^2 = 2\cdot3\cdot x^2$
   $10x^3 = 2\cdot5\cdot x^3$ ⎫ → The GCF of x^2, x^3, and x^1 is x^1 or x.
   $-8x = -1\cdot2\cdot2\cdot2\cdot x^1$ ⎭
   $\text{GCF} = 2\cdot x^1$ or $2x$

b. $-18y^2 = -1\cdot2\cdot3\cdot3\cdot y^2$
   $-63y^3 = -1\cdot3\cdot3\cdot7\cdot y^3$ ⎫ → The GCF of y^2, y^3, and y^4 is y^2.
   $27y^4 = 3\cdot3\cdot3\cdot y^4$ ⎭
   $\text{GCF} = 3\cdot3\cdot y^2$ or $9y^2$

c. The GCF of a^3, a^5, and a^6 is a^3.

   The GCF of b^2, b, and b^2 is b.

   Thus, the GCF of a^3b^2, a^5b, and a^6b^2 is a^3b.   □

PRACTICE

3   Find the GCF of each list of terms.

a. $5y^4$, $15y^2$, and $-20y^3$ **b.** $4x^2$, x^3, and $3x^8$ **c.** a^4b^2, a^3b^5, and a^2b^3

OBJECTIVE

3   Factoring Out the Greatest Common Factor

The first step in factoring a polynomial is to find the GCF of its terms. Once we do so, we can write the polynomial as a product by **factoring out** the GCF.

The polynomial $8x + 14$, for example, contains two terms: $8x$ and 14. The GCF of these terms is 2. We factor out 2 from each term by writing each term as a product of 2 and the term's remaining factors.

$$8x + 14 = 2\cdot4x + 2\cdot7$$

Using the distributive property, we can write

$$8x + 14 = 2\cdot4x + 2\cdot7$$
$$= 2(4x + 7)$$

Thus, a factored form of $8x + 14$ is $2(4x + 7)$. We can check by multiplying:

$$2(4x + 7) = 2\cdot4x + 2\cdot7 = 8x + 14.$$

> ▶ **Helpful Hint**
>
> A factored form of $8x + 14$ is *not*
>
> $$2\cdot4x + 2\cdot7$$
>
> Although the *terms* have been factored (written as a product), the *polynomial* $8x + 14$ has not been factored (written as a product).
>
> A factored form of $8x + 14$ is the *product* $2(4x + 7)$.

✓**CONCEPT CHECK**
Which of the following is/are factored form(s) of $7t + 21$?
  a. 7   **b.** $7 \cdot t + 7 \cdot 3$ **c.** $7(t + 3)$ **d.** $7(t + 21)$

EXAMPLE 4   Factor each polynomial by factoring out the GCF.

a. $6t + 18$ **b.** $y^5 - y^7$

Solution

a. The GCF of terms $6t$ and 18 is 6.

$$6t + 18 = 6 \cdot t + 6 \cdot 3$$
$$= 6(t + 3) \qquad \text{Apply the distributive property.}$$

Our work can be checked by multiplying 6 and $(t + 3)$.

$$6(t + 3) = 6 \cdot t + 6 \cdot 3 = 6t + 18, \text{ the original polynomial.}$$

b. The GCF of y^5 and y^7 is y^5. Thus,

$$y^5 - y^7 = y^5(1) - y^5(y^2)$$
$$= y^5(1 - y^2)$$

▶ **Helpful Hint**
Don't forget the 1.

PRACTICE
   4   Factor each polynomial by factoring out the GCF.

a. $4t + 12$ **b.** $y^8 + y^4$

EXAMPLE 5   Factor: $-9a^5 + 18a^2 - 3a$

Solution

$$-9a^5 + 18a^2 - 3a = (3a)(-3a^4) + (3a)(6a) + (3a)(-1)$$
$$= 3a(-3a^4 + 6a - 1)$$

▶ **Helpful Hint**
Don't forget the −1.

PRACTICE
   5   Factor $-8b^6 + 16b^4 - 8b^2$.

In Example 5, we could have chosen to factor out a $-3a$ instead of $3a$. If we factor out a $-3a$, we have

$$-9a^5 + 18a^2 - 3a = (-3a)(3a^4) + (-3a)(-6a) + (-3a)(1)$$
$$= -3a(3a^4 - 6a + 1)$$

▶ **Helpful Hint**
Notice the changes in signs when factoring out $-3a$.

EXAMPLES   Factor.

6. $6a^4 - 12a = 6a(a^3 - 2)$

7. $\dfrac{3}{7}x^4 + \dfrac{1}{7}x^3 - \dfrac{5}{7}x^2 = \dfrac{1}{7}x^2(3x^2 + x - 5)$

8. $15p^2q^4 + 20p^3q^5 + 5p^3q^3 = 5p^2q^3(3q + 4pq^2 + p)$

PRACTICES
   6–8   Factor.

6. $5x^4 - 20x$ **7.** $\dfrac{5}{9}z^5 + \dfrac{1}{9}z^4 - \dfrac{2}{9}z^3$ **8.** $8a^2b^4 - 20a^3b^3 + 12ab^3$

EXAMPLE 9 Factor: $5(x + 3) + y(x + 3)$

Solution The binomial $(x + 3)$ is the greatest common factor. Use the distributive property to factor out $(x + 3)$.

$$5(x + 3) + y(x + 3) = (x + 3)(5 + y)$$ □

PRACTICE
9 Factor $8(y - 2) + x(y - 2)$.

EXAMPLE 10 Factor: $3m^2n(a + b) - (a + b)$

Solution The greatest common factor is $(a + b)$.

$$3m^2n(a + b) - 1(a + b) = (a + b)(3m^2n - 1)$$ □

PRACTICE
10 Factor $7xy^3(p + q) - (p + q)$

OBJECTIVE
4 Factoring by Grouping ▶

Once the GCF is factored out, we can often continue to factor the polynomial, using a variety of techniques. We discuss here a technique for factoring polynomials called **factoring by grouping.**

EXAMPLE 11 Factor $xy + 2x + 3y + 6$ by grouping. Check by multiplying.

Solution The GCF of the first two terms is x, and the GCF of the last two terms is 3.

$$\begin{aligned} xy + 2x + 3y + 6 &= (xy + 2x) + (3y + 6) \quad \text{Group terms.}\\ &= \underbrace{x(y + 2) + 3(y + 2)} \quad \text{Factor out GCF from each grouping.} \end{aligned}$$

> ▶ **Helpful Hint**
> Notice that this form, $x(y + 2) + 3(y + 2)$, is *not* a factored form of the original polynomial. It is a sum, not a product.

Next we factor out the common binomial factor, $(y + 2)$.

$$x(y + 2) + 3(y + 2) = (y + 2)(x + 3)$$

Now the result is a factored form because it is a product. We were able to write the polynomial as a product because of the common binomial factor, $(y + 2)$, that appeared. If this does not happen, try rearranging the terms of the original polynomial.

Check: Multiply $(y + 2)$ by $(x + 3)$.

$$(y + 2)(x + 3) = xy + 2x + 3y + 6,$$

the original polynomial.
Thus, the factored form of $xy + 2x + 3y + 6$ is the product $(y + 2)(x + 3)$. □

PRACTICE
11 Factor $xy + 3y + 4x + 12$ by grouping. Check by multiplying.

You may want to try these steps when factoring by grouping.

To Factor a Four-Term Polynomial by Grouping

Step 1. Group the terms in two groups of two terms so that each group has a common factor.

Step 2. Factor out the GCF from each group.

Step 3. If there is now a common binomial factor in the groups, factor it out.

Step 4. If not, rearrange the terms and try these steps again.

EXAMPLES Factor by grouping.

12. $15x^3 - 10x^2 + 6x - 4$

$= (15x^3 - 10x^2) + (6x - 4)$ Group the terms.

$= 5x^2(3x - 2) + 2(3x - 2)$ Factor each group.

$= (3x - 2)(5x^2 + 2)$ Factor out the common factor, $(3x - 2)$.

13. $3x^2 + 4xy - 3x - 4y$

$= (3x^2 + 4xy) + (-3x - 4y)$

$= x(3x + 4y) - 1(3x + 4y)$ Factor each group. A -1 is factored from the second pair of terms so that there is a common factor, $(3x + 4y)$.

$= (3x + 4y)(x - 1)$ Factor out the common factor, $(3x + 4y)$.

14. $2a^2 + 5ab + 2a + 5b$

$= (2a^2 + 5ab) + (2a + 5b)$ Factor each group. An understood 1 is written before $(2a + 5b)$ to help remember that $(2a + 5b)$ is $1(2a + 5b)$.

$= a(2a + 5b) + 1(2a + 5b)$

$= (2a + 5b)(a + 1)$ Factor out the common factor, $(2a + 5b)$. □

> **Helpful Hint**
> Notice the factor of 1 is written when $(2a + 5b)$ is factored out.

PRACTICES

12–14

12. Factor $40x^3 - 24x^2 + 15x - 9$ by grouping.

13. Factor $2xy + 3y^2 - 2x - 3y$ by grouping.

14. Factor $7a^3 + 5a^2 + 7a + 5$ by grouping.

EXAMPLES Factor by grouping.

15. $3xy + 2 - 3x - 2y$

Notice that the first two terms have no common factor other than 1. However, if we rearrange these terms, a grouping emerges that does lead to a common factor.

$3xy + 2 - 3x - 2y$

$= (3xy - 3x) + (-2y + 2)$

$= 3x(y - 1) - 2(y - 1)$ Factor -2 from the second group so that there is a common factor, $(y - 1)$.

$= (y - 1)(3x - 2)$ Factor out the common factor, $(y - 1)$.

16. $5x - 10 + x^3 - x^2 = 5(x - 2) + x^2(x - 1)$

There is no common binomial factor that can now be factored out. No matter how we rearrange the terms, no grouping will lead to a common factor. Thus, this polynomial is not factorable by grouping. □

PRACTICES

15–16

15. Factor $4xy + 15 - 12x - 5y$ by grouping.

16. Factor $9y - 18 + y^3 - 4y^2$ by grouping.

> **Helpful Hint**
> One more reminder: When **factoring** a polynomial, make sure the polynomial is written as a **product.** For example, it is true that
>
> $$3x^2 + 4xy - 3x - 4y = \underbrace{x(3x + 4y) - 1(3x + 4y)}_{\text{but is not a factored form}},$$
>
> since it is a **sum (difference)**, not a **product.** A factored form of $3x^2 + 4xy - 3x - 4y$ is the product $(3x + 4y)(x - 1)$.

Factoring out a greatest common factor first makes factoring by any method easier, as we see in the next example.

EXAMPLE 17 Factor: $4ax - 4ab - 2bx + 2b^2$

Solution First, factor out the common factor 2 from all four terms.

$4ax - 4ab - 2bx + 2b^2$

$= 2(2ax - 2ab - bx + b^2)$ Factor out 2 from all four terms.

$= 2[2a(x - b) - b(x - b)]$ Factor each pair of terms. A "$-b$" is factored from the second pair so that there is a common factor, $x - b$.

$= 2(x - b)(2a - b)$ Factor out the common binomial. $\square$

> **Helpful Hint**
> Throughout this chapter, we will be factoring polynomials. Even when the instructions do not so state, it is always a good idea to check your answers by multiplying.

PRACTICE
17   Factor $3xy - 3ay - 6ax + 6a^2$.

Vocabulary, Readiness & Video Check

Use the choices below to fill in each blank. Some choices may be used more than once and some may not be used at all.

greatest common factor   factors   factoring   true   false   least   greatest

1. Since $5 \cdot 4 = 20$, the numbers 5 and 4 are called _____ of 20.

2. The _____ of a list of integers is the largest integer that is a factor of all the integers in the list.

3. The greatest common factor of a list of common variables raised to powers is the variable raised to the _____ exponent in the list.

4. The process of writing a polynomial as a product is called _____.

5. True or false: A factored form of $7x + 21 + xy + 3y$ is $7(x + 3) + y(x + 3)$. _____

6. True or false: A factored form of $3x^3 + 6x + x^2 + 2$ is $3x(x^2 + 2)$. _____

Martin-Gay Interactive Videos

See Video 6.1

Watch the section lecture video and answer the following questions.

OBJECTIVE 1
7. Based on Example 1, give a general definition for the greatest common factor (GCF) of a list of numbers.

OBJECTIVE 2
8. In Example 3, why are the numbers factored out, but not the variables?

OBJECTIVE 3
9. From Example 5, how can the number of terms in the other factor, once you factor out the GCF, help you determine if your factorization is correct?

OBJECTIVE 4
10. In Examples 7 and 8, what are you reminded to always do first when factoring a polynomial? Also, explain how a polynomial looks if it suggests it might be factored by grouping.

6.1 Exercise Set   MyMathLab®

Find the GCF for each list. See Examples 1 through 3.

1. $32, 36$
2. $36, 90$
3. $18, 42, 84$
4. $30, 75, 135$
5. $24, 14, 21$
6. $15, 25, 27$
7. y^2, y^4, y^7
8. x^3, x^2, x^5
9. z^7, z^9, z^{11}
10. y^8, y^{10}, y^{12}
11. $x^{10}y^2, xy^2, x^3y^3$
12. p^7q, p^8q^2, p^9q^3
13. $14x, 21$
14. $20y, 15$
15. $12y^4, 20y^3$
16. $32x^5, 18x^2$
17. $-10x^2, 15x^3$
18. $-21x^3, 14x$
19. $12x^3, -6x^4, 3x^5$
20. $15y^2, 5y^7, -20y^3$

21. $-18x^2y, 9x^3y^3, 36x^3y$ **22.** $7x^3y^3, -21x^2y^2, 14xy^4$

23. $20a^6b^2c^8, 50a^7b$ **24.** $40x^7y^2z, 64x^9y$

Factor out the GCF from each polynomial. See Examples 4 through 10.

25. $3a + 6$ **26.** $18a + 12$

▶ **27.** $30x - 15$ **28.** $42x - 7$

29. $x^3 + 5x^2$ **30.** $y^5 + 6y^4$

31. $6y^4 + 2y^3$ **32.** $5x^2 + 10x^6$

33. $4x - 8y + 4$

34. $7x + 21y - 7$

35. $6x^3 - 9x^2 + 12x$

36. $12x^3 + 16x^2 - 8x$

37. $a^7b^6 - a^3b^2 + a^2b^5 - a^2b^2$

38. $x^9y^6 + x^3y^5 - x^4y^3 + x^3y^3$

39. $8x^5 + 16x^4 - 20x^3 + 12$

40. $9y^6 - 27y^4 + 18y^2 + 6$

41. $\frac{1}{3}x^4 + \frac{2}{3}x^3 - \frac{4}{3}x^5 + \frac{1}{3}x$

42. $\frac{2}{5}y^7 - \frac{4}{5}y^5 + \frac{3}{5}y^2 - \frac{2}{5}y$

▶ **43.** $y(x^2 + 2) + 3(x^2 + 2)$

44. $x(y^2 + 1) - 3(y^2 + 1)$

45. $z(y + 4) - 3(y + 4)$

46. $8(x + 2) - y(x + 2)$

47. $r(z^2 - 6) + (z^2 - 6)$

48. $q(b^3 - 5) + (b^3 - 5)$

Factor a negative number or a GCF with a negative coefficient from each polynomial. See Example 5.

49. $-2x - 14$ **50.** $-7y - 21$

51. $-2x^5 + x^7$ **52.** $-5y^3 + y^6$

53. $-6a^4 + 9a^3 - 3a^2$

54. $-5m^6 + 10m^5 - 5m^3$

Factor each four-term polynomial by grouping. If this is not possible, write "not factorable by grouping." See Examples 11 through 17.

55. $x^3 + 2x^2 + 5x + 10$

56. $x^3 + 4x^2 + 3x + 12$

57. $5x + 15 + xy + 3y$

58. $xy + y + 2x + 2$

59. $6x^3 - 4x^2 + 15x - 10$

60. $16x^3 - 28x^2 + 12x - 21$

61. $5m^3 + 6mn + 5m^2 + 6n$

62. $8w^2 + 7wv + 8w + 7v$

63. $2y - 8 + xy - 4x$

64. $6x - 42 + xy - 7y$

65. $2x^3 - x^2 + 8x - 4$

66. $2x^3 - x^2 - 10x + 5$

67. $3x - 3 + x^3 - 4x^2$

68. $7x - 21 + x^3 - 2x^2$

69. $4x^2 - 8xy - 3x + 6y$

▶ **70.** $5xy - 15x - 6y + 18$

71. $5q^2 - 4pq - 5q + 4p$

72. $6m^2 - 5mn - 6m + 5n$

73. $2x^4 + 5x^3 + 2x^2 + 5x$

74. $4y^4 + y^2 + 20y^3 + 5y$

75. $12x^2y - 42x^2 - 4y + 14$

76. $90 + 15y^2 - 18x - 3xy^2$

MIXED PRACTICE

Factor. See Examples 4 through 17.

77. $32xy - 18x^2$

78. $10xy - 15x^2$

79. $y(x + 2) - 3(x + 2)$

80. $z(y - 4) + 3(y - 4)$

▶ **81.** $14x^3y + 7x^2y - 7xy$

82. $5x^3y - 15x^2y + 10xy$

83. $28x^3 - 7x^2 + 12x - 3$

84. $15x^3 + 5x^2 - 6x - 2$

85. $-40x^8y^6 - 16x^9y^5$

86. $-21x^3y - 49x^2y^2$

▶ **87.** $6a^2 + 9ab^2 + 6ab + 9b^3$

88. $16x^2 + 4xy^2 + 8xy + 2y^3$

REVIEW AND PREVIEW

Multiply. See Section 5.3.

89. $(x + 2)(x + 5)$

90. $(y + 3)(y + 6)$

91. $(b + 1)(b - 4)$

92. $(x - 5)(x + 10)$

Fill in the chart by finding two numbers that have the given product and sum. The first column is filled in for you.

	93.	**94.**	**95.**	**96.**	**97.**	**98.**
Two Numbers	4, 7					
Their Product	28	12	20	8	16	−10	−24
Their Sum	11	8	9	−9	−10	3	−5

CONCEPT EXTENSIONS

See the Concept Checks in this section.

99. Which of the following is/are factored form(s) of $8a - 24$?

    a. $8 \cdot a - 24$ **b.** $8(a - 3)$

    c. $4(2a - 12)$ **d.** $8 \cdot a - 2 \cdot 12$

100. Which of the following is/are factored form(s) of $-2x + 14$?

    a. $-2(x + 7)$ **b.** $-2 \cdot x + 14$

    c. $-2(x - 14)$ **d.** $-2(x - 7)$

Determine whether the following expressions are factored.

101. $(a + 6)(a + 2)$

102. $(x + 5)(x + y)$

103. $5(2y + z) - b(2y + z)$

104. $3x(a + 2b) + 2(a + 2b)$

105. Construct a binomial whose greatest common factor is $5a^3$. (*Hint:* Multiply $5a^3$ by a binomial whose terms contain no common factor other than 1. $5a^3(\square + \square)$.)

106. Construct a trinomial whose greatest common factor is $2x^2$. See the hint for Exercise 105.

107. Explain how you can tell whether a polynomial is written in factored form.

108. Construct a four-term polynomial that can be factored by grouping.

109. The number (in millions) of single digital downloads annually in the United States each year during 2004–2010 can be modeled by the polynomial $-20x^2 + 300x + 120$, where x is the number of years since 2004. (*Source:* Recording Industry Association of America)

a. Find the number of single digital downloads in 2010. To do so, let $x = 6$ and evaluate $-20x^2 + 300x + 120$.

b. Use this expression to predict the number of single digital downloads in 2014.

c. Factor the polynomial $-20x^2 + 300x + 120$ by factoring -20 from each term.

110. The number (in thousands) of students who graduated from U.S. public high schools each year during 2000–2009 can be modeled by $0.8x^2 + 44x + 2552$, where x is the number of years since 2000. (*Source:* Digest of Education Statistics)

a. Find the number of students who graduated from U.S. high schools in 2005. To do so, let $x = 5$ and evaluate $0.8x^2 + 44x + 2552$.

b. Use this expression to predict the number of students who will graduate from U.S. high schools in 2015.

c. Factor the polynomial $0.8x^2 + 44x + 2552$ by factoring out 0.8 from each term.

Write an expression for the area of each shaded region. Then write the expression as a factored polynomial.

△ **111.**   △ **112.**

*Write an expression for the length of each rectangle. (**Hint:** Factor the area binomial and recall that Area = width · length.)*

△ **113.**   △ **114.**

Factor each polynomial by grouping.

115. $x^{2n} + 2x^n + 3x^n + 6$
(**Hint:** Don't forget that $x^{2n} = x^n \cdot x^n$.)

116. $x^{2n} + 6x^n + 10x^n + 60$

117. $3x^{2n} + 21x^n - 5x^n - 35$

118. $12x^{2n} - 10x^n - 30x^n + 25$

6.2 Factoring Trinomials of the Form $x^2 + bx + c$ ▶

OBJECTIVES

1 Factor Trinomials of the Form $x^2 + bx + c$. ▶

2 Factor Out the Greatest Common Factor and Then Factor a Trinomial of the Form $x^2 + bx + c$. ▶

OBJECTIVE

1 Factoring Trinomials of the Form $x^2 + bx + c$ ▶

In this section, we factor trinomials of the form $x^2 + bx + c$, such as

$$x^2 + 4x + 3, \quad x^2 - 8x + 15, \quad x^2 + 4x - 12, \quad r^2 - r - 42$$

Notice that for these trinomials, the coefficient of the squared variable is 1.

Recall that factoring means to write as a product and that factoring and multiplying are reverse processes. Using the FOIL method of multiplying binomials, we have that

$$(x + 3)(x + 1) \overset{\text{F O I L}}{=} x^2 + 1x + 3x + 3$$
$$= x^2 + 4x + 3$$

Thus, a factored form of $x^2 + 4x + 3$ is $(x + 3)(x + 1)$.

Notice that the product of the first terms of the binomials is $x \cdot x = x^2$, the first term of the trinomial. Also, the product of the last two terms of the binomials is $3 \cdot 1 = 3$, the third term of the trinomial. The sum of these same terms is $3 + 1 = 4$, the coefficient of the middle term, x, of the trinomial.

The product of these numbers is 3.

$$x^2 + 4x + 3 = (x + 3)(x + 1)$$

The sum of these numbers is 4.

Many trinomials, such as the one above, factor into two binomials. To factor $x^2 + 7x + 10$, let's assume that it factors into two binomials and begin by writing two pairs of parentheses. The first term of the trinomial is x^2, so we use x and x as the first terms of the binomial factors.

$$x^2 + 7x + 10 = (x + \square)(x + \square)$$

To determine the last term of each binomial factor, we look for two integers whose product is 10 and whose sum is 7. Since our numbers must have a positive product and a positive sum, we list pairs of positive integer factors of 10 only.

Positive Factors of 10	Sum of Factors
1, 10	$1 + 10 = 11$
2, 5	$2 + 5 = 7$

The correct pair of numbers is 2 and 5 because their product is 10 and their sum is 7. Now we can fill in the last terms of the binomial factors.

$$x^2 + 7x + 10 = (x + 2)(x + 5)$$

Check: To see if we have factored correctly, multiply.

$$(x + 2)(x + 5) = x^2 + 5x + 2x + 10$$
$$= x^2 + 7x + 10 \qquad \text{Combine like terms.}$$

▶ **Helpful Hint**

Since multiplication is commutative, the factored form of $x^2 + 7x + 10$ can be written as either $(x + 2)(x + 5)$ or $(x + 5)(x + 2)$.

Factoring a Trinomial of the Form $x^2 + bx + c$

The factored form of $x^2 + bx + c$ is

The product of these numbers is c.

$$x^2 + bx + c = (x + \square)(x + \square)$$

The sum of these numbers is b.

EXAMPLE 1   Factor: $x^2 + 7x + 12$

Solution   We begin by writing the first terms of the binomial factors.

$$(x + \square)(x + \square)$$

Next we look for two numbers whose product is 12 and whose sum is 7. Since our numbers must have a positive product and a positive sum, we look at pairs of positive factors of 12 only.

(Continued on next page)

Positive Factors of 12	Sum of Factors
1, 12	13
2, 6	8
3, 4	7

Correct sum, so the numbers are 3 and 4.

Thus, $x^2 + 7x + 12 = (x + 3)(x + 4)$

Check: $(x + 3)(x + 4) = x^2 + 4x + 3x + 12 = x^2 + 7x + 12.$ □

PRACTICE
1 Factor $x^2 + 5x + 6$.

EXAMPLE 2 Factor: $x^2 - 12x + 35$

Solution Again, we begin by writing the first terms of the binomials.

$$(x + \square)(x + \square)$$

Now we look for two numbers whose product is 35 and whose sum is -12. Since our numbers must have a positive product and a negative sum, we look at pairs of negative factors of 35 only.

Negative Factors of 35	Sum of Factors
$-1, -35$	-36
$-5, -7$	-12

Correct sum, so the numbers are -5 and -7.

Thus, $x^2 - 12x + 35 = (x - 5)(x - 7)$

Check: To check, multiply $(x - 5)(x - 7)$. □

PRACTICE
2 Factor $x^2 - 17x + 70$.

EXAMPLE 3 Factor: $x^2 + 4x - 12$

Solution $x^2 + 4x - 12 = (x + \square)(x + \square)$

We look for two numbers whose product is -12 and whose sum is 4. Since our numbers must have a negative product, we look at pairs of factors with opposite signs.

Factors of −12	Sum of Factors
$-1, 12$	11
$1, -12$	-11
$-2, 6$	4
$2, -6$	-4
$-3, 4$	1
$3, -4$	-1

Correct sum, so the numbers are -2 and 6.

Thus, $x^2 + 4x - 12 = (x - 2)(x + 6)$ □

PRACTICE
3 Factor $x^2 + 5x - 14$.

EXAMPLE 4   Factor: $r^2 - r - 42$

Solution   Because the variable in this trinomial is r, the first term of each binomial factor is r.

$$r^2 - r - 42 = (r + \Box)(r + \Box)$$

Now we look for two numbers whose product is -42 and whose sum is -1, the numerical coefficient of r. The numbers are 6 and -7. Therefore,

$$r^2 - r - 42 = (r + 6)(r - 7)$$ □

PRACTICE
4   Factor $p^2 - 2p - 63$.

EXAMPLE 5   Factor: $a^2 + 2a + 10$

Solution   Look for two numbers whose product is 10 and whose sum is 2. Neither 1 and 10 nor 2 and 5 give the required sum, 2. We conclude that $a^2 + 2a + 10$ is not factorable with integers. A polynomial such as $a^2 + 2a + 10$ is called a **prime polynomial.**   □

PRACTICE
5   Factor $b^2 + 5b + 1$.

EXAMPLE 6   Factor: $x^2 + 7xy + 6y^2$

Solution

$$x^2 + 7xy + 6y^2 = (x + \Box)(x + \Box)$$

Recall that the middle term $7xy$ is the same as $7yx$. Thus, we can see that $7y$ is the "coefficient" of x. We then look for two terms whose product is $6y^2$ and whose sum is $7y$. The terms are $6y$ and $1y$ or $6y$ and y because $6y \cdot y = 6y^2$ and $6y + y = 7y$. Therefore,

$$x^2 + 7xy + 6y^2 = (x + 6y)(x + y)$$ □

PRACTICE
6   Factor $x^2 + 7xy + 12y^2$.

EXAMPLE 7   Factor: $x^4 + 5x^2 + 6$

Solution   As usual, we begin by writing the first terms of the binomials. Since the greatest power of x in this polynomial is x^4, we write

$$(x^2 + \Box)(x^2 + \Box) \quad \text{since } x^2 \cdot x^2 = x^4$$

Now we look for two factors of 6 whose sum is 5. The numbers are 2 and 3. Thus,

$$x^4 + 5x^2 + 6 = (x^2 + 2)(x^2 + 3)$$ □

PRACTICE
7   Factor $x^4 + 13x^2 + 12$.

If the terms of a polynomial are not written in descending powers of the variable, you may want to do so before factoring.

EXAMPLE 8   Factor: $40 - 13t + t^2$

Solution   First, we rearrange terms so that the trinomial is written in descending powers of t.

$$40 - 13t + t^2 = t^2 - 13t + 40$$

(Continued on next page)

Next, try to factor.

$$t^2 - 13t + 40 = (t + \square)(t + \square)$$

Now we look for two factors of 40 whose sum is -13. The numbers are -8 and -5. Thus,

$$t^2 - 13t + 40 = (t - 8)(t - 5)$$ □

PRACTICE
8   Factor $48 - 14x + x^2$.

The following sign patterns may be useful when factoring trinomials.

> ▶ **Helpful Hint**
>
> A positive constant in a trinomial tells us to look for two numbers with the same sign. The sign of the coefficient of the middle term tells us whether the signs are both positive or both negative.
>
> both   same   both   same
> positive   sign   negative   sign
>   ↓   ↙   ↓   ↙
> $$x^2 + 10x + 16 = (x + 2)(x + 8) \qquad x^2 - 10x + 16 = (x - 2)(x - 8)$$
>
> A negative constant in a trinomial tells us to look for two numbers with opposite signs.
>
>   opposite   opposite
>   signs   signs
>   ↓   ↓
> $$x^2 + 6x - 16 = (x + 8)(x - 2) \qquad x^2 - 6x - 16 = (x - 8)(x + 2)$$

OBJECTIVE
2   **Factoring Out the Greatest Common Factor**

Remember that the first step in factoring any polynomial is to factor out the greatest common factor (if there is one other than 1 or -1).

EXAMPLE 9   Factor: $3m^2 - 24m - 60$

Solution   First we factor out the greatest common factor, 3, from each term.

$$3m^2 - 24m - 60 = 3(m^2 - 8m - 20)$$

Now we factor $m^2 - 8m - 20$ by looking for two factors of -20 whose sum is -8. The factors are -10 and 2. Therefore, the complete factored form is

$$3m^2 - 24m - 60 = 3(m + 2)(m - 10)$$ □

> ▶ **Helpful Hint**
>
> Remember to write the common factor 3 as part of the factored form.

PRACTICE
9   Factor $4x^2 - 24x + 36$.

EXAMPLE 10   Factor: $2x^4 - 26x^3 + 84x^2$

Solution

$$2x^4 - 26x^3 + 84x^2 = 2x^2(x^2 - 13x + 42) \qquad \text{Factor out common factor, } 2x^2.$$
$$= 2x^2(x - 6)(x - 7) \qquad \text{Factor } x^2 - 13x + 42.$$ □

PRACTICE
10   Factor $3y^4 - 18y^3 - 21y^2$.

Vocabulary, Readiness & Video Check

Fill in each blank with "true" or "false."

1. To factor $x^2 + 7x + 6$, we look for two numbers whose product is 6 and whose sum is 7. _____

2. We can write the factorization $(y + 2)(y + 4)$ also as $(y + 4)(y + 2)$. _____

3. The factorization $(4x - 12)(x - 5)$ is completely factored. _____

4. The factorization $(x + 2y)(x + y)$ may also be written as $(x + 2y)^2$. _____

Complete each factored form.

5. $x^2 + 9x + 20 = (x + 4)(x \quad\quad)$

6. $x^2 + 12x + 35 = (x + 5)(x \quad\quad)$

7. $x^2 - 7x + 12 = (x - 4)(x \quad\quad)$

8. $x^2 - 13x + 22 = (x - 2)(x \quad\quad)$

9. $x^2 + 4x + 4 = (x + 2)(x \quad\quad)$

10. $x^2 + 10x + 24 = (x + 6)(x \quad\quad)$

Martin-Gay Interactive Videos

See Video 6.2

Watch the section lecture video and answer the following questions.

OBJECTIVE 1

11. In Example 2, why are only negative factors of 15 considered?

OBJECTIVE 2

12. In Example 5, we know we need a positive and a negative factor of -10. How do we determine which factor is negative?

6.2 Exercise Set

MyMathLab®

Factor each trinomial completely. If a polynomial can't be factored, write "prime." See Examples 1 through 8.

1. $x^2 + 7x + 6$

2. $x^2 + 6x + 8$

3. $y^2 - 10y + 9$

4. $y^2 - 12y + 11$

5. $x^2 - 6x + 9$

6. $x^2 - 10x + 25$

7. $x^2 - 3x - 18$

8. $x^2 - x - 30$

9. $x^2 + 3x - 70$

10. $x^2 + 4x - 32$

11. $x^2 + 5x + 2$

12. $x^2 - 7x + 5$

13. $x^2 + 8xy + 15y^2$

14. $x^2 + 6xy + 8y^2$

15. $a^4 - 2a^2 - 15$

16. $y^4 - 3y^2 - 70$

17. $13 + 14m + m^2$

18. $17 + 18n + n^2$

19. $10t - 24 + t^2$

20. $6q - 27 + q^2$

21. $a^2 - 10ab + 16b^2$

22. $a^2 - 9ab + 18b^2$

MIXED PRACTICE

Factor each trinomial completely. Some of these trinomials contain a greatest common factor (other than 1). Don't forget to factor out the GCF first. See Examples 1 through 10.

23. $2z^2 + 20z + 32$

24. $3x^2 + 30x + 63$

25. $2x^3 - 18x^2 + 40x$

26. $3x^3 - 12x^2 - 36x$

27. $x^2 - 3xy - 4y^2$

28. $x^2 - 4xy - 77y^2$

29. $x^2 + 15x + 36$

30. $x^2 + 19x + 60$

31. $x^2 - x - 2$

32. $x^2 - 5x - 14$

33. $r^2 - 16r + 48$

34. $r^2 - 10r + 21$

35. $x^2 + xy - 2y^2$

36. $x^2 - xy - 6y^2$
37. $3x^2 + 9x - 30$
38. $4x^2 - 4x - 48$
39. $3x^2 - 60x + 108$
40. $2x^2 - 24x + 70$
41. $x^2 - 18x - 144$
42. $x^2 + x - 42$
43. $r^2 - 3r + 6$
44. $x^2 + 4x - 10$
45. $x^2 - 8x + 15$
46. $x^2 - 9x + 14$
47. $6x^3 + 54x^2 + 120x$
48. $3x^3 + 3x^2 - 126x$
49. $4x^2y + 4xy - 12y$
50. $3x^2y - 9xy + 45y$
51. $x^2 - 4x - 21$
52. $x^2 - 4x - 32$
53. $x^2 + 7xy + 10y^2$
54. $x^2 - 2xy - 15y^2$
55. $64 + 24t + 2t^2$
56. $50 + 20t + 2t^2$
57. $x^3 - 2x^2 - 24x$
58. $x^3 - 3x^2 - 28x$
59. $2t^5 - 14t^4 + 24t^3$
60. $3x^6 + 30x^5 + 72x^4$
61. $5x^3y - 25x^2y^2 - 120xy^3$
62. $7a^3b - 35a^2b^2 + 42ab^3$
63. $162 - 45m + 3m^2$
64. $48 - 20n + 2n^2$
65. $-x^2 + 12x - 11$ (Factor out -1 first.)
66. $-x^2 + 8x - 7$ (Factor out -1 first.)
67. $\frac{1}{2}y^2 - \frac{9}{2}y - 11$ (Factor out $\frac{1}{2}$ first.)
68. $\frac{1}{3}y^2 - \frac{5}{3}y - 8$ (Factor out $\frac{1}{3}$ first.)
69. $x^3y^2 + x^2y - 20x$
70. $a^2b^3 + ab^2 - 30b$

REVIEW AND PREVIEW

Multiply. See Section 5.3.

71. $(2x + 1)(x + 5)$
72. $(3x + 2)(x + 4)$
73. $(5y - 4)(3y - 1)$
74. $(4z - 7)(7z - 1)$
75. $(a + 3b)(9a - 4b)$
76. $(y - 5x)(6y + 5x)$

CONCEPT EXTENSIONS

77. Write a polynomial that factors as $(x - 3)(x + 8)$.
78. To factor $x^2 + 13x + 42$, think of two numbers whose _____ is 42 and whose _____ is 13.

Complete each sentence in your own words.

79. If $x^2 + bx + c$ is factorable and c is negative, then the signs of the last-term factors of the binomials are opposite because…
80. If $x^2 + bx + c$ is factorable and c is positive, then the signs of the last-term factors of the binomials are the same because…

Remember that perimeter means distance around. Write the perimeter of each rectangle as a simplified polynomial. Then factor the polynomial.

81.
$4x + 33$
$x^2 + 10x$

82.
$12x^2$
$2x^3 + 16x$

83. An object is thrown upward from the top of an 80-foot building with an initial velocity of 64 feet per second. Neglecting air resistance, the height of the object after t seconds is given by $-16t^2 + 64t + 80$. Factor this polynomial.

$-16t^2 + 64t + 80$

84. An object is thrown upward from the top of a 112-foot building with an initial velocity of 96 feet per second. Neglecting air resistance, the height of the object after t seconds is given by $-16t^2 + 96t + 112$. Factor this polynomial.

$-16t^2 + 96t + 112$

Factor each trinomial completely.

85. $x^2 + \dfrac{1}{2}x + \dfrac{1}{16}$

86. $x^2 + x + \dfrac{1}{4}$

87. $z^2(x + 1) - 3z(x + 1) - 70(x + 1)$

88. $y^2(x + 1) - 2y(x + 1) - 15(x + 1)$

Factor each trinomial. (**Hint:** *Notice that $x^{2n} + 4x^n + 3$ factors as $(x^n + 1)(x^n + 3)$.* **Remember:** *$x^n \cdot x^n = x^{n+n}$ or x^{2n}.*)

89. $x^{2n} + 8x^n - 20$

90. $x^{2n} + 5x^n + 6$

Find a positive value of c so that each trinomial is factorable.

91. $x^2 + 6x + c$

92. $t^2 + 8t + c$

93. $y^2 - 4y + c$

94. $n^2 - 16n + c$

Find a positive value of b so that each trinomial is factorable.

95. $x^2 + bx + 15$

96. $y^2 + by + 20$

97. $m^2 + bm - 27$

98. $x^2 + bx - 14$

6.3 Factoring Trinomials of the Form $ax^2 + bx + c$ and Perfect Square Trinomials

OBJECTIVES

1 Factor Trinomials of the Form $ax^2 + bx + c$, Where $a \neq 1$.

2 Factor Out a GCF Before Factoring a Trinomial of the Form $ax^2 + bx + c$.

3 Factor Perfect Square Trinomials.

OBJECTIVE

1 Factoring Trinomials of the Form $ax^2 + bx + c$

In this section, we factor trinomials of the form $ax^2 + bx + c$, such as

$$3x^2 + 11x + 6, \qquad 8x^2 - 22x + 5, \qquad \text{and} \qquad 2x^2 + 13x - 7$$

Notice that the coefficient of the squared variable in these trinomials is a number other than 1. We will factor these trinomials using a trial-and-check method based on our work in the last section.

To begin, let's review the relationship between the numerical coefficients of the trinomial and the numerical coefficients of its factored form. For example, since $(2x + 1)(x + 6) = 2x^2 + 13x + 6$,

a factored form of $2x^2 + 13x + 6$ is $(2x + 1)(x + 6)$

Notice that $2x$ and x are factors of $2x^2$, the first term of the trinomial. Also, 6 and 1 are factors of 6, the last term of the trinomial, as shown:

$$2x^2 + 13x + 6 = (2x + 1)(x + 6)$$

with $2x \cdot x$ and $1 \cdot 6$

Also notice that $13x$, the middle term, is the sum of the following products:

$$2x^2 + 13x + 6 = (2x + 1)(x + 6)$$

$1x$

$+12x$

$13x$ Middle term

Let's use this pattern to factor $5x^2 + 7x + 2$. First, we find factors of $5x^2$. Since all numerical coefficients in this trinomial are positive, we will use factors with positive numerical coefficients only. Thus, the factors of $5x^2$ are $5x$ and x. Let's try these factors as first terms of the binomials. Thus far, we have

$$5x^2 + 7x + 2 = (5x + \square)(x + \square)$$

Next, we need to find positive factors of 2. Positive factors of 2 are 1 and 2. Now we try possible combinations of these factors as second terms of the binomials until we obtain a middle term of $7x$.

$$(5x + 1)(x + 2) = 5x^2 + 11x + 2$$

$$\begin{array}{r} 1x \\ +10x \\ \hline 11x \end{array} \longrightarrow \text{Incorrect middle term}$$

Let's try switching factors 2 and 1.

$$(5x + 2)(x + 1) = 5x^2 + 7x + 2$$

$$\begin{array}{r} 2x \\ +5x \\ \hline 7x \end{array} \longrightarrow \text{Correct middle term}$$

Thus the factored form of $5x^2 + 7x + 2$ is $(5x + 2)(x + 1)$. To check, we multiply $(5x + 2)$ and $(x + 1)$. The product is $5x^2 + 7x + 2$.

EXAMPLE 1 Factor: $3x^2 + 11x + 6$

Solution Since all numerical coefficients are positive, we use factors with positive numerical coefficients. We first find factors of $3x^2$.

$$\text{Factors of } 3x^2: \quad 3x^2 = 3x \cdot x$$

If factorable, the trinomial will be of the form

$$3x^2 + 11x + 6 = (3x + \square)(x + \square)$$

Next we factor 6.

$$\text{Factors of 6:} \quad 6 = 1 \cdot 6, \quad 6 = 2 \cdot 3$$

Now we try combinations of factors of 6 until a middle term of $11x$ is obtained. Let's try 1 and 6 first.

$$(3x + 1)(x + 6) = 3x^2 + 19x + 6$$

$$\begin{array}{r} 1x \\ +18x \\ \hline 19x \end{array} \longrightarrow \textbf{Incorrect} \text{ middle term}$$

Now let's next try 6 and 1.

$$(3x + 6)(x + 1)$$

Before multiplying, notice that the terms of the factor $3x + 6$ have a common factor of 3. The terms of the original trinomial $3x^2 + 11x + 6$ have no common factor other than 1, so the terms of its factors will also contain no common factor other than 1. This means that $(3x + 6)(x + 1)$ is not a factored form.

Next let's try 2 and 3 as last terms.

$$(3x + 2)(x + 3) = 3x^2 + 11x + 6$$

$$\begin{array}{r} 2x \\ +9x \\ \hline 11x \end{array} \longrightarrow \textbf{Correct} \text{ middle term}$$

Thus a factored form of $3x^2 + 11x + 6$ is $(3x + 2)(x + 3)$. $\qquad\square$

PRACTICE

1 Factor: $2x^2 + 11x + 15$.

> ▶ **Helpful Hint**
> If the terms of a trinomial have no common factor (other than 1), then the terms of neither of its binomial factors will contain a common factor (other than 1).

✓ CONCEPT CHECK

Do the terms of $3x^2 + 29x + 18$ have a common factor? Without multiplying, decide which of the following factored forms could not be a factored form of $3x^2 + 29x + 18$.

a. $(3x + 18)(x + 1)$ **b.** $(3x + 2)(x + 9)$ **c.** $(3x + 6)(x + 3)$ **d.** $(3x + 9)(x + 2)$

EXAMPLE 2   Factor: $8x^2 - 22x + 5$

Solution   Factors of $8x^2$: $8x^2 = 8x \cdot x$, $8x^2 = 4x \cdot 2x$

We'll try $8x$ and x.

$$8x^2 - 22x + 5 = (8x + \square)(x + \square)$$

Since the middle term, $-22x$, has a negative numerical coefficient, we factor 5 into negative factors.

$$\text{Factors of 5:}   5 = -1 \cdot -5$$

Let's try -1 and -5.

$$(8x - 1)(x - 5) = 8x^2 - 41x + 5$$

$$\begin{aligned} -1x \\ +(-40x) \\ \hline -41x \end{aligned} \longrightarrow \text{Incorrect middle term}$$

Now let's try -5 and -1.

$$(8x - 5)(x - 1) = 8x^2 - 13x + 5$$

$$\begin{aligned} -5x \\ +(-8x) \\ \hline -13x \end{aligned} \longrightarrow \text{Incorrect middle term}$$

Don't give up yet! We can still try other factors of $8x^2$. Let's try $4x$ and $2x$ with -1 and -5.

$$(4x - 1)(2x - 5) = 8x^2 - 22x + 5$$

$$\begin{aligned} -2x \\ +(-20x) \\ \hline -22x \end{aligned} \longrightarrow \text{Correct middle term}$$

A factored form of $8x^2 - 22x + 5$ is $(4x - 1)(2x - 5)$.   □

PRACTICE
2   Factor: $15x^2 - 22x + 8$.

·· ■

EXAMPLE 3   Factor: $2x^2 + 13x - 7$

Solution   Factors of $2x^2$: $2x^2 = 2x \cdot x$

Factors of -7: $-7 = -1 \cdot 7$, $-7 = 1 \cdot -7$

Answers to Concept Check:
no; a, c, d

(Continued on next page)

We try possible combinations of these factors:

$$(2x + 1)(x - 7) = 2x^2 - 13x - 7 \quad \text{Incorrect middle term}$$
$$(2x - 1)(x + 7) = 2x^2 + 13x - 7 \quad \text{Correct middle term}$$

A factored form of $2x^2 + 13x - 7$ is $(2x - 1)(x + 7)$. □

PRACTICE
3 Factor: $4x^2 + 11x - 3$.

EXAMPLE 4 Factor: $10x^2 - 13xy - 3y^2$

Solution Factors of $10x^2$: $10x^2 = 10x \cdot x$, $10x^2 = 2x \cdot 5x$

Factors of $-3y^2$: $-3y^2 = -3y \cdot y$, $-3y^2 = 3y \cdot -y$

We try some combinations of these factors:

$$\begin{array}{ccc} & \text{Correct} & \text{Correct} \\ & \downarrow & \downarrow \end{array}$$
$$(10x - 3y)(x + y) = 10x^2 + 7xy - 3y^2$$
$$(x + 3y)(10x - y) = 10x^2 + 29xy - 3y^2$$
$$(5x + 3y)(2x - y) = 10x^2 + xy - 3y^2$$
$$(2x - 3y)(5x + y) = 10x^2 - 13xy - 3y^2 \quad \text{Correct middle term}$$

A factored form of $10x^2 - 13xy - 3y^2$ is $(2x - 3y)(5x + y)$. □

PRACTICE
4 Factor: $21x^2 + 11xy - 2y^2$.

EXAMPLE 5 Factor: $3x^4 - 5x^2 - 8$

Solution Factors of $3x^4$: $3x^4 = 3x^2 \cdot x^2$

Factors of -8: $-8 = -2 \cdot 4, 2 \cdot -4, -1 \cdot 8, 1 \cdot -8$

Try combinations of these factors:

$$\begin{array}{ccc} & \text{Correct} & \text{Correct} \\ & \downarrow & \downarrow \end{array}$$
$$(3x^2 - 2)(x^2 + 4) = 3x^4 + 10x^2 - 8$$
$$(3x^2 + 4)(x^2 - 2) = 3x^4 - 2x^2 - 8$$
$$(3x^2 + 8)(x^2 - 1) = 3x^4 + 5x^2 - 8 \quad \text{Incorrect sign on middle term, so switch signs in binomial factors.}$$
$$(3x^2 - 8)(x^2 + 1) = 3x^4 - 5x^2 - 8 \quad \text{Correct middle term.}$$

A factored form of $3x^4 - 5x^2 - 8$ is $(3x^2 - 8)(x^2 + 1)$. □

PRACTICE
5 Factor: $2x^4 - 5x^2 - 7$.

▶ **Helpful Hint**
Study the last two lines of Example 5. If a factoring attempt gives you a middle term whose numerical coefficient is the opposite of the desired numerical coefficient, try switching the signs of the last terms in the binomials.

Switched signs $$(3x^2 + 8)(x^2 - 1) = 3x^4 + 5x^2 - 8 \quad \text{Middle term: } +5x^2$$
$$(3x^2 - 8)(x^2 + 1) = 3x^4 - 5x^2 - 8 \quad \text{Middle term: } -5x^2$$

OBJECTIVE

2   Factoring Out the Greatest Common Factor

Don't forget that the first step in factoring any polynomial is to look for a common factor to factor out.

EXAMPLE 6   Factor: $24x^4 + 40x^3 + 6x^2$

Solution   Notice that all three terms have a common factor of $2x^2$. Thus we factor out $2x^2$ first.

$$24x^4 + 40x^3 + 6x^2 = 2x^2(12x^2 + 20x + 3)$$

Next we factor $12x^2 + 20x + 3$.

Factors of $12x^2$: $12x^2 = 4x \cdot 3x$, $12x^2 = 12x \cdot x$, $12x^2 = 6x \cdot 2x$

Since all terms in the trinomial have positive numerical coefficients, we factor 3 using positive factors only.

Factors of 3: $3 = 1 \cdot 3$

We try some combinations of the factors.

$$2x^2(4x + 3)(3x + 1) = 2x^2(12x^2 + 13x + 3)$$
$$2x^2(12x + 1)(x + 3) = 2x^2(12x^2 + 37x + 3)$$
$$2x^2(2x + 3)(6x + 1) = 2x^2(12x^2 + 20x + 3) \quad \text{Correct middle term}$$

> ▶ **Helpful Hint**
>
> Don't forget to include the common factor in the factored form.

A factored form of $24x^4 + 40x^3 + 6x^2$ is $2x^2(2x + 3)(6x + 1)$.   □

PRACTICE

6   Factor: $3x^3 + 17x^2 + 10x$

When the term containing the squared variable has a negative coefficient, you may want to first factor out a common factor of -1.

EXAMPLE 7   Factor: $-6x^2 - 13x + 5$

Solution   We begin by factoring out a common factor of -1.

$$-6x^2 - 13x + 5 = -1(6x^2 + 13x - 5) \quad \text{Factor out } -1.$$
$$= -1(3x - 1)(2x + 5) \quad \text{Factor } 6x^2 + 13x - 5.$$ □

PRACTICE

7   Factor: $-8x^2 + 2x + 3$

OBJECTIVE

3   Factoring Perfect Square Trinomials

A trinomial that is the square of a binomial is called a **perfect square trinomial.** For example,

$$(x + 3)^2 = (x + 3)(x + 3)$$
$$= x^2 + 6x + 9$$

Thus $x^2 + 6x + 9$ is a perfect square trinomial.

In Chapter 5, we discovered special product formulas for squaring binomials.

$$(a + b)^2 = a^2 + 2ab + b^2 \quad \text{and} \quad (a - b)^2 = a^2 - 2ab + b^2$$

Because multiplication and factoring are reverse processes, we can now use these special products to help us factor perfect square trinomials. If we reverse these equations, we have the following.

> **Factoring Perfect Square Trinomials**
> $$a^2 + 2ab + b^2 = (a + b)^2$$
> $$a^2 - 2ab + b^2 = (a - b)^2$$

> ▶ **Helpful Hint**
> Notice that for both given forms of a perfect square trinomial, the last term is positive. This is because the last term is a square.

To use these equations to help us factor, we must first be able to recognize a perfect square trinomial. A trinomial is a perfect square when

1. two terms, a^2 and b^2, are squares and
2. the remaining term is $2 \cdot a \cdot b$ or $-2 \cdot a \cdot b$. That is, this term is twice the product of a and b, or its opposite.

When a trinomial fits this description, its factored form is $(a + b)^2$ or $(a - b)^2$.

EXAMPLE 8   Factor: $x^2 + 12x + 36$

Solution   First, is this a perfect square trinomial?

$$x^2 + 12x + 36$$

1. $x^2 = (x)^2$ and $36 = 6^2$.
2. Is the middle term $2 \cdot x \cdot 6$? Yes, $2 \cdot x \cdot 6 = 12x$, the middle term.

Thus, $x^2 + 12x + 36$ factors as $(x + 6)^2$.   □

PRACTICE
8   Factor $x^2 + 14x + 49$.

EXAMPLE 9   Factor: $25x^2 + 25xy + 4y^2$

Solution   Is this a perfect square trinomial?

$$25x^2 + 25xy + 4y^2$$

1. $25x^2 = (5x)^2$ and $4y^2 = (2y)^2$.
2. Is the middle term $2 \cdot 5x \cdot 2y$? **No**, $2 \cdot 5x \cdot 2y = 20xy$, **not** the middle term $25xy$.

Therefore, $25x^2 + 25xy + 4y^2$ is not a perfect square trinomial. It is factorable, though. Using earlier techniques, we find that $25x^2 + 25xy + 4y^2$ factors as $(5x + 4y)(5x + y)$.   □

> ▶ **Helpful Hint**
> A perfect square trinomial can also be factored by other methods.

PRACTICE
9   Factor $4x^2 + 20xy + 9y^2$.

EXAMPLE 10   Factor: $4m^4 - 4m^2 + 1$

Solution   Is this a perfect square trinomial?

$$4m^4 - 4m^2 + 1$$

1. $4m^4 = (2m^2)^2$ and $1 = 1^2$.
2. Is the middle term $2 \cdot 2m^2 \cdot 1$ or $-2 \cdot 2m^2 \cdot 1$? Yes, $-2 \cdot 2m^2 \cdot 1 = -4m^2$, the middle term.

Thus, $4m^4 - 4m^2 + 1$ factors as $(2m^2 - 1)^2$.   □

PRACTICE
10   Factor $36n^4 - 12n^2 + 1$.

EXAMPLE 11   Factor: $162x^3 - 144x^2 + 32x$

Solution   Don't forget to look first for a common factor. There is a greatest common factor of $2x$ in this trinomial.

$$162x^3 - 144x^2 + 32x = 2x(81x^2 - 72x + 16)$$
$$= 2x[(9x)^2 - 2 \cdot 9x \cdot 4 + 4^2]$$
$$= 2x(9x - 4)^2$$

PRACTICE

11   Factor $12x^3 - 84x^2 + 147x$.

Vocabulary, Readiness & Video Check

Use the choices below to fill in each blank. Some choices will be used more than once and some not used at all.

| $5y^2$ | $(x + 5y)^2$ | perfect square trinomial |
| $(5y)^2$ | $(x - 5y)^2$ | perfect square binomial |

1. A _____ is a trinomial that is the square of a binomial.

2. The term $25y^2$ written as a square is _____.

3. The expression $x^2 + 10xy + 25y^2$ is called a _____.

4. The factorization $(x + 5y)(x + 5y)$ may also be written as _____.

Complete each factorization.

5. $2x^2 + 5x + 3$ factors as $(2x + 3)(\ ?\ )$.
   a. $(x + 3)$ **b.** $(2x + 1)$ **c.** $(3x + 4)$ **d.** $(x + 1)$

6. $7x^2 + 9x + 2$ factors as $(7x + 2)(\ ?\ )$.
   a. $(3x + 1)$ **b.** $(x + 1)$ **c.** $(x + 2)$ **d.** $(7x + 1)$

Martin-Gay Interactive Videos

See Video 6.3

Watch the section lecture video and answer the following questions.

OBJECTIVE 1   7. From ▭ Example 1, explain in general terms how you would go about factoring a trinomial with a first-term coefficient $\neq 1$.

OBJECTIVE 2   8. From ▭ Examples 3 and 5, how can factoring the GCF from a trinomial help you save time when trying to factor the remaining trinomial?

OBJECTIVE 3   9. Describe in words the special patterns that the trinomials in ▭ Examples 7 and 8 have that identify them as perfect square trinomials.

6.3   Exercise Set   MyMathLab®

Complete each factored form. See Examples 1 through 5, and 8 through 10.

1. $5x^2 + 22x + 8 = (5x + 2)(\quad)$
2. $2y^2 + 27y + 25 = (2y + 25)(\quad)$
3. $50x^2 + 15x - 2 = (5x + 2)(\quad)$
4. $6y^2 + 11y - 10 = (2y + 5)(\quad)$
5. $25x^2 - 20x + 4 = (5x - 2)(\quad)$
6. $4y^2 - 20y + 25 = (2y - 5)(\quad)$

Factor completely. See Examples 1 through 5.

7. $2x^2 + 13x + 15$
8. $3x^2 + 8x + 4$
9. $8y^2 - 17y + 9$
10. $21x^2 - 31x + 10$
11. $2x^2 - 9x - 5$
12. $36r^2 - 5r - 24$
13. $20r^2 + 27r - 8$

14. $3x^2 + 20x - 63$

▶ 15. $10x^2 + 31x + 3$

16. $12x^2 + 17x + 5$

17. $2m^2 + 17m + 10$

18. $3n^2 + 20n + 5$

19. $6x^2 - 13xy + 5y^2$

20. $8x^2 - 14xy + 3y^2$

21. $15m^2 - 16m - 15$

22. $25n^2 - 5n - 6$

Factor completely. See Examples 1 through 7.

23. $12x^3 + 11x^2 + 2x$

24. $8a^3 + 14a^2 + 3a$

25. $21b^2 - 48b - 45$

26. $12x^2 - 14x - 10$

27. $7z + 12z^2 - 12$

28. $16t + 15t^2 - 15$

29. $6x^2y^2 - 2xy^2 - 60y^2$

30. $8x^2y + 34xy - 84y$

▶ 31. $4x^2 - 8x - 21$

32. $6x^2 - 11x - 10$

33. $-x^2 + 2x + 24$

34. $-x^2 + 4x + 21$

▶ 35. $4x^3 - 9x^2 - 9x$

36. $6x^3 - 31x^2 + 5x$

37. $24x^2 - 58x + 9$

38. $36x^2 + 55x - 14$

Factor each perfect square trinomial completely. See Examples 8 through 11.

▶ 39. $x^2 + 22x + 121$

40. $x^2 + 18x + 81$

41. $x^2 - 16x + 64$

42. $x^2 - 12x + 36$

43. $16a^2 - 24a + 9$

44. $25x^2 - 20x + 4$

45. $x^4 + 4x^2 + 4$

46. $m^4 + 10m^2 + 25$

47. $2n^2 - 28n + 98$

48. $3y^2 - 6y + 3$

49. $16y^2 + 40y + 25$

50. $9y^2 + 48y + 64$

MIXED PRACTICE

Factor each trinomial completely. See Examples 1 through 11 and Section 6.2.

51. $2x^2 - 7x - 99$

52. $2x^2 + 7x - 72$

53. $24x^2 + 41x + 12$

54. $24x^2 - 49x + 15$

55. $3a^2 + 10ab + 3b^2$

56. $2a^2 + 11ab + 5b^2$

57. $-9x + 20 + x^2$

58. $-7x + 12 + x^2$

59. $p^2 + 12pq + 36q^2$

60. $m^2 + 20mn + 100n^2$

61. $x^2y^2 - 10xy + 25$

62. $x^2y^2 - 14xy + 49$

63. $40a^2b + 9ab - 9b$

64. $24y^2x + 7yx - 5x$

▶ 65. $30x^3 + 38x^2 + 12x$

66. $6x^3 - 28x^2 + 16x$

67. $6y^3 - 8y^2 - 30y$

68. $12x^3 - 34x^2 + 24x$

69. $10x^4 + 25x^3y - 15x^2y^2$

70. $42x^4 - 99x^3y - 15x^2y^2$

▶ 71. $-14x^2 + 39x - 10$

72. $-15x^2 + 26x - 8$

73. $16p^4 - 40p^3 + 25p^2$

74. $9q^4 - 42q^3 + 49q^2$

75. $x + 3x^2 - 2$

76. $y + 8y^2 - 9$

77. $8x^2 + 6xy - 27y^2$

78. $54a^2 + 39ab - 8b^2$

79. $1 + 6x^2 + x^4$

80. $1 + 16x^2 + x^4$

▶ 81. $9x^2 - 24xy + 16y^2$

82. $25x^2 - 60xy + 36y^2$

83. $18x^2 - 9x - 14$

84. $42a^2 - 43a + 6$

85. $-27t + 7t^2 - 4$

86. $-3t + 4t^2 - 7$

87. $49p^2 - 7p - 2$

88. $3r^2 + 10r - 8$

89. $m^3 + 18m^2 + 81m$

90. $y^3 + 12y^2 + 36y$

91. $5x^2y^2 + 20xy + 1$

92. $3a^2b^2 + 12ab + 1$

93. $6a^5 + 37a^3b^2 + 6ab^4$

94. $5m^5 + 26m^3h^2 + 5mh^4$

REVIEW AND PREVIEW

Multiply the following. See Section 5.4.

95. $(x - 2)(x + 2)$

96. $(y^2 + 3)(y^2 - 3)$

97. $(a + 3)(a^2 - 3a + 9)$

98. $(z - 2)(z^2 + 2z + 4)$

The following graph shows the percent of text message users in each age group. See Section 3.1.

Data from CellSigns, Inc.

99. What range of ages shown has the highest percent of text message users?

100. What range of ages shown has the lowest percent of text message users?

101. Describe any trend you see.

102. Why don't the percents shown in the graph add to 100%?

CONCEPT EXTENSIONS

See the Concept Check in this section.

103. Do the terms of $4x^2 + 19x + 12$ have a common factor (other than 1)?

104. Without multiplying, decide which of the following factored forms is not a factored form of $4x^2 + 19x + 12$.

   a. $(2x + 4)(2x + 3)$ **b.** $(4x + 4)(x + 3)$
   c. $(4x + 3)(x + 4)$ **d.** $(2x + 2)(2x + 6)$

105. Describe a perfect square trinomial.

106. Write the perfect square trinomial that factors as $(x + 3y)^2$.

Write the perimeter of each figure as a simplified polynomial. Then factor the polynomial.

107.

$3x^2 + 1$ $6x + 4$ $x^2 + 15x$

108.

$3y^2$ $-22y + 7$

Factor each trinomial completely.

109. $4x^2 + 2x + \dfrac{1}{4}$

110. $27x^2 + 2x - \dfrac{1}{9}$

111. $4x^2(y - 1)^2 + 10x(y - 1)^2 + 25(y - 1)^2$

112. $3x^2(a + 3)^3 - 10x(a + 3)^3 + 25(a + 3)^3$

113. Fill in the blank so that $x^2 + \underline{\quad} x + 16$ is a perfect square trinomial.

114. Fill in the blank so that $9x^2 + \underline{\quad} x + 25$ is a perfect square trinomial.

The area of the largest square in the figure is $(a + b)^2$. Use this figure to answer Exercises 115 and 116.

△ **115.** Write the area of the largest square as the sum of the areas of the smaller squares and rectangles.

△ **116.** What factoring formula from this section is visually represented by this square?

Find a positive value of b so that each trinomial is factorable.

117. $3x^2 + bx - 5$ **118.** $2y^2 + by + 3$

Find a positive value of c so that each trinomial is factorable.

119. $5x^2 + 7x + c$ **120.** $11y^2 - 40y + c$

Factor completely. Don't forget to first factor out the greatest common factor.

121. $-12x^3y^2 + 3x^2y^2 + 15xy^2$

122. $-12r^3x^2 + 38r^2x^2 + 14rx^2$

123. $4x^2(y - 1)^2 + 20x(y - 1)^2 + 25(y - 1)^2$

124. $3x^2(a + 3)^3 - 28x(a + 3)^3 + 25(a + 3)^3$

Factor.

125. $3x^{2n} + 17x^n + 10$

126. $2x^{2n} + 5x^n - 12$

127. In your own words, describe the steps you will use to factor a trinomial.

6.4 Factoring Trinomials of the Form $ax^2 + bx + c$ by Grouping

OBJECTIVE

1 Use the Grouping Method to Factor Trinomials of the Form $ax^2 + bx + c$.

OBJECTIVE

1   Using the Grouping Method

There is an alternative method that can be used to factor trinomials of the form $ax^2 + bx + c, a \neq 1$. This method is called the **grouping method** because it uses factoring by grouping as we learned in Section 6.1.

To see how this method works, recall from Section 6.2 that to factor a trinomial such as $x^2 + 11x + 30$, we find two numbers such that

$$\underset{\underset{\displaystyle \text{Sum is } 11.}{\downarrow}}{\overset{\overset{\displaystyle \text{Product is } 30}{\downarrow}}{x^2 + 11x + 30}}$$

To factor a trinomial such as $2x^2 + 11x + 12$ by grouping, we use an extension of the method in Section 6.2. Here we look for two numbers such that

$$\underset{\underset{\displaystyle \text{Sum is } 11.}{\downarrow}}{\overset{\overset{\displaystyle \text{Product is } 2 \cdot 12 = 24}{\downarrow \qquad\qquad \downarrow}}{2x^2 + 11x + 12}}$$

This time, we use the two numbers to write

$$2x^2 + 11x + 12 \text{ as}$$
$$= 2x^2 + \Box x + \Box x + 12$$

Then we factor by grouping. Since we want a positive product, 24, and a positive sum, 11, we consider pairs of positive factors of 24 only.

Factors of 24	Sum of Factors	
1, 24	25	
2, 12	14	
3, 8	11	Correct sum

The factors are 3 and 8. Now we use these factors to write the middle term $11x$ as $3x + 8x$ (or $8x + 3x$). We replace $11x$ with $3x + 8x$ in the original trinomial and then we can factor by grouping.

$$
\begin{aligned}
2x^2 + 11x + 12 &= 2x^2 + 3x + 8x + 12 \\
&= (2x^2 + 3x) + (8x + 12) && \text{Group the terms.} \\
&= x(2x + 3) + 4(2x + 3) && \text{Factor each group.} \\
&= (2x + 3)(x + 4) && \text{Factor out } (2x + 3).
\end{aligned}
$$

In general, we have the following procedure.

> **To Factor Trinomials by Grouping**
>
> **Step 1.** Factor out a greatest common factor if there is one other than 1.
> **Step 2.** For the resulting trinomial $ax^2 + bx + c$, find two numbers whose product is $a \cdot c$ and whose sum is b.
> **Step 3.** Write the middle term, bx, using the factors found in Step 2.
> **Step 4.** Factor by grouping.

EXAMPLE 1 Factor $3x^2 + 31x + 10$ by grouping.

Solution

Step 1. The terms of this trinomial contain no greatest common factor other than 1 (or −1).
Step 2. In $3x^2 + 31x + 10$, $a = 3$, $b = 31$, and $c = 10$.

Let's find two numbers whose product is $a \cdot c$ or $3(10) = 30$ and whose sum is b or 31. The numbers are 1 and 30.

Factors of 30	Sum of Factors	
5, 6	11	
3, 10	13	
2, 15	17	
1, 30	31	Correct sum

Step 3. Write $31x$ as $1x + 30x$ so that $3x^2 + 31x + 10 = 3x^2 + 1x + 30x + 10$.

Step 4. Factor by grouping.

$$3x^2 + 1x + 30x + 10 = x(3x + 1) + 10(3x + 1)$$
$$= (3x + 1)(x + 10) \qquad \square$$

PRACTICE
1   Factor $5x^2 + 61x + 12$ by grouping.

EXAMPLE 2   Factor $8x^2 - 14x + 5$ by grouping.

Solution

Step 1. The terms of this trinomial contain no greatest common factor other than 1.

Step 2. This trinomial is of the form $ax^2 + bx + c$ with $a = 8$, $b = -14$, and $c = 5$. Find two numbers whose product is $a \cdot c$ or $8 \cdot 5 = 40$, and whose sum is b or -14.

The numbers are -4 and -10.

Factors of 40	Sum of Factors	
$-40, -1$	-41	
$-20, -2$	-22	
$-10, -4$	-14	Correct sum

Step 3. Write $-14x$ as $-4x - 10x$ so that

$$8x^2 - 14x + 5 = 8x^2 - 4x - 10x + 5$$

Step 4. Factor by grouping.

$$8x^2 - 4x - 10x + 5 = 4x(2x - 1) - 5(2x - 1)$$
$$= (2x - 1)(4x - 5) \qquad \square$$

PRACTICE
2   Factor $12x^2 - 19x + 5$ by grouping.

EXAMPLE 3   Factor $6x^2 - 2x - 20$ by grouping.

Solution

Step 1. First factor out the greatest common factor, 2.

$$6x^2 - 2x - 20 = 2(3x^2 - x - 10)$$

Step 2. Next, notice that $a = 3$, $b = -1$, and $c = -10$ in the resulting trinomial. Find two numbers whose product is $a \cdot c$ or $3(-10) = -30$ and whose sum is b, -1. The numbers are -6 and 5.

Step 3. $3x^2 - x - 10 = 3x^2 - 6x + 5x - 10$

(Continued on next page)

Step 4. $3x^2 - 6x + 5x - 10 = 3x(x-2) + 5(x-2)$
$$= (x-2)(3x+5)$$

The factored form of $6x^2 - 2x - 20 = 2(x-2)(3x+5)$.

$\llcorner$ Don't forget to include the common factor of 2. $\square$

PRACTICE
3 Factor $30x^2 - 14x - 4$ by grouping.

EXAMPLE 4 Factor $18y^4 + 21y^3 - 60y^2$ by grouping.

Solution

Step 1. First factor out the greatest common factor, $3y^2$.
$$18y^4 + 21y^3 - 60y^2 = 3y^2(6y^2 + 7y - 20)$$

Step 2. Notice that $a = 6, b = 7$, and $c = -20$ in the resulting trinomial. Find two numbers whose product is $a \cdot c$ or $6(-20) = -120$ and whose sum is 7. It may help to factor -120 as a product of primes and -1.
$$-120 = 2 \cdot 2 \cdot 2 \cdot 3 \cdot 5 \cdot (-1)$$
Then choose pairings of factors until you have a pairing whose sum is 7.

The numbers are -8 and 15.

Step 3. $6y^2 + 7y - 20 = 6y^2 - 8y + 15y - 20$

Step 4. $6y^2 - 8y + 15y - 20 = 2y(3y-4) + 5(3y-4)$
$$= (3y-4)(2y+5)$$

The factored form of $18y^4 + 21y^3 - 60y^2$ is $3y^2(3y-4)(2y+5)$.

$\llcorner$ Don't forget to include the common factor of $3y^2$. $\square$

PRACTICE
4 Factor $40m^4 + 5m^3 - 35m^2$ by grouping.

EXAMPLE 5 Factor $4x^2 + 20x + 25$ by grouping.

Solution

Step 1. The terms of this trinomial contain no greatest common factor other than 1 (or -1).

Step 2. In $4x^2 + 20x + 25$, $a = 4, b = 20$, and $c = 25$. Find two numbers whose product is $a \cdot c$ or $4 \cdot 25 = 100$ and whose sum is 20. The numbers are 10 and 10.

Step 3. Write $20x$ as $10x + 10x$ so that
$$4x^2 + 20x + 25 = 4x^2 + 10x + 10x + 25$$

Step 4. Factor by grouping.
$$4x^2 + 10x + 10x + 25 = 2x(2x+5) + 5(2x+5)$$
$$= (2x+5)(2x+5)$$

The factored form of $4x^2 + 20x + 25$ is $(2x+5)(2x+5)$ or $(2x+5)^2$. $\square$

PRACTICE
5 Factor $16x^2 + 24x + 9$ by grouping.

A trinomial that is the square of a binomial, such as the trinomial in Example 5, is called a **perfect square trinomial.** From Chapter 5, there are special product formulas we can use to help us recognize and factor these trinomials. To study these formulas further, see Section 6.3, Objective 3. **Remember:** A perfect square trinomial, such as the one in Example 5, may be factored by special product formulas or by other methods of factoring trinomials, such as by grouping.

Vocabulary, Readiness & Video Check

For each trinomial $ax^2 + bx + c$, choose two numbers whose product is $a \cdot c$ and whose sum is b.

1. $x^2 + 6x + 8$
    a. 4, 2   **b.** 7, 1   **c.** 6, 2   **d.** 6, 8

2. $x^2 + 11x + 24$
    a. 6, 4   **b.** 24, 1   **c.** 8, 3   **d.** 2, 12

3. $2x^2 + 13x + 6$
    a. 2, 6   **b.** 12, 1   **c.** 13, 1   **d.** 3, 4

4. $4x^2 + 8x + 3$
    a. 4, 3   **b.** 4, 4   **c.** 12, 1   **d.** 2, 6

Martin-Gay Interactive Videos

See Video 6.4

Watch the section lecture video and answer the following question.

OBJECTIVE
1

5. In the lecture following Example 1, why does writing a term as the sum or difference of two terms suggest we'd then try to factor by grouping?

6.4   Exercise Set   MyMathLab®

Factor each polynomial by grouping. Notice that Step 3 has already been done in these exercises. See Examples 1 through 5.

1. $x^2 + 3x + 2x + 6$

2. $x^2 + 5x + 3x + 15$

3. $y^2 + 8y - 2y - 16$

4. $z^2 + 10z - 7z - 70$

5. $8x^2 - 5x - 24x + 15$

6. $4x^2 - 9x - 32x + 72$

7. $5x^4 - 3x^2 + 25x^2 - 15$

8. $2y^4 - 10y^2 + 7y^2 - 35$

MIXED PRACTICE

Factor each trinomial by grouping. Exercises 9–12 are broken into parts to help you get started. See Examples 1 through 5.

9. $6x^2 + 11x + 3$
    a. Find two numbers whose product is $6 \cdot 3 = 18$ and whose sum is 11.
    b. Write $11x$ using the factors from part (a).
    c. Factor by grouping.

10. $8x^2 + 14x + 3$
    a. Find two numbers whose product is $8 \cdot 3 = 24$ and whose sum is 14.
    b. Write $14x$ using the factors from part (a).
    c. Factor by grouping.

11. $15x^2 - 23x + 4$
    a. Find two numbers whose product is $15 \cdot 4 = 60$ and whose sum is -23.
    b. Write $-23x$ using the factors from part (a).
    c. Factor by grouping.

12. $6x^2 - 13x + 5$
    a. Find two numbers whose product is $6 \cdot 5 = 30$ and whose sum is -13.
    b. Write $-13x$ using the factors from part (a).
    c. Factor by grouping.

13. $21y^2 + 17y + 2$

14. $15x^2 + 11x + 2$

15. $7x^2 - 4x - 11$

16. $8x^2 - x - 9$

▶ **17.** $10x^2 - 9x + 2$

18. $30x^2 - 23x + 3$

19. $2x^2 - 7x + 5$

20. $2x^2 - 7x + 3$

21. $12x + 4x^2 + 9$

22. $20x + 25x^2 + 4$

23. $4x^2 - 8x - 21$

24. $6x^2 - 11x - 10$

25. $10x^2 - 23x + 12$

26. $21x^2 - 13x + 2$

27. $2x^3 + 13x^2 + 15x$

28. $3x^3 + 8x^2 + 4x$

29. $16y^2 - 34y + 18$

30. $4y^2 - 2y - 12$

31. $-13x + 6 + 6x^2$

32. $-25x + 12 + 12x^2$

33. $54a^2 - 9a - 30$

34. $30a^2 + 38a - 20$

35. $20a^3 + 37a^2 + 8a$

36. $10a^3 + 17a^2 + 3a$

▶ **37.** $12x^3 - 27x^2 - 27x$

38. $30x^3 - 155x^2 + 25x$

39. $3x^2y + 4xy^2 + y^3$

40. $6r^2t + 7rt^2 + t^3$

41. $20z^2 + 7z + 1$

42. $36z^2 + 6z + 1$

43. $5x^2 + 50xy + 125y^2$

44. $3x^2 + 42xy + 147y^2$

45. $24a^2 - 6ab - 30b^2$

46. $30a^2 + 5ab - 25b^2$

47. $15p^4 + 31p^3q + 2p^2q^2$

48. $20s^4 + 61s^3t + 3s^2t^2$

49. $162a^4 - 72a^2 + 8$

50. $32n^4 - 112n^2 + 98$

51. $35 + 12x + x^2$

52. $33 + 14x + x^2$

53. $6 - 11x + 5x^2$

54. $5 - 12x + 7x^2$

REVIEW AND PREVIEW

Multiply. See Sections 5.3 and 5.4.

55. $(x - 2)(x + 2)$

56. $(y - 5)(y + 5)$

57. $(y + 4)(y + 4)$

58. $(x + 7)(x + 7)$

59. $(9z + 5)(9z - 5)$

60. $(8y + 9)(8y - 9)$

61. $(x - 3)(x^2 + 3x + 9)$

62. $(2z - 1)(4z^2 + 2z + 1)$

CONCEPT EXTENSIONS

Write the perimeter of each figure as a simplified polynomial. Then factor the polynomial.

63.

Regular Pentagon $2x^2 + 9x + 9$

64.

$7x^2 + 11xy + 4y^2$

Equilateral Triangle

Factor each polynomial by grouping.

65. $x^{2n} + 2x^n + 3x^n + 6$

(*Hint:* Don't forget that $x^{2n} = x^n \cdot x^n$.)

66. $x^{2n} + 6x^n + 10x^n + 60$

67. $3x^{2n} + 16x^n - 35$

68. $12x^{2n} - 40x^n + 25$

69. In your own words, explain how to factor a trinomial by grouping.

6.5 Factoring Binomials

OBJECTIVES

1 Factor the Difference of Two Squares. ▶

2 Factor the Sum or Difference of Two Cubes. ▶

OBJECTIVE

1 Factoring the Difference of Two Squares ▶

When learning to multiply binomials in Chapter 5, we studied a special product, the product of the sum and difference of two terms, a and b:

$$(a + b)(a - b) = a^2 - b^2$$

For example, the product of $x + 3$ and $x - 3$ is

$$(x + 3)(x - 3) = x^2 - 9$$

The binomial $x^2 - 9$ is called a **difference of squares**. In this section, we reverse the pattern for the product of a sum and difference to factor the binomial difference of squares.

> **Factoring the Difference of Two Squares**
>
> $$a^2 - b^2 = (a + b)(a - b)$$

> ▶ **Helpful Hint**
>
> Since multiplication is commutative, remember that the order of factors does not matter. In other words,
>
> $$a^2 - b^2 = (a + b)(a - b) \text{ or } (a - b)(a + b)$$

EXAMPLE 1   Factor: $x^2 - 25$

Solution $x^2 - 25$ is the difference of two squares since $x^2 - 25 = x^2 - 5^2$. Therefore,

$$x^2 - 25 = x^2 - 5^2 = (x + 5)(x - 5)$$

Multiply to check.   □

PRACTICE
1   Factor $x^2 - 81$.

EXAMPLE 2   Factor each difference of squares.

a. $4x^2 - 1$ **b.** $25a^2 - 9b^2$ **c.** $y^2 - \dfrac{4}{9}$

Solution

a. $4x^2 - 1 = (2x)^2 - 1^2 = (2x + 1)(2x - 1)$
b. $25a^2 - 9b^2 = (5a)^2 - (3b)^2 = (5a + 3b)(5a - 3b)$
c. $y^2 - \dfrac{4}{9} = y^2 - \left(\dfrac{2}{3}\right)^2 = \left(y + \dfrac{2}{3}\right)\left(y - \dfrac{2}{3}\right)$ □

PRACTICE
2   Factor each difference of squares.

a. $9x^2 - 1$ **b.** $36a^2 - 49b^2$ **c.** $p^2 - \dfrac{25}{36}$

EXAMPLE 3   Factor: $x^4 - y^6$

Solution   This is a difference of squares since $x^4 = (x^2)^2$ and $y^6 = (y^3)^2$. Thus,

$$x^4 - y^6 = (x^2)^2 - (y^3)^2 = (x^2 + y^3)(x^2 - y^3)$$ □

PRACTICE
3   Factor $p^4 - q^{10}$.

EXAMPLE 4   Factor each binomial.

a. $y^4 - 16$ **b.** $x^2 + 4$

Solution

a. $y^4 - 16 = (y^2)^2 - 4^2$

$\qquad\qquad = (y^2 + 4)\underbrace{(y^2 - 4)}$ Factor the difference of two squares.
This binomial can be factored further since it is the difference of two squares.

$\qquad\qquad = (y^2 + 4)(y + 2)(y - 2)$ Factor the difference of two squares.

(Continued on next page)

b. $x^2 + 4$

Note that the binomial $x^2 + 4$ is the *sum* of two squares since we can write $x^2 + 4$ as $x^2 + 2^2$. We might try to factor using $(x + 2)(x + 2)$ or $(x - 2)(x - 2)$. But when we multiply to check, we find that neither factoring is correct.

$$(x + 2)(x + 2) = x^2 + 4x + 4$$
$$(x - 2)(x - 2) = x^2 - 4x + 4$$

In both cases, the product is a trinomial, not the required binomial. In fact, $x^2 + 4$ is a prime polynomial. ☐

PRACTICE
4 Factor each binomial.

a. $z^4 - 81$ **b.** $m^2 + 49$

▶ **Helpful Hint**

When factoring, don't forget:
• See whether the terms have a greatest common factor (GCF) (other than 1) that can be factored out.
• Other than a GCF, the **sum** of two squares cannot be factored using real numbers.
• Factor completely. Always check to see whether any factors can be factored further.

EXAMPLES Factor each binomial.

5. $4x^3 - 49x = x(4x^2 - 49)$ Factor out the common factor, x.
            $= x[(2x)^2 - 7^2]$
            $= x(2x + 7)(2x - 7)$ Factor the difference of two squares.

6. $162x^4 - 2 = 2(81x^4 - 1)$ Factor out the common factor, 2.
            $= 2(9x^2 + 1)(9x^2 - 1)$ Factor the difference of two squares.
            $= 2(9x^2 + 1)(3x + 1)(3x - 1)$ Factor the difference of two squares. ☐

PRACTICES
5–6 Factor each binomial.

5. $36y^3 - 25y$ **6.** $80y^4 - 5$

EXAMPLE 7 Factor: $-49x^2 + 16$

Solution Factor as is, or, if you like, rearrange terms.

Factor as is: $-49x^2 + 16 = -1(49x^2 - 16)$ Factor out -1.
                     $= -1(7x + 4)(7x - 4)$ Factor the difference of two squares.

Rewrite binomial: $-49x^2 + 16 = 16 - 49x^2 = 4^2 - (7x)^2$
                           $= (4 + 7x)(4 - 7x)$

▶ **Helpful Hint**
When rearranging terms, keep in mind that the sign of a term is in front of the term.

Both factorizations are correct and are equal. To see this, factor -1 from $(4 - 7x)$ in the second factorization. ☐

PRACTICE
7 Factor $-9x^2 + 100$.

OBJECTIVE

2   **Factoring the Sum or Difference of Two Cubes**

Although the sum of two squares usually does not factor, the sum or difference of two cubes can be factored and reveals factoring patterns. The pattern for the sum of cubes is illustrated by multiplying the binomial $x + y$ and the trinomial $x^2 - xy + y^2$.

$$x^2 - xy + y^2$$
$$\underline{x + y}$$
$$x^2y - xy^2 + y^3$$
$$\underline{x^3 - x^2y + xy^2}$$
$$x^3 + y^3$$

Thus, $(x + y)(x^2 - xy + y^2) = x^3 + y^3$ Sum of cubes

The pattern for the difference of two cubes is illustrated by multiplying the binomial $x - y$ by the trinomial $x^2 + xy + y^2$. The result is

$$(x - y)(x^2 + xy + y^2) = x^3 - y^3$$ Difference of cubes

> **Factoring the Sum or Difference of Two Cubes**
> $$a^3 + b^3 = (a + b)(a^2 - ab + b^2)$$
> $$a^3 - b^3 = (a - b)(a^2 + ab + b^2)$$

Recall that "factor" means "to write as a product." Above are patterns for writing sums and differences as products.

EXAMPLE 8   Factor: $x^3 + 8$

Solution   First, write the binomial in the form $a^3 + b^3$.

$$x^3 + 8 = x^3 + 2^3$$ Write in the form $a^3 + b^3$.

If we replace a with x and b with 2 in the formula above, we have

$$x^3 + 2^3 = (x + 2)[x^2 - (x)(2) + 2^2]$$
$$= (x + 2)(x^2 - 2x + 4)$$ □

PRACTICE

8   Factor $x^3 + 64$.

··· ■

> ▶ **Helpful Hint**
>
> When factoring sums or differences of cubes, notice the sign patterns.
>
> same sign
> $$x^3 + y^3 = (x + y)(x^2 - xy + y^2)$$
> opposite signs   always positive
>
> same sign
> $$x^3 - y^3 = (x - y)(x^2 + xy + y^2)$$
> opposite signs   always positive

EXAMPLE 9   Factor: $y^3 - 27$

Solution $y^3 - 27 = y^3 - 3^3$ Write in the form $a^3 - b^3$.
$$= (y - 3)[y^2 + (y)(3) + 3^2]$$
$$= (y - 3)(y^2 + 3y + 9)$$ □

PRACTICE

9   Factor $x^3 - 125$.

··· ■

EXAMPLE 10 Factor: $64x^3 + 1$

Solution
$$64x^3 + 1 = (4x)^3 + 1^3$$
$$= (4x + 1)[(4x)^2 - (4x)(1) + 1^2]$$
$$= (4x + 1)(16x^2 - 4x + 1)$$

PRACTICE
10 Factor $27y^3 + 1$.

EXAMPLE 11 Factor: $54a^3 - 16b^3$

Solution Remember to factor out common factors first before using other factoring methods.

$$54a^3 - 16b^3 = 2(27a^3 - 8b^3) \qquad \text{Factor out the GCF 2.}$$
$$= 2[(3a)^3 - (2b)^3] \quad \text{Difference of two cubes}$$
$$= 2(3a - 2b)[(3a)^2 + (3a)(2b) + (2b)^2]$$
$$= 2(3a - 2b)(9a^2 + 6ab + 4b^2)$$

PRACTICE
11 Factor $32x^3 - 500y^3$.

Graphing Calculator Explorations

Graphing

A graphing calculator is a convenient tool for evaluating an expression at a given replacement value. For example, let's evaluate $x^2 - 6x$ when $x = 2$. To do so, store the value 2 in the variable x and then enter and evaluate the algebraic expression.

The value of $x^2 - 6x$ when $x = 2$ is -8. You may want to use this method for evaluating expressions as you explore the following.

We can use a graphing calculator to explore factoring patterns numerically. Use your calculator to evaluate $x^2 - 2x + 1$, $x^2 - 2x - 1$, and $(x - 1)^2$ for each value of x given in the table. What do you observe?

	$x^2 - 2x + 1$	$x^2 - 2x - 1$	$(x - 1)^2$
$x = 5$			
$x = -3$			
$x = 2.7$			
$x = -12.1$			
$x = 0$			

Notice in each case that $x^2 - 2x - 1 \neq (x - 1)^2$. Because for each x in the table the value of $x^2 - 2x + 1$ and the value of $(x - 1)^2$ are the same, we might guess that $x^2 - 2x + 1 = (x - 1)^2$. We can verify our guess algebraically with multiplication:

$$(x - 1)(x - 1) = x^2 - x - x + 1 = x^2 - 2x + 1$$

Vocabulary, Readiness & Video Check

Use the choices below to fill in each blank. Some choices may be used more than once and some choices may not be used at all.

true	difference of two squares	sum of two cubes
false	difference of two cubes	

1. The expression $x^3 - 27$ is called a _____.
2. The expression $x^2 - 49$ is called a _____.
3. The expression $z^3 + 1$ is called a _____.
4. True or false: The binomial $y^2 + 9$ factors as $(y + 3)^2$. _____

Write each term as a square.
5. $49x^2$ 6. $25y^4$

Write each term as a cube.
7. $8y^3$ 8. x^6

Martin-Gay Interactive Videos

See Video 6.5

Watch the section lecture video and answer the following questions.

OBJECTIVE 1

9. In Examples 1 and 2, what are two reasons the original binomial is rewritten so that each term is a square?

OBJECTIVE 1

10. From Example 3, what is a prime polynomial?

OBJECTIVE 2

11. In Examples 6–8, what tips are given to remember how to factor the sum or difference of two cubes rather than memorizing the formulas?

6.5 Exercise Set

MyMathLab®

Factor each binomial completely. See Examples 1 through 7.

▶ 1. $x^2 - 4$
2. $x^2 - 36$
3. $81p^2 - 1$
4. $49m^2 - 1$
5. $25y^2 - 9$
6. $49a^2 - 16$
▶ 7. $121m^2 - 100n^2$
8. $169a^2 - 49b^2$
9. $x^2y^2 - 1$
10. $a^2b^2 - 16$
11. $x^2 - \dfrac{1}{4}$
12. $y^2 - \dfrac{1}{16}$
13. $-4r^2 + 1$
14. $-9t^2 + 1$
▶ 15. $16r^2 + 1$
16. $49y^2 + 1$
17. $-36 + x^2$

18. $-1 + y^2$
19. $m^4 - 1$
20. $n^4 - 16$
21. $m^4 - n^{18}$
22. $n^4 - r^6$

Factor the sum or difference of two cubes. See Examples 8 through 11.

▶ 23. $x^3 + 125$
24. $p^3 + 1$
25. $8a^3 - 1$
26. $27y^3 - 1$
27. $m^3 + 27n^3$
28. $y^3 + 64z^3$
29. $5k^3 + 40$
30. $6r^3 + 162$
▶ 31. $x^3y^3 - 64$
32. $a^3b^3 - 8$
33. $250r^3 - 128t^3$
34. $24x^3 - 81y^3$

MIXED PRACTICE

Factor each binomial completely. See Examples 1 through 11.

35. $r^2 - 64$

36. $q^2 - 121$

37. $x^2 - 169y^2$

✓ **38.** $x^2 - 225y^2$

39. $27 - t^3$

40. $125 - r^3$

41. $18r^2 - 8$

✓ **42.** $32t^2 - 50$

43. $9xy^2 - 4x$

44. $36x^2y - 25y$

▶ **45.** $8m^3 + 64$

46. $2x^3 + 54$

▶ **47.** $xy^3 - 9xyz^2$

48. $x^3y - 4xy^3$

✓ **49.** $36x^2 - 64y^2$

50. $225a^2 - 81b^2$

51. $144 - 81x^2$

52. $12x^2 - 27$

53. $x^3y^3 - z^6$

54. $a^3b^3 - c^9$

▶ **55.** $49 - \frac{9}{25}m^2$

56. $100 - \frac{4}{81}n^2$

57. $t^3 + 343$

58. $s^3 + 216$

59. $n^3 + 49n$

60. $y^3 + 64y$

61. $x^6 - 81x^2$

62. $n^9 - n^5$

63. $64p^3q - 81pq^3$

64. $100x^3y - 49xy^3$

65. $27x^2y^3 + xy^2$

66. $8x^3y^3 + x^3y$

67. $125a^4 - 64ab^3$

68. $64m^4 - 27mn^3$

69. $16x^4 - 64x^2$

70. $25y^4 - 100y^2$

REVIEW AND PREVIEW

Solve each equation. See Section 2.2.

71. $x - 6 = 0$

72. $y + 5 = 0$

73. $2m + 4 = 0$

74. $3x - 9 = 0$

75. $5z - 1 = 0$

76. $4a + 2 = 0$

CONCEPT EXTENSIONS

Factor each expression completely.

$+ 2)^2 - y^2$

$- 6)^2 - z^2$

79. $a^2(b - 4) - 16(b - 4)$

80. $m^2(n + 8) - 9(n + 8)$

81. $(x^2 + 6x + 9) - 4y^2$ (**Hint:** Factor the trinomial in parentheses first.)

82. $(x^2 + 2x + 1) - 36y^2$

83. $x^{2n} - 100$

84. $x^{2n} - 81$

85. What binomial multiplied by $(x - 6)$ gives the difference of two squares?

86. What binomial multiplied by $(5 + y)$ gives the difference of two squares?

87. In your own words, explain how to tell whether a binomial is a difference of squares. Then explain how to factor a difference of squares.

88. In your own words, explain how to tell whether a binomial is a sum of cubes. Then explain how to factor a sum of cubes.

89. The Toroweap Overlook, on the North Rim of the Grand Canyon, lies 3000 vertical feet above the Colorado River. The view is spectacular, and the sheer drop is dramatic. A film crew creating a documentary about the Grand Canyon has suspended a camera platform 296 feet below the Overlook. A camera filter comes loose and falls to the river below. The height of the filter above the river after t seconds is given by the expression $2704 - 16t^2$.

a. Find the height of the filter above the river after 3 seconds.

b. Find the height of the filter above the river after 7 seconds.

c. To the nearest whole second, estimate when the filter lands in the river.

d. Factor $2704 - 16t^2$.

90. An object is dropped from the top of Pittsburgh's USX Tower, which is 841 feet tall. (*Source: World Almanac research*) The height of the object after t seconds is given by the expression $841 - 16t^2$.

a. Find the height of the object after 2 seconds.

b. Find the height of the object after 5 seconds.

c. To the nearest whole second, estimate when the object hits the ground.

d. Factor $841 - 16t^2$.

841 feet

91. At this writing, the world's second tallest building is the Taipei 101 in Taipei, Taiwan, at a height of 1671 feet. (*Source:* Council on Tall Buildings and Urban Habitat) Suppose a worker is suspended 71 feet below the top of the pinnacle atop the building, at a height of 1600 feet above the ground. If the worker accidentally drops a bolt, the height of the bolt after t seconds is given by the expression $1600 - 16t^2$.

   a. Find the height of the bolt after 3 seconds.

   b. Find the height of the bolt after 7 seconds.

   c. To the nearest whole second, estimate when the bolt hits the ground.

   d. Factor $1600 - 16t^2$.

92. A performer with the Moscow Circus is planning a stunt involving a free fall from the top of the Moscow State University building, which is 784 feet tall. (*Source:* Council on Tall Buildings and Urban Habitat) Neglecting air resistance, the performer's height above gigantic cushions positioned at ground level after t seconds is given by the expression $784 - 16t^2$.

   a. Find the performer's height after 2 seconds.

   b. Find the performer's height after 5 seconds.

   c. To the nearest whole second, estimate when the performer reaches the cushions positioned at ground level.

   d. Factor $784 - 16t^2$.

(Integrated Review) CHOOSING A FACTORING STRATEGY

Sections 6.1–6.5

The following steps may be helpful when factoring polynomials.

> **Factoring a Polynomial**
>
> **Step 1.** Are there any common factors? If so, factor out the GCF.
>
> **Step 2.** How many terms are in the polynomial?
>
>   **a.** If there are **two** terms, decide if one of the following can be applied.
>
>   **i.** Difference of two squares: $a^2 - b^2 = (a + b)(a - b)$.
>
>   **ii.** Difference of two cubes: $a^3 - b^3 = (a - b)(a^2 + ab + b^2)$.
>
>   **iii.** Sum of two cubes: $a^3 + b^3 = (a + b)(a^2 - ab + b^2)$.
>
>   **b.** If there are **three** terms, try one of the following.
>
>   **i.** Perfect square trinomial: $a^2 + 2ab + b^2 = (a + b)^2$
> $a^2 - 2ab + b^2 = (a - b)^2$.
>
>   **ii.** If not a perfect square trinomial, factor using the methods presented in Sections 6.2 through 6.4.
>
>   **c.** If there are **four** or more terms, try factoring by grouping.
>
> **Step 3.** See if any factors in the factored polynomial can be factored further.
>
> **Step 4.** Check by multiplying.

Study the next five examples to help you use the steps above.

   EXAMPLE 1   Factor $10t^2 - 17t + 3$.

Solution

Step 1. The terms of this polynomial have no common factor (other than 1).

Step 2. There are three terms, so this polynomial is a trinomial. This trinomial is not a perfect square trinomial, so factor using methods from earlier sections.

            Factors of $10t^2$: $10t^2 = 2t \cdot 5t$, $10t^2 = t \cdot 10t$

(Continued on next page)

Since the middle term, $-17t$, has a negative numerical coefficient, find negative factors of 3.

$$\text{Factors of 3: } 3 = -1 \cdot -3$$

Try different combinations of these factors. The correct combination is

$$(2t - 3)(5t - 1) = 10t^2 - 17t + 3$$

$$-15t$$
$$-2t$$
$$\overline{-17t} \quad \text{Correct middle term}$$

Step 3. No factor can be factored further, so we have factored completely.

Step 4. To check, multiply $2t - 3$ and $5t - 1$.

$$(2t - 3)(5t - 1) = 10t^2 - 2t - 15t + 3 = 10t^2 - 17t + 3$$

The factored form of $10t^2 - 17t + 3$ is $(2t - 3)(5t - 1)$. ☐

PRACTICE
1   Factor $6x^2 - 11x + 3$.

EXAMPLE 2   Factor $2x^3 + 3x^2 - 2x - 3$.

Solution

Step 1. There are no factors common to all terms.

Step 2. Try factoring by grouping since this polynomial has four terms.

$$2x^3 + 3x^2 - 2x - 3 = x^2(2x + 3) - 1(2x + 3) \quad \text{Factor out the greatest common factor for each pair of terms.}$$

$$= (2x + 3)(x^2 - 1) \quad \text{Factor out } 2x + 3.$$

Step 3. The binomial $x^2 - 1$ can be factored further. It is the difference of two squares.

$$= (2x + 3)(x + 1)(x - 1) \quad \text{Factor } x^2 - 1 \text{ as a difference of squares.}$$

Step 4. Check by finding the product of the three binomials. The polynomial factored completely is $(2x + 3)(x + 1)(x - 1)$. ☐

PRACTICE
2   Factor $3x^3 + x^2 - 12x - 4$.

EXAMPLE 3   Factor $12m^2 - 3n^2$.

Solution

Step 1. The terms of this binomial contain a greatest common factor of 3.

$$12m^2 - 3n^2 = 3(4m^2 - n^2) \quad \text{Factor out the greatest common factor.}$$

Step 2. The binomial $4m^2 - n^2$ is a difference of squares.

$$= 3(2m + n)(2m - n) \quad \text{Factor the difference of squares.}$$

Step 3. No factor can be factored further.

Step 4. We check by multiplying.

$$3(2m + n)(2m - n) = 3(4m^2 - n^2) = 12m^2 - 3n^2$$

The factored form of $12m^2 - 3n^2$ is $3(2m + n)(2m - n)$. ☐

PRACTICE
3   Factor $27x^2 - 3y^2$.

EXAMPLE 4   Factor $x^3 + 27y^3$.

Solution

Step 1. The terms of this binomial contain no common factor (other than 1).

Step 2. This binomial is the sum of two cubes.

$$x^3 + 27y^3 = (x)^3 + (3y)^3$$
$$= (x + 3y)[x^2 - x(3y) + (3y)^2]$$
$$= (x + 3y)(x^2 - 3xy + 9y^2)$$

Step 3. No factor can be factored further.

Step 4. We check by multiplying.

$$(x + 3y)(x^2 - 3xy + 9y^2) = x(x^2 - 3xy + 9y^2) + 3y(x^2 - 3xy + 9y^2)$$
$$= x^3 - 3x^2y + 9xy^2 + 3x^2y - 9xy^2 + 27y^3$$
$$= x^3 + 27y^3$$

Thus, $x^3 + 27y^3$ factored completely is $(x + 3y)(x^2 - 3xy + 9y^2)$. □

PRACTICE
4   Factor $8a^3 + b^3$.

EXAMPLE 5   Factor $30a^2b^3 + 55a^2b^2 - 35a^2b$.

Solution

Step 1. $30a^2b^3 + 55a^2b^2 - 35a^2b = 5a^2b(6b^2 + 11b - 7)$ Factor out the GCF.

Step 2. $= 5a^2b(2b - 1)(3b + 7)$ Factor the resulting trinomial.

Step 3. No factor can be factored further.

Step 4. Check by multiplying.

The trinomial factored completely is $5a^2b(2b - 1)(3b + 7)$. □

PRACTICE
5   Factor $60x^3y^2 - 66x^2y^2 - 36xy^2$.

Factor the following completely.

1. $x^2 + 2xy + y^2$
2. $x^2 - 2xy + y^2$
3. $a^2 + 11a - 12$
4. $a^2 - 11a + 10$
5. $a^2 - a - 6$
6. $a^2 - 2a + 1$
7. $x^2 + 2x + 1$
8. $x^2 + x - 2$
9. $x^2 + 4x + 3$
10. $x^2 + x - 6$
11. $x^2 + 7x + 12$
12. $x^2 + x - 12$
13. $x^2 + 3x - 4$
14. $x^2 - 7x + 10$
15. $x^2 + 2x - 15$
16. $x^2 + 11x + 30$
17. $x^2 - x - 30$
18. $x^2 + 11x + 24$
19. $2x^2 - 98$
20. $3x^2 - 75$
21. $x^2 + 3x + xy + 3y$
22. $3y - 21 + xy - 7x$
23. $x^2 + 6x - 16$
24. $x^2 - 3x - 28$
25. $4x^3 + 20x^2 - 56x$
26. $6x^3 - 6x^2 - 120x$
27. $12x^2 + 34x + 24$
28. $8a^2 + 6ab - 5b^2$
29. $4a^2 - b^2$
30. $28 - 13x - 6x^2$
31. $20 - 3x - 2x^2$
32. $x^2 - 2x + 4$
33. $a^2 + a - 3$
34. $6y^2 + y - 15$
35. $4x^2 - x - 5$
36. $x^2y - y^3$
37. $4t^2 + 36$
38. $x^2 + x + xy + y$
39. $ax + 2x + a + 2$
40. $18x^3 - 63x^2 + 9x$
41. $12a^3 - 24a^2 + 4a$
42. $x^2 + 14x - 32$
43. $x^2 - 14x - 48$
44. $16a^2 - 56ab + 49b^2$
45. $25p^2 - 70pq + 49q^2$
46. $7x^2 + 24xy + 9y^2$
47. $125 - 8y^3$
48. $64x^3 + 27$

49. $-x^2 - x + 30$
50. $-x^2 + 6x - 8$
51. $14 + 5x - x^2$
52. $3 - 2x - x^2$
53. $3x^4y + 6x^3y - 72x^2y$
54. $2x^3y + 8x^2y^2 - 10xy^3$
55. $5x^3y^2 - 40x^2y^3 + 35xy^4$
56. $4x^4y - 8x^3y - 60x^2y$
57. $12x^3y + 243xy$
58. $6x^3y^2 + 8xy^2$
59. $4 - x^2$
60. $9 - y^2$
61. $3rs - s + 12r - 4$
62. $x^3 - 2x^2 + 3x - 6$
▶ **63.** $4x^2 - 8xy - 3x + 6y$
64. $4x^2 - 2xy - 7yz + 14xz$
65. $6x^2 + 18xy + 12y^2$
66. $12x^2 + 46xy - 8y^2$
67. $xy^2 - 4x + 3y^2 - 12$
68. $x^2y^2 - 9x^2 + 3y^2 - 27$
69. $5(x + y) + x(x + y)$
70. $7(x - y) + y(x - y)$
71. $14t^2 - 9t + 1$
72. $3t^2 - 5t + 1$
73. $3x^2 + 2x - 5$
74. $7x^2 + 19x - 6$
75. $x^2 + 9xy - 36y^2$
76. $3x^2 + 10xy - 8y^2$
77. $1 - 8ab - 20a^2b^2$
78. $1 - 7ab - 60a^2b^2$
79. $9 - 10x^2 + x^4$
80. $36 - 13x^2 + x^4$
81. $x^4 - 14x^2 - 32$
82. $x^4 - 22x^2 - 75$
83. $x^2 - 23x + 120$
84. $y^2 + 22y + 96$

85. $6x^3 - 28x^2 + 16x$
86. $6y^3 - 8y^2 - 30y$
87. $27x^3 - 125y^3$
88. $216y^3 - z^3$
89. $x^3y^3 + 8z^3$
90. $27a^3b^3 + 8$
▶ **91.** $2xy - 72x^3y$
92. $2x^3 - 18x$
93. $x^3 + 6x^2 - 4x - 24$
94. $x^3 - 2x^2 - 36x + 72$
95. $6a^3 + 10a^2$
96. $4n^2 - 6n$
97. $a^2(a + 2) + 2(a + 2)$
98. $a - b + x(a - b)$
99. $(x^3 - 28) + (7x^2 - 4x)$
100. $a^3 - 45 - 9a + 5a^2$

CONCEPT EXTENSIONS

Factor.

101. $(x - y)^2 - z^2$
102. $(x + 2y)^2 - 9$
103. $81 - (5x + 1)^2$
104. $b^2 - (4a + c)^2$
105. Explain why it makes good sense to factor out the GCF first, before using other methods of factoring.
106. The sum of two squares usually does not factor. Is the sum of two squares $9x^2 + 81y^2$ factorable?
107. Which of the following are equivalent to $(x + 10)(x - 7)$?
  a. $(x - 7)(x + 10)$ **b.** $-1(x + 10)(x - 7)$
  c. $-1(x + 10)(7 - x)$ **d.** $-1(-x - 10)(7 - x)$
108. Which of the following are equivalent to $(x - 2)(x - 5)$?
  a. $-1(x + 2)(x + 5)$ **b.** $(x - 5)(x - 2)$
  c. $(5 - x)(2 - x)$ **d.** $-1(x + 2)(x - 5)$

6.6 Solving Quadratic Equations by Factoring ▶

In this section, we introduce a new type of equation—the **quadratic equation.**

OBJECTIVES

1 Solve Quadratic Equations by Factoring. ▶

2 Solve Equations with Degree Greater than 2 by Factoring. ▶

3 Find the x-Intercepts of the Graph of a Quadratic Equation in Two Variables. ▶

Quadratic Equation

A quadratic equation is one that can be written in the form

$$ax^2 + bx + c = 0$$

where a, b, and c are real numbers and $a \neq 0$.

Some examples of quadratic equations are shown below.

$$x^2 - 9x - 22 = 0 \qquad 4x^2 - 28 = -49 \qquad x(2x - 7) = 4$$

The form $ax^2 + bx + c = 0$ is called the **standard form** of a quadratic equation. The quadratic equation $x^2 - 9x - 22 = 0$ is the only equation above that is in standard form.

144 feet

Quadratic equations model many real-life situations. For example, let's suppose we want to know how long before a person diving from a 144-foot cliff reaches the ocean. The answer to this question is found by solving the quadratic equation $-16t^2 + 144 = 0$. (See Example 1 in Section 6.7.)

OBJECTIVE

1   Solving Quadratic Equations by Factoring

Some quadratic equations can be solved by making use of factoring and the **zero factor property.**

Zero Factor Theorem

If a and b are real numbers and if $ab = 0$, then $a = 0$ or $b = 0$.

This theorem states that if the product of two numbers is 0, then at least one of the numbers must be 0.

EXAMPLE 1   Solve: $(x - 3)(x + 1) = 0$

Solution   If this equation is to be a true statement, then either the factor $x - 3$ must be 0 or the factor $x + 1$ must be 0. In other words, either

$$x - 3 = 0 \quad \text{or} \quad x + 1 = 0$$

If we solve these two linear equations, we have

$$x = 3 \quad \text{or} \quad x = -1$$

Thus, 3 and -1 are both solutions of the equation $(x - 3)(x + 1) = 0$. To check, we replace x with 3 in the original equation. Then we replace x with -1 in the original equation.

Check: Let $x = 3$.

$(x - 3)(x + 1) = 0$

$(3 - 3)(3 + 1) \stackrel{?}{=} 0$ Replace x with 3.

$0(4) = 0$ True

Let $x = -1$.

$(x - 3)(x + 1) = 0$

$(-1 - 3)(-1 + 1) \stackrel{?}{=} 0$ Replace x with -1.

$(-4)(0) = 0$ True

The solutions are 3 and -1, or we say that the solution set is $\{-1, 3\}$.   □

PRACTICE

1   Solve: $(x + 4)(x - 5) = 0$.

▶ **Helpful Hint**

The zero factor property says that *if a product is 0, then a factor is 0.*

If $a \cdot b = 0$, then $a = 0$ or $b = 0$.
If $x(x + 5) = 0$, then $x = 0$ or $x + 5 = 0$.
If $(x + 7)(2x - 3) = 0$, then $x + 7 = 0$ or $2x - 3 = 0$.

Use this property only when the product is 0.

For example, if $a \cdot b = 8$, we do not know the value of a or b. The values may be $a = 2, b = 4$ or $a = 8, b = 1$, or any other two numbers whose product is 8.

EXAMPLE 2   Solve: $(x - 5)(2x + 7) = 0$

Solution: The product is 0. By the zero factor property, this is true only when a factor is 0. To solve, we set each factor equal to 0 and solve the resulting linear equations.

$$(x - 5)(2x + 7) = 0$$

$$x - 5 = 0 \quad \text{or} \quad 2x + 7 = 0$$

$$x = 5 \qquad\qquad 2x = -7$$

$$x = -\frac{7}{2}$$

(Continued on next page)

Check: Let $x = 5$.

$$(x - 5)(2x + 7) = 0$$
$$(5 - 5)(2 \cdot 5 + 7) \overset{?}{=} 0 \quad \text{Replace } x \text{ with 5.}$$
$$0 \cdot 17 \overset{?}{=} 0$$
$$0 = 0 \quad \text{True}$$

Let $x = -\dfrac{7}{2}$.

$$(x - 5)(2x + 7) = 0$$
$$\left(-\frac{7}{2} - 5\right)\left(2\left(-\frac{7}{2}\right) + 7\right) \overset{?}{=} 0 \quad \text{Replace } x \text{ with } -\frac{7}{2}.$$
$$\left(-\frac{17}{2}\right)(-7 + 7) \overset{?}{=} 0$$
$$\left(-\frac{17}{2}\right) \cdot 0 \overset{?}{=} 0$$
$$0 = 0 \quad \text{True}$$

The solutions are 5 and $-\dfrac{7}{2}$. □

PRACTICE
2   Solve: $(x - 12)(4x + 3) = 0$

■

EXAMPLE 3   Solve: $x(5x - 2) = 0$

Solution
$$x(5x - 2) = 0$$
$$x = 0 \quad \text{or} \quad 5x - 2 = 0 \quad \text{Use the zero factor property.}$$
$$5x = 2$$
$$x = \frac{2}{5}$$

Check: Let $x = 0$.

$$x(5x - 2) = 0$$
$$0(5 \cdot 0 - 2) \overset{?}{=} 0 \quad \text{Replace } x \text{ with 0.}$$
$$0(-2) \overset{?}{=} 0$$
$$0 = 0 \quad \text{True}$$

Let $x = \dfrac{2}{5}$.

$$x(5x - 2) = 0$$
$$\frac{2}{5}\left(5 \cdot \frac{2}{5} - 2\right) \overset{?}{=} 0 \quad \text{Replace } x \text{ with } \frac{2}{5}.$$
$$\frac{2}{5}(2 - 2) \overset{?}{=} 0$$
$$\frac{2}{5}(0) \overset{?}{=} 0$$
$$0 = 0 \quad \text{True}$$

The solutions are 0 and $\dfrac{2}{5}$. □

PRACTICE
3   Solve: $x(7x - 6) = 0$.

■

EXAMPLE 4   Solve: $x^2 - 9x - 22 = 0$

Solution   One side of the equation is 0. However, to use the zero factor property, one side of the equation must be 0 *and* the other side must be written as a product (must be factored). Thus, we must first factor this polynomial.

$$x^2 - 9x - 22 = 0$$
$$(x - 11)(x + 2) = 0 \quad \text{Factor.}$$

Now we can apply the zero factor property.

$$x - 11 = 0 \quad \text{or} \quad x + 2 = 0$$
$$x = 11 \qquad\qquad x = -2$$

Check: Let $x = 11$.

$$x^2 - 9x - 22 = 0$$
$$11^2 - 9 \cdot 11 - 22 \stackrel{?}{=} 0$$
$$121 - 99 - 22 \stackrel{?}{=} 0$$
$$22 - 22 \stackrel{?}{=} 0$$
$$0 = 0 \quad \text{True}$$

Let $x = -2$.

$$x^2 - 9x - 22 = 0$$
$$(-2)^2 - 9(-2) - 22 \stackrel{?}{=} 0$$
$$4 + 18 - 22 \stackrel{?}{=} 0$$
$$22 - 22 \stackrel{?}{=} 0$$
$$0 = 0 \quad \text{True}$$

The solutions are 11 and -2. ☐

PRACTICE

4   Solve: $x^2 - 8x - 48 = 0$.

EXAMPLE 5   Solve: $4x^2 - 28x = -49$

Solution   First we rewrite the equation in standard form so that one side is 0. Then we factor the polynomial.

$$4x^2 - 28x = -49$$
$$4x^2 - 28x + 49 = 0 \qquad \text{Write in standard form by adding 49 to both sides.}$$
$$(2x - 7)(2x - 7) = 0 \qquad \text{Factor.}$$

Next we use the zero factor property and set each factor equal to 0. Since the factors are the same, the related equations will give the same solution.

$$2x - 7 = 0 \quad \text{or} \quad 2x - 7 = 0 \qquad \text{Set each factor equal to 0.}$$
$$2x = 7 \qquad\qquad 2x = 7 \qquad \text{Solve.}$$
$$x = \frac{7}{2} \qquad\qquad x = \frac{7}{2}$$

Check: Although $\frac{7}{2}$ occurs twice, there is a single solution. Check this solution in the original equation. The solution is $\frac{7}{2}$. ☐

PRACTICE

5   Solve: $9x^2 - 24x = -16$.

The following steps may be used to solve a quadratic equation by factoring.

To Solve Quadratic Equations by Factoring

Step 1.   Write the equation in standard form so that one side of the equation is 0.

Step 2.   Factor the quadratic expression completely.

Step 3.   Set each factor containing a variable equal to 0.

Step 4.   Solve the resulting equations.

Step 5.   Check each solution in the original equation.

Since it is not always possible to factor a quadratic polynomial, not all quadratic equations can be solved by factoring. Other methods of solving quadratic equations are presented in Chapter 11.

EXAMPLE 6 Solve: $x(2x - 7) = 4$

Solution First we write the equation in standard form; then we factor.

$$x(2x - 7) = 4$$
$$2x^2 - 7x = 4 \qquad \text{Multiply.}$$
$$2x^2 - 7x - 4 = 0 \qquad \text{Write in standard form.}$$
$$(2x + 1)(x - 4) = 0 \qquad \text{Factor.}$$
$$2x + 1 = 0 \quad \text{or} \quad x - 4 = 0 \qquad \text{Set each factor equal to zero.}$$
$$2x = -1 \qquad\qquad x = 4 \qquad \text{Solve.}$$
$$x = -\frac{1}{2}$$

Check the solutions in the original equation. The solutions are $-\dfrac{1}{2}$ and 4. □

> ▶ **Helpful Hint**
>
> To solve the equation $x(2x - 7) = 4$, do **not** set each factor equal to 4. Remember that to apply the zero factor property, one side of the equation must be 0 and the other side of the equation must be in factored form.

PRACTICE
6 Solve: $x(3x + 7) = 6$.

✓**CONCEPT CHECK**
Explain the error and solve the equation correctly.

$$(x - 3)(x + 1) = 5$$
$$x - 3 = 5 \quad \text{or} \quad x + 1 = 5$$
$$x = 8 \quad \text{or} \quad x = 4$$

EXAMPLE 7 Solve: $-2x^2 - 4x + 30 = 0$.

Solution The equation is in standard form, so we begin by factoring out a common factor of -2.

$$-2x^2 - 4x + 30 = 0$$
$$-2(x^2 + 2x - 15) = 0 \qquad \text{Factor out –2.}$$
$$-2(x + 5)(x - 3) = 0 \qquad \text{Factor the quadratic.}$$

Next, set each factor **containing a variable** equal to 0.

$$x + 5 = 0 \qquad \text{or} \qquad x - 3 = 0 \qquad \text{Set each factor containing a variable equal to 0.}$$
$$x = -5 \qquad \text{or} \qquad x = 3 \qquad \text{Solve.}$$

Note: The factor -2 is a constant term containing no variables and can never equal 0. The solutions are -5 and 3. □

PRACTICE
7 Solve: $-3x^2 - 6x + 72 = 0$.

Answer to Concept Check:
To use the zero factor property, one side of the equation must be 0, not 5. Correctly, $(x - 3)(x + 1) = 5$, $x^2 - 2x - 3 = 5$, $x^2 - 2x - 8 = 0$, $(x - 4)(x + 2) = 0$, $x - 4 = 0$ or $x + 2 = 0$, $x = 4$ or $x = -2$.

OBJECTIVE
2 Solving Equations with Degree Greater than Two by Factoring

Some equations involving polynomials of degree higher than 2 may also be solved by factoring and then applying the zero factor theorem.

EXAMPLE 8 Solve: $3x^3 - 12x = 0$.

Solution Factor the left side of the equation. Begin by factoring out the common factor of $3x$.

$$3x^3 - 12x = 0$$

$$3x(x^2 - 4) = 0 \quad \text{Factor out the GCF } 3x.$$

$$3x(x + 2)(x - 2) = 0 \quad \text{Factor } x^2 - 4, \text{ a difference of squares.}$$

$3x = 0 \quad$ or $\quad x + 2 = 0 \quad$ or $\quad x - 2 = 0 \quad$ Set each factor equal to 0.

$x = 0 \quad$ or $\quad x = -2 \quad$ or $\quad x = 2 \quad$ Solve.

Thus, the equation $3x^3 - 12x = 0$ has three solutions: $0, -2$, and 2. To check, replace x with each solution in the original equation.

Let x = 0.	***Let x = −2.***	***Let x = 2.***
$3(0)^3 - 12(0) \overset{?}{=} 0$	$3(-2)^3 - 12(-2) \overset{?}{=} 0$	$3(2)^3 - 12(2) \overset{?}{=} 0$
$0 = 0$	$3(-8) + 24 \overset{?}{=} 0$	$3(8) - 24 \overset{?}{=} 0$
	$0 = 0$	$0 = 0$

Substituting $0, -2$, or 2 into the original equation results each time in a true equation. The solutions are $0, -2$, and 2. □

PRACTICE

8 Solve: $7x^3 - 63x = 0$.

EXAMPLE 9 Solve: $(5x - 1)(2x^2 + 15x + 18) = 0$.

Solution

$$(5x - 1)(2x^2 + 15x + 18) = 0$$

$$(5x - 1)(2x + 3)(x + 6) = 0 \quad \text{Factor the trinomial.}$$

$5x - 1 = 0 \quad$ or $\quad 2x + 3 = 0 \quad$ or $\quad x + 6 = 0 \quad$ Set each factor equal to 0.

$5x = 1 \quad$ or $\quad 2x = -3 \quad$ or $\quad x = -6 \quad$ Solve.

$$x = \frac{1}{5} \quad \text{or} \quad x = -\frac{3}{2}$$

The solutions are $\frac{1}{5}, -\frac{3}{2}$, and -6. Check by replacing x with each solution in the original equation. The solutions are $-6, -\frac{3}{2}$, and $\frac{1}{5}$. □

PRACTICE

9 Solve: $(3x - 2)(2x^2 - 13x + 15) = 0$.

EXAMPLE 10 Solve: $2x^3 - 4x^2 - 30x = 0$.

Solution Begin by factoring out the GCF $2x$.

$$2x^3 - 4x^2 - 30x = 0$$

$$2x(x^2 - 2x - 15) = 0 \quad \text{Factor out the GCF } 2x.$$

$$2x(x - 5)(x + 3) = 0 \quad \text{Factor the quadratic.}$$

$2x = 0 \quad$ or $\quad x - 5 = 0 \quad$ or $\quad x + 3 = 0 \quad$ Set each factor containing a variable equal to 0.

$x = 0 \quad$ or $\quad x = 5 \quad$ or $\quad x = -3 \quad$ Solve.

Check by replacing x with each solution in the cubic equation. The solutions are $-3, 0$, and 5. □

PRACTICE

10 Solve: $5x^3 + 5x^2 - 30x = 0$.

3 **Finding *x*-Intercepts of the Graph of a Quadratic Equation**

In Chapter 3, we graphed linear equations in two variables, such as $y = 5x - 6$. Recall that to find the *x*-intercept of the graph of a linear equation, let $y = 0$ and solve for *x*. This is also how to find the *x*-intercepts of the graph of a **quadratic equation in two variables,** such as $y = x^2 - 5x + 4$.

EXAMPLE 11 Find the *x*-intercepts of the graph of $y = x^2 - 5x + 4$.

Solution Let $y = 0$ and solve for *x*.

$$y = x^2 - 5x + 4$$
$$0 = x^2 - 5x + 4 \qquad \text{Let } y = 0.$$
$$0 = (x - 1)(x - 4) \qquad \text{Factor.}$$
$$x - 1 = 0 \quad \text{or} \quad x - 4 = 0 \qquad \text{Set each factor equal to 0.}$$
$$x = 1 \quad \text{or} \quad x = 4 \qquad \text{Solve.}$$

The *x*-intercepts of the graph of $y = x^2 - 5x + 4$ are $(1, 0)$ and $(4, 0)$.
The graph of $y = x^2 - 5x + 4$ is shown in the margin. ☐

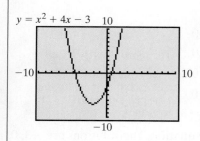

PRACTICE

11 Find the *x*-intercepts of the graph of $y = x^2 - 6x + 8$.

In general, a quadratic equation in two variables is one that can be written in the form $y = ax^2 + bx + c$ where $a \neq 0$. The graph of such an equation is called a **parabola** and will open up or down depending on the sign of *a*.

Notice that the *x*-intercepts of the graph of $y = ax^2 + bx + c$ are the real number solutions of $0 = ax^2 + bx + c$. Also, the real number solutions of $0 = ax^2 + bx + c$ are the *x*-intercepts of the graph of $y = ax^2 + bx + c$. We study more about graphs of quadratic equations in two variables in Chapter 11.

Graph of $y = ax^2 + bx + c$
x-intercepts are solutions of $0 = ax^2 + bx + c$

no solution   1 solution   2 solutions   2 solutions

Graphing Calculator Explorations

$y = x^2 + 4x - 3$

A grapher may be used to find solutions of a quadratic equation whether the related quadratic polynomial is factorable or not. For example, let's use a grapher to approximate the solutions of $0 = x^2 + 4x - 3$. To do so, graph $y_1 = x^2 + 4x - 3$. Recall that the *x*-intercepts of this graph are the solutions of $0 = x^2 + 4x - 3$.

Notice that the graph appears to have an *x*-intercept between -5 and -4 and one between 0 and 1. Many graphers contain a TRACE feature. This feature activates a graph cursor that can be used to *trace* along a graph while the corresponding *x*- and *y*-coordinates are shown on the screen. Use the TRACE feature to confirm that *x*-intercepts lie between -5 and -4 and between 0 and 1. To approximate the *x*-intercepts to the nearest tenth, use a ROOT or a ZOOM feature on your grapher or redefine the viewing window. (A ROOT feature calculates the *x*-intercept. A ZOOM feature magnifies the viewing window around a specific location such as the graph cursor.) If we redefine the window to $[0, 1]$ on the x-axis and $[-1, 1]$ on the y-axis, the graph to the left is generated.

By using the TRACE feature, we can conclude that one x-intercept is approximately 0.6 to the nearest tenth. By repeating these steps for the other x-intercept, we find that it is approximately -4.6.

Use a grapher to approximate the real number solutions to the nearest tenth. If an equation has no real number solution, state so.

1. $3x^2 - 4x - 6 = 0$

2. $x^2 - x - 9 = 0$

3. $2x^2 + x + 2 = 0$

4. $-4x^2 - 5x - 4 = 0$

5. $-x^2 + x + 5 = 0$

6. $10x^2 + 6x - 3 = 0$

Vocabulary, Readiness & Video Check

Use the choices below to fill in each blank. Not all choices will be used.

$-3, 5$	$a = 0$ or $b = 0$	0	linear
$3, -5$	quadratic	1	

1. An equation that can be written in the form $ax^2 + bx + c = 0$, with $a \neq 0$, is called a _____ equation.

2. If the product of two numbers is 0, then at least one of the numbers must be _____.

3. The solutions to $(x - 3)(x + 5) = 0$ are _____.

4. If $a \cdot b = 0$, then _____.

Martin-Gay Interactive Videos

See Video 6.6

Watch the section lecture video and answer the following questions.

OBJECTIVE 1

5. As shown in ▣ Examples 1–3, what two things have to be true in order to use the zero factor theorem?

OBJECTIVE 2

6. ▣ Example 4 implies that the zero factor theorem can be used with any number of factors on one side of the equation so long as the other side of the equation is zero. Why do you think this is true?

OBJECTIVE 3

7. From ▣ Example 5, how does finding the x-intercepts of the graph of a quadratic equation in two variables lead to solving a quadratic equation?

6.6 Exercise Set   MyMathLab®

Solve each equation. See Examples 1 through 3.

1. $(x - 6)(x - 7) = 0$

2. $(x - 10)(x - 5) = 0$

3. $(x - 2)(x + 1) = 0$

4. $(x + 4)(x - 10) = 0$

5. $(x + 9)(x + 17) = 0$

6. $(x + 11)(x + 1) = 0$

7. $x(x + 6) = 0$

8. $x(x - 7) = 0$

9. $3x(x - 8) = 0$

10. $2x(x + 12) = 0$

11. $(2x + 3)(4x - 5) = 0$

12. $(3x - 2)(5x + 1) = 0$

13. $(2x - 7)(7x + 2) = 0$

14. $(9x + 1)(4x - 3) = 0$

15. $\left(x - \dfrac{1}{2}\right)\left(x + \dfrac{1}{3}\right) = 0$

16. $\left(x + \dfrac{2}{9}\right)\left(x - \dfrac{1}{4}\right) = 0$

17. $(x + 0.2)(x + 1.5) = 0$

18. $(x + 1.7)(x + 2.3) = 0$

Solve. See Examples 4 through 7.

19. $x^2 - 13x + 36 = 0$

20. $x^2 + 2x - 63 = 0$

21. $x^2 + 2x - 8 = 0$

22. $x^2 - 5x + 6 = 0$

23. $x^2 - 7x = 0$

24. $x^2 - 3x = 0$

25. $x^2 - 4x = 32$

26. $x^2 - 5x = 24$

27. $x^2 = 16$

28. $x^2 = 9$

29. $(x + 4)(x - 9) = 4x$

30. $(x + 3)(x + 8) = x$

31. $x(3x - 1) = 14$

32. $x(4x - 11) = 3$

33. $-3x^2 + 75 = 0$

34. $-2y^2 + 72 = 0$

35. $24x^2 + 44x = 8$

36. $6x^2 + 57x = 30$

Solve each equation. See Examples 8 through 10.

37. $x^3 - 12x^2 + 32x = 0$

38. $x^3 - 14x^2 + 49x = 0$

39. $(4x - 3)(16x^2 - 24x + 9) = 0$

40. $(2x + 5)(4x^2 + 20x + 25) = 0$

41. $4x^3 - x = 0$ **42.** $4y^3 - 36y = 0$

43. $32x^3 - 4x^2 - 6x = 0$ **44.** $15x^3 + 24x^2 - 63x = 0$

MIXED PRACTICE

Solve each equation. See Examples 1 through 10. (A few exercises are linear equations.)

45. $(x + 3)(x - 2) = 0$ **46.** $(x - 6)(x + 7) = 0$

47. $x^2 + 20x = 0$ **48.** $x^2 + 15x = 0$

49. $4(x - 7) = 6$ **50.** $5(3 - 4x) = 9$

51. $4y^2 - 1 = 0$ **52.** $4y^2 - 81 = 0$

53. $(2x + 3)(2x^2 - 5x - 3) = 0$

54. $(2x - 9)(x^2 + 5x - 36) = 0$

55. $x^2 - 15 = -2x$ **56.** $x^2 - 26 = -11x$

57. $30x^2 - 11x - 30 = 0$ **58.** $12x^2 + 7x - 12 = 0$

59. $5x^2 - 6x - 8 = 0$ **60.** $9x^2 + 7x = 2$

61. $6y^2 - 22y - 40 = 0$ **62.** $3x^2 - 6x - 9 = 0$

63. $(y - 2)(y + 3) = 6$ **64.** $(y - 5)(y - 2) = 28$

65. $3x^3 + 19x^2 - 72x = 0$

66. $36x^3 + x^2 - 21x = 0$

67. $x^2 + 14x + 49 = 0$

68. $x^2 + 22x + 121 = 0$

69. $12y = 8y^2$

70. $9y = 6y^2$

71. $7x^3 - 7x = 0$

72. $3x^3 - 27x = 0$

73. $3x^2 + 8x - 11 = 13 - 6x$

74. $2x^2 + 12x - 1 = 4 + 3x$

75. $3x^2 - 20x = -4x^2 - 7x - 6$

76. $4x^2 - 20x = -5x^2 - 6x - 5$

Find the x-intercepts of the graph of each equation. See Example 11.

77. $y = (3x + 4)(x - 1)$

78. $y = (5x - 3)(x - 4)$

79. $y = x^2 - 3x - 10$

80. $y = x^2 + 7x + 6$

81. $y = 2x^2 + 11x - 6$

82. $y = 4x^2 + 11x + 6$

For Exercises 83 through 88, match each equation with its graph. See Example 11.

83. $y = (x + 2)(x - 1)$ **84.** $y = (x - 5)(x + 2)$

85. $y = x(x + 3)$ **86.** $y = x(x - 4)$

87. $y = 2x^2 - 8$ **88.** $y = 2x^2 - 2$

a.

b.

c.

d.

e.

f.

REVIEW AND PREVIEW

Perform the following operations. Write all results in lowest terms. See Section 1.3.

89. $\dfrac{3}{5} + \dfrac{4}{9}$ **90.** $\dfrac{2}{3} + \dfrac{3}{7}$

91. $\dfrac{7}{10} - \dfrac{5}{12}$ **92.** $\dfrac{5}{9} - \dfrac{5}{12}$

93. $\dfrac{7}{8} \div \dfrac{7}{15}$ **94.** $\dfrac{5}{12} - \dfrac{3}{10}$

95. $\dfrac{4}{5} \cdot \dfrac{7}{8}$ **96.** $\dfrac{3}{7} \cdot \dfrac{12}{17}$

CONCEPT EXTENSIONS

For Exercises 97 and 98, see the Concept Check in this section.

97. Explain the error and solve correctly:

$$x(x - 2) = 8$$
$$x = 8 \quad \text{or} \quad x - 2 = 8$$
$$x = 10$$

98. Explain the error and solve correctly:

$$(x - 4)(x + 2) = 0$$
$$x = -4 \quad \text{or} \quad x = 2$$

99. Write a quadratic equation that has two solutions, 6 and -1. Leave the polynomial in the equation in factored form.

100. Write a quadratic equation that has two solutions, 0 and -2. Leave the polynomial in the equation in factored form.

101. Write a quadratic equation in standard form that has two solutions, 5 and 7.

102. Write an equation that has three solutions, 0, 1, and 2.

103. A compass is accidentally thrown upward and out of an air balloon at a height of 300 feet. The height, y, of the compass at time x in seconds is given by the equation

$$y = -16x^2 + 20x + 300$$

300 ft

a. Find the height of the compass at the given times by filling in the table below.

time, x	0	1	2	3	4	5	6
height, y							

b. Use the table to determine when the compass strikes the ground.

c. Use the table to approximate the maximum height of the compass.

d. Plot the points (x, y) on a rectangular coordinate system and connect them with a smooth curve. Explain your results.

104. A rocket is fired upward from the ground with an initial velocity of 100 feet per second. The height, y, of the rocket at any time x is given by the equation

$$y = -16x^2 + 100x$$

y

a. Find the height of the rocket at the given times by filling in the table below.

time, x	0	1	2	3	4	5	6	7
height, y								

b. Use the table to approximate when the rocket strikes the ground to the nearest second.

c. Use the table to approximate the maximum height of the rocket.

d. Plot the points (x, y) on a rectangular coordinate system and connect them with a smooth curve. Explain your results.

Solve each equation. First, multiply the binomial.

To solve $(x - 6)(2x - 3) = (x + 2)(x + 9)$, see below.

$$(x - 6)(2x - 3) = (x + 2)(x + 9)$$
$$2x^2 - 15x + 18 = x^2 + 11x + 18$$
$$x^2 - 26x = 0$$
$$x(x - 26) = 0$$
$$x = 0 \quad \text{or} \quad x - 26 = 0$$
$$x = 26$$

105. $(x - 3)(3x + 4) = (x + 2)(x - 6)$

106. $(2x - 3)(x + 6) = (x - 9)(x + 2)$

107. $(2x - 3)(x + 8) = (x - 6)(x + 4)$

108. $(x + 6)(x - 6) = (2x - 9)(x + 4)$

6.7 | Quadratic Equations and Problem Solving

OBJECTIVE

1 Solve Problems That Can Be Modeled by Quadratic Equations.

OBJECTIVE

1 Solving Problems Modeled by Quadratic Equations

Some problems may be modeled by quadratic equations. To solve these problems, we use the same problem-solving steps that were introduced in Section 2.4. When solving these problems, keep in mind that a solution of an equation that models a problem may not be a solution to the problem. For example, a person's age or the length of a rectangle is always a positive number. Discard solutions that do not make sense as solutions of the problem.

EXAMPLE 1 **Finding Free-Fall Time**

Since the 1940s, one of the top tourist attractions in Acapulco, Mexico, is watching the cliff divers off the La Quebrada.
The divers' platform is about 144 feet above the sea. These
divers must time their descent just right, since they land in
the crashing Pacific, in an inlet that is at most $9\frac{1}{2}$ feet deep.
Neglecting air resistance, the height h in feet of a cliff diver
above the ocean after t seconds is given by the quadratic equation $h = -16t^2 + 144$.

  Find out how long it takes the diver to reach the ocean.

Solution

1. UNDERSTAND. Read and reread the problem. Then draw a
    picture of the problem.

    The equation $h = -16t^2 + 144$ models the height of the fall-
    ing diver at time t. Familiarize yourself with this equation by finding
    the height of the diver at time $t = 1$ second and $t = 2$ seconds.
        When $t = 1$ second, the height of the diver is $h = -16(1)^2 + 144 = 128$ feet.
        When $t = 2$ seconds, the height of the diver is $h = -16(2)^2 + 144 = 80$ feet.

2. TRANSLATE. To find out how long it takes the diver to reach the ocean, we want
    to know the value of t for which $h = 0$.

3. SOLVE.

$0 = -16t^2 + 144$	
$0 = -16(t^2 - 9)$	Factor out -16.
$0 = -16(t - 3)(t + 3)$	Factor completely.
$t - 3 = 0$ or $t + 3 = 0$	Set each factor containing a variable equal to 0.
$t = 3$ or $t = -3$	Solve.

4. INTERPRET. Since the time t cannot be negative, the proposed solution is
    3 seconds.

Check: Verify that the height of the diver when t is 3 seconds is 0.

    When $t = 3$ seconds, $h = -16(3)^2 + 144 = -144 + 144 = 0$.

State: It takes the diver 3 seconds to reach the ocean.

PRACTICE

1   Cliff divers also frequent the falls at Waimea Falls Park in Oahu, Hawaii. One
of the popular diving spots is 64 feet high. Neglecting air resistance, the height of a
diver above the pool after t seconds is $h = -16t^2 + 64$. Find how long it takes a diver
to reach the pool.

EXAMPLE 2 **Finding an Unknown Number**

The square of a number plus three times the number is 70. Find the number.

Solution

1. UNDERSTAND. Read and reread the problem. Suppose that the number is 5.
    The square of 5 is 5^2 or 25. Three times 5 is 15. Then $25 + 15 = 40$, not 70, so the
    number is not 5. Remember, the purpose of proposing a number, such as 5, is to un-
    derstand the problem better. Now that we do, we will let $x =$ the number.

2. TRANSLATE.

the square of a number	plus	three times the number	is	70
↓	↓	↓	↓	↓
x^2	$+$	$3x$	$=$	70

3. SOLVE.

$$x^2 + 3x = 70$$
$$x^2 + 3x - 70 = 0 \qquad \text{Subtract 70 from both sides.}$$
$$(x + 10)(x - 7) = 0 \qquad \text{Factor.}$$
$$x + 10 = 0 \quad \text{or} \quad x - 7 = 0 \quad \text{Set each factor equal to 0.}$$
$$x = -10 \qquad\qquad x = 7 \quad \text{Solve.}$$

4. INTERPRET.

Check: The square of -10 is $(-10)^2$, or 100. Three times -10 is $3(-10)$ or -30. Then $100 + (-30) = 70$, the correct sum, so -10 checks.

The square of 7 is 7^2 or 49. Three times 7 is $3(7)$, or 21. Then $49 + 21 = 70$, the correct sum, so 7 checks.

State: There are two numbers. They are -10 and 7.   □

PRACTICE

2   The square of a number minus eight times the number is equal to forty-eight. Find the number.

.... ▪

△   **EXAMPLE 3**   **Finding the Dimensions of a Sail**

The height of a triangular sail is 2 meters less than twice the length of the base. If the sail has an area of 30 square meters, find the length of its base and the height.

Solution

1. **UNDERSTAND.** Read and reread the problem. Since we are finding the length of the base and the height, we let

$$x = \text{the length of the base}$$

and since the height is 2 meters less than twice the base,

$$2x - 2 = \text{the height}$$

An illustration is shown to the right.

Height = $2x - 2$

Base = x

2. **TRANSLATE.** We are given that the area of the triangle is 30 square meters, so we use the formula for area of a triangle.

area of triangle	$=$	$\dfrac{1}{2}$	$\cdot$	base	$\cdot$	height
↓		↓		↓		↓
30	$=$	$\dfrac{1}{2}$	$\cdot$	x	$\cdot$	$(2x - 2)$

(Continued on next page)

3. SOLVE. Now we solve the quadratic equation.

$$30 = \frac{1}{2}x(2x - 2)$$

$$30 = x^2 - x \qquad \text{Multiply.}$$

$$x^2 - x - 30 = 0 \qquad \text{Write in standard form.}$$

$$(x - 6)(x + 5) = 0 \qquad \text{Factor.}$$

$$x - 6 = 0 \quad \text{or} \quad x + 5 = 0 \qquad \text{Set each factor equal to 0.}$$

$$x = 6 \qquad\qquad x = -5$$

4. INTERPRET. Since x represents the length of the base, we discard the solution -5. The base of a triangle cannot be negative. The base is then 6 meters and the height is $2(6) - 2 = 10$ meters.

Check: To check this problem, we recall that $\frac{1}{2}$base $\cdot$ height $=$ area, or

$$\frac{1}{2}(6)(10) = 30 \quad \text{The required area}$$

State: The base of the triangular sail is 6 meters and the height is 10 meters. □

PRACTICE

3 An engineering team from Georgia Tech earned second place in a flight competition, with their triangular shaped paper hang glider. The base of their prize-winning entry was 1 foot less than three times the height. If the area of the triangular glider wing was 210 square feet, find the dimensions of the wing. (*Source: The Technique* [Georgia Tech's newspaper], April 18, 2003)

. . . . ■

Study the following diagrams for a review of consecutive integers.

Examples

If x is the first integer, then consecutive integers are $x, x + 1, x + 2, \ldots$

If x is the first even integer, then consecutive even integers are $x, x + 2, x + 4, \ldots$

If x is the first odd integer, then consecutive odd integers are $x, x + 2, x + 4, \ldots$

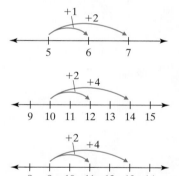

EXAMPLE 4 **Finding Consecutive Even Integers**

Find two consecutive even integers whose product is 34 more than their sum.

Solution

1. UNDERSTAND. Read and reread the problem. Let's just choose two consecutive even integers to help us better understand the problem. Let's choose 10 and 12. Their product is $10(12) = 120$ and their sum is $10 + 12 = 22$. The product is $120 - 22$, or 98 greater than the sum. Thus our guess is incorrect, but we have a better understanding of this example.

Let's let x and $x + 2$ be the consecutive even integers.

2. TRANSLATE.

Product of integers	is	34	more than	sum of integers
↓	↓	↓	↓	↓
$x(x + 2)$	$=$	34	$+$	$x + (x + 2)$

3. SOLVE. Now we solve the equation.

$$x(x + 2) = 34 + x + (x + 2)$$
$$x^2 + 2x = 34 + x + x + 2 \qquad \text{Multiply.}$$
$$x^2 + 2x = 2x + 36 \qquad \text{Combine like terms.}$$
$$x^2 - 36 = 0 \qquad \text{Write in standard form.}$$
$$(x + 6)(x - 6) = 0 \qquad \text{Factor.}$$
$$x + 6 = 0 \quad \text{or} \quad x - 6 = 0 \qquad \text{Set each factor equal to 0.}$$
$$x = -6 \qquad\qquad x = 6 \qquad \text{Solve.}$$

4. INTERPRET. If $x = -6$, then $x + 2 = -6 + 2$, or -4.
If $x = 6$, then $x + 2 = 6 + 2$, or 8.

Check: $\quad -6, -4 \qquad\qquad\qquad\qquad\qquad 6, 8$

$$-6(-4) \overset{?}{=} 34 + (-6) + (-4) \qquad\qquad 6(8) \overset{?}{=} 34 + 6 + 8$$
$$24 \overset{?}{=} 34 + (-10) \qquad\qquad\qquad 48 \overset{?}{=} 34 + 14$$
$$24 = 24 \qquad\qquad \text{True} \qquad\qquad 48 = 48 \qquad\qquad \text{True}$$

State: The two consecutive even integers are -6 and -4 or 6 and 8. □

PRACTICE

4 Find two consecutive integers whose product is 41 more than their sum.

··· ■

The next example uses the **Pythagorean theorem** and consecutive integers. Before we review this theorem, recall that a **right triangle** is a triangle that contains a 90° or right angle. The **hypotenuse** of a right triangle is the side opposite the right angle and is the longest side of the triangle. The **legs** of a right triangle are the other sides of the triangle.

> ▶ **Helpful Hint**
> If you use this formula, don't forget that c represents the length of the hypotenuse.

Pythagorean Theorem

In a right triangle, the sum of the squares of the lengths of the two legs is equal to the square of the length of the hypotenuse.

$$(\text{leg})^2 + (\text{leg})^2 = (\text{hypotenuse})^2 \qquad \text{or} \qquad a^2 + b^2 = c^2$$

leg b hypotenuse c

leg a

△ **EXAMPLE 5** **Finding the Dimensions of a Triangle**

Find the lengths of the sides of a right triangle if the lengths can be expressed as three consecutive even integers.

(Continued on next page)

Solution

1. UNDERSTAND. Read and reread the problem. Let's suppose that the length of one leg of the right triangle is 4 units. Then the other leg is the next even integer, or 6 units, and the hypotenuse of the triangle is the next even integer, or 8 units. Remember that the hypotenuse is the longest side. Let's see if a triangle with sides of these lengths forms a right triangle. To do this, we check to see whether the Pythagorean theorem holds true.

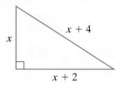

$$4^2 + 6^2 \stackrel{?}{=} 8^2$$

$$16 + 36 \stackrel{?}{=} 64$$

$$52 = 64 \quad \text{False}$$

Our proposed numbers do not check, but we now have a better understanding of the problem.

We let x, $x + 2$, and $x + 4$ be three consecutive even integers. Since these integers represent lengths of the sides of a right triangle, we have the following.

$$x = \text{one leg}$$

$$x + 2 = \text{other leg}$$

$$x + 4 = \text{hypotenuse (longest side)}$$

2. TRANSLATE. By the Pythagorean theorem, we have that

$$(\text{leg})^2 + (\text{leg})^2 = (\text{hypotenuse})^2$$

$$(x)^2 + (x + 2)^2 = (x + 4)^2$$

3. SOLVE. Now we solve the equation.

$$x^2 + (x + 2)^2 = (x + 4)^2$$

$$x^2 + x^2 + 4x + 4 = x^2 + 8x + 16 \qquad \text{Multiply.}$$

$$2x^2 + 4x + 4 = x^2 + 8x + 16 \qquad \text{Combine like terms.}$$

$$x^2 - 4x - 12 = 0 \qquad \text{Write in standard form.}$$

$$(x - 6)(x + 2) = 0 \qquad \text{Factor.}$$

$$x - 6 = 0 \quad \text{or} \quad x + 2 = 0 \qquad \text{Set each factor equal to 0.}$$

$$x = 6 \qquad\qquad x = -2$$

4. INTERPRET. We discard $x = -2$ since length cannot be negative. If $x = 6$, then $x + 2 = 8$ and $x + 4 = 10$.

Check: Verify that

$$(\text{leg})^2 + (\text{leg})^2 = (\text{hypotenuse})^2$$

$$6^2 + 8^2 \stackrel{?}{=} 10^2$$

$$36 + 64 \stackrel{?}{=} 100$$

$$100 = 100 \qquad\qquad \text{True}$$

State: The sides of the right triangle have lengths 6 units, 8 units, and 10 units.

PRACTICE

5   Find the dimensions of a right triangle where the second leg is 1 unit less than double the first leg, and the hypotenuse is 1 unit more than double the length of the first leg.

Vocabulary, Readiness & Video Check

Martin-Gay Interactive Videos

See Video 6.7

Watch the section lecture video and answer the following question.

OBJECTIVE 1

1. In each of Examples 1–3, why aren't both solutions of the translated equation accepted as solutions to the application?

6.7 Exercise Set   MyMathLab®

MIXED PRACTICE

See Examples 1 through 5 for all exercises.

TRANSLATING

For Exercises 1 through 6, represent each given condition using a single variable, x.

△ 1. The length and width of a rectangle whose length is 4 centimeters more than its width

△ 2. The length and width of a rectangle whose length is twice its width

3. Two consecutive odd integers

4. Two consecutive even integers

△ 5. The base and height of a triangle whose height is one more than four times its base

△ 6. The base and height of a trapezoid whose base is three less than five times its height

Use the information given to find the dimensions of each figure.

△ 7. The *area* of the square is 121 square units. Find the length of its sides.

△ 8. The *area* of the rectangle is 84 square inches. Find its length and width.

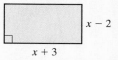

△ 9. The *perimeter* of the quadrilateral is 120 centimeters. Find the lengths of the sides.

△ 10. The *perimeter* of the triangle is 85 feet. Find the lengths of its sides.

△ 11. The *area* of the parallelogram is 96 square miles. Find its base and height.

△ 12. The *area* of the circle is 25π square kilometers. Find its radius.

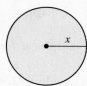

Solve.

▶ **13.** An object is thrown upward from the top of an 80-foot building with an initial velocity of 64 feet per second. The height h of the object after t seconds is given by the quadratic equation $h = -16t^2 + 64t + 80$. When will the object hit the ground?

14. A hang glider pilot accidentally drops her compass from the top of a 400-foot cliff. The height h of the compass after t seconds is given by the quadratic equation $h = -16t^2 + 400$. When will the compass hit the ground?

△ **15.** The width of a rectangle is 7 centimeters less than twice its length. Its area is 30 square centimeters. Find the dimensions of the rectangle.

△ **16.** The length of a rectangle is 9 inches more than its width. Its area is 112 square inches. Find the dimensions of the rectangle.

The equation $D = \dfrac{1}{2}n(n - 3)$ gives the number of diagonals D for a polygon with n sides. For example, a polygon with 6 sides has $D = \dfrac{1}{2} \cdot 6(6 - 3)$ or $D = 9$ diagonals. (See if you can count all 9 diagonals. Some are shown in the figure.) Use this equation, $D = \dfrac{1}{2}n(n - 3)$, for Exercises 17 through 20.

△ **17.** Find the number of diagonals for a polygon that has 12 sides.

△ **18.** Find the number of diagonals for a polygon that has 15 sides.

△ **19.** Find the number of sides n for a polygon that has 35 diagonals.

△ **20.** Find the number of sides n for a polygon that has 14 diagonals.

Solve.

21. The sum of a number and its square is 132. Find the number(s).

▶ **22.** The sum of a number and its square is 182. Find the number(s).

23. The product of two consecutive room numbers is 210. Find the room numbers.

▶ **24.** The product of two consecutive page numbers is 420. Find the page numbers.

25. A ladder is leaning against a building so that the distance from the ground to the top of the ladder is one foot less than the length of the ladder. Find the length of the ladder if the distance from the bottom of the ladder to the building is 5 feet.

26. Use the given figure to find the length of the guy wire.

△ **27.** If the sides of a square are increased by 3 inches, the area becomes 64 square inches. Find the length of the sides of the original square.

△ **28.** If the sides of a square are increased by 5 meters, the area becomes 100 square meters. Find the length of the sides of the original square.

29. One leg of a right triangle is 4 millimeters longer than the smaller leg and the hypotenuse is 8 millimeters longer than the smaller leg. Find the lengths of the sides of the triangle.

30. One leg of a right triangle is 9 centimeters longer than the other leg and the hypotenuse is 45 centimeters. Find the lengths of the legs of the triangle.

31. The length of the base of a triangle is twice its height. If the area of the triangle is 100 square kilometers, find the height.

32. The height of a triangle is 2 millimeters less than the base. If the area is 60 square millimeters, find the base.

33. Find the length of the shorter leg of a right triangle if the longer leg is 12 feet more than the shorter leg and the hypotenuse is 12 feet less than twice the shorter leg.

34. Find the length of the shorter leg of a right triangle if the longer leg is 10 miles more than the shorter leg and the hypotenuse is 10 miles less than twice the shorter leg.

35. An object is dropped from 39 feet below the tip of the pinnacle atop one of the 1483-foot-tall Petronas Twin Towers in Kuala Lumpur, Malaysia. (*Source:* Council on Tall Buildings and Urban Habitat) The height h of the object after t seconds is given by the equation $h = -16t^2 + 1444$. Find how many seconds pass before the object reaches the ground.

36. An object is dropped from the top of 311 South Wacker Drive, a 961-foot-tall office building in Chicago. (*Source:* Council on Tall Buildings and Urban Habitat) The height h of the object after t seconds is given by the equation $h = -16t^2 + 961$. Find how many seconds pass before the object reaches the ground.

37. At the end of 2 years, P dollars invested at an interest rate r compounded annually increases to an amount, A dollars, given by

$$A = P(1 + r)^2$$

Find the interest rate if $100 increased to $144 in 2 years. Write your answer as a percent.

38. At the end of 2 years, P dollars invested at an interest rate r compounded annually increases to an amount, A dollars, given by

$$A = P(1 + r)^2$$

Find the interest rate if $2000 increased to $2420 in 2 years. Write your answer as a percent.

39. Find the dimensions of a rectangle whose width is 7 miles less than its length and whose area is 120 square miles.

40. Find the dimensions of a rectangle whose width is 2 inches less than half its length and whose area is 160 square inches.

41. If the cost, C, for manufacturing x units of a certain product is given by $C = x^2 - 15x + 50$, find the number of units manufactured at a cost of $9500.

42. If a switchboard handles n telephones, the number C of telephone connections it can make simultaneously is given by the equation $C = \dfrac{n(n - 1)}{2}$. Find how many telephones are handled by a switchboard making 120 telephone connections simultaneously.

REVIEW AND PREVIEW

The following double-line graph shows a comparison of the number of annual visitors (in millions) to Glacier National Park and Gettysburg National Military Park for the years shown. Use this graph to answer Exercises 43 through 50. See Section 3.1.

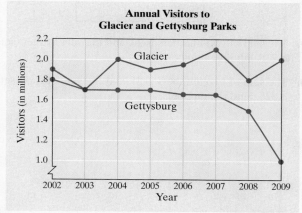

43. Approximate the number of visitors to Glacier National Park in 2009.

44. Approximate the number of visitors to Gettysburg National Military Park in 2009.

45. Approximate the number of visitors to Glacier National Park in 2005.

46. Approximate the number of visitors to Gettysburg National Military Park in 2005.

47. Determine the year that the colored lines in this graph intersect.

48. For what years on the graph is the number of visitors to Glacier Park greater than the number of visitors to Gettysburg Park?

49. In your own words, explain the meaning of the point of intersection in the graph.

50. Describe the trends shown in this graph and speculate as to why these trends have occurred.

Write each fraction in simplest form. See Section 1.3.

51. $\dfrac{20}{35}$ **52.** $\dfrac{24}{32}$ **53.** $\dfrac{27}{18}$

54. $\dfrac{15}{27}$ **55.** $\dfrac{14}{42}$ **56.** $\dfrac{45}{50}$

CONCEPT EXTENSIONS

△ **57.** Two boats travel at right angles to each other after leaving the same dock at the same time. One hour later, the boats are 17 miles apart. If one boat travels 7 miles per hour faster than the other boat, find the rate of each boat.

△ **58.** The side of a square equals the width of a rectangle. The length of the rectangle is 6 meters longer than its width. The sum of the areas of the square and the rectangle is 176 square meters. Find the side of the square.

59. The sum of two numbers is 20, and the sum of their squares is 218. Find the numbers.

60. The sum of two numbers is 25, and the sum of their squares is 325. Find the numbers.

△ **61.** A rectangular pool is surrounded by a walk 4 meters wide. The pool is 6 meters longer than its width. If the total area of the pool and walk is 576 square meters more than the area of the pool, find the dimensions of the pool.

△ **62.** A rectangular garden is surrounded by a walk of uniform width. The area of the garden is 180 square yards. If the dimensions of the garden plus the walk are 16 yards by 24 yards, find the width of the walk.

63. Write down two numbers whose sum is 10. Square each number and find the sum of the squares. Use this work to write a word problem like Exercise 59. Then give the word problem to a classmate to solve.

64. Write down two numbers whose sum is 12. Square each number and find the sum of the squares. Use this work to write a word problem like Exercise 60. Then give the word problem to a classmate to solve.

Chapter 6 Vocabulary Check

Fill in each blank with one of the words or phrases listed below. Not all choices will be used and some choices may be used more than once.

factoring	quadratic equation	perfect square trinomial	0
greatest common factor	hypotenuse	sum of two cubes	1
difference of two cubes	difference of two squares	triangle	leg

1. An equation that can be written in the form $ax^2 + bx + c = 0$ (with a not 0) is called a _____.

2. _____ is the process of writing an expression as a product.

3. The _____ of a list of terms is the product of all common factors.

4. A trinomial that is the square of some binomial is called a _____.

5. The expression $a^2 - b^2$ is called a _____.

6. The expression $a^3 - b^3$ is called a _____.

7. The expression $a^3 + b^3$ is called a _____.

8. By the zero factor property, if the product of two numbers is 0, then at least one of the numbers must be _____.

9. In a right triangle, the side opposite the right angle is called the _____.

10. In a right triangle, each side adjacent to the right angle is called a _____.

11. The Pythagorean theorem states that $(\text{leg})^2 + (\text{leg})^2 = ($_____$)^2$.

Chapter 6 Highlights

DEFINITIONS AND CONCEPTS	EXAMPLES

Section 6.1   The Greatest Common Factor and Factoring by Grouping

Factoring is the process of writing an expression as a product.	Factor: $\qquad\qquad 6 = 2 \cdot 3$ $$x^2 + 5x + 6 = (x + 2)(x + 3)$$
To Find the GCF of a List of Integers	Find the GCF of 12, 36, and 48.
Step 1. Write each number as a product of primes.	$12 = 2 \cdot 2 \cdot 3$
Step 2. Identify the common prime factors.	$36 = 2 \cdot 2 \cdot 3 \cdot 3$
Step 3. The product of all common factors is the greatest common factor. If there are no common prime factors, the GCF is 1.	$48 = 2 \cdot 2 \cdot 2 \cdot 2 \cdot 3$ $\text{GCF} = 2 \cdot 2 \cdot 3 = 12$
The GCF of a list of common variables raised to powers is the variable raised to the smallest exponent in the list.	The GCF of z^5, z^3, and z^{10} is z^3.
The GCF of a list of terms is the product of all common factors.	Find the GCF of $8x^2y$, $10x^3y^2$, and $26x^2y^3$. The GCF of 8, 10, and 26 is 2. The GCF of x^2, x^3, and x^2 is x^2. The GCF of y, y^2, and y^3 is y. The GCF of the terms is $2x^2y$.
To Factor by Grouping	Factor $10ax + 15a - 6xy - 9y$.
Step 1. Arrange the terms so that the first two terms have a common factor and the last two have a common factor.	**Step 1.** $10ax + 15a - 6xy - 9y$
Step 2. For each pair of terms, factor out the pair's GCF.	**Step 2.** $5a(2x + 3) - 3y(2x + 3)$
Step 3. If there is now a common binomial factor, factor it out.	**Step 3.** $(2x + 3)(5a - 3y)$
Step 4. If there is no common binomial factor, begin again, rearranging the terms differently. If no rearrangement leads to a common binomial factor, the polynomial cannot be factored.	

Section 6.2   Factoring Trinomials of the Form $x^2 + bx + c$

The product of these numbers is c. $$x^2 + bx + c = (x + \square)(x + \square)$$ The sum of these numbers is b.	Factor: $x^2 + 7x + 12$ $3 + 4 = 7 \qquad 3 \cdot 4 = 12$ $$x^2 + 7x + 12 = (x + 3)(x + 4)$$

DEFINITIONS AND CONCEPTS	EXAMPLES

Section 6.3   Factoring Trinomials of the Form $ax^2 + bx + c$ and Perfect Square Trinomials

To factor $ax^2 + bx + c$, try various combinations of factors of ax^2 and c until a middle term of bx is obtained when checking.

Factor: $3x^2 + 14x - 5$

Factors of $3x^2$: $3x, x$

Factors of -5: $-1, 5$ and $1, -5$.

$$(3x - 1)(x + 5)$$
$$-1x$$
$$+15x \quad \textbf{Correct} \text{ middle term}$$
$$14x$$

A **perfect square trinomial** is a trinomial that is the square of some binomial.

Perfect square trinomial = square of binomial
$$x^2 + 4x + 4 = (x + 2)^2$$
$$25x^2 - 10x + 1 = (5x - 1)^2$$

Factoring Perfect Square Trinomials:
$$a^2 + 2ab + b^2 = (a + b)^2$$
$$a^2 - 2ab + b^2 = (a - b)^2$$

Factor:
$$x^2 + 6x + 9 = x^2 + 2 \cdot x \cdot 3 + 3^2 = (x + 3)^2$$
$$4x^2 - 12x + 9 = (2x)^2 - 2 \cdot 2x \cdot 3 + 3^2 = (2x - 3)^2$$

Section 6.4   Factoring Trinomials of the Form $ax^2 + bx + c$ by Grouping

To Factor $ax^2 + bx + c$ by Grouping

Step 1. Find two numbers whose product is $a \cdot c$ and whose sum is b.

Step 2. Rewrite bx, using the factors found in Step 1.

Step 3. Factor by grouping.

Factor: $3x^2 + 14x - 5$

Step 1. Find two numbers whose product is $3 \cdot (-5)$ or -15 and whose sum is 14. They are 15 and -1.

Step 2. $3x^2 + 14x - 5$
$$= 3x^2 + 15x - 1x - 5$$

Step 3. $= 3x(x + 5) - 1(x + 5)$
$$= (x + 5)(3x - 1)$$

Section 6.5   Factoring Binomials

Difference of Squares
$$a^2 - b^2 = (a + b)(a - b)$$

Sum or Difference of Cubes
$$a^3 + b^3 = (a + b)(a^2 - ab + b^2)$$
$$a^3 - b^3 = (a - b)(a^2 + ab + b^2)$$

Factor:
$$x^2 - 9 = x^2 - 3^2 = (x + 3)(x - 3)$$

$$y^3 + 8 = y^3 + 2^3 = (y + 2)(y^2 - 2y + 4)$$
$$125z^3 - 1 = (5z)^3 - 1^3 = (5z - 1)(25z^2 + 5z + 1)$$

Integrated Review—Choosing a Factoring Strategy

To Factor a Polynomial,

Step 1. Factor out the GCF.

Step 2. **a.** If two terms,
  i. $a^2 - b^2 = (a + b)(a - b)$
  ii. $a^3 - b^3 = (a - b)(a^2 + ab + b^2)$
  iii. $a^3 + b^3 = (a + b)(a^2 - ab + b^2)$
 b. If three terms,
  i. $a^2 + 2ab + b^2 = (a + b)^2$
  ii. Methods in Sections 6.2 and 6.3
 c. If four or more terms, try factoring by grouping.

Factor: $2x^4 - 6x^2 - 8$

Step 1. $2x^4 - 6x^2 - 8 = 2(x^4 - 3x^2 - 4)$

Step 2.   b. ii. $\quad = 2(x^2 + 1)(x^2 - 4)$

(continued)

DEFINITIONS AND CONCEPTS	EXAMPLES

Integrated Review—Choosing a Factoring Strategy (continued)

Step 3. See if any factors can be factored further.

Step 4. Check by multiplying.

Step 3. $= 2(x^2 + 1)(x + 2)(x - 2)$

Step 4. Check by multiplying.

$$2(x^2 + 1)(x + 2)(x - 2) = 2(x^2 + 1)(x^2 - 4)$$
$$= 2(x^4 - 3x^2 - 4)$$
$$= 2x^4 - 6x^2 - 8$$

Section 6.6   Solving Quadratic Equations by Factoring

A **quadratic equation** is an equation that can be written in the form $ax^2 + bx + c = 0$ with a not 0.

The form $ax^2 + bx + c = 0$ is called the **standard form** of a quadratic equation.

Quadratic Equation	*Standard Form*
$x^2 = 16$	$x^2 - 16 = 0$
$y = -2y^2 + 5$	$2y^2 + y - 5 = 0$

Zero Factor Theorem

If a and b are real numbers and if $ab = 0$, then $a = 0$ or $b = 0$.

If $(x + 3)(x - 1) = 0$, then $x + 3 = 0$ or $x - 1 = 0$

To solve quadratic equations by factoring,

Solve: $3x^2 = 13x - 4$

Step 1. Write the equation in standard form: $ax^2 + bx + c = 0$.

Step 1. $3x^2 - 13x + 4 = 0$

Step 2. Factor the quadratic.

Step 2. $(3x - 1)(x - 4) = 0$

Step 3. Set each factor containing a variable equal to 0.

Step 3. $3x - 1 = 0$ or $x - 4 = 0$

Step 4. Solve the equations.

Step 4. $3x = 1$ or $x = 4$

$$x = \frac{1}{3}$$

Step 5. Check in the original equation.

Step 5. Check both $\frac{1}{3}$ and 4 in the original equation.

Section 6.7   Quadratic Equations and Problem Solving

Problem-Solving Steps

A garden is in the shape of a rectangle whose length is two feet more than its width. If the area of the garden is 35 square feet, find its dimensions.

1. UNDERSTAND the problem.

1. Read and reread the problem. Guess a solution and check your guess.

Let x be the width of the rectangular garden. Then $x + 2$ is the length.

2. TRANSLATE.

2. In words: length   ·   width   =   area

Translate: $(x + 2)$ · x =   35

(continued)

.FINITIONS AND CONCEPTS	EXAMPLES

Section 6.7   Quadratic Equations and Problem Solving (continued)

	3.
E.	$(x + 2)x = 35$
	$x^2 + 2x - 35 = 0$
	$(x - 5)(x + 7) = 0$
	$x - 5 = 0$ or $x + 7 = 0$
	$x = 5$ or $x = -7$
4. INTERPRET.	4. Discard the solution of -7 since x represents width.

Check: If x is 5 feet then $x + 2 = 5 + 2 = 7$ feet. The area of a rectangle whose width is 5 feet and whose length is 7 feet is (5 feet)(7 feet) or 35 square feet.

State: The garden is 5 feet by 7 feet.

Chapter 6 Review

(6.1) *Complete the factoring.*

1. $6x^2 - 15x = 3x(\quad)$
2. $2x^3y + 6x^2y^2 + 8xy^3 = 2xy(\quad)$

Factor the GCF from each polynomial.

3. $20x^2 + 12x$
4. $6x^2y^2 - 3xy^3$
5. $3x(2x + 3) - 5(2x + 3)$
6. $5x(x + 1) - (x + 1)$

Factor each polynomial by grouping.

7. $3x^2 - 3x + 2x - 2$
8. $3a^2 + 9ab + 3b^2 + ab$
9. $10a^2 + 5ab + 7b^2 + 14ab$
10. $6x^2 + 10x - 3x - 5$

(6.2) *Factor each trinomial.*

11. $x^2 + 6x + 8$
12. $x^2 - 11x + 24$
13. $x^2 + x + 2$ 14. $x^2 - x + 2$
15. $x^2 + 4xy - 12y^2$
16. $x^2 + 8xy + 15y^2$
17. $72 - 18x - 2x^2$
18. $32 + 12x - 4x^2$
19. $10a^3 - 110a^2 + 100a$
20. $5y^3 - 50y^2 + 120y$
21. To factor $x^2 + 2x - 48$, think of two numbers whose product is ____ and whose sum is ____.
22. What is the first step in factoring $3x^2 + 15x + 30$?

(6.3) *or* **(6.4)** *Factor each trinomial.*

23. $2x^2 + 13x + 6$
24. $4x^2 + 4x - 3$
25. $6x^2 + 5xy - 4y^2$
26. $18x^2 - 9xy - 20y^2$
27. $10y^3 + 25y^2 - 60y$
28. $60y^3 - 39y^2 + 6y$
29. $18x^2 - 60x + 50$
30. $4x^2 - 28xy + 49y^2$

(6.5) *Factor each binomial.*

31. $4x^2 - 9$
32. $9t^2 - 25s^2$
33. $16x^2 + y^2$
34. $x^3 - 8y^3$
35. $8x^3 + 27$
36. $2x^3 + 8x$
37. $54 - 2x^3y^3$
38. $9x^2 - 4y^2$
39. $16x^4 - 1$
40. $x^4 + 16$

(6.6) *Solve the following equations.*

41. $(x + 6)(x - 2) = 0$
42. $3x(x + 1)(7x - 2) = 0$
43. $4(5x + 1)(x + 3) = 0$
44. $x^2 + 8x + 7 = 0$
45. $x^2 - 2x - 24 = 0$

46. $x^2 + 10x = -25$

47. $x(x - 10) = -16$

48. $(3x - 1)(9x^2 - 6x + 1) = 0$

49. $56x^2 - 5x - 6 = 0$

50. $20x^2 - 7x - 6 = 0$

51. $5(3x + 2) = 4$

52. $6x^2 - 3x + 8 = 0$

53. $12 - 5t = -3$

54. $5x^3 + 20x^2 + 20x = 0$

55. $4t^3 - 5t^2 - 21t = 0$

56. Write a quadratic equation that has the two solutions 4 and 5.

(6.7) Use the given information to choose the correct dimensions.

△ **57.** The perimeter of a rectangle is 24 inches. The length is twice the width. Find the dimensions of the rectangle.

  a. 5 inches by 7 inches

  b. 5 inches by 10 inches

  c. 4 inches by 8 inches

  d. 2 inches by 10 inches

△ **58.** The area of a rectangle is 80 square meters. The length is one more than three times the width. Find the dimensions of the rectangle.

  a. 8 meters by 10 meters

  b. 4 meters by 13 meters

  c. 4 meters by 20 meters

  d. 5 meters by 16 meters

Use the given information to find the dimensions of each figure.

△ **59.** The *area* of the square is 81 square units. Find the length of a side.

△ **60.** The *perimeter* of the quadrilateral is 47 units. Find the lengths of the sides.

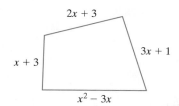

△ **61.** A flag for a local organization is in the shape of a rectangle whose length is 15 inches less than twice its width. If the area of the flag is 500 square inches, find its dimensions.

△ **62.** The base of a triangular sail is four times its height. If the area of the triangle is 162 square yards, find the base.

63. Find two consecutive positive integers whose product is 380.

64. Find two consecutive positive even integers whose product is 440.

65. A rocket is fired from the ground with an initial velocity of 440 feet per second. Its height h after t seconds is given by the equation

$$h = -16t^2 + 440t$$

2800 ft

  a. Find how many seconds pass before the rocket reaches a height of 2800 feet. Explain why two answers are obtained.

  b. Find how many seconds pass before the rocket reaches the ground again.

△ **66.** An architect's squaring instrument is in the shape of a right triangle. Find the length of the longer leg of the right triangle if the hypotenuse is 8 centimeters longer than the longer leg and the shorter leg is 8 centimeters shorter than the longer leg.

MIXED REVIEW

Factor completely.

67. $7x - 63$

68. $11x(4x - 3) - 6(4x - 3)$

69. $m^2 - \dfrac{4}{25}$

70. $3x^3 - 4x^2 + 6x - 8$

71. $xy + 2x - y - 2$

72. $2x^2 + 2x - 24$

73. $3x^3 - 30x^2 + 27x$

74. $4x^2 - 81$

75. $2x^2 - 18$

76. $16x^2 - 24x + 9$

77. $5x^2 + 20x + 20$

78. $2x^2 + 5x - 12$

79. $4x^2y - 6xy^2$

80. $125x^3 + 27$

81. $24x^2 - 3x - 18$

82. $(x + 7)^2 - y^2$

83. $x^2(x + 3) - 4(x + 3)$

84. $54a^3b - 2b$

Write the perimeter of each figure as a simplified polynomial. Then factor each polynomial.

△ **85.**

△ **86.**

Solve.

87. $2x^2 - x - 28 = 0$

88. $x^2 - 2x = 15$

89. $2x(x + 7)(x + 4) = 0$

90. $x(x - 5) = -6$

91. $x^2 = 16x$

Solve.

△ **92.** The perimeter of the following triangle is 48 inches. Find the lengths of its sides.

93. The width of a rectangle is 4 inches less than its length. Its area is 12 square inches. Find the dimensions of the rectangle.

94. A 6-foot-tall person drops an object from the top of the Westin Peachtree Plaza in Atlanta, Georgia. The Westin building is 723 feet tall. (*Source: World Almanac* research) The height h of the object after t seconds is given by the equation $h = -16t^2 + 729$. Find how many seconds pass before the object reaches the ground.

723 ft

Write an expression for the area of the shaded region. Then write the expression as a factored polynomial.

△ **95.**

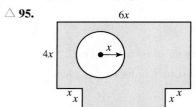

Chapter 6 Test   MyMathLab®   CHAPTER Test Prep VIDEOS   ▶ You Tube

Factor each polynomial completely. If a polynomial cannot be factored, write "prime."

▶ **1.** $x^2 + 11x + 28$

▶ **2.** $49 - m^2$

▶ **3.** $y^2 + 22y + 121$

▶ **4.** $4(a + 3) - y(a + 3)$

▶ **5.** $x^2 + 4$

▶ **6.** $y^2 - 8y - 48$

▶ **7.** $x^2 + x - 10$

▶ **8.** $9x^3 + 39x^2 + 12x$

▶ **9.** $3a^2 + 3ab - 7a - 7b$

▶ **10.** $3x^2 - 5x + 2$

▶ **11.** $x^2 + 14xy + 24y^2$

▶ **12.** $180 - 5x^2$

▶ **13.** $6t^2 - t - 5$

▶ **14.** $xy^2 - 7y^2 - 4x + 28$

▶ **15.** $x - x^5$

▶ **16.** $-xy^3 - x^3y$

▶ **17.** $64x^3 - 1$

▶ **18.** $8y^3 - 64$

Solve each equation.

▶ **19.** $(x - 3)(x + 9) = 0$

▶ **20.** $x^2 + 5x = 14$

▶ **21.** $x(x + 6) = 7$

▶ **22.** $3x(2x - 3)(3x + 4) = 0$

▶ **23.** $5t^3 - 45t = 0$

▶ **24.** $t^2 - 2t - 15 = 0$

▶ **25.** $6x^2 = 15x$

Solve each problem.

26. A deck for a home is in the shape of a triangle. The length of the base of the triangle is 9 feet longer than its altitude. If the area of the triangle is 68 square feet, find the length of the base.

Base

Altitude

27. The sum of two numbers is 17 and the sum of their squares is 145. Find the numbers.

28. An object is dropped from the top of the Woolworth Building on Broadway in New York City. The height h of the object after t seconds is given by the equation

$$h = -16t^2 + 784$$

Find how many seconds pass before the object reaches the ground.

29. Find the lengths of the sides of a right triangle if the hypotenuse is 10 centimeters longer than the shorter leg and 5 centimeters longer than the longer leg.

Chapter 6 Cumulative Review

1. Translate each sentence into a mathematical statement.
  a. Nine is less than or equal to eleven.
  b. Eight is greater than one.
  c. Three is not equal to four.

2. Insert $<$ or $>$ in the space to make each statement true.
  a. $|-5|$ _____ $|-3|$
  b. $|0|$ _____ $|-2|$

3. Simplify each fraction (write it in lowest terms).
  a. $\dfrac{42}{49}$ **b.** $\dfrac{11}{27}$ **c.** $\dfrac{88}{20}$

4. Evaluate $\dfrac{x}{y} + 5x$ if $x = 20$ and $y = 10$.

5. Simplify: $\dfrac{8 + 2 \cdot 3}{2^2 - 1}$

6. Evaluate $\dfrac{x}{y} + 5x$ if $x = -20$ and $y = 10$.

7. Add.
  a. $3 + (-7) + (-8)$
  b. $[7 + (-10)] + [-2 + |-4|]$

8. Evaluate $\dfrac{x}{y} + 5x$ if $x = -20$ and $y = -10$.

9. Multiply.
  a. $(-8)(4)$
  b. $14(-1)$
  c. $(-9)(-10)$

10. Simplify: $5 - 2(3x - 7)$

11. Simplify each expression by combining like terms.
  a. $7x - 3x$ **b.** $10y^2 + y^2$
  c. $8x^2 + 2x - 3x$ **d.** $9n^2 - 5n^2 + n^2$

12. Solve: $0.8y + 0.2(y - 1) = 1.8$

Solve.

13. $\dfrac{y}{7} = 20$

14. $\dfrac{x}{-7} = -4$

15. $-3x = 33$

16. $-\dfrac{2}{3}x = -22$

17. $8(2 - t) = -5t$

18. $-z = \dfrac{7z + 3}{5}$

19. Balsa wood sticks are commonly used to build models (for example, bridge models). A 48-inch balsa wood stick is to be cut into two pieces so that the longer piece is 3 times the shorter. Find the length of each piece.

20. Solve $3x + 9 \le 5(x - 1)$. Write the solution set using interval notation.

21. Graph the linear equation $y = -\dfrac{1}{3}x + 2$.

22. Is the ordered pair $(-1, 2)$ a solution of $-7x - 8y = -9$?

23. Find the slope and the y-intercept of the line whose equation is $3x - 4y = 4$.

24. Find the slope of the line through $(5, -6)$ and $(5, 2)$.

25. Evaluate each expression for the given value of x.
  a. $2x^3$; x is 5 **b.** $\dfrac{9}{x^2}$; x is -3

26. Find the slope and y-intercept of the line whose equation is $7x - 3y = 2$.

27. Find the degree of each term.
  a. $3x^2$ **b.** -2^3x^5 **c.** y
  d. $12x^2yz^3$ **e.** 5

28. Find an equation of the vertical line through $(0, 7)$.

29. Subtract: $(2x^3 + 8x^2 - 6x) - (2x^3 - x^2 + 1)$

30. Find an equation of the line with slope 4 and y-intercept $\left(0, \frac{1}{2}\right)$. Write the equation in standard form.

31. Multiply $(3x + 2)(2x - 5)$.

32. Write an equation of the line through $(-4, 0)$ and $(6, -1)$. Write the equation in standard form.

33. Multiply $(3y + 1)^2$.

34. Solve the system: $\begin{cases} -x + 3y = 18 \\ -3x + 2y = 19 \end{cases}$

35. Simplify by writing each expression with positive exponents only.

  a. 3^{-2} **b.** $2x^{-3}$

  c. $2^{-1} + 4^{-1}$ **d.** $(-2)^{-4}$

  e. y^{-4}

36. Simplify: $\dfrac{(5a^7)^2}{a^5}$

37. Write each number in scientific notation.
  a. 367,000,000
  b. 0.000003
  c. 20,520,000,000
  d. 0.00085

38. Multiply $(3x - 7y)^2$.

39. Divide $x^2 + 7x + 12$ by $x + 3$ using long division.

40. Simplify: $\dfrac{(xy)^{-3}}{(x^5y^6)^3}$

41. Find the GCF of each list of terms.
  a. x^3, x^7, and x^5 **b.** y, y^4, and y^7

Factor.

42. $z^3 + 7z + z^2 + 7$

43. $x^2 + 7x + 12$

44. $2x^3 + 2x^2 - 84x$

45. $8x^2 - 22x + 5$

46. $-4x^2 - 23x + 6$

47. $25a^2 - 9b^2$

48. $9xy^2 - 16x$

49. Solve: $(x - 3)(x + 1) = 0$

50. Solve $x^2 - 13x = -36$.

Appendix A

Operations on Decimals/Table of Percent, Decimal, and Fraction Equivalents

A.1 Operations on Decimals

To **add** or **subtract** decimals, write the numbers vertically with decimal points lined up. Add or subtract as with whole numbers and place the decimal point in the answer directly below the decimal points in the problem.

EXAMPLE 1   Add $5.87 + 23.279 + 0.003$.

Solution

$$
\begin{array}{r}
5.87 \\
23.279 \\
+\,0.003 \\
\hline
29.152
\end{array}
$$

     □

EXAMPLE 2   Subtract $32.15 - 11.237$.

Solution

$$
\begin{array}{rccccc}
 & & & 1 & 11 & 4 & 10 \\
 & 3 & 2 \,.\, & 1 & 5 & 0 \\
- & 1 & 1 \,.\, & 2 & 3 & 7 \\
\hline
 & 2 & 0 \,.\, & 9 & 1 & 3
\end{array}
$$

     □

To **multiply** decimals, multiply the numbers as if they were whole numbers. The decimal point in the product is placed so that the number of decimal places in the product is the same as the sum of the number of decimal places in the factors.

EXAMPLE 3   Multiply 0.072×3.5.

Solution

$$
\begin{array}{rl}
0.072 & \text{3 decimal places} \\
\times \quad 3.5 & \text{1 decimal place} \\
\hline
360 & \\
216 & \\
\hline
0.2520 & \text{4 decimal places}
\end{array}
$$

     □

To **divide** decimals, move the decimal point in the divisor to the right of the last digit. Move the decimal point in the dividend the same number of places that the decimal point in the divisor was moved. The decimal point in the quotient lies directly above the decimal point in the dividend.

EXAMPLE 4   Divide $9.46 \div 0.04$.

Solution

$$
\begin{array}{r}
236.5 \\
04.\overline{)946.0} \\
-8 \\
\hline
14 \\
-12 \\
\hline
26 \\
-24 \\
\hline
20 \\
-20 \\
\hline
\end{array}
$$

     □

A Exercise Set   MyMathLab®

Perform the indicated operations.

1. 9.076 + 8.004

2.   6.3
    × 0.05
    ───────

3.   27.004
    −14.2
    ───────

4.   0.0036
    7.12
    32.502
    + 0.05
    ───────

5. 107.92
    + 3.04
    ───────

6. 7.2 ÷ 4

7. 10 − 7.6

8. 40 ÷ 0.25

9. 126.32 − 97.89

10.   3.62
    7.11
    12.36
    4.15
    + 2.29
    ───────

11.   3.25
    × 70
    ───────

12.   26.014
    − 7.8
    ───────

13. 8.1 ÷ 3

14.   1.2366
    0.005
    15.17
    + 0.97
    ───────

15. 55.405 − 6.1711

16. 8.09 + 0.22

17. 60 ÷ 0.75

18. 20 − 12.29

19. 7.612 ÷ 100

20.   8.72
    1.12
    14.86
    3.98
    + 1.99
    ───────

21. 12.312 ÷ 2.7

22. 0.443 ÷ 100

23.   569.2
    71.25
    + 8.01
    ───────

24. 3.706 − 2.91

25. 768 − 0.17

26. 63 ÷ 0.28

27. 12 + 0.062

28. 0.42 + 18

29. 76 − 14.52

30. 1.1092 ÷ 0.47

31. 3.311 ÷ 0.43

32. 7.61 + 0.0004

33.   762.12
    89.7
    + 11.55
    ───────

34. 444 ÷ 0.6

35. 23.4 − 0.821

36. 3.7 + 5.6

37. 476.12 − 112.97

38. 19.872 ÷ 0.54

39. 0.007 + 7

40.   51.77
    + 3.6
    ───────

A.2 Table of Percent, Decimal, and Fraction Equivalents

Percent, Decimal, and Fraction Equivalents		
Percent	*Decimal*	*Fraction*
1%	0.01	$\frac{1}{100}$
5%	0.05	$\frac{1}{20}$
10%	0.1	$\frac{1}{10}$
12.5% or $12\frac{1}{2}$%	0.125	$\frac{1}{8}$
$16.\overline{6}$% or $16\frac{2}{3}$%	$0.1\overline{6}$	$\frac{1}{6}$
20%	0.2	$\frac{1}{5}$
25%	0.25	$\frac{1}{4}$
30%	0.3	$\frac{3}{10}$
$33.\overline{3}$% or $33\frac{1}{3}$%	$0.\overline{3}$	$\frac{1}{3}$
37.5% or $37\frac{1}{2}$%	0.375	$\frac{3}{8}$
40%	0.4	$\frac{2}{5}$
50%	0.5	$\frac{1}{2}$
60%	0.6	$\frac{3}{5}$
62.5% or $62\frac{1}{2}$%	0.625	$\frac{5}{8}$
$66.\overline{6}$% or $66\frac{2}{3}$%	$0.\overline{6}$	$\frac{2}{3}$
70%	0.7	$\frac{7}{10}$
75%	0.75	$\frac{3}{4}$
80%	0.8	$\frac{4}{5}$
$83.\overline{3}$% or $83\frac{1}{3}$%	$08.\overline{3}$	$\frac{5}{6}$
87.5% or $87\frac{1}{2}$%	0.875	$\frac{7}{8}$
90%	0.9	$\frac{9}{10}$
100%	1.0	1
110%	1.1	$1\frac{1}{10}$
125%	1.25	$1\frac{1}{4}$
$133.\overline{3}$% or $133\frac{1}{3}$%	$1.\overline{3}$	$1\frac{1}{3}$
150%	1.5	$1\frac{1}{2}$
$166.\overline{6}$% or $166\frac{2}{3}$%	$1.\overline{6}$	$1\frac{2}{3}$
175%	1.75	$1\frac{3}{4}$
200%	2.0	2

Appendix B

Review of Algebra Topics

Recall that equations model many real-life problems. For example, we can use a linear equation to calculate the increase in the number (in millions) of Wi-Fi-enabled cell phones.

Wi-Fi-enabled cell phones let you carry your Internet access with you. There are already several of these smart phones available, and this technology will continue to expand. Predicted numbers of Wi-Fi-enabled cell phones in the United States for various years are shown below.

Projected Growth of Wi-Fi-Enabled Cell Phones in the U.S.

To find the projected increase in the number of Wi-Fi-enabled cell phones in the United States from 2014 to 2015, for example, we can use the equation below.

In words:	Increase in cell phones	is	cell phones in 2015	minus	cell phones in 2014
Translate:	x	$=$	149	$-$	138

Since our variable x (increase in Wi-Fi-enabled cell phones) is by itself on one side of the equation, we can find the value of x by simplifying the right side.

$$x = 11$$

The projected increase in the number of Wi-Fi-enabled cell phones from 2014 to 2015 is 11 million.

The **equation** $x = 149 - 138$ is a linear equation in one variable. In this section, we review solving linear equations and quadratic equations that can be solved by factoring. We will learn other methods for solving quadratic equations in Chapter 11.

B.1 | Equations (Linear and Quadratic Solved by Factoring)

OBJECTIVE

1 Solve linear and quadratic equations. ▶

OBJECTIVE

1 Solving Linear and Quadratic Equations

EXAMPLE 1   Solve: $2(x - 3) = 5x - 9$.

Solution   First, use the distributive property.

$$2(x - 3) = 5x - 9$$

$$2x - 6 = 5x - 9 \quad \text{Use the distributive property.}$$

Next, get variable terms on the same side of the equation by subtracting $5x$ from both sides.

$$2x - 6 - 5x = 5x - 9 - 5x \quad \text{Subtract } 5x \text{ from both sides.}$$

$$-3x - 6 = -9 \quad \text{Simplify.}$$

$$-3x - 6 + 6 = -9 + 6 \quad \text{Add 6 to both sides.}$$

$$-3x = -3 \quad \text{Simplify.}$$

$$\frac{-3x}{-3} = \frac{-3}{-3} \quad \text{Divide both sides by } -3.$$

$$x = 1$$

Let $x = 1$ in the original equation to see that 1 is the solution.   □

PRACTICE

1   Solve: $3(x - 5) = 6x - 3$.

Don't forget, if an equation contains fractions, you may want to first clear the equation of fractions by multiplying both sides of the equation by the *least common denominator* (LCD) of all fractions in the equation.

EXAMPLE 2   Solve for y: $\dfrac{y}{3} - \dfrac{y}{4} = \dfrac{1}{6}$.

Solution   First, clear the equation of fractions by multiplying both sides of the equation by 12, the LCD of denominators 3, 4, and 6.

$$\frac{y}{3} - \frac{y}{4} = \frac{1}{6}$$

$$12\left(\frac{y}{3} - \frac{y}{4}\right) = 12\left(\frac{1}{6}\right) \quad \text{Multiply both sides by the LCD 12.}$$

$$12\left(\frac{y}{3}\right) - 12\left(\frac{y}{4}\right) = 2 \quad \text{Apply the distributive property.}$$

$$4y - 3y = 2 \quad \text{Simplify.}$$

$$y = 2 \quad \text{Simplify.}$$

Check: To check, let $y = 2$ in the original equation.

$$\frac{y}{3} - \frac{y}{4} = \frac{1}{6} \quad \text{Original equation.}$$

$$\frac{2}{3} - \frac{2}{4} \stackrel{?}{=} \frac{1}{6} \quad \text{Let } y = 2.$$

$$\frac{8}{12} - \frac{6}{12} \stackrel{?}{=} \frac{1}{6} \quad \text{Write fractions with the LCD.}$$

$$\frac{2}{12} \stackrel{?}{=} \frac{1}{6} \quad \text{Subtract.}$$

$$\frac{1}{6} = \frac{1}{6} \quad \text{Simplify.}$$

This is a true statement, so the solution is 2. □

PRACTICE
2   Solve for y: $\dfrac{y}{2} - \dfrac{y}{5} = \dfrac{1}{4}$.

EXAMPLE 3   Solve: $3(x^2 + 4) + 5 = -6(x^2 + 2x) + 13$.

Solution   Rewrite the equation so that one side is 0.

$$3(x^2 + 4) + 5 = -6(x^2 + 2x) + 13$$
$$3x^2 + 12 + 5 = -6x^2 - 12x + 13 \qquad \text{Apply the distributive property.}$$
$$9x^2 + 12x + 4 = 0 \qquad \text{Rewrite the equation so that one side is 0.}$$
$$(3x + 2)(3x + 2) = 0 \qquad \text{Factor.}$$
$$3x + 2 = 0 \quad \text{or} \quad 3x + 2 = 0 \qquad \text{Set each factor equal to 0.}$$
$$3x = -2 \quad \text{or} \qquad 3x = -2$$
$$x = -\frac{2}{3} \quad \text{or} \qquad x = -\frac{2}{3} \qquad \text{Solve each equation.}$$

The solution is $-\dfrac{2}{3}$. Check by substituting $-\dfrac{2}{3}$ into the original equation. □

PRACTICE
3   Solve: $8(x^2 + 3) + 4 = -8x(x + 3) + 19$.

EXAMPLE 4   Solve for x: $\dfrac{x + 5}{2} + \dfrac{1}{2} = 2x - \dfrac{x - 3}{8}$.

Solution   Multiply both sides of the equation by 8, the LCD of 2 and 8.

$$8\left(\frac{x + 5}{2} + \frac{1}{2}\right) = 8\left(2x - \frac{x - 3}{8}\right) \qquad \text{Multiply both sides by 8.}$$

$$8\left(\frac{x + 5}{2}\right) + 8 \cdot \frac{1}{2} = 8 \cdot 2x - 8\left(\frac{x - 3}{8}\right) \qquad \text{Apply the distributive property.}$$

$$4(x + 5) + 4 = 16x - (x - 3) \qquad \text{Simplify.}$$
$$4x + 20 + 4 = 16x - x + 3 \qquad \text{Use the distributive property to remove parentheses.}$$
$$4x + 24 = 15x + 3 \qquad \text{Combine like terms.}$$
$$-11x + 24 = 3 \qquad \text{Subtract } 15x \text{ from both sides.}$$
$$-11x = -21 \qquad \text{Subtract 24 from both sides.}$$
$$\frac{-11x}{-11} = \frac{-21}{-11} \qquad \text{Divide both sides by } -11.$$

$$x = \frac{21}{11} \qquad \text{Simplify.}$$

> ▶ **Helpful Hint**
> When we multiply both sides of an equation by a number, the distributive property tells us that each term of the equation is multiplied by the number.

Check: To check, verify that replacing x with $\dfrac{21}{11}$ makes the original equation true. The solution is $\dfrac{21}{11}$. □

PRACTICE
4   Solve for x: $x - \dfrac{x - 2}{12} = \dfrac{x + 3}{4} + \dfrac{1}{4}$.

EXAMPLE 5 Solve: $2x^2 = \dfrac{17}{3}x + 1$.

Solution

$$2x^2 = \dfrac{17}{3}x + 1$$

$$3(2x^2) = 3\left(\dfrac{17}{3}x + 1\right) \quad \text{Clear the equation of fractions.}$$

$$6x^2 = 17x + 3 \quad \text{Apply the distributive property.}$$

$$6x^2 - 17x - 3 = 0 \quad \text{Rewrite the equation in standard form.}$$

$$(6x + 1)(x - 3) = 0 \quad \text{Factor.}$$

$$6x + 1 = 0 \quad \text{or} \quad x - 3 = 0 \quad \text{Set each factor equal to zero.}$$

$$6x = -1$$

$$x = -\dfrac{1}{6} \quad \text{or} \quad x = 3 \quad \text{Solve each equation.}$$

The solutions are $-\dfrac{1}{6}$ and 3.

PRACTICE
5 Solve: $4x^2 = \dfrac{15}{2}x + 1$.

B.1 Exercise Set

MyMathLab®

MIXED PRACTICE

Solve each equation. See Examples 1 through 5.

1. $x^2 + 11x + 24 = 0$
2. $y^2 - 10y + 24 = 0$
3. $3x - 4 - 5x = x + 4 + x$
4. $13x - 15x + 8 = 4x + 2 - 24$
5. $12x^2 + 5x - 2 = 0$
6. $3y^2 - y - 14 = 0$
7. $z^2 + 9 = 10z$
8. $n^2 + n = 72$
9. $5(y + 4) = 4(y + 5)$
10. $6(y - 4) = 3(y - 8)$
11. $0.6x - 10 = 1.4x - 14$
12. $0.3x + 2.4 = 0.1x + 4$
13. $x(5x + 2) = 3$
14. $n(2n - 3) = 2$
15. $6x - 2(x - 3) = 4(x + 1) + 4$
16. $10x - 2(x + 4) = 8(x - 2) + 6$
17. $\dfrac{3}{8} + \dfrac{b}{3} = \dfrac{5}{12}$
18. $\dfrac{a}{2} + \dfrac{7}{4} = 5$
19. $x^2 - 6x = x(8 + x)$
20. $n(3 + n) = n^2 + 4n$
21. $\dfrac{z^2}{6} - \dfrac{z}{2} - 3 = 0$

22. $\dfrac{c^2}{20} - \dfrac{c}{4} + \dfrac{1}{5} = 0$
23. $-z + 3(2 + 4z) = 6(z + 1) + 5z$
24. $4(m - 6) - m = 8(m - 3) - 5m$
25. $\dfrac{x^2}{2} + \dfrac{x}{20} = \dfrac{1}{10}$
26. $\dfrac{y^2}{30} = \dfrac{y}{15} + \dfrac{1}{2}$
27. $\dfrac{4t^2}{5} = \dfrac{t}{5} + \dfrac{3}{10}$
28. $\dfrac{5x^2}{6} - \dfrac{7x}{2} + \dfrac{2}{3} = 0$
29. $\dfrac{3t + 1}{8} = \dfrac{5 + 2t}{7} + 2$
30. $4 - \dfrac{2z + 7}{9} = \dfrac{7 - z}{12}$
31. $\dfrac{m - 4}{3} - \dfrac{3m - 1}{5} = 1$
32. $\dfrac{n + 1}{8} - \dfrac{2 - n}{3} = \dfrac{5}{6}$
33. $3x^2 = -x$
34. $y^2 = -5y$
35. $x(x - 3) = x^2 + 5x + 7$
36. $z^2 - 4z + 10 = z(z - 5)$
37. $3(t - 8) + 2t = 7 + t$
38. $7c - 2(3c + 1) = 5(4 - 2c)$
39. $-3(x - 4) + x = 5(3 - x)$

40. $-4(a + 1) - 3a = -7(2a - 3)$

41. $(x - 1)(x + 4) = 24$

42. $(2x - 1)(x + 2) = -3$

43. $\dfrac{x^2}{4} - \dfrac{5}{2}x + 6 = 0$

44. $\dfrac{x^2}{18} + \dfrac{x}{2} + 1 = 0$

45. $y^2 + \dfrac{1}{4} = -y$

46. $\dfrac{x^2}{10} + \dfrac{5}{2} = x$

47. Which solution strategies are incorrect? Why?

   a. Solve $(y - 2)(y + 2) = 4$ by setting each factor equal to 4.

   b. Solve $(x + 1)(x + 3) = 0$ by setting each factor equal to 0.

   c. Solve $z^2 + 5z + 6 = 0$ by factoring $z^2 + 5z + 6$ and setting each factor equal to 0.

   d. Solve $x^2 + 6x + 8 = 10$ by factoring $x^2 + 6x + 8$ and setting each factor equal to 0.

48. Describe two ways a linear equation differs from a quadratic equation.

Find the value of K such that the equations are equivalent.

49. $3.2x + 4 = 5.4x - 7$
$3.2x = 5.4x + K$

50. $-7.6y - 10 = -1.1y + 12$
$-7.6y = -1.1y + K$

51. $\dfrac{x}{6} + 4 = \dfrac{x}{3}$
$x + K = 2x$

52. $\dfrac{5x}{4} + \dfrac{1}{2} = \dfrac{x}{2}$
$5x + K = 2x$

Solve and check.

53. $2.569x = -12.48534$

54. $-9.112y = -47.537304$

55. $2.86z - 8.1258 = -3.75$

56. $1.25x - 20.175 = -8.15$

B.2 Problem Solving

OBJECTIVES

1 Write Algebraic Expressions That Can Be Simplified.

2 Apply the Steps for Problem Solving.

OBJECTIVE
1   Writing and Simplifying Algebraic Expressions

In order to prepare for problem solving, we practice writing algebraic expressions that can be simplified.

    Our first example involves consecutive integers and perimeter. Recall that *consecutive integers* are integers that follow one another in order. Study the examples of consecutive, even, and odd integers and their representations.

Consecutive Integers:

Consecutive Even Integers:

Consecutive Odd Integers:

EXAMPLE 1   Write the following as algebraic expressions. Then simplify.

  a. The sum of three consecutive integers, if x is the first consecutive integer.

△ **b.** The perimeter of the triangle with sides of length x, $5x$, and $6x - 3$.

(Continued on next page)

Solution

a. Recall that if x is the first integer, then the next consecutive integer is 1 more, or $x + 1$, and the next consecutive integer is 1 more than $x + 1$, or $x + 2$.

In words:	first integer	plus	next consecutive integer	plus	next consecutive integer
	↓	↓	↓	↓	↓
Translate:	x	$+$	$(x + 1)$	$+$	$(x + 2)$

Then
$$x + (x + 1) + (x + 2) = x + x + 1 + x + 2$$
$$= 3x + 3 \quad \text{Simplify by combining like terms.}$$

b. The perimeter of a triangle is the sum of the lengths of the sides.

In words:	side	+	side	+	side
	↓		↓		↓
Translate:	x	$+$	$5x$	$+$	$(6x - 3)$

Then
$$x + 5x + (6x - 3) = x + 5x + 6x - 3$$
$$= 12x - 3 \quad \text{Simplify.} \qquad \square$$

PRACTICE

1 Write the following algebraic expressions. Then simplify.

a. The sum of three consecutive odd integers if x is the first consecutive odd integer

b. The perimeter of a trapezoid with bases x and $2x$ and sides of $x + 2$ and $2x - 3$

....■

EXAMPLE 2 **Writing Algebraic Expressions Representing Metropolitan Regions**

The most populous metropolitan region in the United States is New York City, although it is only the sixth most populous metropolis in the world. Tokyo is the most populous metropolitan region. Mexico City is the fifth most populous metropolis in the world. Mexico City's population is 0.03 million more than New York's, and Tokyo's is twice that of New York, decreased by 2.19 million. Write the sum of the populations of these three metropolitan regions as an algebraic expression. Let x be the population of New York (in millions). (*Source:* United Nations, Department of Economic and Social Affairs)

Solution:

If x = the population of New York (in millions), then
$x + 0.03$ = the population of Mexico City (in millions) and
$2x - 2.19$ = the population of Tokyo (in millions)

In words:	population of New York		population of Mexico City		population of Tokyo
	↓		↓		↓
Translate:	x	$+$	$(x + 0.03)$	$+$	$(2x - 2.19)$

Then $x + (x + 0.03) + (2x - 2.19) = x + x + 2x + 0.03 - 2.19$
$$= 4x - 2.16 \quad \text{Combine like terms.}$$

In Exercise 57, we will find the actual populations of these cities. $\qquad \square$

PRACTICE

2 The three busiest airports in Europe are in London, England; Paris, France; and Frankfurt, Germany. The airport in London has 12.9 million more arrivals and departures than the Frankfurt airport. The Paris airport has 5.2 million more arrivals and departures than the Frankfurt airport. Write the sum of the arrivals and departures from these three cities as a simplified algebraic expression. Let x be the number of arrivals and departures at the Frankfurt airport. (*Source:* Association of European Airlines)

OBJECTIVE

2 Applying Steps for Problem Solving

Our main purpose for studying algebra is to solve problems. The following problem-solving strategy will be used throughout this text and may also be used to solve real-life problems that occur outside the mathematics classroom.

General Strategy for Problem Solving

1. UNDERSTAND the problem. During this step, become comfortable with the problem. Some ways of doing this are to:

   Read and reread the problem.

   Propose a solution and check. Pay careful attention to how you check your proposed solution. This will help when writing an equation to model the problem.

   Construct a drawing.

   Choose a variable to represent the unknown. (Very important part)

2. TRANSLATE the problem into an equation.

3. SOLVE the equation.

4. INTERPRET the results: *Check* the proposed solution in the stated problem and *state* your conclusion.

Let's review this strategy by solving a problem involving unknown numbers.

EXAMPLE 3 **Finding Unknown Numbers**

Find three numbers such that the second number is 3 more than twice the first number, and the third number is four times the first number. The sum of the three numbers is 164.

Solution

> **Helpful Hint**
>
> The purpose of guessing a solution is not to guess correctly but to gain confidence and to help understand the problem and how to model it.

1. UNDERSTAND the problem. First let's read and reread the problem and then propose a solution. For example, if the first number is 25, then the second number is 3 more than twice 25, or 53. The third number is four times 25, or 100. The sum of 25, 53, and 100 is 178, not the required sum, but we have gained some valuable information about the problem. First, we know that the first number is less than 25 since our guess led to a sum greater than the required sum. Also, we have gained some information as to how to model the problem.

   Next let's assign a variable and use this variable to represent any other unknown quantities. If we let

$$x = \text{the first number, then}$$
$$2x + 3 = \text{the second number}$$

3 more than
twice the first number

$$4x = \text{the third number}$$

(Continued on next page)

2. TRANSLATE the problem into an equation. To do so, we use the fact that the sum of the numbers is 164. First let's write this relationship in words and then translate to an equation.

In words:

first number	added to	second number	added to	third number	is	164
↓	↓	↓	↓	↓	↓	↓

Translate: $\quad\quad x \quad\quad + \quad\quad (2x + 3) \quad\quad + \quad\quad 4x \quad\quad = \quad\quad 164$

3. SOLVE the equation.

$$x + (2x + 3) + 4x = 164$$
$$x + 2x + 4x + 3 = 164 \quad \text{Remove parentheses.}$$
$$7x + 3 = 164 \quad \text{Combine like terms.}$$
$$7x = 161 \quad \text{Subtract 3 from both sides.}$$
$$x = 23 \quad \text{Divide both sides by 7.}$$

4. INTERPRET. Here, we *check* our work and *state* the solution. Recall that if the first number $x = 23$, then the second number $2x + 3 = 2 \cdot 23 + 3 = 49$ and the third number $4x = 4 \cdot 23 = 92$.

Check: Is the second number 3 more than twice the first number? Yes, since 3 more than twice 23 is $46 + 3$, or 49. Also, their sum, $23 + 49 + 92 = 164$, is the required sum.

State: The three numbers are 23, 49, and 92. □

PRACTICE

3 Find three numbers such that the second number is 8 less than triple the first number, the third number is five times the first number, and the sum of the three numbers is 118.

Many of today's rates and statistics are given as percents. Interest rates, tax rates, nutrition labeling, and percent of households in a given category are just a few examples. Before we practice solving problems containing percents, let's briefly review the meaning of percent and how to find a percent of a number.

The word *percent* means "per hundred," and the symbol % denotes percent.

This means that 23% is 23 per hundred, or $\dfrac{23}{100}$. Also,

$$41\% = \frac{41}{100} = 0.41$$

To find a percent of a number, we multiply.

$$16\% \text{ of } 25 = 16\% \cdot 25 = 0.16 \cdot 25 = 4$$

Thus, 16% of 25 is 4.

Study the table below. It will help you become more familiar with finding percents.

Percent	*Meaning/Shortcut*	*Example*
50%	$\dfrac{1}{2}$ or half of a number	50% of 60 is 30.
25%	$\dfrac{1}{4}$ or a quarter of a number	25% of 60 is 15.
10%	0.1 or $\dfrac{1}{10}$ of a number (move the decimal point 1 place to the left)	10% of 60 is 6.0 or 6.
1%	0.01 or $\dfrac{1}{100}$ of a number (move the decimal point 2 places to the left)	1% of 60 is 0.60 or 0.6.
100%	1 or all of a number	100% of 60 is 60.
200%	2 or double a number	200% of 60 is 120.

Next, we solve a problem containing a percent.

EXAMPLE 4   **Finding the Original Price of a Computer**

Suppose that a computer store just announced an 8% decrease in the price of a particular computer model. If this computer sells for $2162 after the decrease, find the original price of this computer.

Solution

1. UNDERSTAND. Read and reread the problem. Recall that a percent decrease means a percent of the original price. Let's guess that the original price of the computer is $2500. The amount of decrease is then 8% of $2500, or $(0.08)(\$2500) = \$200$. This means that the new price of the computer is the original price minus the decrease, or $\$2500 - \$200 = \$2300$. Our guess is incorrect, but we now have an idea of how to model this problem. In our model, we will let x = the original price of the computer.

2. TRANSLATE.

In words:	the original price of computer	minus	8% of the original price	is	the new price
	↓	↓	↓	↓	↓
Translate:	x	$-$	$0.08x$	$=$	2162

3. SOLVE the equation.

$$x - 0.08x = 2162$$
$$0.92x = 2162 \qquad \text{Combine like terms.}$$
$$x = \frac{2162}{0.92} = 2350 \quad \text{Divide both sides by 0.92.}$$

4. INTERPRET.

Check: If the original price of the computer was $2350, the new price is
$$\$2350 - (0.08)(\$2350) = \$2350 - \$188$$
$$= \$2162 \qquad \text{The given new price}$$

State: The original price of the computer was $2350.   ☐

PRACTICE
4   At the end of the season, the cost of a snowboard was reduced by 40%. If the snowboard sells for $270 after the decrease, find the original price of the board.

Vocabulary & Readiness Check

Fill in each blank with $<$, $>$, *or* $=$. *(Assume that the unknown number is a positive number.)*

1. 130% of a number _____ the number.

2. 70% of a number _____ the number.

3. 100% of a number _____ the number.

4. 200% of a number _____ the number.

Complete the table. The first row has been completed for you.

	First Integer	All Described Integers
Three consecutive integers	18	18, 19, 20
5. Four consecutive integers	31	
6. Three consecutive odd integers	31	
7. Three consecutive even integers	18	
8. Four consecutive even integers	92	
9. Three consecutive integers	y	
10. Three consecutive even integers	z (z is even)	
11. Four consecutive integers	p	
12. Three consecutive odd integers	s (s is odd)	

B.2 Exercise Set   MyMathLab®

Write the following as algebraic expressions. Then simplify. See Examples 1 and 2.

△ **1.** The perimeter of a square with side length y.

△ **2.** The perimeter of a rectangle with length x and width $x - 5$.

▶ **3.** The sum of three consecutive integers if the first is z.

4. The sum of three consecutive odd integers if the first integer is z.

▶ **5.** The total amount of money (in cents) in x nickels, $(x + 3)$ dimes, and $2x$ quarters. (*Hint:* The value of a nickel is 5 cents, the value of a dime is 10 cents, and the value of a quarter is 25 cents.)

6. The total amount of money (in cents) in y quarters, $7y$ dimes, and $(2y - 1)$ nickels. (Use the hint for Exercise 5.)

△ **7.** A piece of land along Bayou Liberty is to be fenced and subdivided as shown so that each rectangle has the same dimensions. Express the total amount of fencing needed as an algebraic expression in x.

8. A flooded piece of land near the Mississippi River in New Orleans is to be surveyed and divided into 4 rectangles of equal dimension. Express the total amount of fencing needed as an algebraic expression in x.

△ **9.** Write the perimeter of the floor plan shown as an algebraic expression in x.

10. Write the perimeter of the floor plan shown as an algebraic expression in x.

Solve. For Exercises 11 and 12, the solutions have been started for you. See Example 3.

11. Four times the difference of a number and 2 is the same as 2, increased by four times the number, plus twice the number. Find the number.

Start the solution:

1. UNDERSTAND the problem. Reread it as many times as needed.

2. TRANSLATE into an equation. (Fill in the blanks below.)

Four times	the difference of a number and 2	is the same as	2	increased by	four times the number	plus	twice the number
↓	↓	↓	↓	↓	↓	↓	↓
4 ·	(x − 2)	=	2	___			

Finish with:

3. SOLVE and 4. INTERPRET

12. Twice the sum of a number and 3 is the same as five times the number, minus 1, minus four times the number. Find the number.

Start the solution:

1. UNDERSTAND the problem. Reread it as many times as needed.

2. TRANSLATE into an equation. (Fill in the blanks below.)

Twice	the sum of a number and 3	is the same as	five times the number	minus	1	minus	four times the number
↓	↓	↓	↓	↓	↓	↓	↓
2	(x + 3)	=	___	___	1	___	___

Finish with:

3. SOLVE and 4. INTERPRET

▷ 13. A second number is five times a first number. A third number is 100 more than the first number. If the sum of the three numbers is 415, find the numbers.

14. A second number is 6 less than a first number. A third number is twice the first number. If the sum of the three numbers is 306, find the numbers.

Solve. See Example 4.

15. The United States consists of 2271 million acres of land. Approximately 29% of this land is federally owned. Find the number of acres that are not federally owned. (*Source:* U.S. General Services Administration)

16. The state of Nevada contains the most federally owned acres of land in the United States. If 90% of the state's 70 million acres of land is federally owned, find the number of acres that are not federally owned. (*Source:* U.S. General Services Administration)

17. In 2010, 8476 earthquakes occurred in the United States. Of these, 91.4% were minor tremors with magnitudes of 3.9 or less on the Richter scale. How many minor earthquakes occurred in the United States in 2010? Round to the nearest whole. (*Source:* U.S. Geological Survey National Earthquake Information Center)

18. Of the 1543 tornadoes that occurred in the United States during 2010, 27.7% occurred during the month of June. How many tornadoes occurred in the United States during June 2010? Round to the nearest whole. (*Source:* Storm Prediction Center)

19. In a recent survey, 15% of online shoppers in the United States say that they prefer to do business only with large, well-known retailers. In a group of 1500 online shoppers, how many are willing to do business with any size retailers? (*Source:* Inc.com)

20. In 2010, the restaurant industry employed 9% of the U.S. workforce. If there are estimated to be 141 million Americans in the workforce, how many people are employed by the restaurant industry? Round to the nearest tenth. (*Source:* National Restaurant Association, U.S. Bureau of Labor Statistics)

The following graph is called a circle graph or a pie chart. The circle represents a whole, or in this case, 100%. This particular graph shows the number of minutes per day that people use email at work. Use this graph to answer Exercises 21 through 24.

Time Spent on Email at Work

Source: Pew Internet & American Life Project

21. What percent of email users at work spend less than 15 minutes on email per day?

22. Among email users at work, what is the most common time spent on email per day?

23. If it were estimated that a large company has 4633 employees, how many of these would you expect to be using email more than 3 hours per day?

24. If it were estimated that a medium-size company has 250 employees, how many of these would you expect to be using email between 2 and 3 hours per day?

MIXED PRACTICE

Use the diagrams to find the unknown measures of angles or lengths of sides. Recall that the sum of the angle measures of a triangle is 180°.

25.

26.

27.

(4x) m   (5x + 1) m

(5x + 3) m

Perimeter is 102 meters.

28.

(2x) cm

(3.5x) cm

(3x + 7) cm

Perimeter is 75 centimeters.

29.

(2.5x − 9) in.

x in.   Isoceles Trapezoid   x in.

1.5x in.

Perimeter is 99 inches.

30.

(9.2x − 3) ft

7.3x ft   Parallelogram   7.3x ft

(9.2x − 3) ft

Perimeter is 324 feet.

Solve.

31. The sum of three consecutive integers is 228. Find the integers.

32. The sum of three consecutive odd integers is 327. Find the integers.

33. The ZIP codes of three Nevada locations—Fallon, Fernley, and Gardnerville Ranchos—are three consecutive even integers. If twice the first integer added to the third is 268,222, find each ZIP code.

34. During a recent year, the average SAT scores in math for the states of Alabama, Louisiana, and Michigan were 3 consecutive integers. If the sum of the first integer, second integer, and three times the third integer is 2637, find each score.

Many companies predict the growth or decline of various technologies. The following data is based on information from Techcrunchies, a technological information site. Notice that the first table is the predicted increase in the number of Wi-Fi-enabled cell phones (in millions), and the second is the predicted percent increase in the number of Wi-Fi-enabled cell phones in the United States.

35. Use the middle column in the table to find the predicted number of Wi-Fi-enabled cell phones for each year.

Year	Increase in Wi-Fi-Enabled Cell Phones	Predicted Number
2010	$2x - 21$	
2012	$\frac{5}{2}x + 2$	
2014	$3x + 24$	
Total	290 million	

36. Use the middle column in the table to find the predicted percent increase in the number of Wi-Fi-enabled cell phones for each year.

Year	Percent Increase in Wi-Fi-Enabled Cell Phones since 2009	Predicted Percent Increase
2010	x	
2011	$2x + 10$	
2012	$4x - 25$	
	300%	

Solve.

37. The occupations of biomedical engineers, skin care specialists, and physician assistants are among the 10 with the largest growth from 2008 to 2018. The number of physician assistant jobs will grow 7 thousand less than three times the number of biomedical engineer jobs. The number of skin care specialist jobs will grow 9 thousand more than half the number of biomedical engineer jobs. If the total growth of these three jobs is predicted to be 56 thousand, find the predicted growth of each job. (*Source:* U.S. Department of Labor, Bureau of Labor Statistics)

38. The occupations of farmer or rancher, file clerk, and telemarketer are among the 10 jobs with the largest decline from 2008 to 2018. The number of file clerk jobs is predicted to decline 11 thousand more than the number of telemarketer jobs. The number of farmer or rancher jobs is predicted to decline 3 thousand more than twice the number of telemarketer jobs. If the total decline of these three jobs is predicted to be 166 thousand, find the predicted decline of each job. (*Source:* U.S. Department of Labor, Bureau of Labor Statistics)

39. The B767-300ER aircraft has 88 more seats than the B737-200 aircraft. The F-100 has 32 fewer seats than the B737-200 aircraft. If their total number of seats is 413, find the number of seats for each aircraft. (*Source:* Air Transport Association of America)

40. Cowboy Stadium, home of the Dallas Cowboys of the NFL, seats approximately 9800 more fans than does Candlestick Park, home of the San Francisco 49ers. Soldier Field, home of the Chicago Bears, seats 8700 fewer fans than Candlestick Park. If the total seats in these three stadiums is 211,700, how many seats are in each of the three stadiums?

41. A new fax machine was recently purchased for an office in Hopedale for $464.40 including tax. If the tax rate in Hopedale is 8%, find the price of the fax machine before tax.

42. A premedical student at a local university was complaining that she had just paid $158.60 for her human anatomy book, including tax. Find the price of the book before taxes if the tax rate at this university is 9%.

43. The median compensation for a U.S. university president was $436,000 for the 2008–2009 academic year. Calculate the salary of a university president who received a 2.3% raise.

44. In 2009, the population of Brazil was 191.5 million. This represented a decrease in population of 3.7% from 2000. What was the population of Brazil in 2000? Round to the nearest tenth of a million. (*Source:* Population Reference Bureau)

45. In 2010, the population of Swaziland was 1,200,000 people. From 2010 to 2050, Swaziland's population is expected to increase by 50%. Find the expected population of Swaziland in 2050. (*Source:* Population Reference Bureau)

46. Dana, an auto parts supplier headquartered in Toledo, Ohio, recently announced it would be cutting 11,000 jobs worldwide. This is equivalent to 15% of Dana's workforce. Find the size of Dana's workforce prior to this round of job layoffs. Round to the nearest whole. (*Source:* Dana Corporation)

Recall that two angles are complements of each other if their sum is 90°. Two angles are supplements of each other if their sum is 180°. Find the measure of each angle.

47. One angle is three times its supplement increased by 20°. Find the measures of the two supplementary angles.

48. One angle is twice its complement increased by 30°. Find the measure of the two complementary angles.

Recall that the sum of the angle measures of a triangle is 180°.

△ **49.** Find the measures of the angles of a triangle if the measure of one angle is twice the measure of a second angle and the third angle measures 3 times the second angle decreased by 12.

△ **50.** Find the angles of an isoceles triangle whose two base angles are equal and whose third angle is 10° less than three times a base angle.

▶ **51.** Two frames are needed with the same perimeter: one frame in the shape of a square and one in the shape of an equilateral triangle. Each side of the triangle is 6 centimeters longer than each side of the square. Find the dimensions of each frame. (An equilateral triangle has sides that are the same length.)

52. Two frames are needed with the same perimeter: one frame in the shape of a square and one in the shape of a regular pentagon. Each side of the square is 7 inches longer than each side of the pentagon. Find the dimensions of each frame. (A regular polygon has sides that are the same length.)

53. The sum of the first and third of three consecutive even integers is 156. Find the three even integers.

54. The sum of the second and fourth of four consecutive integers is 110. Find the four integers.

55. Daytona International Speedway in Florida has 37,000 more grandstand seats than twice the number of grandstand seats at Darlington Motor Raceway in South Carolina. Together, these two race tracks seat 220,000 NASCAR fans. How many seats does each race track have? (*Source:* NASCAR)

56. For the 2010–2011 National Hockey League season, the payroll for the San Jose Sharks was $5,986,667 more than that for the Montreal Canadiens. The total payroll for these two teams was $113,103,333. What were the payrolls for these two teams for the 2010–2011 NHL season?

57. The sum of the populations of the metropolitan regions of New York, Tokyo, and Mexico City is 75.56 million. Use this information and Example 2 in this section to find the population of each metropolitan region. (*Source:* United Nations Department of Economic and Social Affairs)

58. The airports in London, Paris, and Frankfurt have a total of 177.1 million annual arrivals and departures. Use this information and Practice 2 in this section to find the number from each airport.

59. Suppose the perimeter of the triangle in Example 1b in this section is 483 feet. Find the length of each side.

60. Suppose the perimeter of the trapezoid in Practice 1b in this section is 110 meters. Find the lengths of its sides and bases.

61. Incandescent, fluorescent, and halogen bulbs are lasting longer today than ever before. On average, the number of bulb hours for a fluorescent bulb is 25 times the number of bulb hours for a halogen bulb. The number of bulb hours for an incandescent bulb is 2500 less than the halogen bulb. If the total number of bulb hours for the three types of bulbs is 105,500, find the number of bulb hours for each type. (*Source: Popular Science* magazine)

62. Falkland Islands, Iceland, and Norway are the top three countries that have the greatest Internet penetration rate (percent of population) in the world. Falkland Islands has a 6.8 percent greater penetration rate than Iceland. Norway has a 2.3 percent less penetration rate than Iceland. If the sum of the penetration rates is 284.1, find the Internet penetration rate in each of these countries. (*Source:* Internet World Stats)

63. During the 2010 Major League Baseball season, the number of wins for the Milwaukee Brewers, Houston Astros, and Chicago Cubs was three consecutive integers. Of these three teams, the Milwaukee Brewers had the most wins. The Chicago Cubs had the least wins. The total number of wins by these three teams was 228. How many wins did each team have in the 2010 season?

64. In the 2010 Winter Olympics, Austria won more medals than the Russian Federation, which won more medals than South Korea. If the numbers of medals won by these three countries is three consecutive integers whose sum is 45, find the number of medals won by each. (*Source:* Vancouver 2010)

65. The three tallest hospitals in the world are Guy's Tower in London, Queen Mary Hospital in Hong Kong, and Galter Pavilion in Chicago. These buildings have a total height of 1320 feet. Guy's Tower is 67 feet taller than Galter Pavilion, and the Queen Mary Hospital is 47 feet taller than Galter Pavilion. Find the heights of the three hospitals.

△ **66.** The official manual for traffic signs is the *Manual on Uniform Traffic Control Devices* published by the Government Printing Office. The rectangular sign below has a length 12 inches more than twice its height. If the perimeter of the sign is 312 inches, find its dimensions.

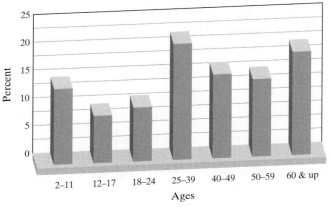

B.3 Graphing ▶

OBJECTIVE

1 **Plotting Ordered Pairs** ▶

Graphs are widely used today in newspapers, magazines, and all forms of newsletters. A few examples of graphs are shown here.

Percent of People Who Go to the Movies

Source: Motion Picture Association of America

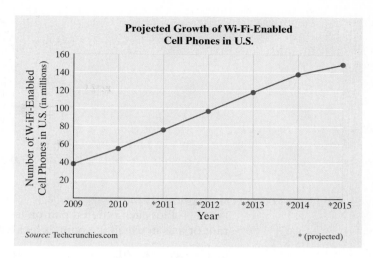

Projected Growth of Wi-Fi-Enabled Cell Phones in U.S.

Source: Techcrunchies.com

* (projected)

To review how to read these graphs, we review their origin—the rectangular coordinate system. One way to locate points on a plane is by using a **rectangular coordinate system,** which is also called a **Cartesian coordinate system** after its inventor, René Descartes (1596–1650). The next diagram to the left shows the rectangular coordinate system. For further review of this system, see Section 3.1.

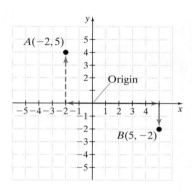

Recall that the location of point A in the figure above is described as 2 units to the left of the origin along the x-axis and 5 units upward parallel to the y-axis. Thus, we identify point A with the ordered pair $(-2, 5)$. Notice that the order of these numbers is *critical.* The x-value -2 is called the **x-coordinate** and is associated with the x-axis. The y-value 5 is called the **y-coordinate** and is associated with the y-axis. Compare the location of point A with the location of point B, which corresponds to the ordered pair $(5, -2)$.

Keep in mind that **each ordered pair corresponds to exactly one point in the real plane and that each point in the plane corresponds to exactly one ordered pair.** Thus, we may refer to the ordered pair (x, y) as the point (x, y).

EXAMPLE 1 Plot each ordered pair on a Cartesian coordinate system and name the quadrant or axis in which the point is located.

a. $(2, -1)$ **b.** $(0, 5)$ **c.** $(-3, 5)$

d. $(-2, 0)$ **e.** $\left(-\dfrac{1}{2}, -4\right)$ **f.** $(1.5, 1.5)$

Solution The six points are graphed as shown on the next page.

a. $(2, -1)$ is in quadrant IV. **b.** $(0, 5)$ is on the y-axis.

c. $(-3, 5)$ is in quadrant II. **d.** $(-2, 0)$ is on the x-axis.

e. $\left(-\dfrac{1}{2}, -4\right)$ is in quadrant III. **f.** $(1.5, 1.5)$ is in quadrant I.

(Continued on next page)

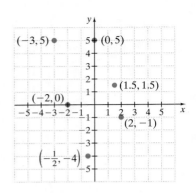

PRACTICE

1 Plot each ordered pair on a Cartesian coordinate system and name the quadrant or axis in which the point is located.

a. $(3, -4)$ **b.** $(0, -2)$ **c.** $(-2, 4)$ **d.** $(4, 0)$ **e.** $\left(-1\frac{1}{2}, -2\right)$ **f.** $(2.5, 3.5)$

Notice that the y-coordinate of any point on the x-axis is 0. For example, the point with coordinates $(-2, 0)$ lies on the x-axis. Also, the x-coordinate of any point on the y-axis is 0. For example, the point with coordinates $(0, 5)$ lies on the y-axis. These points that lie on the axes do not lie in any quadrants.

✓**CONCEPT CHECK**

Which of the following correctly describes the location of the point $(3, -6)$ in a rectangular coordinate system?

a. 3 units to the left of the y-axis and 6 units above the x-axis

b. 3 units above the x-axis and 6 units to the left of the y-axis

c. 3 units to the right of the y-axis and 6 units below the x-axis

d. 3 units below the x-axis and 6 units to the right of the y-axis

---

OBJECTIVE

2 Graphing Linear Equations

Recall that an equation such as $3x - y = 12$ is called a linear equation in two variables, and **the graph of every linear equation in two variables is a line.**

> **Linear Equation in Two Variables**
>
> A linear equation in two variables is an equation that can be written in the form
>
> $$Ax + By = C$$
>
> where A and B are not both 0. This form is called **standard form.**

Some examples of equations in standard form:

$$3x - y = 12$$
$$-2.1x + 5.6y = 0$$

> ▶ **Helpful Hint**
>
> Remember: A linear equation is written in standard form when all of the variable terms are on one side of the equation and the constant is on the other side.

Answer to Concept Check:
c

EXAMPLE 2 Graph the equation $y = -2x + 3$.

Solution This is a linear equation. (In standard form it is $2x + y = 3$.) Find three ordered pair solutions, and plot the ordered pairs. The line through the plotted points is the graph. Since the equation is solved for y, let's choose three x-values. We'll choose $0, 2$, and then -1 for x to find our three ordered pair solutions.

Let $x = 0$
$y = -2x + 3$
$y = -2 \cdot 0 + 3$
$y = 3$ Simplify.

Let $x = 2$
$y = -2x + 3$
$y = -2 \cdot 2 + 3$
$y = -1$ Simplify.

Let $x = -1$
$y = -2x + 3$
$y = -2(-1) + 3$
$y = 5$ Simplify.

The three ordered pairs $(0, 3)$, $(2, -1)$, and $(-1, 5)$ are listed in the table and the graph is shown.

x	y
0	3
2	-1
-1	5

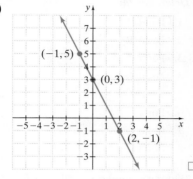

PRACTICE
2 Graph the equation $y = -3x - 2$.

Notice that the graph crosses the y-axis at the point $(0, 3)$. This point is called the **y-intercept.** (You may sometimes see just the number 3 called the y-intercept.) This graph also crosses the x-axis at the point $\left(\dfrac{3}{2}, 0\right)$. This point is called the **x-intercept.** (You may also see just the number $\dfrac{3}{2}$ called the x-intercept.)

Since every point on the y-axis has an x-value of 0, we can find the y-intercept of a graph by letting $x = 0$ and solving for y. Also, every point on the x-axis has a y-value of 0. To find the x-intercept, we let $y = 0$ and solve for x.

> **Finding x- and y-Intercepts**
>
> To find an x-intercept, let $y = 0$ and solve for x.
> To find a y-intercept, let $x = 0$ and solve for y.

EXAMPLE 3 Graph the linear equation $y = \dfrac{1}{3}x$.

Solution To graph, we find ordered pair solutions, plot the ordered pairs, and draw a line through the plotted points. We will choose x-values and substitute in the equation. To avoid fractions, we choose x-values that are multiples of 3. To find the y-intercept, we let $x = 0$.

> **▶ Helpful Hint**
> Notice that by using multiples of 3 for x, we avoid fractions.

> **▶ Helpful Hint**
> Since the equation $y = \dfrac{1}{3}x$ is solved for y, we choose x-values for finding points. This way, we simply need to evaluate an expression to find the y-value, as shown.

$$y = \frac{1}{3}x$$

If $x = 0$, then $y = \dfrac{1}{3}(0)$, or 0.

If $x = 6$, then $y = \dfrac{1}{3}(6)$, or 2.

If $x = -3$, then $y = \dfrac{1}{3}(-3)$, or -1.

x	y
0	0
6	2
-3	-1

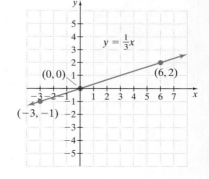

(Continued on next page)

This graph crosses the x-axis at $(0, 0)$ and the y-axis at $(0, 0)$. This means that the x-intercept is $(0, 0)$ and that the y-intercept is $(0, 0)$. □

PRACTICE 3 Graph the linear equation $y = -\dfrac{1}{2}x$.

■

B.3 Exercise Set MyMathLab®

Determine the coordinates of each point on the graph.

1. Point A
2. Point B
3. Point C
4. Point D
5. Point E
6. Point F
7. Point G
8. Point H

Without graphing, visualize the location of each point. Then give its location by quadrant or x- or y-axis. See Example 1.

9. $(2, 3)$
10. $(0, 5)$
11. $(-2, 7)$
12. $(-3, 0)$
13. $(-1, -4)$
14. $(4, -2)$
15. $(0, -100)$
16. $(10, 30)$
17. $(-10, -30)$
18. $(0, 0)$
19. $(-87, 0)$
20. $(-42, 17)$

Given that x is a positive number and that y is a positive number, determine the quadrant or axis in which each point lies.

21. $(x, -y)$
22. $(-x, y)$
23. $(x, 0)$
24. $(0, -y)$
25. $(-x, -y)$
26. $(0, 0)$

Graph each linear equation. See Examples 2 and 3.

27. $y = -x - 2$
28. $y = -2x + 1$
29. $3x - 4y = 8$
30. $x - 9y = 3$
31. $y = \dfrac{1}{3}x$
32. $y = \dfrac{3}{2}x$
33. $y + 4 = 0$
34. $x = -1.5$

Recall that if $f(2) = 7$, for example, this corresponds to the ordered pair $(2, 7)$ on the graph of f. Use this information and the graphs of f and g below to answer Exercises 35 through 42.

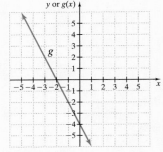

35. $f(4) =$
36. $f(0) =$
37. $g(0) =$
38. $g(-1) =$
39. Find all values for x such that $f(x) = 0$.
40. Find all values for x such that $g(x) = 0$.
41. If $(-1, -2)$ is a point on the graph of g, write this using function notation.
42. If $(-1, 2)$ is a point on the graph of f, write this using function notation.

B.4 | Polynomials and Factoring

OBJECTIVES

1 Review Operations on Polynomials.

2 Review Factoring Polynomials.

OBJECTIVE
1 Operations on Polynomials

B.4 Exercise Set, Part 1 MyMathLab®

Perform each indicated operation.

1. $(-y^2 + 6y - 1) + (3y^2 - 4y - 10)$
2. $(5z^4 - 6z^2 + z + 1) - (7z^4 - 2z + 1)$
3. Subtract $(x - 5)$ from $(x^2 - 6x + 2)$.
4. $(2x^2 + 6x - 5) + (5x^2 - 10x)$
5. $(5x - 3)^2$
6. $(5x^2 - 14x - 3) \div (5x + 1)$

7. $(2x^4 - 3x^2 + 5x - 2) \div (x + 2)$

8. $(4x - 1)(x^2 - 3x - 2)$

OBJECTIVE

2   Factoring Strategies

The key to proficiency in factoring polynomials is to practice until you are comfortable with each technique. A strategy for factoring polynomials completely is given next.

Factoring a Polynomial

Step 1.   Are there any common factors? If so, factor out the greatest common factor.

Step 2.   How many terms are in the polynomial?

    a. If there are *two* terms, decide if one of the following formulas may be applied:

        i. Difference of two squares: $a^2 - b^2 = (a - b)(a + b)$

        ii. Difference of two cubes: $a^3 - b^3 = (a - b)(a^2 + ab + b^2)$

        iii. Sum of two cubes: $a^3 + b^3 = (a + b)(a^2 - ab + b^2)$

    b. If there are *three* terms, try one of the following:

        i. Perfect square trinomial: $a^2 + 2ab + b^2 = (a + b)^2$
$$a^2 - 2ab + b^2 = (a - b)^2$$

        ii. If not a perfect square trinomial, factor by using the methods presented in Sections 6.2 through 6.4.

    c. If there are *four* or more terms, try factoring by grouping.

Step 3.   See whether any factors in the factored polynomial can be factored further.

A few examples are worked for you below.

EXAMPLE 1   Factor each polynomial completely.

a. $8a^2b - 4ab$ **b.** $36x^2 - 9$ **c.** $2x^2 - 5x - 7$

d. $5p^2 + 5 + qp^2 + q$ **e.** $9x^2 + 24x + 16$ **f.** $y^2 + 25$

Solution

a. Step 1.   The terms have a common factor of $4ab$, which we factor out.

$$8a^2b - 4ab = 4ab(2a - 1)$$

    Step 2.   There are two terms, but the binomial $2a - 1$ is not the difference of two squares or the sum or difference of two cubes.

    Step 3.   The factor $2a - 1$ cannot be factored further.

b. Step 1.   Factor out a common factor of 9.

$$36x^2 - 9 = 9(4x^2 - 1)$$

    Step 2.   The factor $4x^2 - 1$ has two terms, and it is the difference of two squares.

$$9(4x^2 - 1) = 9(2x + 1)(2x - 1)$$

    Step 3.   No factor with more than one term can be factored further.

c. Step 1.   The terms of $2x^2 - 5x - 7$ contain no common factor other than 1 or -1.

    Step 2.   There are three terms. The trinomial is not a perfect square, so we factor by methods from Section 6.3 or 6.4.

$$2x^2 - 5x - 7 = (2x - 7)(x + 1)$$

    Step 3.   No factor with more than one term can be factored further.

(Continued on next page)

d. Step 1. There is no common factor of all terms of $5p^2 + 5 + qp^2 + q$.

Step 2. The polynomial has four terms, so try factoring by grouping.

$$5p^2 + 5 + qp^2 + q = (5p^2 + 5) + (qp^2 + q) \quad \text{Group the terms.}$$
$$= 5(p^2 + 1) + q(p^2 + 1)$$
$$= (p^2 + 1)(5 + q)$$

Step 3. No factor can be factored further.

e. Step 1. The terms of $9x^2 + 24x + 16$ contain no common factor other than 1 or -1.

Step 2. The trinomial $9x^2 + 24x + 16$ is a perfect square trinomial, and $9x^2 + 24x + 16 = (3x + 4)^2$.

Step 3. No factor can be factored further.

f. Step 1. There is no common factor of $y^2 + 25$ other than 1.

Step 2. This binomial is the sum of two squares and is prime.

Step 3. The binomial $y^2 + 25$ cannot be factored further. ☐

PRACTICE

1 Factor each polynomial completely.

a. $12x^2y - 3xy$

b. $49x^2 - 4$

c. $5x^2 + 2x - 3$

d. $3x^2 + 6 + x^3 + 2x$

e. $4x^2 + 20x + 25$

f. $b^2 + 100$

EXAMPLE 2 Factor each polynomial completely.

a. $27a^3 - b^3$

b. $3n^2m^4 - 48m^6$

c. $2x^2 - 12x + 18 - 2z^2$

d. $8x^4y^2 + 125xy^2$

e. $(x - 5)^2 - 49y^2$

Solution

a. This binomial is the difference of two cubes.

$$27a^3 - b^3 = (3a)^3 - b^3$$
$$= (3a - b)[(3a)^2 + (3a)(b) + b^2]$$
$$= (3a - b)(9a^2 + 3ab + b^2)$$

b. $3n^2m^4 - 48m^6 = 3m^4(n^2 - 16m^2)$ Factor out the GCF $3m^4$.

$\qquad\qquad\qquad = 3m^4(n + 4m)(n - 4m)$ Factor the difference of squares.

c. $2x^2 - 12x + 18 - 2z^2 = 2(x^2 - 6x + 9 - z^2)$ The GCF is 2.

$\qquad\qquad\qquad\qquad = 2[(x^2 - 6x + 9) - z^2]$ Group the first three terms together.

$\qquad\qquad\qquad\qquad = 2[(x - 3)^2 - z^2]$ Factor the perfect square trinomial.

$\qquad\qquad\qquad\qquad = 2[(x - 3) + z][(x - 3) - z]$ Factor the difference of squares.

$\qquad\qquad\qquad\qquad = 2(x - 3 + z)(x - 3 - z)$

d. $8x^4y^2 + 125xy^2 = xy^2(8x^3 + 125)$ The GCF is xy^2.

$\qquad\qquad\qquad = xy^2[(2x)^3 + 5^3]$

$\qquad\qquad\qquad = xy^2(2x + 5)[(2x)^2 - (2x)(5) + 5^2]$ Factor the sum of cubes.

$\qquad\qquad\qquad = xy^2(2x + 5)(4x^2 - 10x + 25)$

e. This binomial is the difference of squares.

$$(x - 5)^2 - 49y^2 = (x - 5)^2 - (7y)^2$$
$$= [(x - 5) + 7y][(x - 5) - 7y]$$
$$= (x - 5 + 7y)(x - 5 - 7y) \qquad ☐$$

PRACTICE
2   Factor each polynomial completely.

a. $64x^3 + y^3$
b. $7x^2y^2 - 63y^4$
c. $3x^2 + 12x + 12 - 3b^2$
d. $x^5y^4 + 27x^2y$
e. $(x + 7)^2 - 81y^2$

B.4 Exercise Set, Part 2   MyMathLab®

Factor completely.

9. $x^2 - 8x + 16 - y^2$
10. $12x^2 - 22x - 20$
11. $x^4 - x$
12. $(2x + 1)^2 - 3(2x + 1) + 2$
13. $14x^2y - 2xy$
14. $24ab^2 - 6ab$
15. $4x^2 - 16$
16. $9x^2 - 81$
17. $3x^2 - 8x - 11$
18. $5x^2 - 2x - 3$
19. $4x^2 + 8x - 12$
20. $6x^2 - 6x - 12$
21. $4x^2 + 36x + 81$
22. $25x^2 + 40x + 16$
23. $8x^3 + 125y^3$
24. $27x^3 - 64y^3$
25. $64x^2y^3 - 8x^2$
26. $27x^5y^4 - 216x^2y$
27. $(x + 5)^3 + y^3$
28. $(y - 1)^3 + 27x^3$
29. $(5a - 3)^2 - 6(5a - 3) + 9$
30. $(4r + 1)^2 + 8(4r + 1) + 16$
31. $7x^2 - 63x$
32. $20x^2 + 23x + 6$

33. $ab - 6a + 7b - 42$
34. $20x^2 - 220x + 600$
35. $x^4 - 1$
36. $15x^2 - 20x$
37. $10x^2 - 7x - 33$
38. $45m^3n^3 - 27m^2n^2$
39. $5a^3b^3 - 50a^3b$
40. $x^4 + x$
41. $16x^2 + 25$
42. $20x^3 + 20y^3$
43. $10x^3 - 210x^2 + 1100x$
44. $9y^2 - 42y + 49$
45. $64a^3b^4 - 27a^3b$
46. $y^4 - 16$
47. $2x^3 - 54$
48. $2sr + 10s - r - 5$
49. $3y^5 - 5y^4 + 6y - 10$
50. $64a^2 + b^2$
51. $100z^3 + 100$
52. $250x^4 - 16x$
53. $4b^2 - 36b + 81$
54. $2a^5 - a^4 + 6a - 3$
55. $(y - 6)^2 + 3(y - 6) + 2$
56. $(c + 2)^2 - 6(c + 2) + 5$

△ **57.** Express the area of the shaded region as a polynomial. Factor the polynomial completely.

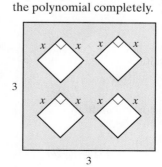

B.5 | Rational Expressions ▶

OBJECTIVE

1 Perform Operations on Rational Expressions and Solve Equations Containing Rational Expressions. ▶

OBJECTIVE

1 Performing Operations on Rational Expressions and Solving Equations Containing Rational Expressions ▶

It is very important that you understand the difference between an expression and an equation containing rational expressions. An equation contains an equal sign; an expression does not.

Expression to be Simplified

$$\frac{x}{2} + \frac{x}{6}$$

Write both rational expressions with the LCD, 6, as the denominator.

$$\frac{x}{2} + \frac{x}{6} = \frac{x \cdot 3}{2 \cdot 3} + \frac{x}{6}$$

$$= \frac{3x}{6} + \frac{x}{6}$$

$$= \frac{4x}{6} = \frac{2x}{3}$$

Equation to be Solved

$$\frac{x}{2} + \frac{x}{6} = \frac{2}{3}$$

Multiply both sides by the LCD, 6.

$$6\left(\frac{x}{2} + \frac{x}{6}\right) = 6\left(\frac{2}{3}\right)$$

$$3x + x = 4$$

$$4x = 4$$

$$x = 1$$

Check to see that the solution is 1.

> ▶ **Helpful Hint**
> Remember: Equations can be cleared of fractions; expressions cannot.

EXAMPLE 1 Multiply. $\dfrac{x^3 - 1}{-3x + 3} \cdot \dfrac{15x^2}{x^2 + x + 1}$

Solution

$$\frac{x^3 - 1}{-3x + 3} \cdot \frac{15x^2}{x^2 + x + 1} = \frac{(x - 1)(x^2 + x + 1)}{-3(x - 1)} \cdot \frac{15x^2}{x^2 + x + 1} \qquad \text{Factor.}$$

$$= \frac{(x - 1)(x^2 + x + 1) \cdot 3 \cdot 5x^2}{-1 \cdot 3(x - 1)(x^2 + x + 1)} \qquad \text{Factor.}$$

$$= \frac{5x^2}{-1} = -5x^2 \qquad \text{Simplest form} \qquad \square$$

PRACTICE

1 Multiply.

a. $\dfrac{2 + 5n}{3n} \cdot \dfrac{6n + 3}{5n^2 - 3n - 2}$

b. $\dfrac{x^3 - 8}{-6x + 12} \cdot \dfrac{6x^2}{x^2 + 2x + 4}$

EXAMPLE 2 Divide. $\dfrac{8m^2}{3m^2 - 12} \div \dfrac{40}{2 - m}$

Solution

$$\frac{8m^2}{3m^2 - 12} \div \frac{40}{2 - m} = \frac{8m^2}{3m^2 - 12} \cdot \frac{2 - m}{40} \qquad \text{Multiply by the reciprocal of the divisor.}$$

$$= \frac{8m^2(2 - m)}{3(m + 2)(m - 2) \cdot 40} \qquad \text{Factor and multiply.}$$

$$= \frac{8\,m^2 \cdot -1\,(m - 2)}{3(m + 2)\,(m - 2) \cdot 8 \cdot 5} \qquad \text{Write } (2 - m) \text{ as } -1(m - 2).$$

$$= -\frac{m^2}{15(m + 2)} \qquad \text{Simplify.} \qquad \square$$

PRACTICE

2   Divide.

a. $\dfrac{6y^3}{3y^2 - 27} \div \dfrac{42}{3 - y}$

b. $\dfrac{10x^2 + 23x - 5}{5x^2 - 51x + 10} \div \dfrac{2x^2 + 9x + 10}{7x^2 - 68x - 20}$

EXAMPLE 3   Perform the indicated operation.

$$\frac{3}{x + 2} + \frac{2x}{x - 2}$$

Solution   The LCD is the product of the two denominators: $(x + 2)(x - 2)$.

$$\frac{3}{x + 2} + \frac{2x}{x - 2} = \frac{3 \cdot (x - 2)}{(x + 2) \cdot (x - 2)} + \frac{2x \cdot (x + 2)}{(x - 2) \cdot (x + 2)} \quad \text{Write equivalent rational expressions.}$$

$$= \frac{3x - 6}{(x + 2)(x - 2)} + \frac{2x^2 + 4x}{(x + 2)(x - 2)} \quad \text{Multiply in the numerators.}$$

$$= \frac{3x - 6 + 2x^2 + 4x}{(x + 2)(x - 2)} \quad \text{Add the numerators.}$$

$$= \frac{2x^2 + 7x - 6}{(x + 2)(x - 2)} \quad \text{Simplify the numerator.} \quad \square$$

PRACTICE

3   Perform the indicated operation.

a. $\dfrac{4}{p^3 q} + \dfrac{3}{5p^4 q}$

b. $\dfrac{4}{y + 3} + \dfrac{5y}{y - 3}$

c. $\dfrac{3z - 18}{z - 5} - \dfrac{3}{5 - z}$

EXAMPLE 4   Solve: $\dfrac{2x}{x - 3} + \dfrac{6 - 2x}{x^2 - 9} = \dfrac{x}{x + 3}$.

Solution   We factor the second denominator to find that the LCD is $(x + 3)(x - 3)$. We multiply both sides of the equation by $(x + 3)(x - 3)$. By the distributive property, this is the same as multiplying each term by $(x + 3)(x - 3)$.

$$\frac{2x}{x - 3} + \frac{6 - 2x}{x^2 - 9} = \frac{x}{x + 3}$$

$$(x + 3)(x - 3) \cdot \frac{2x}{x - 3} + (x + 3)(x - 3) \cdot \frac{6 - 2x}{(x + 3)(x - 3)}$$

$$= (x + 3)(x - 3)\left(\frac{x}{x + 3}\right)$$

$$2x(x + 3) + (6 - 2x) = x(x - 3) \quad \text{Simplify.}$$

$$2x^2 + 6x + 6 - 2x = x^2 - 3x \quad \text{Use the distributive property.}$$

Next we solve this quadratic equation by the factoring method. To do so, we first write the equation so that one side is 0.

$$x^2 + 7x + 6 = 0$$

$$(x + 6)(x + 1) = 0 \quad \text{Factor.}$$

$$x = -6 \quad \text{or} \quad x = -1 \quad \text{Set each factor equal to 0.}$$

Neither -6 nor -1 makes any denominator 0, so they are both solutions. The solutions are -6 and -1. $\quad \square$

PRACTICE

4   Solve: $\dfrac{2}{x - 2} - \dfrac{5 + 2x}{x^2 - 4} = \dfrac{x}{x + 2}$.

B.5 Exercise Set MyMathLab®

Perform each indicated operation and simplify, or solve the equation for the variable.

1. $\dfrac{x}{2} = \dfrac{1}{8} + \dfrac{x}{4}$

2. $\dfrac{x}{4} = \dfrac{3}{2} + \dfrac{x}{10}$

3. $\dfrac{1}{8} + \dfrac{x}{4}$

4. $\dfrac{3}{2} + \dfrac{x}{10}$

5. $\dfrac{4}{x + 2} - \dfrac{2}{x - 1}$

6. $\dfrac{5}{x - 2} - \dfrac{10}{x + 4}$

7. $\dfrac{4}{x + 2} = \dfrac{2}{x - 1}$

8. $\dfrac{5}{x - 2} = \dfrac{10}{x + 4}$

9. $\dfrac{2}{x^2 - 4} = \dfrac{1}{x + 2} - \dfrac{3}{x - 2}$

10. $\dfrac{3}{x^2 - 25} = \dfrac{1}{x + 5} + \dfrac{2}{x - 5}$

11. $\dfrac{5}{x^2 - 3x} + \dfrac{4}{2x - 6}$

12. $\dfrac{5}{x^2 - 3x} \div \dfrac{4}{2x - 6}$

13. $\dfrac{x - 1}{x + 1} + \dfrac{x + 7}{x - 1} = \dfrac{4}{x^2 - 1}$

14. $\left(1 - \dfrac{y}{x}\right) \div \left(1 - \dfrac{x}{y}\right)$

15. $\dfrac{a^2 - 9}{a - 6} \cdot \dfrac{a^2 - 5a - 6}{a^2 - a - 6}$

16. $\dfrac{2}{a - 6} + \dfrac{3a}{a^2 - 5a - 6} - \dfrac{a}{5a + 5}$

17. $\dfrac{2x + 3}{3x - 2} = \dfrac{4x + 1}{6x + 1}$

18. $\dfrac{5x - 3}{2x} = \dfrac{10x + 3}{4x + 1}$

19. $\dfrac{a}{9a^2 - 1} + \dfrac{2}{6a - 2}$

20. $\dfrac{3}{4a - 8} - \dfrac{a + 2}{a^2 - 2a}$

21. $-\dfrac{3}{x^2} - \dfrac{1}{x} + 2 = 0$

22. $\dfrac{x}{2x + 6} + \dfrac{5}{x^2 - 9}$

23. $\dfrac{x - 8}{x^2 - x - 2} + \dfrac{2}{x - 2}$

24. $\dfrac{x - 8}{x^2 - x - 2} + \dfrac{2}{x - 2} = \dfrac{3}{x + 1}$

25. $\dfrac{3}{a} - 5 = \dfrac{7}{a} - 1$

26. $\dfrac{7}{3z - 9} + \dfrac{5}{z}$

Use $\dfrac{x}{5} - \dfrac{x}{4} = \dfrac{1}{10}$ and $\dfrac{x}{5} - \dfrac{x}{4} + \dfrac{1}{10}$ for Exercises 27 and 28.

27. a. Which one above is an expression?

  b. Describe the first step to simplify this expression.

  c. Simplify the expression.

28. a. Which one above is an equation?

  b. Describe the first step to solve this equation.

  c. Solve the equation.

For each exercise, choose the correct statement.* Each figure represents a real number, and no denominators are 0.

29. a. $\dfrac{\triangle + \square}{\triangle} = \square$ **b.** $\dfrac{\triangle + \square}{\triangle} = 1 + \dfrac{\square}{\triangle}$

  c. $\dfrac{\triangle + \square}{\triangle} = \dfrac{\square}{\triangle}$ **d.** $\dfrac{\triangle + \square}{\triangle} = 1 + \square$

  e. $\dfrac{\triangle + \square}{\triangle - \square} = -1$

*My thanks to Kelly Champagne for permission to use her Exercises for 29 through 33.

▶ **Helpful Hint**
Remember: Equations can be cleared of fractions; expressions cannot.

30. **a.** $\dfrac{\triangle}{\square} + \dfrac{\square}{\triangle} = \dfrac{\triangle + \square}{\square + \triangle} = 1$

b. $\dfrac{\triangle}{\square} + \dfrac{\square}{\triangle} = \dfrac{\triangle + \square}{\triangle\square}$

c. $\dfrac{\triangle}{\square} + \dfrac{\square}{\triangle} = \triangle\triangle + \square\square$

d. $\dfrac{\triangle}{\square} + \dfrac{\square}{\triangle} = \dfrac{\triangle\triangle + \square\square}{\square\triangle}$

e. $\dfrac{\triangle}{\square} + \dfrac{\square}{\triangle} = \dfrac{\triangle\square}{\square\triangle} = 1$

31. **a.** $\dfrac{\triangle}{\square} \cdot \dfrac{\bigcirc}{\square} = \dfrac{\triangle\bigcirc}{\square}$
b. $\dfrac{\triangle}{\square} \cdot \dfrac{\bigcirc}{\square} = \triangle\bigcirc$

c. $\dfrac{\triangle}{\square} \cdot \dfrac{\bigcirc}{\square} = \dfrac{\triangle + \bigcirc}{\square + \square}$
d. $\dfrac{\triangle}{\square} \cdot \dfrac{\bigcirc}{\square} = \dfrac{\triangle\bigcirc}{\square\square}$

32. **a.** $\dfrac{\triangle}{\square} \div \dfrac{\bigcirc}{\triangle} = \dfrac{\triangle\triangle}{\square\bigcirc}$
b. $\dfrac{\triangle}{\square} \div \dfrac{\bigcirc}{\triangle} = \dfrac{\bigcirc\square}{\triangle\triangle}$

c. $\dfrac{\triangle}{\square} \div \dfrac{\bigcirc}{\triangle} = \dfrac{\bigcirc}{\square}$
d. $\dfrac{\triangle}{\square} \div \dfrac{\bigcirc}{\triangle} = \dfrac{\triangle + \triangle}{\square + \bigcirc}$

33. **a.** $\dfrac{\dfrac{\triangle + \square}{\bigcirc}}{\dfrac{\triangle}{\bigcirc}} = \square$
b. $\dfrac{\dfrac{\triangle + \square}{\bigcirc}}{\dfrac{\triangle}{\bigcirc}} = \dfrac{\triangle\triangle + \triangle\square}{\bigcirc\bigcirc}$

c. $\dfrac{\dfrac{\triangle + \square}{\bigcirc}}{\dfrac{\triangle}{\bigcirc}} = 1 + \square$
d. $\dfrac{\dfrac{\triangle + \square}{\bigcirc}}{\dfrac{\triangle}{\bigcirc}} = \dfrac{\triangle + \square}{\triangle}$

Appendix C

An Introduction to Using a Graphing Utility

The Viewing Window and Interpreting Window Settings

In this appendix, we will use the term **graphing utility** to mean a graphing calculator or a computer software graphing package. All graphing utilities graph equations by plotting points on a screen. While plotting several points can be slow and sometimes tedious for us, a graphing utility can quickly and accurately plot hundreds of points. How does a graphing utility show plotted points? A computer or calculator screen is made up of a grid of small rectangular areas called **pixels.** If a pixel contains a point to be plotted, the pixel is turned "on"; otherwise, the pixel remains "off." The graph of an equation is then a collection of pixels turned "on." The graph of $y = 3x + 1$ from a graphing calculator is shown in Figure A-1. Notice the irregular shape of the line caused by the rectangular pixels.

Figure A-1

The portion of the coordinate plane shown on the screen in Figure A-1 is called the **viewing window** or the **viewing rectangle.** Notice the x-axis and the y-axis on the graph. While tick marks are shown on the axes, they are not labeled. This means that from this screen alone, we do not know how many units each tick mark represents. To see what each tick mark represents and the minimum and maximum values on the axes, check the window setting of the graphing utility. It defines the viewing window. The window of the graph of $y = 3x + 1$ shown in Figure A-1 has the following settings (Figure A-2):

Xmin = −10	The minimum x-value is −10.
Xmax = 10	The maximum x-value is 10.
Xscl = 1	The x-axis scale is 1 unit per tick mark.
Ymin = −10	The minimum y-value is −10.
Ymax = 10	The maximum y-value is 10.
Yscl = 1	The y-axis scale is 1 unit per tick mark.

By knowing the scale, we can find the minimum and the maximum values on the axes simply by counting tick marks. For example, if both the Xscl (x-axis scale) and the Yscl (y-axis scale) are 1 unit per tick mark on the graph in Figure A-3, we can count the tick marks and find that the minimum x-value is −10 and the maximum x-value is 10. Also, the minimum y-value is −10 and the maximum y-value is 10. If the Xscl changes to 2 units per tick mark (shown in Figure A-4), by counting tick marks, we see that the minimum x-value is now −20 and the maximum x-value is now 20.

Figure A-2

Figure A-3

Figure A-4

Figure A-5

It is also true that if we know the Xmin and the Xmax values, we can calculate the Xscl by the displayed axes. For example, the Xscl of the graph in Figure A-5 must be 3 units per tick mark for the maximum and minimum *x*-values to be as shown. Also, the Yscl of that graph must be 2 units per tick mark for the maximum and minimum *y*-values to be as shown.

We will call the viewing window in Figure A-3 a *standard* viewing window or rectangle. Although a standard viewing window is sufficient for much of this text, special care must be taken to ensure that all key features of a graph are shown. Figures A-6, A-7, and A-8 show the graph of $y = x^2 + 11x - 1$ on three different viewing windows. Note that certain viewing windows for this equation are misleading.

Figure A-6

Figure A-7

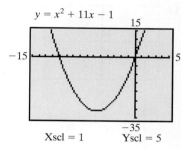

Figure A-8

How do we ensure that all distinguishing features of the graph of an equation are shown? It helps to know about the equation that is being graphed. For example, the equation $y = x^2 + 11x - 1$ is not a linear equation and its graph is not a line. This equation is a quadratic equation and, therefore, its graph is a parabola. By knowing this information, we know that the graph shown in Figure A-6, although correct, is misleading. Of the three viewing rectangles shown, the graph in Figure A-8 is best because it shows more of the distinguishing features of the parabola. Properties of equations needed for graphing will be studied in this text.

The Viewing Window and Interpreting Window Settings Exercise Set

In Exercises 1–4, determine whether all ordered pairs listed will lie within a standard viewing rectangle.

1. $(-9, 0), (5, 8), (1, -8)$

2. $(4, 7), (0, 0), (-8, 9)$

3. $(-11, 0), (2, 2), (7, -5)$

4. $(3, 5), (-3, -5), (15, 0)$

In Exercises 5–10, choose an Xmin, Xmax, Ymin, and Ymax so that all ordered pairs listed will lie within the viewing rectangle.

5. $(-90, 0), (55, 80), (0, -80)$

6. $(4, 70), (20, 20), (-18, 90)$

7. $(-11, 0), (2, 2), (7, -5)$

8. $(3, 5), (-3, -5), (15, 0)$

9. $(200, 200), (50, -50), (70, -50)$

10. $(40, 800), (-30, 500), (15, 0)$

Write the window setting for each viewing window shown. Use the following format:

Xmin =	Ymin =
Xmax =	Ymax =
Xscl =	Yscl =

11.

12.

13.

14.

15.

16.

19.

20.

Xscl = 5, Yscl = 10

Xscl = 100, Yscl = 200

17.

Xscl = 1, Yscl = 3

18.

Xscl = 10, Yscl = 2

Graphing Equations and Square Viewing Window

In general, the following steps may be used to graph an equation on a standard viewing window.

> **Graphing an Equation in *X* and *Y* with a Graphing Utility on a Standard Viewing Window**
>
> **Step 1:** Solve the equation for *y*.
>
> **Step 2:** Using your graphing utility, enter the equation in the form
> Y = *expression involving x*.
>
> **Step 3:** Activate the graphing utility.

Special care must be taken when entering the *expression involving x* in Step 2. You must be sure that the graphing utility you are using interprets the expression as you want it to. For example, let's graph $3y = 4x$. To do so,

Step 1: Solve the equation for *y*.

$$3y = 4x$$
$$\frac{3y}{3} = \frac{4x}{3}$$
$$y = \frac{4}{3}x$$

Figure A-9

Step 2: Using your graphing utility, enter the expression $\frac{4}{3}x$ after the Y = prompt. In order for your graphing utility to correctly interpret the expression, you may need to enter $(4/3)x$ or $(4 \div 3)x$.

Step 3: Activate the graphing utility. The graph should appear as in Figure A-9.

Distinguishing features of the graph of a line include showing all the intercepts of the line. For example, the window of the graph of the line in Figure A-10 does not show both intercepts of the line, but the window of the graph of the same line in Figure A-11 does show both intercepts. Notice the notation below each graph. This is a shorthand notation of the range setting of the graph. This notation means [Xmin, Xmax] by [Ymin, Ymax].

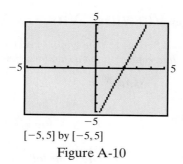

[-5, 5] by [-5, 5]

Figure A-10

[-4, 8] by [-8, 5]

Figure A-11

On a standard viewing window, the tick marks on the *y*-axis are closer together than the tick marks on the *x*-axis. This happens because the viewing window is a rectangle, and so 10 equally spaced tick marks on the positive *y*-axis will be closer together than 10 equally spaced tick marks on the positive *x*-axis. This causes the appearance of graphs to be distorted.

For example, notice the different appearances of the same line graphed using different viewing windows. The line in Figure A-12 is distorted because the tick marks along the *x*-axis are farther apart than the tick marks along the *y*-axis. The graph of the same line in Figure A-13 is not distorted because the viewing rectangle has been selected so that there is equal spacing between tick marks on both axes.

Figure A-12

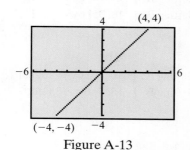

Figure A-13

We say that the line in Figure A-13 is graphed on a *square* setting. Some graphing utilities have a built-in program that, if activated, will automatically provide a square setting. A square setting is especially helpful when we are graphing perpendicular lines, circles, or when a true geometric perspective is desired. Some examples of square screens are shown in Figures A-14 and A-15.

Figure A-14

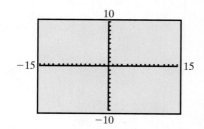

Figure A-15

Other features of a graphing utility such as Trace, Zoom, Intersect, and Table are discussed in appropriate Graphing Calculator Explorations in this text.

Graphing Equations and Square Viewing Window Exercise Set

Graph each linear equation in two variables using the two different range settings given. Determine which setting shows all intercepts of a line.

1. $y = 2x + 12$
   Setting A: $[-10, 10]$ by $[-10, 10]$
   Setting B: $[-10, 10]$ by $[-10, 15]$

2. $y = -3x + 25$
   Setting A: $[-5, 5]$ by $[-30, 10]$
   Setting B: $[-10, 10]$ by $[-10, 30]$

3. $y = -x - 41$
   Setting A: $[-50, 10]$ by $[-10, 10]$
   Setting B: $[-50, 10]$ by $[-50, 15]$

4. $y = 6x - 18$
   Setting A: $[-10, 10]$ by $[-20, 10]$
   Setting B: $[-10, 10]$ by $[-10, 10]$

5. $y = \frac{1}{2}x - 15$
   Setting B: $[-10, 10]$ by $[-20, 10]$
   Setting B: $[-10, 35]$ by $[-20, 15]$

6. $y = -\frac{2}{3}x - \frac{29}{3}$
   Setting A: $[-10, 10]$ by $[-10, 10]$
   Setting B: $[-15, 5]$ by $[-15, 5]$

The graph of each equation is a line. Use a graphing utility and a standard viewing window to graph each equation.

7. $3x = 5y$
8. $7y = -3x$
9. $9x - 5y = 30$
10. $4x + 6y = 20$
11. $y = -7$
12. $y = 2$
13. $x + 10y = -5$
14. $x - 5y = 9$

Graph the following equations using the square setting given. Some keystrokes that may be helpful are given.

15. $y = \sqrt{x}$ $[-12, 12]$ by $[-8, 8]$
    Suggested keystrokes: $\sqrt{\ } x$

16. $y = \sqrt{2x}$ $[-12, 12]$ by $[-8, 8]$
    Suggested keystrokes: $\sqrt{\ }(2x)$

17. $y = x^2 + 2x + 1$ $[-15, 15]$ by $[-10, 10]$
    Suggested keystrokes: $x\text{^}2 + 2x + 1$

18. $y = x^2 - 5$ $[-15, 15]$ by $[-10, 10]$
    Suggested keystrokes: $x\text{^}2 - 5$

19. $y = |x|$ $[-9, 9]$ by $[-6, 6]$
    Suggested keystrokes: $ABS(x)$

20. $y = |x - 2|$ $[-9, 9]$ by $[-6, 6]$
    Suggested keystrokes: $ABS(x - 2)$

Graph each line. Use a standard viewing window; then, if necessary, change the viewing window so that all intercepts of each line show.

21. $x + 2y = 30$
22. $1.5x - 3.7y = 40.3$

Appendix D

Solving Systems of Equations by Matrices

OBJECTIVES

1 Use Matrices to Solve a System of Two Equations. ▶

2 Use Matrices to Solve a System of Three Equations. ▶

By now, you may have noticed that the solution of a system of equations depends on the coefficients of the equations in the system and not on the variables. In this section, we introduce solving a system of equations by a **matrix.**

OBJECTIVE

1 Using Matrices to Solve a System of Two Equations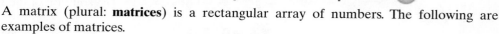

A matrix (plural: **matrices**) is a rectangular array of numbers. The following are examples of matrices.

$$\begin{bmatrix} 1 & 0 \\ 0 & 1 \end{bmatrix} \qquad \begin{bmatrix} 2 & 1 & 3 & -1 \\ 0 & -1 & 4 & 5 \\ -6 & 2 & 1 & 0 \end{bmatrix} \qquad \begin{bmatrix} a & b & c \\ d & e & f \end{bmatrix}$$

The numbers aligned horizontally in a matrix are in the same **row.** The numbers aligned vertically are in the same **column.**

$$\begin{array}{l} \text{row 1} \rightarrow \\ \text{row 2} \rightarrow \end{array} \begin{bmatrix} 2 & 1 & 0 \\ -1 & 6 & 2 \end{bmatrix}$$

column 1, column 2, column 3

This matrix has 2 rows and 3 columns. It is called a 2×3 (read "two by three") matrix.

To see the relationship between systems of equations and matrices, study the example below.

> **Helpful Hint**
>
> Before writing the corresponding matrix associated with a system of equations, make sure that the equations are written in standard form.

System of Equations (in standard form)

$$\begin{cases} 2x - 3y = 6 & \text{Equation 1} \\ x + y = 0 & \text{Equation 2} \end{cases}$$

Corresponding Matrix

$$\begin{bmatrix} 2 & -3 & \vdots & 6 \\ 1 & 1 & \vdots & 0 \end{bmatrix} \begin{array}{l} \text{Row 1} \\ \text{Row 2} \end{array}$$

Notice that the rows of the matrix correspond to the equations in the system. The coefficients of each variable are placed to the left of a vertical dashed line. The constants are placed to the right. Each of the numbers in the matrix is called an **element.**

The method of solving systems by matrices is to write this matrix as an equivalent matrix from which we easily identify the solution. Two matrices are equivalent if they represent systems that have the same solution set. The following **row operations** can be performed on matrices, and the result is an equivalent matrix.

> **Helpful Hint**
>
> Notice that these *row* operations are the same operations that we can perform on *equations* in a system.

Elementary Row Operations

1. Any two rows in a matrix may be interchanged.

2. The elements of any row may be multiplied (or divided) by the same nonzero number.

3. The elements of any row may be multiplied (or divided) by a nonzero number and added to their corresponding elements in any other row.

To solve a system of two equations in x and y by matrices, write the corresponding matrix associated with the system. Then use elementary row operations to write equivalent matrices until you have a matrix of the form

$$\begin{bmatrix} 1 & a & \vdots & b \\ 0 & 1 & \vdots & c \end{bmatrix},$$

where a, b, and c are constants. Why? If a matrix associated with a system of equations is in this form, we can easily solve for x and y. For example,

Matrix		*System of Equations*

$$\begin{bmatrix} 1 & 2 & \vdots & -3 \\ 0 & 1 & \vdots & 5 \end{bmatrix} \quad \text{corresponds to} \quad \begin{cases} 1x + 2y = -3 \\ 0x + 1y = 5 \end{cases} \quad \text{or} \quad \begin{cases} x + 2y = -3 \\ y = 5 \end{cases}$$

In the second equation, we have $y = 5$. Substituting this in the first equation, we have $x + 2(5) = -3$ or $x = -13$. The solution of the system is the ordered pair $(-13, 5)$.

EXAMPLE 1   Use matrices to solve the system.

$$\begin{cases} x + 3y = 5 \\ 2x - y = -4 \end{cases}$$

**Solution**   The corresponding matrix is $\begin{bmatrix} 1 & 3 & \vdots & 5 \\ 2 & -1 & \vdots & -4 \end{bmatrix}$. We use elementary row

operations to write an equivalent matrix that looks like $\begin{bmatrix} 1 & a & \vdots & b \\ 0 & 1 & \vdots & c \end{bmatrix}$.

For the matrix given, the element in the first row, first column is already 1, as desired. Next we write an equivalent matrix with a 0 below the 1. To do this, we multiply row 1 by -2 and add to row 2. *We will change only row 2.*

$$\begin{bmatrix} 1 & 3 & \vdots & 5 \\ -2(1) + 2 & -2(3) + (-1) & \vdots & -2(5) + (-4) \end{bmatrix} \quad \text{simplifies to} \quad \begin{bmatrix} 1 & 3 & \vdots & 5 \\ 0 & -7 & \vdots & -14 \end{bmatrix}$$

row 1   row 2   row 1   row 2   row 1   row 2
element element element element element element

Now we change the -7 to a 1 by use of an elementary row operation. We divide row 2 by -7, then

$$\begin{bmatrix} 1 & 3 & \vdots & 5 \\ \dfrac{0}{-7} & \dfrac{-7}{-7} & \vdots & \dfrac{-14}{-7} \end{bmatrix} \quad \text{simplifies to} \quad \begin{bmatrix} 1 & 3 & \vdots & 5 \\ 0 & 1 & \vdots & 2 \end{bmatrix}$$

This last matrix corresponds to the system

$$\begin{cases} x + 3y = 5 \\ y = 2 \end{cases}$$

To find x, we let $y = 2$ in the first equation, $x + 3y = 5$.

$$\begin{aligned} x + 3y &= 5 && \text{First equation} \\ x + 3(2) &= 5 && \text{Let } y = 2. \\ x &= -1 \end{aligned}$$

The ordered pair solution is $(-1, 2)$. Check to see that this ordered pair satisfies both equations.   □

PRACTICE
1   Use matrices to solve the system.

$$\begin{cases} x + 4y = -2 \\ 3x - y = 7 \end{cases}$$

EXAMPLE 2   Use matrices to solve the system.

$$\begin{cases} 2x - y = 3 \\ 4x - 2y = 5 \end{cases}$$

Solution   The corresponding matrix is $\begin{bmatrix} 2 & -1 & \vdots & 3 \\ 4 & -2 & \vdots & 5 \end{bmatrix}$. To get 1 in the row 1, column 1 position, we divide the elements of row 1 by 2.

$$\begin{bmatrix} \dfrac{2}{2} & -\dfrac{1}{2} & \vdots & \dfrac{3}{2} \\ 4 & -2 & \vdots & 5 \end{bmatrix} \quad \text{simplifies to} \quad \begin{bmatrix} 1 & -\dfrac{1}{2} & \vdots & \dfrac{3}{2} \\ 4 & -2 & \vdots & 5 \end{bmatrix}$$

To get 0 under the 1, we multiply the elements of row 1 by -4 and add the new elements to the elements of row 2.

$$\begin{bmatrix} 1 & -\dfrac{1}{2} & \vdots & \dfrac{3}{2} \\ -4(1) + 4 & -4\left(-\dfrac{1}{2}\right) - 2 & \vdots & -4\left(\dfrac{3}{2}\right) + 5 \end{bmatrix} \quad \text{simplifies to} \quad \begin{bmatrix} 1 & -\dfrac{1}{2} & \vdots & \dfrac{3}{2} \\ 0 & 0 & \vdots & -1 \end{bmatrix}$$

The corresponding system is $\begin{cases} x - \dfrac{1}{2}y = \dfrac{3}{2} \\ 0 = -1 \end{cases}$. The equation $0 = -1$ is false for all y or x values; hence, the system is inconsistent and has no solution. The solution set is $\{\ \}$ or $\varnothing$.

PRACTICE
2   Use matrices to solve the system.

$$\begin{cases} x - 3y = 3 \\ -2x + 6y = 4 \end{cases}$$

✓**CONCEPT CHECK**
Consider the system

$$\begin{cases} 2x - 3y = 8 \\ x + 5y = -3 \end{cases}$$

What is wrong with its corresponding matrix shown below?

$$\begin{bmatrix} 2 & -3 & \vdots & 8 \\ 0 & 5 & \vdots & -3 \end{bmatrix}$$

OBJECTIVE
2   Using Matrices to Solve a System of Three Equations

To solve a system of three equations in three variables using matrices, we will write the corresponding matrix in the form

$$\begin{bmatrix} 1 & a & b & \vdots & d \\ 0 & 1 & c & \vdots & e \\ 0 & 0 & 1 & \vdots & f \end{bmatrix}$$

Answer to Concept Check:

matrix should be $\begin{bmatrix} 2 & -3 & \vdots & 8 \\ 1 & 5 & \vdots & -3 \end{bmatrix}$

EXAMPLE 3 Use matrices to solve the system.

$$\begin{cases} x + 2y + z = 2 \\ -2x - y + 2z = 5 \\ x + 3y - 2z = -8 \end{cases}$$

Solution The corresponding matrix is $\begin{bmatrix} 1 & 2 & 1 & \vdots & 2 \\ -2 & -1 & 2 & \vdots & 5 \\ 1 & 3 & -2 & \vdots & -8 \end{bmatrix}$. Our goal is to write

an equivalent matrix with 1's along the diagonal (see the numbers in red) and 0's below the 1's. The element in row 1, column 1 is already 1. Next we get 0's for each element in the rest of column 1. To do this, first we multiply the elements of row 1 by 2 and add the new elements to row 2. Also, we multiply the elements of row 1 by −1 and add the new elements to the elements of row 3. We *do not change row 1*. Then

$$\begin{bmatrix} 1 & 2 & 1 & \vdots & 2 \\ 2(1) - 2 & 2(2) - 1 & 2(1) + 2 & \vdots & 2(2) + 5 \\ -1(1) + 1 & -1(2) + 3 & -1(1) - 2 & \vdots & -1(2) - 8 \end{bmatrix} \text{ simplifies to } \begin{bmatrix} 1 & 2 & 1 & \vdots & 2 \\ 0 & 3 & 4 & \vdots & 9 \\ 0 & 1 & -3 & \vdots & -10 \end{bmatrix}$$

We continue down the diagonal and use elementary row operations to get 1 where the element 3 is now. To do this, we interchange rows 2 and 3.

$$\begin{bmatrix} 1 & 2 & 1 & \vdots & 2 \\ 0 & 3 & 4 & \vdots & 9 \\ 0 & 1 & -3 & \vdots & -10 \end{bmatrix} \text{ is equivalent to } \begin{bmatrix} 1 & 2 & 1 & \vdots & 2 \\ 0 & 1 & -3 & \vdots & -10 \\ 0 & 3 & 4 & \vdots & 9 \end{bmatrix}$$

Next we want the new row 3, column 2 element to be 0. We multiply the elements of row 2 by −3 and add the result to the elements of row 3.

$$\begin{bmatrix} 1 & 2 & 1 & \vdots & 2 \\ 0 & 1 & -3 & \vdots & -10 \\ -3(0) + 0 & -3(1) + 3 & -3(-3) + 4 & \vdots & -3(-10) + 9 \end{bmatrix} \text{ simplifies to }$$

$$\begin{bmatrix} 1 & 2 & 1 & \vdots & 2 \\ 0 & 1 & -3 & \vdots & -10 \\ 0 & 0 & 13 & \vdots & 39 \end{bmatrix}$$

Finally, we divide the elements of row 3 by 13 so that the final diagonal element is 1.

$$\begin{bmatrix} 1 & 2 & 1 & \vdots & 2 \\ 0 & 1 & -3 & \vdots & -10 \\ \frac{0}{13} & \frac{0}{13} & \frac{13}{13} & \vdots & \frac{39}{13} \end{bmatrix} \text{ simplifies to } \begin{bmatrix} 1 & 2 & 1 & \vdots & 2 \\ 0 & 1 & -3 & \vdots & -10 \\ 0 & 0 & 1 & \vdots & 3 \end{bmatrix}$$

This matrix corresponds to the system

$$\begin{cases} x + 2y + z = 2 \\ y - 3z = -10 \\ z = 3 \end{cases}$$

We identify the z-coordinate of the solution as 3. Next, we replace z with 3 in the second equation and solve for y.

$$y - 3z = -10 \quad \text{Second equation}$$
$$y - 3(3) = -10 \quad \text{Let } z = 3.$$
$$y = -1$$

To find x, we let $z = 3$ and $y = -1$ in the first equation.

$$x + 2y + z = 2 \quad \text{First equation}$$
$$x + 2(-1) + 3 = 2 \quad \text{Let } z = 3 \text{ and } y = -1.$$
$$x = 1$$

The ordered triple solution is $(1, -1, 3)$. Check to see that it satisfies all three equations in the original system. □

PRACTICE
3 Use matrices to solve the system.

$$\begin{cases} x + 3y - z = 0 \\ 2x + y + 3z = 5 \\ -x - 2y + 4z = 7 \end{cases}$$

D Exercise Set MyMathLab®

Solve each system of linear equations using matrices. See Example 1.

1. $\begin{cases} x + y = 1 \\ x - 2y = 4 \end{cases}$

2. $\begin{cases} 2x - y = 8 \\ x + 3y = 11 \end{cases}$

3. $\begin{cases} x + 3y = 2 \\ x + 2y = 0 \end{cases}$

4. $\begin{cases} 4x - y = 5 \\ 3x + 3y = 0 \end{cases}$

Solve each system of linear equations using matrices. See Example 2.

5. $\begin{cases} x - 2y = 4 \\ 2x - 4y = 4 \end{cases}$

6. $\begin{cases} -x + 3y = 6 \\ 3x - 9y = 9 \end{cases}$

7. $\begin{cases} 3x - 3y = 9 \\ 2x - 2y = 6 \end{cases}$

8. $\begin{cases} 9x - 3y = 6 \\ -18x + 6y = -12 \end{cases}$

Solve each system of linear equations using matrices. See Example 3.

9. $\begin{cases} x + y = 3 \\ 2y = 10 \\ 3x + 2y - 4z = 12 \end{cases}$

10. $\begin{cases} 5x = 5 \\ 2x + y = 4 \\ 3x + y - 5z = -15 \end{cases}$

11. $\begin{cases} 2y - z = -7 \\ x + 4y + z = -4 \\ 5x - y + 2z = 13 \end{cases}$

12. $\begin{cases} 4y + 3z = -2 \\ 5x - 4y = 1 \\ -5x + 4y + z = -3 \end{cases}$

MIXED PRACTICE

Solve each system of linear equations using matrices. See Examples 1 through 3.

13. $\begin{cases} x - 4 = 0 \\ x + y = 1 \end{cases}$

14. $\begin{cases} 3y = 6 \\ x + y = 7 \end{cases}$

15. $\begin{cases} x + y + z = 2 \\ 2x - z = 5 \\ 3y + z = 2 \end{cases}$

16. $\begin{cases} x + 2y + z = 5 \\ x - y - z = 3 \\ y + z = 2 \end{cases}$

17. $\begin{cases} 5x - 2y = 27 \\ -3x + 5y = 18 \end{cases}$

18. $\begin{cases} 4x - y = 9 \\ 2x + 3y = -27 \end{cases}$

19. $\begin{cases} 4x - 7y = 7 \\ 12x - 21y = 24 \end{cases}$

20. $\begin{cases} 2x - 5y = 12 \\ -4x + 10y = 20 \end{cases}$

21. $\begin{cases} 4x - y + 2z = 5 \\ 2y + z = 4 \\ 4x + y + 3z = 10 \end{cases}$

22. $\begin{cases} 5y - 7z = 14 \\ 2x + y + 4z = 10 \\ 2x + 6y - 3z = 30 \end{cases}$

23. $\begin{cases} 4x + y + z = 3 \\ -x + y - 2z = -11 \\ x + 2y + 2z = -1 \end{cases}$

24. $\begin{cases} x + y + z = 9 \\ 3x - y + z = -1 \\ -2x + 2y - 3z = -2 \end{cases}$

CONCEPT EXTENSIONS

Solve. See the Concept Check in this section.

25. For the system $\begin{cases} x + z = 7 \\ y + 2z = -6, \\ 3x - y = 0 \end{cases}$ which is the correct corresponding matrix?

a. $\begin{bmatrix} 1 & 1 & | & 7 \\ 1 & 2 & | & -6 \\ 3 & -1 & | & 0 \end{bmatrix}$

b. $\begin{bmatrix} 1 & 0 & 1 & | & 7 \\ 1 & 2 & 0 & | & -6 \\ 3 & -1 & 0 & | & 0 \end{bmatrix}$

c. $\begin{bmatrix} 1 & 0 & 1 & | & 7 \\ 0 & 1 & 2 & | & -6 \\ 3 & -1 & 0 & | & 0 \end{bmatrix}$

Appendix E

Solving Systems of Equations by Determinants

OBJECTIVES

1 Define and Evaluate a 2 × 2 Determinant.

2 Use Cramer's Rule to Solve a System of Two Linear Equations in Two Variables.

3 Define and Evaluate a 3 × 3 Determinant.

4 Use Cramer's Rule to Solve a System of Three Linear Equations in Three Variables.

We have solved systems of two linear equations in two variables in four different ways: graphically, by substitution, by elimination, and by matrices. Now we analyze another method, called **Cramer's rule.**

Recall that a matrix is a rectangular array of numbers. If a matrix has the same number of rows and columns, it is called a **square matrix.** Examples of square matrices are

$$\begin{bmatrix} 1 & 6 \\ 5 & 2 \end{bmatrix} \qquad \begin{bmatrix} 2 & 4 & 1 \\ 0 & 5 & 2 \\ 3 & 6 & 9 \end{bmatrix}$$

A **determinant** is a real number associated with a square matrix. The determinant of a square matrix is denoted by placing vertical bars about the array of numbers. Thus,

The determinant of the square matrix $\begin{bmatrix} 1 & 6 \\ 5 & 2 \end{bmatrix}$ is $\begin{vmatrix} 1 & 6 \\ 5 & 2 \end{vmatrix}$.

The determinant of the square matrix $\begin{bmatrix} 2 & 4 & 1 \\ 0 & 5 & 2 \\ 3 & 6 & 9 \end{bmatrix}$ is $\begin{vmatrix} 2 & 4 & 1 \\ 0 & 5 & 2 \\ 3 & 6 & 9 \end{vmatrix}$.

We define the determinant of a 2 × 2 matrix first. (Recall that 2 × 2 is read "two by two." It means that the matrix has 2 rows and 2 columns.)

Determinant of a 2 × 2 Matrix

$$\begin{vmatrix} a & b \\ c & d \end{vmatrix} = ad - bc$$

EXAMPLE 1 Evaluate each determinant

a. $\begin{vmatrix} -1 & 2 \\ 3 & -4 \end{vmatrix}$ **b.** $\begin{vmatrix} 2 & 0 \\ 7 & -5 \end{vmatrix}$

Solution First we identify the values of a, b, c, and d. Then we perform the evaluation.

a. Here $a = -1, b = 2, c = 3$, and $d = -4$.

$$\begin{vmatrix} -1 & 2 \\ 3 & -4 \end{vmatrix} = ad - bc = (-1)(-4) - (2)(3) = -2$$

b. In this example, $a = 2, b = 0, c = 7$, and $d = -5$.

$$\begin{vmatrix} 2 & 0 \\ 7 & -5 \end{vmatrix} = ad - bc = 2(-5) - (0)(7) = -10$$

OBJECTIVE

2   Using Cramer's Rule to Solve a System of Two Linear Equations

To develop Cramer's rule, we solve the system $\begin{cases} ax + by = h \\ cx + dy = k \end{cases}$ using elimination. First, we eliminate y by multiplying both sides of the first equation by d and both sides of the second equation by $-b$ so that the coefficients of y are opposites. The result is that

$$\begin{cases} d(ax + by) = d \cdot h \\ -b(cx + dy) = -b \cdot k \end{cases} \quad \text{simplifies to} \quad \begin{cases} adx + bdy = hd \\ -bcx - bdy = -kb \end{cases}$$

We now add the two equations and solve for x.

$$\begin{array}{rl} adx + bdy &= hd \\ \underline{-bcx - bdy} &= \underline{-kb} \\ adx - bcx &= hd - kb \quad \text{Add the equations.} \\ (ad - bc)x &= hd - kb \\ x &= \dfrac{hd - kb}{ad - bc} \quad \text{Solve for } x. \end{array}$$

When we replace x with $\dfrac{hd - kb}{ad - bc}$ in the equation $ax + by = h$ and solve for y, we find that $y = \dfrac{ak - ch}{ad - bc}$.

Notice that the numerator of the value of x is the determinant of

$$\begin{vmatrix} h & b \\ k & d \end{vmatrix} = hd - kb$$

Also, the numerator of the value of y is the determinant of

$$\begin{vmatrix} a & h \\ c & k \end{vmatrix} = ak - hc$$

Finally, the denominators of the values of x and y are the same and are the determinant of

$$\begin{vmatrix} a & b \\ c & d \end{vmatrix} = ad - bc$$

This means that the values of x and y can be written in determinant notation:

$$x = \frac{\begin{vmatrix} h & b \\ k & d \end{vmatrix}}{\begin{vmatrix} a & b \\ c & d \end{vmatrix}} \quad \text{and} \quad y = \frac{\begin{vmatrix} a & h \\ c & k \end{vmatrix}}{\begin{vmatrix} a & b \\ c & d \end{vmatrix}}$$

For convenience, we label the determinants D, D_x, and D_y.

x-coefficients ────────────────┐

┌─ y-coefficients ─┐

$$\begin{vmatrix} a & b \\ c & d \end{vmatrix} = D \qquad \begin{vmatrix} h & b \\ k & d \end{vmatrix} = D_x \qquad \begin{vmatrix} a & h \\ c & k \end{vmatrix} = D_y$$

x-column replaced y-column replaced
by constants   by constants

These determinant formulas for the coordinates of the solution of a system are known as **Cramer's rule.**

Cramer's Rule for Two Linear Equations in Two Variables

The solution of the system $\begin{cases} ax + by = h \\ cx + dy = k \end{cases}$ is given by

$$x = \frac{\begin{vmatrix} h & b \\ k & d \end{vmatrix}}{\begin{vmatrix} a & b \\ c & d \end{vmatrix}} = \frac{D_x}{D} \qquad y = \frac{\begin{vmatrix} a & h \\ c & k \end{vmatrix}}{\begin{vmatrix} a & b \\ c & d \end{vmatrix}} = \frac{D_y}{D}$$

as long as $D = ad - bc$ is not 0.

When $D = 0$, the system is either inconsistent or the equations are dependent. When this happens, we need to use another method to see which is the case.

EXAMPLE 2 Use Cramer's rule to solve the system

$$\begin{cases} 3x + 4y = -7 \\ x - 2y = -9 \end{cases}$$

Solution First we find $D, D_x,$ and $D_y.$

$$\begin{cases} 3x + 4y = -7 \\ x - 2y = -9 \end{cases}$$

$$D = \begin{vmatrix} a & b \\ c & d \end{vmatrix} = \begin{vmatrix} 3 & 4 \\ 1 & -2 \end{vmatrix} = 3(-2) - 4(1) = -10$$

$$D_x = \begin{vmatrix} h & b \\ k & d \end{vmatrix} = \begin{vmatrix} -7 & 4 \\ -9 & -2 \end{vmatrix} = (-7)(-2) - 4(-9) = 50$$

$$D_y = \begin{vmatrix} a & h \\ c & k \end{vmatrix} = \begin{vmatrix} 3 & -7 \\ 1 & -9 \end{vmatrix} = 3(-9) - (-7)(1) = -20$$

Then $x = \dfrac{D_x}{D} = \dfrac{50}{-10} = -5$ and $y = \dfrac{D_y}{D} = \dfrac{-20}{-10} = 2.$

The ordered pair solution is $(-5, 2).$
As always, check the solution in both original equations.

EXAMPLE 3 Use Cramer's rule to solve the system

$$\begin{cases} 5x + y = 5 \\ -7x - 2y = -7 \end{cases}$$

Solution First we find $D, D_x,$ and $D_y.$

$$D = \begin{vmatrix} 5 & 1 \\ -7 & -2 \end{vmatrix} = 5(-2) - (-7)(1) = -3$$

$$D_x = \begin{vmatrix} 5 & 1 \\ -7 & -2 \end{vmatrix} = 5(-2) - (-7)(1) = -3$$

$$D_y = \begin{vmatrix} 5 & 5 \\ -7 & -7 \end{vmatrix} = 5(-7) - 5(-7) = 0$$

Then

$$x = \frac{D_x}{D} = \frac{-3}{-3} = 1 \qquad y = \frac{D_y}{D} = \frac{0}{-3} = 0$$

The ordered pair solution is $(1, 0)$. □

OBJECTIVE

3 Evaluating 3 × 3 Determinants

A 3×3 determinant can be used to solve a system of three equations in three variables. The determinant of a 3×3 matrix, however, is considerably more complex than a 2×2 one.

Determinant of a 3 × 3 Matrix

$$\begin{vmatrix} a_1 & b_1 & c_1 \\ a_2 & b_2 & c_2 \\ a_3 & b_3 & c_3 \end{vmatrix} = a_1 \cdot \begin{vmatrix} b_2 & c_2 \\ b_3 & c_3 \end{vmatrix} - a_2 \cdot \begin{vmatrix} b_1 & c_1 \\ b_3 & c_3 \end{vmatrix} + a_3 \cdot \begin{vmatrix} b_1 & c_1 \\ b_2 & c_2 \end{vmatrix}$$

Notice that the determinant of a 3×3 matrix is related to the determinants of three 2×2 matrices. Each determinant of these 2×2 matrices is called a **minor,** and every element of a 3×3 matrix has a minor associated with it. For example, the minor of c_2 is the determinant of the 2×2 matrix found by deleting the row and column containing c_2.

$$\begin{matrix} a_1 & b_1 & c_1 \\ a_2 & b_2 & c_2 \\ a_3 & b_3 & c_3 \end{matrix} \qquad \text{The minor of } c_2 \text{ is} \qquad \begin{vmatrix} a_1 & b_1 \\ a_3 & b_3 \end{vmatrix}$$

Also, the minor of element a_1 is the determinant of the 2×2 matrix that has no row or column containing a_1.

$$\begin{matrix} a_1 & b_1 & c_1 \\ a_2 & b_2 & c_2 \\ a_3 & b_3 & c_3 \end{matrix} \qquad \text{The minor of } a_1 \text{ is} \qquad \begin{vmatrix} b_2 & c_2 \\ b_3 & c_3 \end{vmatrix}$$

So the determinant of a 3×3 matrix can be written as

$$a_1 \cdot (\text{minor of } a_1) - a_2 \cdot (\text{minor of } a_2) + a_3 \cdot (\text{minor of } a_3)$$

Finding the determinant by using minors of elements in the first column is called **expanding** by the minors of the first column. *The value of a determinant can be found by expanding by the minors of any row or column.* The following **array of signs** is helpful in determining whether to add or subtract the product of an element and its minor.

$$\begin{matrix} + & - & + \\ - & + & - \\ + & - & + \end{matrix}$$

If an element is in a position marked $+$, we add. If marked $-$, we subtract.

EXAMPLE 4 Evaluate by expanding by the minors of the given row or column.

$$\begin{vmatrix} 0 & 5 & 1 \\ 1 & 3 & -1 \\ -2 & 2 & 4 \end{vmatrix}$$

a. First column   **b.** Second row

Solution

a. The elements of the first column are 0, 1, and −2. The first column of the array of signs is +, −, +.

$$\begin{vmatrix} 0 & 5 & 1 \\ 1 & 3 & -1 \\ -2 & 2 & 4 \end{vmatrix} = 0 \cdot \begin{vmatrix} 3 & -1 \\ 2 & 4 \end{vmatrix} - 1 \cdot \begin{vmatrix} 5 & 1 \\ 2 & 4 \end{vmatrix} + (-2) \cdot \begin{vmatrix} 5 & 1 \\ 3 & -1 \end{vmatrix}$$

$$= 0(12 - (-2)) - 1(20 - 2) + (-2)(-5 - 3)$$
$$= 0 - 18 + 16 = -2$$

b. The elements of the second row are 1, 3, and −1. This time, the signs begin with − and again alternate.

$$\begin{vmatrix} 0 & 5 & 1 \\ 1 & 3 & -1 \\ -2 & 2 & 4 \end{vmatrix} = -1 \cdot \begin{vmatrix} 5 & 1 \\ 2 & 4 \end{vmatrix} + 3 \cdot \begin{vmatrix} 0 & 1 \\ -2 & 4 \end{vmatrix} - (-1) \cdot \begin{vmatrix} 0 & 5 \\ -2 & 2 \end{vmatrix}$$

$$= -1(20 - 2) + 3(0 - (-2)) - (-1)(0 - (-10))$$
$$= -18 + 6 + 10 = -2$$

Notice that the determinant of the 3 × 3 matrix is the same regardless of the row or column you select to expand by. □

✓CONCEPT CHECK

Why would expanding by minors of the second row be a good choice for the determinant $\begin{vmatrix} 3 & 4 & -2 \\ 5 & 0 & 0 \\ 6 & -3 & 7 \end{vmatrix}$?

OBJECTIVE

4 **Using Cramer's Rule to Solve a System of Three Linear Equations**

A system of three equations in three variables may be solved with Cramer's rule also. Using the elimination process to solve a system with unknown constants as coefficients leads to the following.

Cramer's Rule for Three Equations in Three Variables

The solution of the system $\begin{cases} a_1x + b_1y + c_1z = k_1 \\ a_2x + b_2y + c_2z = k_2 \\ a_3x + b_3y + c_3z = k_3 \end{cases}$ is given by

$$x = \frac{D_x}{D} \qquad y = \frac{D_y}{D} \qquad \text{and} \qquad z = \frac{D_z}{D}$$

where

$$D = \begin{vmatrix} a_1 & b_1 & c_1 \\ a_2 & b_2 & c_2 \\ a_3 & b_3 & c_3 \end{vmatrix} \qquad D_x = \begin{vmatrix} k_1 & b_1 & c_1 \\ k_2 & b_2 & c_2 \\ k_3 & b_3 & c_3 \end{vmatrix}$$

$$D_y = \begin{vmatrix} a_1 & k_1 & c_1 \\ a_2 & k_2 & c_2 \\ a_3 & k_3 & c_3 \end{vmatrix} \qquad D_z = \begin{vmatrix} a_1 & b_1 & k_1 \\ a_2 & b_2 & k_2 \\ a_3 & b_3 & k_3 \end{vmatrix}$$

as long as D is not 0.

Answer to Concept Check:
Two elements of the second row are 0, which makes calculations easier.

EXAMPLE 5   Use Cramer's rule to solve the system

$$\begin{cases} x - 2y + z = 4 \\ 3x + y - 2z = 3 \\ 5x + 5y + 3z = -8 \end{cases}$$

Solution   First we find $D, D_x, D_y,$ and $D_z.$ Beginning with $D,$ we expand by the minors of the first column.

$$D = \begin{vmatrix} 1 & -2 & 1 \\ 3 & 1 & -2 \\ 5 & 5 & 3 \end{vmatrix} = 1 \cdot \begin{vmatrix} 1 & -2 \\ 5 & 3 \end{vmatrix} - 3 \cdot \begin{vmatrix} -2 & 1 \\ 5 & 3 \end{vmatrix} + 5 \cdot \begin{vmatrix} -2 & 1 \\ 1 & -2 \end{vmatrix}$$

$$= 1(3 - (-10)) - 3(-6 - 5) + 5(4 - 1)$$

$$= 13 + 33 + 15 = 61$$

$$D_x = \begin{vmatrix} 4 & -2 & 1 \\ 3 & 1 & -2 \\ -8 & 5 & 3 \end{vmatrix} = 4 \cdot \begin{vmatrix} 1 & -2 \\ 5 & 3 \end{vmatrix} - 3 \cdot \begin{vmatrix} -2 & 1 \\ 5 & 3 \end{vmatrix} + (-8) \cdot \begin{vmatrix} -2 & 1 \\ 1 & -2 \end{vmatrix}$$

$$= 4(3 - (-10)) - 3(-6 - 5) + (-8)(4 - 1)$$

$$= 52 + 33 - 24 = 61$$

$$D_y = \begin{vmatrix} 1 & 4 & 1 \\ 3 & 3 & -2 \\ 5 & -8 & 3 \end{vmatrix} = 1 \cdot \begin{vmatrix} 3 & -2 \\ -8 & 3 \end{vmatrix} - 3 \cdot \begin{vmatrix} 4 & 1 \\ -8 & 3 \end{vmatrix} + 5 \cdot \begin{vmatrix} 4 & 1 \\ 3 & -2 \end{vmatrix}$$

$$= 1(9 - 16) - 3(12 - (-8)) + 5(-8 - 3)$$

$$= -7 - 60 - 55 = -122$$

$$D_z = \begin{vmatrix} 1 & -2 & 4 \\ 3 & 1 & 3 \\ 5 & 5 & -8 \end{vmatrix} = 1 \cdot \begin{vmatrix} 1 & 3 \\ 5 & -8 \end{vmatrix} - 3 \cdot \begin{vmatrix} -2 & 4 \\ 5 & -8 \end{vmatrix} + 5 \cdot \begin{vmatrix} -2 & 4 \\ 1 & 3 \end{vmatrix}$$

$$= 1(-8 - 15) - 3(16 - 20) + 5(-6 - 4)$$

$$= -23 + 12 - 50 = -61$$

From these determinants, we calculate the solution:

$$x = \frac{D_x}{D} = \frac{61}{61} = 1 \quad y = \frac{D_y}{D} = \frac{-122}{61} = -2 \quad z = \frac{D_z}{D} = \frac{-61}{61} = -1$$

The ordered triple solution is $(1, -2, -1).$ Check this solution by verifying that it satisfies each equation of the system.   ☐

E Exercise Set   MyMathLab®

Evaluate. See Example 1.

1. $\begin{vmatrix} 3 & 5 \\ -1 & 7 \end{vmatrix}$

2. $\begin{vmatrix} -5 & 1 \\ 0 & -4 \end{vmatrix}$

3. $\begin{vmatrix} 9 & -2 \\ 4 & -3 \end{vmatrix}$

4. $\begin{vmatrix} 4 & 0 \\ 9 & 8 \end{vmatrix}$

5. $\begin{vmatrix} -2 & 9 \\ 4 & -18 \end{vmatrix}$

6. $\begin{vmatrix} -40 & 8 \\ 70 & -14 \end{vmatrix}$

Use Cramer's rule, if possible, to solve each system of linear equations. See Examples 2 and 3.

7. $\begin{cases} 2y - 4 = 0 \\ x + 2y = 5 \end{cases}$

8. $\begin{cases} 4x - y = 5 \\ 3x - 3 = 0 \end{cases}$

9. $\begin{cases} 3x + y = 1 \\ 2y = 2 - 6x \end{cases}$

10. $\begin{cases} y = 2x - 5 \\ 8x - 4y = 20 \end{cases}$

11. $\begin{cases} 5x - 2y = 27 \\ -3x + 5y = 18 \end{cases}$

12. $\begin{cases} 4x - y = 9 \\ 2x + 3y = -27 \end{cases}$

Evaluate. See Example 4.

13. $\begin{vmatrix} 2 & 1 & 0 \\ 0 & 5 & -3 \\ 4 & 0 & 2 \end{vmatrix}$

14. $\begin{vmatrix} -6 & 4 & 2 \\ 1 & 0 & 5 \\ 0 & 3 & 1 \end{vmatrix}$

15. $\begin{vmatrix} 4 & -6 & 0 \\ -2 & 3 & 0 \\ 4 & -6 & 1 \end{vmatrix}$

16. $\begin{vmatrix} 5 & 2 & 1 \\ 3 & -6 & 0 \\ -2 & 8 & 0 \end{vmatrix}$

17. $\begin{vmatrix} 3 & 6 & -3 \\ -1 & -2 & 3 \\ 4 & -1 & 6 \end{vmatrix}$

18. $\begin{vmatrix} 2 & -2 & 1 \\ 4 & 1 & 3 \\ 3 & 1 & 2 \end{vmatrix}$

Use Cramer's rule, if possible, to solve each system of linear equations. See Example 5.

19. $\begin{cases} 3x \quad\ + z = -1 \\ -x - 3y + z = 7 \\ \quad\ 3y + z = 5 \end{cases}$

20. $\begin{cases} \quad\ 4y - 3z = -2 \\ 8x - 4y \quad\ = 4 \\ -8x + 4y + z = -2 \end{cases}$

21. $\begin{cases} x + y + z = 8 \\ 2x - y - z = 10 \\ x - 2y + 3z = 22 \end{cases}$

22. $\begin{cases} 5x + y + 3z = 1 \\ x - y - 3z = -7 \\ -x + y \quad\ = 1 \end{cases}$

MIXED PRACTICE

Evaluate.

23. $\begin{vmatrix} 10 & -1 \\ -4 & 2 \end{vmatrix}$

24. $\begin{vmatrix} -6 & 2 \\ 5 & -1 \end{vmatrix}$

25. $\begin{vmatrix} 1 & 0 & 4 \\ 1 & -1 & 2 \\ 3 & 2 & 1 \end{vmatrix}$

26. $\begin{vmatrix} 0 & 1 & 2 \\ 3 & -1 & 2 \\ 3 & 2 & -2 \end{vmatrix}$

▶ 27. $\begin{vmatrix} \frac{3}{4} & \frac{5}{2} \\ -\frac{1}{6} & \frac{7}{3} \end{vmatrix}$

28. $\begin{vmatrix} \frac{5}{7} & \frac{1}{3} \\ \frac{6}{7} & \frac{2}{3} \end{vmatrix}$

29. $\begin{vmatrix} 4 & -2 & 2 \\ 6 & -1 & 3 \\ 2 & 1 & 1 \end{vmatrix}$

30. $\begin{vmatrix} 1 & 5 & 0 \\ 7 & 9 & -4 \\ 3 & 2 & -2 \end{vmatrix}$

31. $\begin{vmatrix} -2 & 5 & 4 \\ 5 & -1 & 3 \\ 4 & 1 & 2 \end{vmatrix}$

32. $\begin{vmatrix} 5 & -2 & 4 \\ -1 & 5 & 3 \\ 1 & 4 & 2 \end{vmatrix}$

Use Cramer's rule, if possible, to solve each system of linear equations.

▶ 33. $\begin{cases} 2x - 5y = 4 \\ x + 2y = -7 \end{cases}$

34. $\begin{cases} 3x - y = 2 \\ -5x + 2y = 0 \end{cases}$

35. $\begin{cases} 4x + 2y = 5 \\ 2x + y = -1 \end{cases}$

36. $\begin{cases} 3x + 6y = 15 \\ 2x + 4y = 3 \end{cases}$

37. $\begin{cases} 2x + 2y + z = 1 \\ -x + y + 2z = 3 \\ x + 2y + 4z = 0 \end{cases}$

38. $\begin{cases} 2x - 3y + z = 5 \\ x + y + z = 0 \\ 4x + 2y + 4z = 4 \end{cases}$

39. $\begin{cases} \frac{2}{3}x - \frac{3}{4}y = -1 \\ -\frac{1}{6}x + \frac{3}{4}y = \frac{5}{2} \end{cases}$

40. $\begin{cases} \frac{1}{2}x - \frac{1}{3}y = -3 \\ \frac{1}{8}x + \frac{1}{6}y = 0 \end{cases}$

41. $\begin{cases} 0.7x - 0.2y = -1.6 \\ 0.2x - y = -1.4 \end{cases}$

42. $\begin{cases} -0.7x + 0.6y = 1.3 \\ 0.5x - 0.3y = -0.8 \end{cases}$

43. $\begin{cases} -2x + 4y - 2z = 6 \\ x - 2y + z = -3 \\ 3x - 6y + 3z = -9 \end{cases}$

44. $\begin{cases} -x - y + 3z = 2 \\ 4x + 4y - 12z = -8 \\ -3x - 3y + 9z = 6 \end{cases}$

45. $\begin{cases} x - 2y + z = -5 \\ 3y + 2z = 4 \\ 3x - y \quad\ = -2 \end{cases}$

46. $\begin{cases} 4x + 5y \quad\ = 10 \\ 3y + 2z = -6 \\ x + y + z = 3 \end{cases}$

CONCEPT EXTENSIONS

Find the value of x such that each is a true statement.

47. $\begin{vmatrix} 1 & x \\ 2 & 7 \end{vmatrix} = -3$

48. $\begin{vmatrix} 6 & 1 \\ -2 & x \end{vmatrix} = 26$

49. If all the elements in a single row of a square matrix are zero, to what does the determinant evaluate? Explain your answer.

50. If all the elements in a single column of a square matrix are 0, to what does the determinant evaluate? Explain your answer.

51. Suppose you are interested in finding the determinant of a 4×4 matrix. Study the pattern shown in the array of signs for a 3×3 matrix. Use the pattern to expand the array of signs for use with a 4×4 matrix.

52. Why would expanding by minors of the second row be a good choice for the determinant $\begin{vmatrix} 3 & 4 & -2 \\ 5 & 0 & 0 \\ 6 & -3 & 7 \end{vmatrix}$?

Find the value of each determinant. To evaluate a 4×4 determinant, select any row or column and expand by the minors. The array of signs for a 4×4 determinant is the same as for a 3×3 determinant except expanded.

53. $\begin{vmatrix} 5 & 0 & 0 & 0 \\ 0 & 4 & 2 & -1 \\ 1 & 3 & -2 & 0 \\ 0 & -3 & 1 & 2 \end{vmatrix}$

54. $\begin{vmatrix} 1 & 7 & 0 & -1 \\ 1 & 3 & -2 & 0 \\ 1 & 0 & -1 & 2 \\ 0 & -6 & 2 & 4 \end{vmatrix}$

55. $\begin{vmatrix} 4 & 0 & 2 & 5 \\ 0 & 3 & -1 & 1 \\ 0 & 0 & 2 & 0 \\ 0 & 0 & 0 & 1 \end{vmatrix}$

56. $\begin{vmatrix} 2 & 0 & -1 & 4 \\ 6 & 0 & 4 & 1 \\ 2 & 4 & 3 & -1 \\ 4 & 0 & 5 & -4 \end{vmatrix}$

Appendix F

Mean, Median, and Mode

It is sometimes desirable to be able to describe a set of data, or a set of numbers, by a single "middle" number. Three such **measures of central tendency** are the mean, the median, and the mode.

The most common measure of central tendency is the mean (sometimes called the arithmetic mean or the average). The **mean** of a set of data items, denoted by $\bar{x}$, is the sum of the items divided by the number of items.

EXAMPLE 1 Seven students in a psychology class conducted an experiment on mazes. Each student was given a pencil and asked to successfully complete the same maze. The timed results are below.

Student	Ann	Thanh	Carlos	Jesse	Melinda	Ramzi	Dayni
Time (Seconds)	13.2	11.8	10.7	16.2	15.9	13.8	18.5

a. Who completed the maze in the shortest time? Who completed the maze in the longest time?

b. Find the mean.

c. How many students took longer than the mean time? How many students took shorter than the mean time?

Solution

a. Carlos completed the maze in 10.7 seconds, the shortest time. Dayni completed the maze in 18.5 seconds, the longest time.

b. To find the mean, $\bar{x}$, find the sum of the data items and divide by 7, the number of items.

$$\bar{x} = \frac{13.2 + 11.8 + 10.7 + 16.2 + 15.9 + 13.8 + 18.5}{7} = \frac{100.1}{7} = 14.3$$

c. Three students, Jesse, Melinda, and Dayni, had times longer than the mean time. Four students, Ann, Thanh, Carlos, and Ramzi, had times shorter than the mean time. ☐

Two other measures of central tendency are the median and the mode.

The **median** of an ordered set of numbers is the middle number. If the number of items is even, the median is the mean of the two middle numbers. The **mode** of a set of numbers is the number that occurs most often. It is possible for a data set to have no mode or more than one mode.

EXAMPLE 2 Find the median and the mode of the following list of numbers. These numbers were high temperatures for fourteen consecutive days in a city in Montana.

$$76, 80, 85, 86, 89, 87, 82, 77, 76, 79, 82, 89, 89, 92$$

(Continued on next page)

Solution

First, write the numbers in order.

$$76, 76, 77, 79, 80, 82, \underbrace{82, 85}_{\substack{\text{two} \\ \text{middle numbers}}}, 86, 87, \underbrace{89, 89, 89}_{\text{mode}}, 92$$

Since there is an even number of items, the median is the mean of the two middle numbers.

$$\text{median} = \frac{82 + 85}{2} = 83.5$$

The mode is 89, since 89 occurs most often. □

F Exercise Set

MyMathLab®

For each of the following data sets, find the mean, the median, and the mode. If necessary, round the mean to one decimal place.

1. 21, 28, 16, 42, 38

2. 42, 35, 36, 40, 50

3. 7.6, 8.2, 8.2, 9.6, 5.7, 9.1

4. 4.9, 7.1, 6.8, 6.8, 5.3, 4.9

5. 0.2, 0.3, 0.5, 0.6, 0.6, 0.9, 0.2, 0.7, 1.1

6. 0.6, 0.6, 0.8, 0.4, 0.5, 0.3, 0.7, 0.8, 0.1

7. 231, 543, 601, 293, 588, 109, 334, 268

8. 451, 356, 478, 776, 892, 500, 467, 780

The eight tallest buildings in the United States are listed below. Use this table for Exercises 9 through 12.

Building	Height (feet)
Willis Tower, Chicago, IL	1454
Empire State, New York, NY	1250
Amoco, Chicago, IL	1136
John Hancock Center, Chicago, IL	1127
First Interstate World Center, Los Angeles, CA	1107
Chrysler, New York, NY	1046
NationsBank Tower, Atlanta, GA	1023
Texas Commerce Tower, Houston, TX	1002

9. Find the mean height for the five tallest buildings.
10. Find the median height for the five tallest buildings.
11. Find the median height for the eight tallest buildings.
12. Find the mean height for the eight tallest buildings.

During an experiment, the following times (in seconds) were recorded: 7.8, 6.9, 7.5, 4.7, 6.9, 7.0.

13. Find the mean. Round to the nearest tenth.
14. Find the median.
15. Find the mode.

In a mathematics class, the following test scores were recorded for a student: 86, 95, 91, 74, 77, 85.

16. Find the mean. Round to the nearest hundredth.
17. Find the median.
18. Find the mode.

The following pulse rates were recorded for a group of fifteen students: 78, 80, 66, 68, 71, 64, 82, 71, 70, 65, 70, 75, 77, 86, 72.

19. Find the mean.
20. Find the median.
21. Find the mode.
22. How many rates were higher than the mean?
23. How many rates were lower than the mean?
24. Have each student in your algebra class take his/her pulse rate. Record the data and find the mean, the median, and the mode.

Find the missing numbers in each list of numbers. (These numbers are not necessarily in numerical order.)

25. __, __, 16, 18, __
    The mode is 21.   The mean is 20.

26. __, __, __, __, 40
    The mode is 35.   The median is 37.   The mean is 38.

Appendix G

Review of Angles, Lines, and Special Triangles

The word **geometry** is formed from the Greek words **geo,** meaning earth, and **metron,** meaning measure. Geometry literally means to measure the earth.

This section contains a review of some basic geometric ideas. It will be assumed that fundamental ideas of geometry such as point, line, ray, and angle are known. In this appendix, the notation $\angle 1$ is read "angle 1" and the notation $m\angle 1$ is read "the measure of angle 1."

We first review types of angles.

Angles

A **right angle** is an angle whose measure is 90°. A right angle can be indicated by a square drawn at the vertex of the angle, as shown below.

An angle whose measure is more than 0° but less than 90° is called an **acute angle.**

An angle whose measure is greater than 90° but less than 180° is called an **obtuse angle.**

An angle whose measure is 180° is called a **straight angle.**

Two angles are said to be **complementary** if the sum of their measures is 90°. Each angle is called the **complement** of the other.

Two angles are said to be **supplementary** if the sum of their measures is 180°. Each angle is called the **supplement** of the other.

Acute angle   Right angle   Obtuse angle   Straight angle

Complementary angles
$m\angle 1 + m\angle 2 = 90°$

Supplementary angles
$m\angle 3 + m\angle 4 = 180°$

EXAMPLE 1   If an angle measures 28°, find its complement.

Solution   Two angles are complementary if the sum of their measures is 90°. The complement of a 28° angle is an angle whose measure is $90° - 28° = 62°$. To check, notice that $28° + 62° = 90°$.   □

Plane is an undefined term that we will describe. A plane can be thought of as a flat surface with infinite length and width, but no thickness. A plane is two dimensional.

The arrows in the following diagram indicate that a plane extends indefinitely and has no boundaries.

Figures that lie on a plane are called **plane figures.** Lines that lie in the same plane are called **coplanar.**

Lines

Two lines are **parallel** if they lie in the same plane but never meet.

Intersecting lines meet or cross in one point.

Two lines that form right angles when they intersect are said to be **perpendicular.**

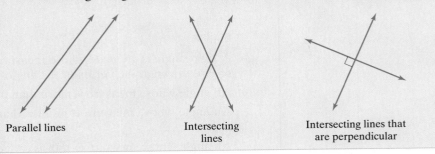

Parallel lines   Intersecting lines   Intersecting lines that are perpendicular

---

Two intersecting lines form **vertical angles.** Angles 1 and 3 are vertical angles. Also, angles 2 and 4 are vertical angles. It can be shown that **vertical angles have equal measures.**

$$m\angle 1 = m\angle 3$$
$$m\angle 2 = m\angle 4$$

Adjacent angles have the same vertex and share a side. Angles 1 and 2 are adjacent angles. Other pairs of adjacent angles are angles 2 and 3, angles 3 and 4, and angles 4 and 1.

A **transversal** is a line that intersects two or more lines in the same plane. Line l is a transversal that intersects lines m and n. The eight angles formed are numbered and certain pairs of these angles are given special names.

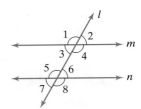

Corresponding angles: $\angle 1$ and $\angle 5$, $\angle 3$ and $\angle 7$, $\angle 2$ and $\angle 6$, and $\angle 4$ and $\angle 8$.

Exterior angles: $\angle 1$, $\angle 2$, $\angle 7$, and $\angle 8$.

Interior angles: $\angle 3$, $\angle 4$, $\angle 5$, and $\angle 6$.

Alternate interior angles: $\angle 3$ and $\angle 6$, $\angle 4$ and $\angle 5$.

These angles and parallel lines are related in the following manner.

> **Parallel Lines Cut by a Transversal**
>
> 1. If two parallel lines are cut by a transversal, then
>   a. corresponding angles are equal and
>   b. alternate interior angles are equal.
> 2. If corresponding angles formed by two lines and a transversal are equal, then the lines are parallel.
> 3. If alternate interior angles formed by two lines and a transversal are equal, then the lines are parallel.

EXAMPLE 2   Given that lines m and n are parallel and that the measure of angle 1 is 100°, find the measures of angles 2, 3, and 4.

Solution $m\angle 2 = 100°$, since angles 1 and 2 are vertical angles.

$m\angle 4 = 100°$, since angles 1 and 4 are alternate interior angles.

$m\angle 3 = 180° - 100° = 80°$, since angles 4 and 3 are supplementary angles.   □

A **polygon** is the union of three or more coplanar line segments that intersect each other only at each end point, with each end point shared by exactly two segments.

A **triangle** is a polygon with three sides. The sum of the measures of the three angles of a triangle is 180°. In the following figure, $m\angle 1 + m\angle 2 + m\angle 3 = 180°$.

EXAMPLE 3   Find the measure of the third angle of the triangle shown.

Solution   The sum of the measures of the angles of a triangle is 180°. Since one angle measures 45° and the other angle measures 95°, the third angle measures $180° - 45° - 95° = 40°$.   □

Two triangles are **congruent** if they have the same size and the same shape. In congruent triangles, the measures of corresponding angles are equal and the lengths of corresponding sides are equal. The following triangles are congruent.

Corresponding angles are equal: $m\angle 1 = m\angle 4$, $m\angle 2 = m\angle 5$, and $m\angle 3 = m\angle 6$. Also, lengths of corresponding sides are equal: $a = x$, $b = y$, and $c = z$.

Any one of the following may be used to determine whether two triangles are congruent.

Congruent Triangles

1. If the measures of two angles of a triangle equal the measures of two angles of another triangle and the lengths of the sides between each pair of angles are equal, the triangles are congruent.

$$m\angle 1 = m\angle 3$$
$$m\angle 2 = m\angle 4$$
and
$$a = x$$

2. If the lengths of the three sides of a triangle equal the lengths of corresponding sides of another triangle, the triangles are congruent.

$$a = x$$
$$b = y$$
and
$$c = z$$

3. If the lengths of two sides of a triangle equal the lengths of corresponding sides of another triangle, and the measures of the angles between each pair of sides are equal, the triangles are congruent.

$$a = x$$
$$b = y$$
and
$$m\angle 1 = m\angle 2$$

Two triangles are **similar** if they have the same shape. In similar triangles, the measures of corresponding angles are equal and corresponding sides are in proportion. The following triangles are similar. (All similar triangles drawn in this appendix will be oriented the same.)

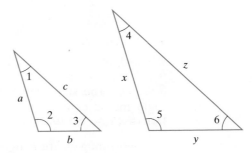

Corresponding angles are equal: $m\angle 1 = m\angle 4$, $m\angle 2 = m\angle 5$, and $m\angle 3 = m\angle 6$.

Also, corresponding sides are proportional: $\dfrac{a}{x} = \dfrac{b}{y} = \dfrac{c}{z}$.

Any one of the following may be used to determine whether two triangles are similar.

> ## Similar Triangles
>
> **1.** If the measures of two angles of a triangle equal the measures of two angles of another triangle, the triangles are similar.
>
>
>
> **2.** If three sides of one triangle are proportional to three sides of another triangle, the triangles are similar.
>
>
>
> **3.** If two sides of a triangle are proportional to two sides of another triangle and the measures of the included angles are equal, the triangles are similar.
>
>

EXAMPLE 4   Given that the following triangles are similar, find the missing length x.

**Solution**   Since the triangles are similar, corresponding sides are in proportion. Thus, $\frac{2}{3} = \frac{10}{x}$. To solve this equation for x, we multiply both sides by the LCD, $3x$.

$$3x\left(\frac{2}{3}\right) = 3x\left(\frac{10}{x}\right)$$
$$2x = 30$$
$$x = 15$$

The missing length is 15 units.   □

A **right triangle** contains a right angle. The side opposite the right angle is called the **hypotenuse,** and the other two sides are called the **legs.** The **Pythagorean theorem** gives a formula that relates the lengths of the three sides of a right triangle.

> ## The Pythagorean Theorem
>
> If a and b are the lengths of the legs of a right triangle, and c is the length of the hypotenuse, then $a^2 + b^2 = c^2$.
>
>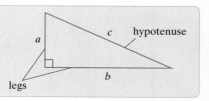

EXAMPLE 5 Find the length of the hypotenuse of a right triangle whose legs have lengths of 3 centimeters and 4 centimeters.

3 centimeters

4 centimeters

Solution Because we have a right triangle, we use the Pythagorean theorem. The legs are 3 centimeters and 4 centimeters, so let $a = 3$ and $b = 4$ in the formula.

$$a^2 + b^2 = c^2$$
$$3^2 + 4^2 = c^2$$
$$9 + 16 = c^2$$
$$25 = c^2$$

Since c represents a length, we assume that c is positive. Thus, if c^2 is 25, c must be 5. The hypotenuse has a length of 5 centimeters.

G Exercise Set · MyMathLab®

Find the complement of each angle. See Example 1.

1. $19°$
2. $65°$
3. $70.8°$
4. $45\frac{2}{3}°$
5. $11\frac{1}{4}°$
6. $19.6°$

Find the supplement of each angle.

7. $150°$
8. $90°$
9. $30.2°$
10. $81.9°$
11. $79\frac{1}{2}°$
12. $165\frac{8}{9}°$

13. If lines m and n are parallel, find the measures of angles 1 through 7. See Example 2.

14. If lines m and n are parallel, find the measures of angles 1 through 5. See Example 2.

In each of the following, the measures of two angles of a triangle are given. Find the measure of the third angle. See Example 3.

15. $11°, 79°$
16. $8°, 102°$
17. $25°, 65°$
18. $44°, 19°$
19. $30°, 60°$
20. $67°, 23°$

In each of the following, the measure of one angle of a right triangle is given. Find the measures of the other two angles.

21. $45°$
22. $60°$
23. $17°$
24. $30°$
25. $39\frac{3}{4}°$
26. $72.6°$

Given that each of the following pairs of triangles is similar, find the missing lengths. See Example 4.

27.
28.
29.

30.

Use the Pythagorean theorem to find the missing lengths in the right triangles. See Example 5.

31.

32.

33.

34.

Contents of Student Resources

Study Skills Builders

Attitude and Study Tips:

Organizing Your Work:

MyMathLab and MathXL:

Additional Help Inside and Outside Your Textbook:

The Bigger Picture—Study Guide Outline

Practice Final Exam

Answers to Selected Exercises

Student Resources

Study Skills Builders

Attitude and Study Tips

Study Skills Builder 1

Have You Decided to Complete This Course Successfully?

Ask yourself if one of your current goals is to complete this course successfully.

If it is not a goal of yours, ask yourself why. One common reason is fear of failure. Amazingly enough, fear of failure alone can be strong enough to keep many of us from doing our best in any endeavor.

Another common reason is that you simply haven't taken the time to think about or write down your goals for this course. To help accomplish this, answer the following questions.

Exercises

1. Write down your goal(s) for this course.

2. Now list steps you will take to make sure your goal(s) in Exercise 1 are accomplished.

3. Rate your commitment to this course with a number between 1 and 5. Use the diagram below to help.

High Commitment		Average Commitment		Not Committed at All
5	4	3	2	1

4. If you have rated your personal commitment level (from the exercise above) as a 1, 2, or 3, list the reasons why this is so. Then determine whether it is possible to increase your commitment level to a 4 or 5.

Good luck, and don't forget that a positive attitude will make a big difference.

Study Skills Builder 2

Tips for Studying for an Exam

To prepare for an exam, try the following study techniques:

- Start the study process days before your exam.
- Make sure that you are up to date on your assignments.
- If there is a topic that you are unsure of, use one of the many resources that are available to you. For example,
  - See your instructor.
  - View a lecture video on the topic.
  - Visit a learning resource center on campus.
  - Read the textbook material and examples on the topic.
- Reread your notes and carefully review the Chapter Highlights at the end of any chapter.
- Work the review exercises at the end of the chapter.
- Find a quiet place to take the Chapter Test found at the end of the chapter. Do not use any resources when taking this sample test. This way, you will have a clear indication of how prepared you are for your exam. Check your answers and use the Chapter Test Prep Videos to make sure that you correct any missed exercises.

Good luck, and keep a positive attitude.

Exercises

Let's see how you did on your last exam.

1. How many days before your last exam did you start studying for that exam?

2. Were you up to date on your assignments at that time or did you need to catch up on assignments?

3. List the most helpful text supplement (if you used one).

4. List the most helpful campus supplement (if you used one).

5. List your process for preparing for a mathematics test.

6. Was this process helpful? In other words, were you satisfied with your performance on your exam?

7. If not, what changes can you make in your process that will make it more helpful to you?

Study Skills Builder 3
What to Do the Day of an Exam

Your first exam may be soon. On the day of an exam, don't forget to try the following:

- Allow yourself plenty of time to arrive.
- Read the directions on the test carefully.
- Read each problem carefully as you take your test. Make sure that you answer the question asked.
- Watch your time and pace yourself so that you may attempt each problem on your test.
- Check your work and answers.
- **Do not turn your test in early.** If you have extra time, spend it double-checking your work.

Good luck!

Exercises

Answer the following questions based on your most recent mathematics exam, whenever that was.

1. How soon before class did you arrive?
2. Did you read the directions on the test carefully?
3. Did you make sure you answered the question asked for each problem on the exam?
4. Were you able to attempt each problem on your exam?
5. If your answer to Exercise 4 is no, list reasons why.
6. Did you have extra time on your exam?
7. If your answer to Exercise 6 is yes, describe how you spent that extra time.

Study Skills Builder 4
Are You Satisfied with Your Performance on a Particular Quiz or Exam?

If not, don't forget to analyze your quiz or exam and look for common errors. Were most of your errors a result of:

- *Carelessness?* Did you turn in your quiz or exam before the allotted time expired? If so, resolve to use any extra time to check your work.
- *Running out of time?* Answer the questions you are sure of first. Then attempt the questions you are unsure of and delay checking your work until all questions have been answered.
- *Not understanding a concept?* If so, review that concept and correct your work so that you make sure you understand it before the next quiz or the final exam.
- *Test conditions?* When studying for a quiz or exam, make sure you place yourself in conditions similar to test conditions. For example, before your next quiz or exam, take a sample test without the aid of your notes or text.

(For a sample test, see your instructor or use the Chapter Test at the end of each chapter.)

Exercises

1. Have you corrected all your previous quizzes and exams?
2. List any errors you have found common to two or more of your graded papers.
3. Is one of your common errors not understanding a concept? If so, are you making sure you understand all the concepts for the next quiz or exam?
4. Is one of your common errors making careless mistakes? If so, are you now taking all the time allotted to check over your work so that you can minimize the number of careless mistakes?
5. Are you satisfied with your grades thus far on quizzes and tests?
6. If your answer to Exercise 5 is no, are there any more suggestions you can make to your instructor or yourself to help? If so, list them here and share these with your instructor.

Study Skills Builder 5
How Are You Doing?

If you haven't done so yet, take a few moments to think about how you are doing in this course. Are you working toward your goal of successfully completing this course? Is your performance on homework, quizzes, and tests satisfactory? If not, you might want to see your instructor to see whether he/she has any suggestions on how you can improve your performance. Reread Section 1.1 for ideas on places to get help with your mathematics course.

Exercises

Answer the following.

1. List any textbook supplements you are using to help you through this course.
2. List any campus resources you are using to help you through this course.
3. Write a short paragraph describing how you are doing in your mathematics course.
4. If improvement is needed, list ways that you can work toward improving your situation as described in Exercise 3.

Study Skills Builder 6
Are You Preparing for Your Final Exam?

To prepare for your final exam, try the following study techniques:

- Review the material that you will be responsible for on your exam. This includes material from your textbook, your notebook, and any handouts from your instructor.
- Review any formulas that you may need to memorize.
- Check to see if your instructor or mathematics department will be conducting a final exam review.
- Check with your instructor to see whether final exams from previous semesters/quarters are available to students for review.

- Use your previously taken exams as a practice final exam. To do so, rewrite the test questions in mixed order on blank sheets of paper. This will help you prepare for exam conditions.
- If you are unsure of a few concepts, see your instructor or visit a learning lab for assistance. Also, view the video segment of any troublesome sections.
- If you need further exercises to work, try the Cumulative Reviews at the end of the chapters.

Once again, good luck! I hope you are enjoying this textbook and your mathematics course.

Organizing Your Work

Study Skills Builder 7
Learning New Terms

Many of the terms used in this text may be new to you. It will be helpful to make a list of new mathematical terms and symbols as you encounter them and to review them frequently. Placing these new terms (including page references) on 3×5 index cards might help you later when you're preparing for a quiz.

Exercises

1. Name one way you might place a word and its definition on a 3×5 card.
2. How do new terms stand out in this text so that they can be found?

Study Skills Builder 8
Are You Organized?

Have you ever had trouble finding a completed assignment? When it's time to study for a test, are your notes neat and organized? Have you ever had trouble reading your own mathematics handwriting? (Be honest—I have.)

When any of these things happen, it's time to get organized. Here are a few suggestions:

- Write your notes and complete your homework assignments in a notebook with pockets (spiral or ring binder).
- Take class notes in this notebook, and then follow the notes with your completed homework assignment.
- When you receive graded papers or handouts, place them in the notebook pocket so that you will not lose them.
- Mark (possibly with an exclamation point) any note(s) that seem extra important to you.
- Mark (possibly with a question mark) any notes or homework that you are having trouble with.
- See your instructor or a math tutor to help you with the concepts or exercises that you are having trouble understanding.
- If you are having trouble reading your own handwriting, *slow down* and write your mathematics work clearly!

Exercises

1. Have you been completing your assignments on time?
2. Have you been correcting any exercises you may be having difficulty with?
3. If you are having trouble with a mathematical concept or correcting any homework exercises, have you visited your instructor, a tutor, or your campus math lab?
4. Are you taking lecture notes in your mathematics course? (By the way, these notes should include worked-out examples solved by your instructor.)
5. Is your mathematics course material (handouts, graded papers, lecture notes) organized?
6. If your answer to Exercise 5 is no, take a moment to review your course material. List at least two ways that you might organize it better.

Study Skills Builder 9
Organizing a Notebook

It's never too late to get organized. If you need ideas about organizing a notebook for your mathematics course, try some of these:

- Use a spiral or ring binder notebook with pockets and use it for mathematics only.
- Start each page by writing the book's section number you are working on at the top.
- When your instructor is lecturing, take notes. *Always* include any examples your instructor works for you.
- Place your worked-out homework exercises in your notebook immediately after the lecture notes from that section. This way, a section's worth of material is together.
- Homework exercises: Attempt and check all assigned homework.
- Place graded quizzes in the pockets of your notebook or a special section of your binder.

Exercises

Check your notebook organization by answering the following questions.

1. Do you have a spiral or ring binder notebook for your mathematics course only?
2. Have you ever had to flip through several sheets of notes and work in your mathematics notebook to determine what section's work you are in?
3. Are you now writing the textbook's section number at the top of each notebook page?
4. Have you ever lost or had trouble finding a graded quiz or test?
5. Are you now placing all your graded work in a dedicated place in your notebook?
6. Are you attempting all of your homework and placing all of your work in your notebook?
7. Are you checking and correcting your homework in your notebook? If not, why not?
8. Are you writing in your notebook the examples your instructor works for you in class?

Study Skills Builder 10

How Are Your Homework Assignments Going?

It is very important in mathematics to keep up with homework. Why? Many concepts build on each other. Often your understanding of a day's concepts depends on an understanding of the previous day's material.

Remember that completing your homework assignment involves a lot more than attempting a few of the problems assigned.

To complete a homework assignment, remember these four things:

- Attempt all of it.
- Check it.
- Correct it.
- If needed, ask questions about it.

Exercises

Take a moment to review your completed homework assignments. Answer the questions below based on this review.

1. Approximate the fraction of your homework you have attempted.
2. Approximate the fraction of your homework you have checked (if possible).
3. If you are able to check your homework, have you corrected it when errors have been found?
4. When working homework, if you do not understand a concept, what do you do?

MyMathLab and MathXL

Study Skills Builder 11

Tips for Turning in Your Homework on Time

It is very important to keep up with your mathematics homework assignments. Why? Many concepts in mathematics build upon each other.

Remember these four tips to help ensure that your work is completed on time:

- Know the assignments and due dates set by your instructor.
- Do not wait until the last minute to submit your homework.
- Set a goal to submit your homework 6–8 hours before the scheduled due date in case you have unexpected technology trouble.
- Schedule enough time to complete each assignment.

Following these tips will also help you avoid losing points for late or missed assignments.

Exercises

Take a moment to consider your work on your homework assignments to date and answer the following questions:

1. What percentage of your assignments have you turned in on time?
2. Why might it be a good idea to submit your homework 6–8 hours before the scheduled deadline?
3. If you have missed submitting any homework by the due date, list some of the reasons this occurred.
4. What steps do you plan to take in the future to ensure that your homework is submitted on time?

Study Skills Builder 12

Tips for Doing Your Homework Online

Practice is one of the main keys to success in any mathematics course. Did you know that MyMathLab/MathXL provides you with **immediate feedback** for each exercise? If you are incorrect, you are given hints to work the exercise correctly. You have **unlimited practice opportunities** and can rework any exercises you have trouble with until you master them, and submit homework assignments unlimited times before the deadline.

Remember these success tips when doing your homework online:

- Attempt all assigned exercises.
- Write down (neatly) your step-by-step work for each exercise before entering your answer.
- Use the immediate feedback provided by the program to help you check and correct your work for each exercise.
- Rework any exercises you have trouble with until you master them.

- Work through your homework assignment as many times as necessary until you are satisfied.

Exercises

Take a moment to think about your homework assignments to date and answer the following:

1. Have you attempted all assigned exercises?
2. Of the exercises attempted, have you also written out your work before entering your answer so that you can check it?
3. Are you familiar with how to enter answers using the MathXL player so that you avoid answer entry–type errors?
4. List some ways the immediate feedback and practice supports have helped you with your homework. If you have not used these supports, how do you plan to use them with the given success tips on your next assignment?

Study Skills Builder 13

Organizing Your Work

Have you ever used any readily available paper (such as the back of a flyer, another course assignment, Post-it notes, etc.) to work out homework exercises before entering the answer in MathXL? To save time, have you ever entered answers directly into MathXL without working the exercises on paper? When it's time to study, have you ever been unable to find your completed work or read and follow your own mathematics handwriting?

When any of these things happen, it's time to get organized. Here are some suggestions:

- Write your step-by-step work for each homework exercise (neatly) on lined, loose-leaf paper and keep this in a 3-ring binder.
- Refer to your step-by-step work when you receive feedback that your answer is incorrect in MathXL. Double-check against the steps and hints provided by the program and correct your work accordingly.
- Keep your written homework with your class notes for that section.

- Identify any exercises you are having trouble with and ask questions about them.
- Keep all graded quizzes and tests in this binder as well to study later.

If you follow these suggestions, you and your instructor or tutor will be able to follow your steps and correct any mistakes. You will have a written copy of your work to refer to later to ask questions and study for tests.

Exercises

1. Why is it important to write out your step-by-step work to homework exercises and keep a hard copy of all work submitted online?
2. If you have gotten an incorrect answer, are you able to follow your steps and find your error?
3. If you were asked today to review your previous homework assignments and first test, could you find them? If not, list some ways you might organize your work better.

Study Skills Builder 14

Getting Help with Your Homework Assignments

Many helpful resources are available to you through MathXL to help you work through any homework exercises you may have trouble with. It is important for you to know what these resources are and when and how to use them.

Let's review these features, found in the homework exercises:

- **Help Me Solve This**—provides step-by-step help for the exercise you are working. You must work an additional exercise of the same type (without this help) before you can get credit for having worked it correctly.

- **View an Example**—allows you to view a correctly worked exercise similar to the one you are having trouble with. You can go back to your original exercise and work it on your own.

- **E-Book**—allows you to read examples from your text and find similar exercises.

- **Video****—your text author, Elayn Martin-Gay, works an exercise similar to the one you need help with. **Not all exercises have an accompanying video clip.

- **Ask My Instructor**—allows you to email your instructor for help with an exercise.

Exercises

1. How does the "Help Me Solve This" feature work?

2. If the "View an Example" feature is used, is it necessary to work an additional problem before continuing the assignment?

3. When might be a good time to use the "Video" feature? Do all exercises have an accompanying video clip?

4. Which of the features above have you used? List those you found the most helpful to you.

5. If you haven't used the features discussed, list those you plan to try on your next homework assignment.

Study Skills Builder 15

Tips for Preparing for an Exam

Did you know that you can rework your previous homework assignments in MyMathLab and MathXL? This is a great way to prepare for tests. To do this, open a previous homework assignment and click "similar exercise." This will generate new exercises similar to the homework you have submitted. You can then rework the exercises and assignments until you feel confident that you understand them.

To prepare for an exam, follow these tips:

- Review your written work for your previous homework assignments along with your class notes.

- Identify any exercises or topics that you have questions on or have difficulty understanding.

- Rework your previous assignments in MyMathLab and MathXL until you fully understand them and can do them without help.

- Get help for any topics you feel unsure of or for which you have questions.

Exercises

1. Are your current homework assignments up to date and is your written work for them organized in a binder or notebook? If the answer is no, it's time to get organized. For tips on this, see Study Skills Builder 13—Organizing Your Work.

2. How many days in advance of an exam do you usually start studying?

3. List some ways you think that practicing previous homework assignments can help you prepare for your test.

4. List two or three resources you can use to get help for any topics you are unsure of or have questions on.

Good luck!

Study Skills Builder 16

How Well Do You Know the Resources Available to You in MyMathLab?

Many helpful resources are available to you in MyMathLab. Let's take a moment to locate and explore a few of them now. Go into your MyMathLab course and visit the multimedia library, tools for success, and E-book.

Let's see what you found.

Exercises

1. List the resources available to you in the Multimedia Library.

2. List the resources available to you in the Tools for Success folder.

3. Where did you find the English/Spanish Audio Glossary?

4. Can you view videos from the E-book?

5. Did you find any resources you did not know about? If so, which ones?

6. Which resources have you used most often or found most helpful?

Additional Help Inside and Outside Your Textbook

Study Skills Builder 17

How Well Do You Know Your Textbook?

The following questions will help determine whether you are familiar with your textbook. For additional information, see Section 1.1 in this text.

1. What does the ▶ icon mean?

2. What does the ◥ icon mean?

3. What does the △ icon mean?

4. Where can you find a review for each chapter? What answers to this review can be found in the back of your text?

5. Each chapter contains an overview of the chapter along with examples. What is this feature called?

6. Each chapter contains a review of vocabulary. What is this feature called?

7. Practice exercises are contained in this text. What are they and how can they be used?

8. This text contains a student section in the back entitled Student Resources. List the contents of this section and how they might be helpful.

9. What exercise answers are available in this text? Where are they located?

Study Skills Builder 18

Are You Familiar with Your Textbook Supplements?

Below is a review of some of the student supplements available for additional study. Check to see whether you are using the ones most helpful to you.

- Chapter Test Prep Videos. These videos provide video clip solutions to the Chapter Test exercises in this text. You will find this extremely useful when studying for tests or exams.
- Interactive DVD Lecture Series. These are keyed to each section of the text. The material is presented by me, Elayn Martin-Gay, and I have placed a ▶ by the exercises in the text that I have worked on the video.
- The *Student Solutions Manual*. This contains worked-out solutions to odd-numbered exercises as well as every exercise in the Integrated Reviews, Chapter Reviews, Chapter Tests, and Cumulative Reviews and every Practice exercise.
- Pearson Tutor Center. Mathematics questions may be phoned, faxed, or emailed to this center.
- MyMathLab is a text-specific online course. MathXL is an online homework, tutorial, and assessment system. Take a moment to determine whether these are available to you.

As usual, your instructor is your best source of information.

Exercises

Let's see how you are doing with textbook supplements.

1. Name one way the Lecture Videos can be helpful to you.
2. Name one way the Chapter Test Prep Video can help you prepare for a chapter test.
3. List any textbook supplements that you have found useful.
4. Have you located and visited a learning resource lab located on your campus?
5. List the textbook supplements that are currently housed in your campus's learning resource lab.

Study Skills Builder 19

Are You Getting All the Mathematics Help That You Need?

Remember that, in addition to your instructor, there are many places to get help with your mathematics course. For example:

- This text has an accompanying video lesson by the author for every section. There are also worked-out video solutions by the author to every Chapter Test exercise.
- The back of the book contains answers to odd-numbered exercises.
- A *Student Solutions Manual* is available that contains worked-out solutions to odd-numbered exercises as well as solutions to every exercise in the Integrated Reviews, Chapter Reviews, Chapter Tests, and Cumulative Reviews and every Practice exercise.
- Don't forget to check with your instructor for other local resources available to you, such as a tutor center.

Exercises

1. List items you find helpful in the text and all student supplements to this text.
2. List all the campus help that is available to you for this course.
3. List any help (besides the textbook) from Exercises 1 and 2 above that you are using.
4. List any help (besides the textbook) that you feel you should try.
5. Write a goal for yourself that includes trying everything you listed in Exercise 4 during the next week.

The Bigger Picture—Study Guide Outline

Simplifying Expressions and Solving Equations and Inequalities

I. Simplifying Expressions

A. Real Numbers

1. **Add:** (Sec. 1.5)

   $$-1.7 + (-0.21) = -1.91$$ Adding like signs.
   Add absolute values. Attach common sign.

   $$-7 + 3 = -4$$ Adding different signs.
   Subtract absolute values. Attach the sign of the number with the larger absolute value.

2. **Subtract:** Add the first number to the opposite of the second number. (Sec. 1.6)

   $$17 - 25 = 17 + (-25) = -8$$

3. **Multiply or divide:** Multiply or divide the two numbers as usual. If the signs are the same, the answer is positive. If the signs are different, the answer is negative. (Sec. 1.7)

   $$-10 \cdot 3 = -30, \qquad -81 \div (-3) = 27$$

B. Exponents (Secs. 5.1 and 5.5)

$$x^7 \cdot x^5 = x^{12}; \ (x^7)^5 = x^{35}; \ \frac{x^7}{x^5} = x^2; \ x^0 = 1; \ 8^{-2} = \frac{1}{8^2} = \frac{1}{64}$$

C. Polynomials

1. **Add:** Combine like terms. (Sec. 5.2)

   $$(3y^2 + 6y + 7) + (9y^2 - 11y - 15) = 3y^2 + 6y + 7 + 9y^2 - 11y - 15$$
   $$= 12y^2 - 5y - 8$$

2. **Subtract:** Change the sign of the terms of the polynomial being subtracted, then add. (Sec. 5.2)

   $$(3y^2 + 6y + 7) - (9y^2 - 11y - 15) = 3y^2 + 6y + 7 - 9y^2 + 11y + 15$$
   $$= -6y^2 + 17y + 22$$

3. **Multiply:** Multiply each term of one polynomial by each term of the other polynomial. (Secs. 5.3 and 5.4)

   $$(x + 5)(2x^2 - 3x + 4) = x(2x^2 - 3x + 4) + 5(2x^2 - 3x + 4)$$
   $$= 2x^3 - 3x^2 + 4x + 10x^2 - 15x + 20$$
   $$= 2x^3 + 7x^2 - 11x + 20$$

4. **Divide:** (Sec. 5.6)

   a. To divide by a monomial, divide each term of the polynomial by the monomial.

   $$\frac{8x^2 + 2x - 6}{2x} = \frac{8x^2}{2x} + \frac{2x}{2x} - \frac{6}{2x} = 4x + 1 - \frac{3}{x}$$

b. To divide by a polynomial other than a monomial, use long division.

$$2x + 5 \overline{)2x^2 - 7x + 10} \quad x - 6 + \dfrac{40}{2x + 5}$$

$$\underline{2x^2 + 5x}$$
$$-12x + 10$$
$$\underline{+12x + 30}$$
$$40$$

D. Factoring Polynomials

See the Chapter 6 Integrated Review for steps.

$$3x^4 - 78x^2 + 75 = 3(x^4 - 26x^2 + 25) \quad \text{Factor out GCF—always first step.}$$
$$= 3(x^2 - 25)(x^2 - 1) \quad \text{Factor trinomial.}$$
$$= 3(x + 5)(x - 5)(x + 1)(x - 1) \quad \text{Factor further—each difference of squares.}$$

E. Rational Expressions

1. **Simplify:** Factor the numerator and denominator. Then divide out factors of 1 by dividing out common factors in the numerator and denominator. (Sec. 7.1)

$$\frac{x^2 - 9}{7x^2 - 21x} = \frac{(x + 3)(x - 3)}{7x(x - 3)} = \frac{x + 3}{7x}$$

2. **Multiply:** Multiply numerators, then multiply denominators. (Sec. 7.2)

$$\frac{5z}{2z^2 - 9z - 18} \cdot \frac{22z + 33}{10z} = \frac{5 \cdot z}{(2z + 3)(z - 6)} \cdot \frac{11(2z + 3)}{2 \cdot 5 \cdot z} = \frac{11}{2(z - 6)}$$

3. **Divide:** First fraction times the reciprocal of the second fraction. (Sec. 7.2)

$$\frac{14}{x + 5} \div \frac{x + 1}{2} = \frac{14}{x + 5} \cdot \frac{2}{x + 1} = \frac{28}{(x + 5)(x + 1)}$$

4. **Add or subtract:** Must have same denominator. If not, find the LCD and write each fraction as an equivalent fraction with the LCD as denominator. (Sec. 7.4)

$$\frac{9}{10} - \frac{x + 1}{x + 5} = \frac{9(x + 5)}{10(x + 5)} - \frac{10(x + 1)}{10(x + 5)}$$
$$= \frac{9x + 45 - 10x - 10}{10(x + 5)} = \frac{-x + 35}{10(x + 5)}$$

F. Radicals

1. **Simplify square roots:** If possible, factor the radicand so that one factor is a perfect square. Then use the product rule and simplify. (Sec. 10.3)

$$\sqrt{75} = \sqrt{25 \cdot 3} = \sqrt{25} \cdot \sqrt{3} = 5\sqrt{3}$$

2. **Add or subtract:** Only like radicals (same index and radicand) can be added or subtracted. (Sec. 10.4)

$$8\sqrt{10} - \sqrt{40} + \sqrt{5} = 8\sqrt{10} - 2\sqrt{10} + \sqrt{5} = 6\sqrt{10} + \sqrt{5}$$

3. **Multiply or divide:** $\sqrt{a} \cdot \sqrt{b} = \sqrt{ab}$; $\dfrac{\sqrt{a}}{\sqrt{b}} = \sqrt{\dfrac{a}{b}}$. (Sec. 10.4)

$$\sqrt{11} \cdot \sqrt{3} = \sqrt{33}; \quad \frac{\sqrt{140}}{\sqrt{7}} = \sqrt{\frac{140}{7}} = \sqrt{20} = \sqrt{4 \cdot 5} = 2\sqrt{5}$$

4. **Rationalizing the denominator:** (Sec. 10.5)

   a. If denominator is one term,

$$\frac{5}{\sqrt{11}} = \frac{5 \cdot \sqrt{11}}{\sqrt{11} \cdot \sqrt{11}} = \frac{5\sqrt{11}}{11}$$

b. If denominator is two terms, multiply by 1 in the form of $\dfrac{\text{conjugate of denominator}}{\text{conjugate of denominator}}$.

$$\frac{13}{3 + \sqrt{2}} = \frac{13}{3 + \sqrt{2}} \cdot \frac{3 - \sqrt{2}}{3 - \sqrt{2}} = \frac{13(3 - \sqrt{2})}{9 - 2} = \frac{13(3 - \sqrt{2})}{7}$$

II. Solving Equations

A. Linear Equations: (Sec. 2.3)

$$5(x - 2) = \frac{4(2x + 1)}{3}$$

$$3 \cdot 5(x - 2) = \cancel{3} \cdot \frac{4(2x + 1)}{\cancel{3}}$$

$$15x - 30 = 8x + 4$$

$$7x = 34$$

$$x = \frac{34}{7}$$

B. Quadratic and Higher-Degree Equations (Secs. 6.6, 11.1, 11.2, 11.3)

$$2x^2 - 7x = 9$$

$$2x^2 - 7x - 9 = 0$$

$$(2x - 9)(x + 1) = 0$$

$$2x - 9 = 0 \quad \text{or} \quad x + 1 = 0$$

$$x = \frac{9}{2} \quad \text{or} \quad x = -1$$

$$2x^2 + x - 2 = 0$$

$$a = 2, \ b = 1, \ c = -2$$

$$x = \frac{-1 \pm \sqrt{1^2 - 4(2)(-2)}}{2 \cdot 2}$$

$$x = \frac{-1 \pm \sqrt{17}}{4}$$

C. Equations with Rational Expressions (Sec. 7.5)

$$\frac{7}{x - 1} + \frac{3}{x + 1} = \frac{x + 3}{x^2 - 1}$$

$$\cancel{(x - 1)}(x + 1) \cdot \frac{7}{\cancel{x - 1}} + (x - 1)\cancel{(x + 1)} \cdot \frac{3}{\cancel{x + 1}}$$

$$= \cancel{(x - 1)}\cancel{(x + 1)} \cdot \frac{x + 3}{\cancel{(x - 1)}\cancel{(x + 1)}}$$

$$7(x + 1) + 3(x - 1) = x + 3$$

$$7x + 7 + 3x - 3 = x + 3$$

$$9x = -1$$

$$x = -\frac{1}{9}$$

D. Proportions: An equation with two ratios equal. Set cross products equal, then solve. Make sure the proposed solution does not make the denominator 0. (Sec. 7.6)

$$\frac{5}{x} \gtreqqless \frac{9}{2x - 3}$$

$$5(2x - 3) = 9 \cdot x \qquad \text{Set cross products equal.}$$

$$10x - 15 = 9x \qquad \text{Multiply.}$$

$$x = 15 \qquad \text{Write equation with variable terms on one side and constants on the other.}$$

E. Absolute Value Equations (Sec. 9.2)

$$|3x - 1| = 8$$

$3x - 1 = 8$ or $3x - 1 = -8$

$3x = 9$ or $\quad 3x = -7$

$x = 3$ or $\quad x = -\dfrac{7}{3}$

$$|x - 5| = |x + 1|$$

$x - 5 = x + 1$ or $x - 5 = -(x + 1)$

$\underbrace{-5 = 1}_{\text{No solution}}$ or $x - 5 = -x - 1$

or $\quad 2x = 4$

$\quad x = 2$

F. Equations with Radicals (Sec. 10.6)

$$\sqrt{5x + 10} - 2 = x$$
$$\sqrt{5x + 10} = x + 2$$
$$(\sqrt{5x + 10})^2 = (x + 2)^2$$
$$5x + 10 = x^2 + 4x + 4$$
$$0 = x^2 - x - 6$$
$$0 = (x - 3)(x + 2)$$

$x - 3 = 0$ or $x + 2 = 0$

$x = 3$ or $\quad x = -2$

Both solutions check.

G. Exponential Equations (Secs. 12.3, 12.8)

$$9^x = 27^{x+1}$$
$$(3^2)^x = (3^3)^{x+1}$$
$$3^{2x} = 3^{3x+3}$$
$$2x = 3x + 3$$
$$-3 = x$$

$$5^x = 7$$
$$\log 5^x = \log 7$$
$$x \log 5 = \log 7$$
$$x = \dfrac{\log 7}{\log 5}$$

H. Logarithmic Equations (Sec. 12.8)

$$\log 7 + \log(x + 3) = \log 5$$
$$\log 7(x + 3) = \log 5$$
$$7(x + 3) = 5$$
$$7x + 21 = 5$$
$$7x = -16$$
$$x = -\dfrac{16}{7}$$

III. Solving Inequalities
A. Linear Inequalities (Sec. 2.8)

$$-3(x + 2) \geq 6$$
$$-3x - 6 \geq 6$$
$$-3x \geq 12$$
$$\dfrac{-3x}{-3} \leq \dfrac{12}{-3}$$
$$x \leq -4 \quad \text{or} \quad (-\infty, -4]$$

B. Compound Inequalities (Sec. 9.1)

$x \leq 3 \quad and \quad x < -7$

$x \leq 3$

$x < -7$

and

$(-\infty, -7)$

$x \leq 3 \quad or \quad x < -7$

$x \leq 3$

$x < -7$

or

$(-\infty, 3]$

C. Absolute Value Inequalities (Sec. 9.3)

$|x - 5| - 8 < -2$

$|x - 5| < 6$

$-6 < x - 5 < 6$

$-1 < x < 11$

$(-1, 11)$

$|2x + 1| \geq 17$

$2x + 1 \geq 17 \quad or \quad 2x + 1 \leq -17$

$2x \geq 16 \quad or \quad 2x \leq -18$

$x \geq 8 \quad or \quad x \leq -9$

$(-\infty, -9] \cup [8, \infty)$

D. Nonlinear Inequalities (Sec. 11.4)

$x^2 - x < 6$

$x^2 - x - 6 < 0$

$(x - 3)(x + 2) < 0$

$(-2, 3)$

$\dfrac{x - 5}{x + 1} \geq 0$

$(-\infty, -1) \cup [5, \infty)$

Evaluate.

1. $6[5 + 2(3 - 8) - 3]$

2. -3^4

3. 4^{-3}

4. $\dfrac{1}{2} - \dfrac{5}{6}$

Perform the indicated operations and simplify if possible.

5. $5x^3 + x^2 + 5x - 2 - (8x^3 - 4x^2 + x - 7)$

6. $(4x - 2)^2$

7. $(3x + 7)(x^2 + 5x + 2)$

Factor.

8. $y^2 - 8y - 48$

9. $9x^3 + 39x^2 + 12x$

10. $180 - 5x^2$

11. $3a^2 + 3ab - 7a - 7b$

12. $8y^3 - 64$

Simplify. Write answer with positive exponents only.

13. $\left(\dfrac{x^2 y^3}{x^3 y^{-4}}\right)^2$

Solve each equation or inequality. Write inequality answers using interval notation.

14. $-4(a + 1) - 3a = -7(2a - 3)$

15. $3x - 5 \geq 7x + 3$

16. $x(x + 6) = 7$

Graph the following.

17. $5x - 7y = 10$

18. $x - 3 = 0$

Find the slope of each line.

19. Through $(6, -5)$ and $(-1, 2)$

20. $-3x + y = 5$

Write equations of the following lines. Write each equation in standard form.

21. Through $(2, -5)$ and $(1, 3)$

22. Through $(-5, -1)$ and parallel to $x = 7$

Solve each system of equations.

23. $\begin{cases} \dfrac{1}{2}x + 2y = -\dfrac{15}{4} \\ \quad\quad 4x = -y \end{cases}$

24. $\begin{cases} 4x - 6y = 7 \\ -2x + 3y = 0 \end{cases}$

25. Divide by long division: $\dfrac{27x^3 - 8}{3x + 2}$

Answer the questions about functions.

26. If $h(x) = x^3 - x$, find
   a. $h(-1)$
   b. $h(0)$
   c. $h(4)$

27. Identify the *x*- and *y*-intercepts. Then find the domain and range of the function graphed.

Solve each application.

28. Some states have a single area code for the entire state. Two such states have area codes where one is double the other. If the sum of these integers is 1203, find the two area codes.

29. Two trains leave Los Angeles simultaneously traveling on the same track in opposite directions at speeds of 50 and 64 mph. How long will it take before they are 285 miles apart?

30. Find the amount of a 12% saline solution a lab assistant should add to 80 cc (cubic centimeters) of a 22% saline solution in order to have a 16% solution.

31. Find the domain of the rational function

$$g(x) = \frac{9x^2 - 9}{x^2 + 4x + 3}.$$

Perform the indicated operations and simplify if possible.

32. $\dfrac{15x}{2x + 5} - \dfrac{6 - 4x}{2x + 5}$

33. $\dfrac{x^2 - 9}{x^2 - 3x} \div \dfrac{xy + 5x + 3y + 15}{2x + 10}$

34. $\dfrac{5a}{a^2 - a - 6} - \dfrac{2}{a - 3}$

35. $\dfrac{5 - \dfrac{1}{y^2}}{\dfrac{1}{y} + \dfrac{2}{y^2}}$

Solve each equation.

36. $\dfrac{4}{y} - \dfrac{5}{3} = -\dfrac{1}{5}$

37. $\dfrac{5}{y+1} = \dfrac{4}{y+2}$

38. $\dfrac{a}{a-3} = \dfrac{3}{a-3} - \dfrac{3}{2}$

Solve.

39. One number plus five times its reciprocal is equal to six. Find the number.

Simplify. If needed, write answers with positive exponents only.

40. $\sqrt{216}$

41. $\left(\dfrac{1}{125}\right)^{-1/3}$

42. $\left(\dfrac{64c^{4/3}}{a^{-2/3}b^{5/6}}\right)^{1/2}$

Perform the indicated operations and simplify if possible.

43. $\sqrt{125x^3} - 3\sqrt{20x^3}$

44. $(\sqrt{5} + 5)(\sqrt{5} - 5)$

Solve each equation or inequality. Write inequality solutions using interval notation.

45. $|6x - 5| - 3 = -2$

46. $-3 < 2(x - 3) \le 4$

47. $|3x + 1| > 5$

48. $y^2 - 3y = 5$

49. $x = \sqrt{x - 2} + 2$

50. $2x^2 - 7x > 15$

Graph the following.

51. $y > -4x$

52. $g(x) = -|x + 2| - 1$. Also, find the domain and range of this function.

53. $h(x) = x^2 - 4x + 4$. Label the vertex and any intercepts.

54. $f(x) = \begin{cases} -\dfrac{1}{2}x & \text{if } x \le 0 \\ 2x - 3 & \text{if } x > 0 \end{cases}$. Also, find the domain and range of this function.

Write equations of the following lines. Write each equation using function notation.

55. Through $(4, -2)$ and $(6, -3)$

56. Through $(-1, 2)$ and perpendicular to $3x - y = 4$

Find the distance or midpoint.

57. Find the distance between the points $(-6, 3)$ and $(-8, -7)$.

58. Find the midpoint of the line segment whose endpoints are $(-2, -5)$ and $(-6, 12)$.

Rationalize each denominator. Assume that variables represent positive numbers.

59. $\sqrt{\dfrac{9}{y}}$

60. $\dfrac{4 - \sqrt{x}}{4 + 2\sqrt{x}}$

Solve.

61. Suppose that W is inversely proportional to V. If $W = 20$ when $V = 12$, find W when $V = 15$.

62. Given the diagram shown, approximate to the nearest foot how many feet of walking distance a person saves by cutting across the lawn instead of walking on the sidewalk.

63. A stone is thrown upward from a bridge. The stone's height in feet, $s(t)$, above the water t seconds after the stone is thrown is a function given by the equation

$$s(t) = -16t^2 + 32t + 256$$

a. Find the maximum height of the stone.

b. Find the time it takes the stone to hit the water. Round the answer to two decimal places.

COMPLEX NUMBERS: CHAPTER 10

Perform the indicated operation and simplify. Write the result in the form $a + bi$.

64. $-\sqrt{-8}$

65. $(12 - 6i) - (12 - 3i)$

66. $(4 + 3i)^2$

67. $\dfrac{1 + 4i}{1 - i}$

INVERSE, EXPONENTIAL, AND LOGARITHMIC FUNCTIONS: CHAPTER 12

68. If $g(x) = x - 7$ and $h(x) = x^2 - 6x + 5$, find $(g \circ h)(x)$.

69. Determine whether $f(x) = 6 - 2x$ is a one-to-one function. If it is, find its inverse.

70. Use properties of logarithms to write the expression as a single logarithm.

$$\log_5 x + 3\log_5 x - \log_5(x + 1)$$

Solve. Give exact solutions.

71. $8^{x-1} = \dfrac{1}{64}$

72. $3^{2x+5} = 4$ Give an exact solution and a 4-decimal-place approximation.

73. $\log_8(3x - 2) = 2$

74. $\log_4(x + 1) - \log_4(x - 2) = 3$

75. $\ln\sqrt{e} = x$

76. Graph $y = \left(\dfrac{1}{2}\right)^x + 1$

77. The prairie dog population of the Grand Forks area now stands at 57,000 animals. If the population is growing at a rate of 2.6% annually, how many prairie dogs will there be in that area 5 years from now?

CONIC SECTIONS: CHAPTER 13

Sketch the graph of each equation.

78. $x^2 - y^2 = 36$

79. $16x^2 + 9y^2 = 144$

80. $x^2 + y^2 + 6x = 16$

81. Solve the system: $\begin{cases} x^2 + y^2 = 26 \\ x^2 - 2y^2 = 23 \end{cases}$

SEQUENCES, SERIES, AND THE BINOMIAL THEOREM: CHAPTER 14

82. Find the first five terms of the sequence $a_n = \dfrac{(-1)^n}{n + 4}$.

83. Find the partial sum S_5 of the sequence $a_n = 5(2)^{n-1}$.

84. Find S_∞ of the sequence $\dfrac{3}{2}, -\dfrac{3}{4}, \dfrac{3}{8}, \ldots$

85. Find $\displaystyle\sum_{i=1}^{4} i(i - 2)$

86. Expand: $(2x + y)^5$

Answers to Selected Exercises

CHAPTER 1 REVIEW OF REAL NUMBERS

Section 1.2
Practice Exercises

1. a. $<$ **b.** $>$ **c.** $<$ **2. a.** True **b.** False **c.** True **d.** True **3. a.** $3 < 8$ **b.** $15 \geq 9$ **c.** $6 \neq 7$ **4.** -10 **5. a.** 25
b. 25 **c.** $25, -15, -99$ **d.** $25, \frac{7}{3}, -15, -\frac{3}{4}, -3.7, 8.8, -99$ **e.** $\sqrt{5}$ **f.** $25, \frac{7}{3}, -15, -\frac{3}{4}, \sqrt{5}, -3.7, 8.8, -99$ **6. a.** $<$ **b.** $>$ **c.** $=$
7. a. 8 **b.** 9 **c.** 2.5 **d.** $\frac{5}{11}$ **e.** $\sqrt{3}$ **8. a.** $=$ **b.** $>$ **c.** $<$ **d.** $>$ **e.** $<$

Vocabulary, Readiness & Video Check 1.2
1. whole **3.** inequality **5.** real **7.** irrational **9.** To form a true statement: $0 < 7$. **11.** 0 belongs to the whole numbers, the integers, the rational numbers, and the real numbers; because 0 is a rational number, it cannot also be an irrational number

Exercise Set 1.2
1. $>$ **3.** $=$ **5.** $<$ **7.** $<$ **9.** $32 < 212$ **11.** $30 \leq 45$ **13.** true **15.** false **17.** false **19.** true **21.** false **23.** $8 < 12$
25. $5 \geq 4$ **27.** $15 \neq -2$ **29.** $14,494; -282$ **31.** $-28,000$ **33.** $350; -126$ **35.** whole, integers, rational, real **37.** integers, rational, real
39. natural, whole, integers, rational, real **41.** rational, real **43.** irrational, real **45.** false **47.** true **49.** true **51.** true **53.** false
55. $>$ **57.** $>$ **59.** $<$ **61.** $<$ **63.** $>$ **65.** $=$ **67.** $<$ **69.** $<$ **71.** 2009 **73.** 2009, 2010 **75.** 280 million $<$ 281 million
77. 49 million $>$ 16 million **79.** 38 million pounds less, or -38 million **81.** $-0.04 > -26.7$ **83.** sun **85.** sun **87.** $20 \leq 25$ **89.** $6 > 0$
91. $-12 < -10$ **93.** answers may vary

Section 1.3
Practice Exercises

1. a. $2 \cdot 2 \cdot 3 \cdot 3$ **b.** $2 \cdot 2 \cdot 2 \cdot 5 \cdot 5$ **2. a.** $\frac{7}{8}$ **b.** $\frac{16}{3}$ **c.** $\frac{7}{25}$ **3.** $\frac{7}{24}$ **4. a.** $\frac{27}{16}$ **b.** $\frac{1}{36}$ **c.** $\frac{5}{2}$ **5. a.** 1 **b.** $\frac{6}{5}$ **c.** $\frac{4}{5}$ **d.** $\frac{1}{2}$
6. $\frac{14}{21}$ **7. a.** $\frac{46}{77}$ **b.** $\frac{1}{14}$ **c.** $\frac{1}{2}$ **8.** $22\frac{11}{15}$ **9.** $40\frac{5}{6}$

Vocabulary, Readiness & Video Check 1.3

1. fraction **3.** product **5.** factors, product **7.** equivalent **9.** The division operation changes to multiplication and the second fraction $\frac{1}{20}$ changes to its reciprocal $\frac{20}{1}$. **11.** The number $4\frac{7}{6}$ is not in proper mixed number form as the fraction part, $\frac{7}{6}$, should not be an improper fraction.

Exercise Set 1.3

1. $\frac{3}{8}$ **3.** $\frac{5}{7}$ **5.** $3 \cdot 11$ **7.** $2 \cdot 7 \cdot 7$ **9.** $2 \cdot 2 \cdot 5$ **11.** $3 \cdot 5 \cdot 5$ **13.** $3 \cdot 3 \cdot 5$ **15.** $\frac{1}{2}$ **17.** $\frac{2}{3}$ **19.** $\frac{3}{7}$ **21.** $\frac{3}{5}$ **23.** $\frac{30}{61}$ **25.** $\frac{3}{8}$
27. $\frac{1}{2}$ **29.** $\frac{6}{7}$ **31.** 15 **33.** $\frac{1}{6}$ **35.** $\frac{25}{27}$ **37.** $\frac{11}{20}$ sq mi **39.** $\frac{7}{36}$ sq ft **41.** $\frac{3}{5}$ **43.** 1 **45.** $\frac{1}{3}$ **47.** $\frac{9}{35}$ **49.** $\frac{21}{30}$ **51.** $\frac{4}{18}$
53. $\frac{16}{20}$ **55.** $\frac{23}{21}$ **57.** $\frac{11}{60}$ **59.** $\frac{5}{66}$ **61.** $\frac{7}{5}$ **63.** $\frac{1}{5}$ **65.** $\frac{3}{8}$ **67.** $\frac{1}{9}$ **69.** $18\frac{20}{27}$ **71.** $2\frac{28}{29}$ **73.** $48\frac{1}{15}$ **75.** $7\frac{1}{12}$ **77.** $\frac{5}{7}$
79. $\frac{65}{21}$ **81.** $\frac{2}{5}$ **83.** $\frac{10}{9}$ **85.** $\frac{17}{3}$ **87.** 37 **89.** $\frac{5}{66}$ **91.** $\frac{1}{5}$ **93.** $5\frac{1}{6}$ **95.** $\frac{17}{18}$ **97.** $55\frac{1}{4}$ ft **99.** answers may vary
101. $3\frac{3}{8}$ mi **103.** $\frac{21}{100}$ **105.** multiplexes **107.** incorrect; $\frac{12}{24} = \frac{2 \cdot 2 \cdot 3}{2 \cdot 2 \cdot 2 \cdot 3} = \frac{1}{2}$ **109.** incorrect; $\frac{2}{7} + \frac{9}{7} = \frac{11}{7}$

Section 1.4
Practice Exercises

1. a. 1 **b.** 25 **c.** $\frac{1}{100}$ **d.** 9 **e.** $\frac{8}{125}$ **2. a.** 33 **b.** 11 **c.** $\frac{32}{9}$ or $3\frac{5}{9}$ **d.** 36 **e.** $\frac{3}{16}$ **3.** $\frac{31}{11}$ **4.** 4 **5.** $\frac{9}{22}$ **6. a.** 9
b. $\frac{8}{15}$ **c.** $\frac{19}{10}$ **d.** 33 **7.** No **8. a.** $6x$ **b.** $x - 8$ **c.** $x \cdot 9$ or $9x$ **d.** $2x + 3$ **e.** $7 + x$ **9. a.** $x + 7 = 13$ **b.** $x - 2 = 11$
c. $2x + 9 \neq 25$ **d.** $5(11) \geq x$

Graphing Calculator Explorations 1.4
1. 625 **3.** 59,049 **5.** 30 **7.** 9857 **9.** 2376

Vocabulary, Readiness & Video Check 1.4
1. base; exponent **3.** variable **5.** equation **7.** solving **9.** The replacement value for z is not used because it's not needed–there is no variable z in the given algebraic expression. **11.** We translate phrases to mathematical expressions and sentences to mathematical equations.

Exercise Set 1.4

1. 243 **3.** 27 **5.** 1 **7.** 5 **9.** 49 **11.** $\frac{16}{81}$ **13.** $\frac{1}{125}$ **15.** 1.44 **17.** 0.000064 **19.** 17 **21.** 20 **23.** 10 **25.** 21

27. 45 **29.** 0 **31.** 30 **33.** 2 **35.** $\frac{7}{18}$ **37.** $\frac{27}{10}$ **39.** $\frac{7}{5}$ **41.** 32 **43.** $\frac{23}{27}$ **45. a.** 64 **b.** 43 **c.** 19 **d.** 22 **47.** 9

49. 1 **51.** 1 **53.** 11 **55.** 8 **57.** 45 **59.** 27 **61.** 132 **63.** $\frac{37}{18}$ **65.** 16; 64; 144; 256 **67.** yes **69.** no **71.** no **73.** yes

75. no **77.** $x + 15$ **79.** $x - 5$ **81.** $\frac{x}{4}$ **83.** $3x + 22$ **85.** $1 + 2 = 9 \div 3$ **87.** $3 \neq 4 \div 2$ **89.** $5 + x = 20$ **91.** $7.6x = 17$

93. $13 - 3x = 13$ **95.** multiply **97.** subtract **99.** no; answers may vary **101.** 14 in., 12 sq in. **103.** 14 in., 9.01 sq in. **105.** Rectangles with the same perimeter can have different areas. **107.** $(20 - 4) \cdot 4 \div 2$ **109. a.** expression **b.** equation **c.** equation **d.** expression **e.** expression **111.** answers may vary **113.** answers may vary, for example, $-2(5) - 1$ **115.** 12,000 sq ft **117.** 51 mph

Section 1.5
Practice Exercises

1. **2.** **3. a.** -13 **b.** -32 **4.**

5. a. -3 **b.** 1 **c.** -0.2 **6. a.** -1 **b.** -6 **c.** 0.5 **d.** $\frac{1}{70}$ **7. a.** -6 **b.** -6 **8.** 4°F **9. a.** $\frac{5}{9}$ **b.** -8 **c.** -6.2

d. 3 **10. a.** -15 **b.** $\frac{3}{5}$ **c.** $5y$ **d.** 8

Vocabulary, Readiness & Video Check 1.5
1. opposites **3.** n **5.** absolute values **7.** Negative temperatures; the high temperature for the day was -6°F

Exercise Set 1.5

1. 9 **3.** -14 **5.** 1 **7.** -12 **9.** -5 **11.** -12 **13.** -4 **15.** 7 **17.** -2 **19.** 0 **21.** -19 **23.** 31 **25.** -47

27. -2.1 **29.** -8 **31.** 38 **33.** -13.1 **35.** $\frac{2}{8} = \frac{1}{4}$ **37.** $-\frac{3}{16}$ **39.** $-\frac{13}{10}$ **41.** -8 **43.** -59 **45.** -9 **47.** 5 **49.** 11

51. -18 **53.** 19 **55.** -0.7 **57.** -6° **59.** 146 ft **61.** $-\$6.9$ million **63.** -16 **65.** -6 **67.** 2 **69.** 0 **71.** -6 **73.** -2

75. 0 **77.** $-\frac{2}{3}$ **79.** yes **81.** no **83.** July **85.** October **87.** 4.7°F **89.** -3 **91.** -22 **93.** negative **95.** positive **97.** true

99. false **101.** answers may vary **103.** answers may vary

Section 1.6
Practice Exercises

1. a. -13 **b.** -7 **c.** 12 **d.** -2 **2. a.** 10.9 **b.** $-\frac{1}{2}$ **c.** $-\frac{19}{20}$ **3.** -7 **4. a.** -6 **b.** 6.1 **5. a.** -20 **b.** 13 **6. a.** 2

b. 13 **7.** \$357 **8. a.** 28° **b.** 137°

Vocabulary, Readiness & Video Check 1.6
1. $7 - x$ **3.** $x - 7$ **5.** $7 - x$ **7.** $-10 - (-14)$; d **9.** addition; opposite **11.** There's a minus sign in the numerator and the replacement value is negative (notice parentheses are used around the replacement value), and it's always good to be careful when working with negative signs. **13.** In Example 9, you have two supplementary angles and know the measure of one of them. From the definition, you know that two supplementary angles must sum to 180°. Therefore you can subtract the known angle measure from 180° to get the measure of the other angle.

Exercise Set 1.6

1. -10 **3.** -5 **5.** 19 **7.** $\frac{1}{6}$ **9.** 2 **11.** -11 **13.** 11 **15.** 5 **17.** 37 **19.** -6.4 **21.** -71 **23.** 0 **25.** 4.1

27. $\frac{2}{11}$ **29.** $-\frac{11}{12}$ **31.** 8.92 **33.** 13 **35.** -5 **37.** -1 **39.** -23 **41.** -26 **43.** -24 **45.** 3 **47.** -45 **49.** -4

51. 13 **53.** 6 **55.** 9 **57.** -9 **59.** -7 **61.** $\frac{7}{5}$ **63.** 21 **65.** $\frac{1}{4}$ **67.** 100°F **69.** 265°F **71.** 35,653 ft **73.** -308 ft

75. 19,852 ft **77.** 130° **79.** 30° **81.** no **83.** no **85.** yes **87.** $-5 + x$ **89.** $-20 - x$ **91.** -4.4°; 2.6°; 12°; 23.5°; 15.3° **93.** May **95.** answers may vary **97.** 16 **99.** -20 **101.** true; answers may vary **103.** false; answers may vary **105.** negative, $-30,387$

Integrated Review

1. negative **2.** negative **3.** positive **4.** 0 **5.** positive **6.** 0 **7.** positive **8.** positive **9.** $-\frac{1}{7}; \frac{1}{7}$ **10.** $\frac{12}{5}; \frac{12}{5}$ **11.** 3; 3

12. $-\frac{9}{11}; \frac{9}{11}$ **13.** -42 **14.** 10 **15.** 2 **16.** -18 **17.** -7 **18.** -39 **19.** -2 **20.** -9 **21.** -3.4 **22.** -9.8 **23.** $-\frac{25}{28}$

24. $-\frac{5}{24}$ **25.** -4 **26.** -24 **27.** 6 **28.** 20 **29.** 6 **30.** 61 **31.** -6 **32.** -16 **33.** -19 **34.** -13 **35.** -4 **36.** -1

37. $\frac{13}{20}$ **38.** $-\frac{29}{40}$ **39.** 4 **40.** 9 **41.** -1 **42.** -3 **43.** 8 **44.** 10 **45.** 47 **46.** $\frac{2}{3}$

Section 1.7
Practice Exercises

1. a. -40 **b.** 12 **c.** -54 **2. a.** -30 **b.** 24 **c.** 0 **d.** 26 **3. a.** -0.046 **b.** $-\dfrac{4}{15}$ **c.** 14 **4. a.** 36 **b.** -36 **c.** -64 **d.** -64 **5. a.** $\dfrac{3}{8}$ **b.** $\dfrac{1}{15}$ **c.** $-\dfrac{7}{2}$ **d.** $-\dfrac{1}{5}$ **6. a.** -8 **b.** -4 **c.** 5 **7. a.** 3 **b.** -16 **c.** $-\dfrac{6}{5}$ **d.** $-\dfrac{1}{18}$ **8. a.** 0 **b.** undefined **c.** undefined **9. a.** $-\dfrac{84}{5}$ **b.** 11 **10. a.** -9 **b.** 33 **c.** $\dfrac{5}{3}$ **11.** -52

Graphing Calculator Explorations 1.7
1. 38 **3.** -441 **5.** $163.\overline{3}$ **7.** 54,499 **9.** 15,625

Vocabulary, Readiness & Video Check 1.7
1. 0; 0 **3.** positive **5.** negative **7.** positive **9.** The parentheses, or lack of them, determine the base of the expression. In Example 6, $(-2)^4$, the base is -2 and all of -2 is raised to 4. In Example 7, -2^4, the base is 2 and only 2 is raised to 4. **11.** Yes; because division of real numbers is defined in terms of multiplication. **13.** The football team lost 4 yards on each play and a loss of yardage is represented by a negative number.

Exercise Set 1.7
1. -24 **3.** -2 **5.** 50 **7.** -12 **9.** 0 **11.** -18 **13.** $\dfrac{3}{10}$ **15.** $\dfrac{2}{3}$ **17.** -7 **19.** 0.14 **21.** -800 **23.** -28 **25.** 25 **27.** $-\dfrac{8}{27}$ **29.** -121 **31.** $-\dfrac{1}{4}$ **33.** -30 **35.** 23 **37.** -7 **39.** true **41.** false **43.** 16 **45.** -1 **47.** 25 **49.** -49 **51.** $\dfrac{1}{9}$ **53.** $\dfrac{3}{2}$ **55.** $-\dfrac{1}{14}$ **57.** $-\dfrac{11}{3}$ **59.** $\dfrac{1}{0.2}$ **61.** -6.3 **63.** -9 **65.** 4 **67.** -4 **69.** 0 **71.** -5 **73.** undefined **75.** 3 **77.** -15 **79.** $-\dfrac{18}{7}$ **81.** $\dfrac{20}{27}$ **83.** -1 **85.** $-\dfrac{9}{2}$ **87.** -4 **89.** 16 **91.** -3 **93.** $-\dfrac{16}{7}$ **95.** 2 **97.** $\dfrac{6}{5}$ **99.** -5 **101.** $\dfrac{3}{2}$ **103.** -21 **105.** 41 **107.** -134 **109.** 3 **111.** 0 **113.** $-71 \cdot x$ or $-71x$ **115.** $-16 - x$ **117.** $-29 + x$ **119.** $\dfrac{x}{-33}$ or $x \div (-33)$ **121.** $3 \cdot (-4) = -12$; a loss of 12 yd **123.** $5(-20) = -100$; a depth of 100 ft **125.** yes **127.** no **129.** yes **131.** $-162°F$ **133.** answers may vary **135.** 1, -1 **137.** positive **139.** not possible **141.** negative **143.** $-2 + \dfrac{-15}{3}$; -7 **145.** $2[-5 + (-3)]$; -16

Section 1.8
Practice Exercises
1. a. $8 \cdot x$ **b.** $17 + x$ **2. a.** $2 + (9 + 7)$ **b.** $(-4 \cdot 2) \cdot 7$ **3. a.** $x + 14$ **b.** $-30x$ **4. a.** $5x - 5y$ **b.** $-24 - 12t$ **c.** $6x - 8y - 2z$ **d.** $-3 + y$ **e.** $-x + 7 - 2s$ **f.** $x + 11$ **5. a.** $5(w + 3)$ **b.** $9(w + z)$ **6. a.** commutative property of multiplication **b.** associative property of addition **c.** identity element for addition **d.** multiplicative inverse property **e.** commutative property of addition **f.** additive inverse property **g.** commutative and associative properties of multiplication

Vocabulary, Readiness & Video Check 1.8
1. commutative property of addition **3.** distributive property **5.** associative property of addition **7.** opposites or additive inverses **9.** 2 is outside the parentheses, so the point is made that you should only distribute the -9 to the terms within the parentheses and not also to the 2.

Exercise Set 1.8
1. $16 + x$ **3.** $y \cdot (-4)$ **5.** yx **7.** $13 + 2x$ **9.** $x \cdot (yz)$ **11.** $(2 + a) + b$ **13.** $(4a) \cdot b$ **15.** $a + (b + c)$ **17.** $17 + b$ **19.** $24y$ **21.** y **23.** $26 + a$ **25.** $-72x$ **27.** s **29.** $2 + x$ **31.** $4x + 4y$ **33.** $9x - 54$ **35.** $6x + 10$ **37.** $28x - 21$ **39.** $18 + 3x$ **41.** $-2y + 2z$ **43.** $-21y - 35$ **45.** $5x + 20m + 10$ **47.** $-4 + 8m - 4n$ **49.** $-5x - 2$ **51.** $-r + 3 + 7p$ **53.** $3x + 4$ **55.** $-x + 3y$ **57.** $6r + 8$ **59.** $-36x - 70$ **61.** $-16x - 25$ **63.** $4(1 + y)$ **65.** $11(x + y)$ **67.** $-1(5 + x)$ **69.** $30(a + b)$ **71.** commutative property of multiplication **73.** associative property of addition **75.** distributive property **77.** associative property of multiplication **79.** identity element of addition **81.** distributive property **83.** commutative and associative properties of multiplication **85.** $-8; \dfrac{1}{8}$ **87.** $-x; \dfrac{1}{x}$ **89.** $2x; -2x$ **91.** false **93.** no **95.** yes **97.** yes **99.** no **101. a.** commutative property of addition **b.** commutative property of addition **c.** associative property of addition **103.** answers may vary **105.** answers may vary

Chapter 1 Vocabulary Check
1. inequality symbols **2.** equation **3.** absolute value **4.** variable **5.** opposites **6.** numerator **7.** solution **8.** reciprocals **9.** base; exponent **10.** denominator **11.** grouping symbols **12.** set

Chapter 1 Review
1. $<$ **3.** $>$ **5.** $<$ **7.** $=$ **9.** $>$ **11.** $4 \geq -3$ **13.** $0.03 < 0.3$ **15. a.** 1, 3 **b.** 0, 1, 3 **c.** $-6, 0, 1, 3$ **d.** $-6, 0, 1, 1\dfrac{1}{2}, 3, 9.62$ **e.** π **f.** $-6, 0, 1, 1\dfrac{1}{2}, 3, \pi, 9.62$ **17.** Friday **19.** $2 \cdot 2 \cdot 3 \cdot 3$ **21.** $\dfrac{12}{25}$ **23.** $\dfrac{13}{10}$ **25.** $9\dfrac{3}{8}$ **27.** 15 **29.** $\dfrac{7}{12}$ **31.** $A = 1\dfrac{1}{6}$ sq m; $P = 4\dfrac{5}{12}$ m **33.** $14\dfrac{1}{8}$ lb **35.** $18\dfrac{7}{16}$ lb **37.** Baby E **39.** c **41.** $\dfrac{4}{49}$ **43.** 37 **45.** $\dfrac{18}{7}$ **47.** $20 - 12 = 2 \cdot 4$ **49.** 18 **51.** 5 **53.** $63°$ **55.** yes **57.** 9 **59.** -2 **61.** -11 **63.** $-\dfrac{3}{16}$ **65.** -13.9 **67.** -14

69. 5 **71.** -19 **73.** a **75.** $51 **77.** $-\dfrac{1}{6}$ **79.** -48 **81.** 3 **83.** undefined **85.** undefined **87.** -12 **89.** 9

91. $-7 \cdot x$ or $-7x$ **93.** $-20 - x$ **95.** commutative property of addition **97.** distributive property **99.** associative property of addition **101.** distributive property **103.** multiplicative inverse property **105.** $5y - 10$ **107.** $-7 + x - 4z$ **109.** $-12z - 27$ **111.** $<$

113. -15.3 **115.** -80 **117.** $-\dfrac{1}{4}$ **119.** 16 **121.** -5 **123.** $-\dfrac{5}{6}$ **125.** $1\dfrac{3}{8}$ ft

Chapter 1 Test

1. $|-7| > 5$ **2.** $9 + 5 \geq 4$ **3.** -5 **4.** -11 **5.** -3 **6.** -39 **7.** 12 **8.** -2 **9.** undefined **10.** -8 **11.** $-\dfrac{1}{3}$ **12.** $4\dfrac{5}{8}$

13. 1.275 **14.** -32 **15.** -48 **16.** 3 **17.** 0 **18.** $>$ **19.** $>$ **20.** $<$ **21.** $=$ **22.** $2221 < 10{,}993$ **23. a.** 1, 7 **b.** 0, 1, 7

c. $-5, -1, 0, 1, 7$ **d.** $-5, -1, 0, \dfrac{1}{4}, 1, 7, 11.6$ **e.** $\sqrt{7}, 3\pi$ **f.** $-5, -1, 0, \dfrac{1}{4}, 1, 7, 11.6, \sqrt{7}, 3\pi$ **24.** 40 **25.** 12 **26.** 22 **27.** -1

28. associative property of addition **29.** commutative property of multiplication **30.** distributive property **31.** multiplicative inverse property

32. 9 **33.** -3 **34.** second down **35.** yes **36.** $17°$ **37.** $650 million **38.** $420

CHAPTER 2 EQUATIONS, INEQUALITIES, AND PROBLEM SOLVING

Section 2.1
Practice Exercises

1. a. 1 **b.** -7 **c.** $-\dfrac{1}{5}$ **d.** 43 **e.** -1 **2. a.** like terms **b.** unlike terms **c.** like terms **d.** like terms **3. a.** $8y$ **b.** $5x^2$

c. $5x + 5x^2$ **d.** $21y^2$ **4. a.** $11y - 5$ **b.** $5x - 6$ **c.** $-\dfrac{1}{4}t$ **d.** $12.2y + 13$ **e.** $5z - 3z^4$ **5. a.** $6x - 21$ **b.** $-5x + 2.5z + 25$

c. $-2x + y - z + 2$ **6. a.** $36x + 10$ **b.** $-11x + 1$ **c.** $-30x - 17$ **7.** $-5x + 4$ **8. a.** $2x + 3$ **b.** $x - 1$ **c.** $2x + 10$ **d.** $\dfrac{13}{2}x$

Vocabulary, Readiness & Video Check 2.1

1. expression; term **3.** numerical coefficient **5.** numerical coefficient **7.** Although these terms have exactly the same variables, the exponents on each are not exactly the same—the exponents on x differ in each term. **9.** -1

Exercise Set 2.1

1. -7 **3.** 1 **5.** 17 **7.** like **9.** unlike **11.** like **13.** $15y$ **15.** $13w$ **17.** $-7b - 9$ **19.** $-m - 6$ **21.** -8 **23.** $7.2x - 5.2$
25. $4x - 3$ **27.** $5x^2$ **29.** $1.3x + 3.5$ **31.** $5y - 20$ **33.** $-2x - 4$ **35.** $7d - 11$ **37.** $-10x + 15y - 30$ **39.** $-3x + 2y - 1$
41. $2x + 14$ **43.** $10x - 3$ **45.** $-4x - 9$ **47.** $-4m - 3$ **49.** $k - 6$ **51.** $-15x + 18$ **53.** 16 **55.** $x + 5$ **57.** $x + 2$

59. $2k + 10$ **61.** $-3x + 5$ **63.** -11 **65.** $3y + \dfrac{5}{6}$ **67.** $-22 + 24x$ **69.** $0.9m + 1$ **71.** $10 - 6x - 9y$ **73.** $-x - 38$ **75.** $5x - 7$

77. $2x - 4$ **79.** $2x + 7$ **81.** $\dfrac{3}{4}x + 12$ **83.** $-2 + 12x$ **85.** $8(x + 6)$ or $8x + 48$ **87.** $x - 10$ **89.** $7x - 7$ **91.** 2 **93.** -23

95. -25 **97.** $(18x - 2)$ ft **99.** balanced **101.** balanced **103.** answers may vary **105.** $(15x + 23)$ in. **107.** answers may vary
109. $5b^2c^3 + b^3c^2$ **111.** $5x^2 + 9x$ **113.** $-7x^2y$

Section 2.2
Practice Exercises

1. -8 **2.** -1.8 **3.** -10 **4.** 18 **5.** 20 **6.** -12 **7.** 65 **8.** -3 **9. a.** 7 **b.** $9 - x$ **c.** $(9 - x)$ ft **10.** $3x + 6$

Vocabulary, Readiness & Video Check 2.2

1. equation; expression **3.** solution **5.** addition **7.** multiplication **9.** true **11.** both sides **13.** addition property; multiplication property; answers may vary

Exercise Set 2.2

1. 3 **3.** -2 **5.** -14 **7.** 0.5 **9.** -3 **11.** -0.7 **13.** 3 **15.** 11 **17.** 0 **19.** -3 **21.** 16 **23.** -4 **25.** 0 **27.** 12
29. 10 **31.** -12 **33.** 3 **35.** -2 **37.** 0 **39.** answers may vary **41.** 10 **43.** -20 **45.** 0 **47.** -5 **49.** 0

51. $-\dfrac{3}{2}$ **53.** -21 **55.** $\dfrac{11}{2}$ **57.** 1 **59.** $-\dfrac{1}{4}$ **61.** 12 **63.** -30 **65.** $\dfrac{9}{10}$ **67.** -30 **69.** 2 **71.** -2 **73.** 23

75. $20 - p$ **77.** $(10 - x)$ ft **79.** $(180 - x)°$ **81.** $(n + 284)$ votes **83.** $(m - 60)$ ft **85.** $(n - 28{,}000)$ students **87.** $7x$ sq mi
89. $2x + 2$ **91.** $2x + 2$ **93.** $5x + 20$ **95.** $7x - 12$ **97.** 1 **99.** $>$ **101.** $=$ **103.** $(173 - 3x)°$ **105.** answers may vary

107. 4 **109.** answers may vary **111.** answers may vary **113.** -48 **115.** $\dfrac{700}{3}$ mg **117.** solution **119.** -2.95 **121.** 0.02

Section 2.3
Practice Exercises

1. 3 **2.** $\dfrac{21}{13}$ **3.** -15 **4.** 3 **5.** 0 **6.** no solution **7.** all real numbers

Graphing Calculator Explorations 2.3

1. solution   **3.** not a solution   **5.** solution

Vocabulary, Readiness & Video Check 2.3

1. equation   **3.** expression   **5.** expression   **7.** equation   **9.** 3; distributive property, addition property of equality, multiplication property of equality   **11.** The number of decimal places in each number helps you determine what power of 10 you can multiply through by so you are no longer dealing with decimals.

Exercise Set 2.3

1. -6 **3.** 3   **5.** 1   **7.** $\frac{3}{2}$ **9.** 0   **11.** -1 **13.** 4   **15.** -4 **17.** -3 **19.** 2   **21.** 50   **23.** 1   **25.** $\frac{7}{3}$ **27.** 0.2
29. all real numbers   **31.** no solution   **33.** no solution   **35.** all real numbers   **37.** 18   **39.** $\frac{19}{9}$ **41.** $\frac{14}{3}$ **43.** 13   **45.** 4
47. all real numbers   **49.** $-\frac{3}{5}$ **51.** -5 **53.** 10   **55.** no solution   **57.** 3   **59.** -17 **61.** -4 **63.** 3   **65.** all real numbers
67. $-8 - x$ **69.** $-3 + 2x$ **71.** $9(x + 20)$ **73.** $(6x - 8)$ m   **75. a.** all real numbers   **b.** answers may vary   **c.** answers may vary
77. A   **79.** B   **81.** C   **83.** answers may vary   **85. a.** $x + x + x + 2x + 2x = 28$ **b.** $x = 4$ **c.** $x = 4$ cm; $2x = 8$ cm   **87.** answers may vary   **89.** 15.3   **91.** -0.2 **93.** $-\frac{7}{8}$ **95.** no solution

Integrated Review

1. 6   **2.** -17 **3.** 12   **4.** -26 **5.** -3 **6.** -1 **7.** $\frac{27}{2}$ **8.** $\frac{25}{2}$ **9.** 8   **10.** -64 **11.** 2   **12.** -3 **13.** no solution
14. no solution   **15.** -2 **16.** -2 **17.** $-\frac{5}{6}$ **18.** $\frac{1}{6}$ **19.** 1   **20.** 6   **21.** 4   **22.** 1   **23.** $\frac{9}{5}$ **24.** $-\frac{6}{5}$ **25.** all real numbers
26. all real numbers   **27.** 0   **28.** -1.6 **29.** $\frac{4}{19}$ **30.** $-\frac{5}{19}$ **31.** $\frac{7}{2}$ **32.** $-\frac{1}{4}$ **33.** 2   **34.** 2   **35.** no solution   **36.** no solution
37. $\frac{7}{6}$ **38.** $\frac{1}{15}$

Section 2.4
Practice Exercises

1. 9   **2.** 2   **3.** 9 in. and 36 in.   **4.** 29 Republican and 20 Democratic governors   **5.** $25°, 75°, 80°$ **6.** $46, 48, 50$

Vocabulary, Readiness & Video Check 2.4

1. $2x; 2x - 31$ **3.** $x + 5; 2(x + 5)$ **5.** $20 - y; \frac{20 - y}{3}$ or $(20 - y) \div 3$ **7.** in the statement of the application   **9.** That the 3 angle measures are consecutive even integers and that they sum to $180°$.

Exercise Set 2.4

1. $6x + 1 = 5x; -1$ **3.** $3x - 6 = 2x + 8; 14$ **5.** $2(x - 8) = 3(x + 3); -25$ **7.** $2(-2 + x) = x - \frac{1}{2}; \frac{7}{2}$ **9.** 3 in.; 6 in.; 16 in.
11. 1st piece: 5 in.; 2nd piece: 10 in.; 3rd piece: 25 in.   **13.** 7837 screens; 31,710; In 2010, 7837 screens were 3D.   **15.** 1st angle: $37.5°$; 2nd angle: $37.5°$; 3rd angle: $105°$ **17.** $3x + 3$ **19.** $x + 2; x + 4; 2x + 4$ **21.** $x + 1; x + 2; x + 3; 4x + 6$ **23.** $x + 2; x + 4; 2x + 6$
25. 234, 235   **27.** Belgium: 32; France: 33; Spain: 34   **29.** Sahara: 3,500,000 sq mi; Gobi: 500,000 sq mi   **31.** 5 ft, 12 ft   **33.** $\frac{5}{4}$
35. Botswana: 32,000,000 carats; Angola: 8,000,000 carats   **37.** $58°, 60°, 62°$ **39.** South Korea: 14; Russia: 15; Austria: 16   **41.** -16 **43.** $43°, 137°$
45. 1   **47.** $\frac{3}{2}$ **49.** Maglev: 361 mph; TGV: 357.2 mph   **51.** $\frac{5}{2}$ **53.** California: 58; Montana: 56   **55.** 111°   **57.** 1st piece: 3 ft; 2nd piece: 12 ft; 3rd piece: 15 ft   **59.** Eagles: *Their Greatest Hits, 1971–1975*   **61.** *Thriller*: $27 million; *The Wall*: $23 million   **63.** answers may vary   **65.** 34   **67.** 225π **69.** 15 ft by 24 ft   **71.** 5400 chirps per hour; 129,600 chirps per day; 47,304,000 chirps per year   **73.** answers may vary   **75.** answers may vary   **77.** c

Section 2.5
Practice Exercises

1. 116 sec or 1 min 56 sec   **2.** 9 ft   **3.** 46.4°F   **4.** length: 28 in.; width: 5 in.   **5.** $r = \frac{I}{Pt}$ **6.** $s = \frac{H - 10a}{5a}$ **7.** $d = \frac{N - F}{n - 1}$
8. $B = \frac{2A - ab}{a}$

Vocabulary, Readiness & Video Check 2.5

1. relationships   **3.** To show that the process of solving this equation for x—dividing both sides by 5, the coefficient of x—is the same process used to solve a formula for a specific variable. Treat whatever is multiplied by that specific variable as the coefficient—the coefficient is all the factors except that specific variable.

Exercise Set 2.5

1. $h = 3$ **3.** $h = 3$ **5.** $h = 20$ **7.** $c = 12$ **9.** $r \approx 2.5$ **11.** $T = 3$ **13.** $h \approx 15$ **15.** $h = \frac{f}{5g}$ **17.** $w = \frac{V}{lh}$ **19.** $y = 7 - 3x$
21. $R = \frac{A - P}{PT}$ **23.** $A = \frac{3V}{h}$ **25.** $a = P - b - c$ **27.** $h = \frac{S - 2\pi r^2}{2\pi r}$ **29.** 120 ft   **31. a.** area: 103.5 sq ft; perimeter: 41 ft

b. baseboard: perimeter; carpet: area **33. a.** area: 480 sq in.; perimeter: 120 in. **b.** frame: perimeter; glass: area **35.** −10°C **37.** length: 78 ft; width: 52 ft **39.** 18 ft, 36 ft, 48 ft **41.** 55.2 mph **43.** 96 piranhas **45.** 61.5°F **47.** 60 chirps per minute **49.** increases **51.** 2 bags **53.** one 16-in. pizza **55.** $x = 6$ m, $2.5x = 15$ m **57.** 22 hr **59.** 13 in. **61.** 2.25 hr **63.** 12,090 ft **65.** 50°C **67.** 332.6°F **69.** 449 cu in. **71.** 0.32 **73.** 2.00 or 2 **75.** 17% **77.** 720% **79.** multiplies the volume by 8; answers may vary **81.** $53\frac{1}{3}$

83. $V = G(N - R)$ **85.** ● $=$ ■$-$▲ / ■ **87.** 500 sec or $8\frac{1}{3}$ min **89.** 608.33 ft **91.** 4.42 min **93.** $35\frac{11}{17}$ mph

Section 2.6
Practice Exercises

1. 62.5% **2.** 360 **3. a.** 42% **b.** 98% **c.** 79.3 million dogs **4.** discount: $408; new price: $72 **5.** 42.6% **6.** 3554 screens **7.** 2 liters of 5% eyewash; 4 liters of 2% eyewash

Vocabulary, Readiness & Video Check 2.6

1. no **3.** yes **5. a.** equals; $=$ **b.** multiplication; · **c.** Drop the percent symbol and move the decimal point two places to the left. **7.** You must first find the actual amount of increase in price by subtracting the original price from the new price.

Exercise Set 2.6

1. 11.2 **3.** 55% **5.** 180 **7.** 4% **9.** 9990 **11.** discount: $1480; new price: $17,020 **13.** $46.58 **15.** 9.8% **17.** 30% **19.** $104 **21.** $42,500 **23.** 2 gal **25.** 7 lb **27.** 4.6 **29.** 50 **31.** 30% **33.** 23% **35.** 90,405 **37.** 59%; 5%; 26%; 2%; 99% due to rounding **39.** decrease: $64; sale price: $192 **41.** 27.2% **43.** 239 million **45.** 300% **47.** 400 oz **49.** 66.7% **51.** 120 employees **53.** 361 college students **55.** 400 oz **57.** 854 thousand Scoville units **59.** $>$ **61.** $=$ **63.** $>$ **65.** no; answers may vary **67.** no; answers may vary **69.** 9.6% **71.** 26.9%; yes **73.** 17.1%

Section 2.7
Practice Exercises

1. 2.2 hr **2.** eastbound: 62 mph; westbound: 52 mph **3.** 106 $5 bills; 59 $20 bills **4.** $18,000 at 11.5%; $12,000 at 6%

Vocabulary, Readiness & Video Check 2.7

1.

	r ·	t =	d
bus	55	x	55x
car	50	x + 3	50(x + 3)

; $55x = 50(x + 3)$

3.

	P ·	R ·	T =	I
	x	0.06	1	0.06x
	36,000 − x	0.04	1	0.04(36,000 − x)

; $0.06x = 0.04(36{,}000 - x)$

Exercise Set 2.7

1. $666\frac{2}{3}$ mi **3.** 55 mph **5.** 0.10 y **7.** 0.05(x + 7) **9.** 20(4y) or 80y **11.** 50(35 − x) **13.** 12 $10 bills; 32 $5 bills **15.** $11,500 at 8%; $13,500 at 9% **17.** $7000 at 11% profit; $3000 at 4% loss **19.** 187 adult tickets; 313 child tickets **21.** 2 hr **23.** $30,000 at 8%; $24,000 at 10% **25.** 2 hr $37\frac{1}{2}$ min **27.** 36 mph; 46 mph **29.** 483 dimes; 161 nickels **31.** 4 hr **33.** 2.5 hr **35.** $4500 **37.** 2.2 mph; 3.3 mph **39.** 27.5 mi **41.** −4 **43.** $\frac{9}{16}$ **45.** −4 **47.** 25 $100 bills; 71 $50 bills; 175 $20 bills **49.** 25 skateboards **51.** 800 books **53.** answers may vary

Section 2.8
Practice Exercises

1. $(-\infty, 5)$ **2.** $[-5, \infty)$ **3.** $(-\infty, 3]$ **4.** $(-3, \infty)$

5. $[7, \infty)$ **6.** $(-\infty, -7]$ **7.** $\left(-\infty, \frac{9}{4}\right)$ **8.** $[0, \infty)$

9. $[-3, 1)$ **10.** $(-2, 2]$ **11.** $\left(-\frac{16}{3}, \frac{4}{3}\right)$ **12.** all numbers less than 10

13. Kasonga can afford at most 3 classes.

Vocabulary, Readiness & Video Check 2.8

1. expression **3.** inequality **5.** −5 **7.** The graph of Example 1 is shaded from −∞ to and including −1, as indicated by a bracket. To write interval notation, you write down what is shaded for the inequality from left to right. A parenthesis is always used with −∞, so from the graph, the interval notation is $(-\infty, -1]$. **9.** You would divide the left, middle, and right by −3 instead of 3, which would reverse the directions of both inequality symbols.

Exercise Set 2.8

1. $x \geq 2$ **3.** $x < -5$ **5.** $(-\infty, -1]$ **7.** $\left(-\infty, \frac{1}{2}\right)$ **9.** $[5, \infty)$ **11.** $x < -3,$ $(-\infty, -3)$ **13.** $x \geq -5,$ $[-5, \infty)$ **15.** $x \geq -2$ $[2, \infty)$ **17.** $x > -3,$ $(-3, \infty)$ **19.** $x \leq 1,$ $(-\infty, 1]$ **21.** $x > -5,$ $(-5, \infty)$ **23.** $x \leq -2,$ $(-\infty, -2]$ **25.** $x \leq -8,$ $(-\infty, -8]$

27. $x > 4$, ⟵———→ (4) $\quad (4, \infty)$ **29.** $x \geq 20$, ⟵———→ (20) $\quad [20, \infty)$ **31.** $x > 16$, ⟵———→ (16) $\quad (16, \infty)$

33. $x > -3$, ⟵———→ (-3) $\quad (-3, \infty)$ **35.** $x \leq -\dfrac{2}{3}$, ⟵———→ $\quad \left(-\infty, -\dfrac{2}{3}\right]$ **37.** $x > \dfrac{8}{3}$, ⟵———→ $\quad \left(\dfrac{8}{3}, \infty\right)$

39. $x > -13$, ⟵———→ (-13) $\quad (-13, \infty)$ **41.** $x < 0$, ⟵———→ (0) $\quad (-\infty, 0)$ **43.** $x \leq 0$, ⟵———→ (0) $\quad (-\infty, 0]$

45. $x > 3$, ⟵———→ (3) $\quad (3, \infty)$ **47.** $x > \dfrac{8}{3}$ ⟵———→ $\quad \left(\dfrac{8}{3}, \infty\right)$ **49.** ⟵———→ $\quad (-1, 3)$ **51.** ⟵———→ $\quad [0, 2)$

53. ⟵———→ $\quad (-1, 2)$ **55.** ⟵———→ $\quad [4, 5]$ **57.** ⟵———→ $\quad (1, 5]$ **59.** ⟵———→ $\quad (1, 4)$

61. ⟵———→ $\quad \left(0, \dfrac{14}{3}\right]$ **63.** all numbers greater than -10 **65.** 35 cm **67.** at least 193 **69.** 86 people **71.** at least 35 min

73. $-3 < x < 3$ **75.** 8 **77.** 1 **79.** $\dfrac{16}{49}$ **81.** $>$ **83.** $\geq$ **85.** when multiplying or dividing by a negative number

87. final exam score ≥ 78.5 **89.** answers may vary **91.** answers may vary **93.** $0.924 \leq d \leq 0.987$ **95.** ⟵———→ (1) $\quad (1, \infty)$

97. ⟵———→ $\quad \left(-\infty, \dfrac{5}{8}\right)$

Chapter 2 Vocabulary Check

1. like terms **2.** unlike terms **3.** linear equation in one variable **4.** linear inequality in one variable **5.** compound inequalities **6.** formula
7. numerical coefficient **8.** equivalent equations **9.** all real numbers **10.** no solution **11.** the same **12.** reversed

Chapter 2 Review

1. $6x$ **3.** $4x - 2$ **5.** $3n - 18$ **7.** $-6x + 7$ **9.** $3x - 7$ **11.** 4 **13.** 6 **15.** 0 **17.** -23 **19.** $5; 5$ **21.** b **23.** b **25.** -12
27. 0 **29.** 0.75 **31.** -6 **33.** -1 **35.** $-\dfrac{1}{5}$ **37.** $3x + 3$ **39.** -4 **41.** 2 **43.** no solution **45.** $\dfrac{3}{4}$ **47.** 20 **49.** $\dfrac{23}{7}$

51. 102 **53.** 6665.5 in. **55.** Kellogg: 35 plants; Keebler: 18 plants **57.** 3 **59.** $w = 9$ **61.** $m = \dfrac{y - b}{x}$ **63.** $x = \dfrac{2y - 7}{5}$ **65.** $\pi = \dfrac{C}{D}$
67. 15 m **69.** 1 hr 20 min **71.** 20% **73.** 110 **75.** mark-up: \$209; new price: \$2109 **77.** 40% solution: 10 gal; 10% solution: 20 gal
79. 18% **81.** 966 customers **83.** 32% **85.** 50 km **87.** 80 nickels **89.** $(0, \infty)$ ⟵———→ (0) **91.** $[0.5, 1.5)$ ⟵———→

93. $(-\infty, -4)$ ⟵———→ (-4) **95.** $(-\infty, 4]$ ⟵———→ (4) **97.** $\left(-\dfrac{1}{2}, \dfrac{3}{4}\right)$ ⟵———→ **99.** $\left(-\infty, \dfrac{19}{3}\right]$ ⟵———→

101. \$2500 **103.** 4 **105.** $-\dfrac{3}{2}$ **107.** all real numbers **109.** -13 **111.** $h = \dfrac{3V}{A}$ **113.** 160 **115.** $(9, \infty)$ ⟵———→ (9)
117. $(-\infty, 0]$ ⟵———→ (0)

Chapter 2 Test

1. $y - 10$ **2.** $5.9x + 1.2$ **3.** $-2x + 10$ **4.** $10y + 1$ **5.** -5 **6.** 8 **7.** $\dfrac{7}{10}$ **8.** 0 **9.** 27 **10.** 3 **11.** 0.25 **12.** $\dfrac{25}{7}$

13. no solution **14.** $x = 6$ **15.** $h = \dfrac{V}{\pi r^2}$ **16.** $y = \dfrac{3x - 10}{4}$ **17.** $(-\infty, -2]$ ⟵———→ (-2) **18.** $(-\infty, 4)$ ⟵———→ (4)

19. $\left(-1, \dfrac{7}{3}\right)$ ⟵———→ **20.** $\left(\dfrac{2}{5}, \infty\right)$ ⟵———→ **21.** 21 **22.** 62 ft by 64 ft **23.** 401, 802 **24.** \$8500 at 10%; \$17,000 at 12%

25. $2\dfrac{1}{2}$ hr **26.** 552 **27.** 40% **28.** 16%

Chapter 2 Cumulative Review

1. a. $11, 112$ **b.** $0, 11, 112$ **c.** $-3, -2, 0, 11, 112$ **d.** $-3, -2, -1.5, 0, \dfrac{1}{4}, 11, 112$ **e.** $\sqrt{2}$ **f.** all numbers in the given set; Sec. 1.2, Ex. 5

3. a. 4 **b.** 5 **c.** 0 **d.** $\dfrac{1}{2}$ **e.** 5.6; Sec. 1.2, Ex. 7 **5. a.** $2 \cdot 2 \cdot 2 \cdot 5$ **b.** $3 \cdot 3 \cdot 7$; Sec. 1.3, Ex. 1 **7.** $\dfrac{8}{20}$; Sec. 1.3, Ex. 6 **9.** 66; Sec. 1.4, Ex. 4

11. 2 is a solution; Sec. 1.4, Ex. 7 **13.** -3; Sec. 1.5, Ex. 2 **15.** 2; Sec. 1.5, Ex. 4 **17. a.** 10 **b.** $\dfrac{1}{2}$ **c.** $2x$ **d.** -6; Sec. 1.5, Ex. 10

19. a. 9.9 **b.** $-\dfrac{4}{5}$ **c.** $\dfrac{2}{15}$; Sec. 1.6, Ex. 2 **21. a.** $52°$ **b.** $118°$; Sec. 1.6, Ex. 8 **23. a.** -0.06 **b.** $-\dfrac{7}{15}$ **c.** 16; Sec. 1.7, Ex. 3

25. a. 6 **b.** -12 **c.** $-\dfrac{8}{15}$ **d.** $-\dfrac{1}{6}$; Sec. 1.7, Ex. 7 **27. a.** $5 + x$ **b.** $x \cdot 3$; Sec. 1.8, Ex. 1 **29. a.** $8(2 + x)$ **b.** $7(s + t)$; Sec. 1.8, Ex. 5

31. $-2x - 1$; Sec. 2.1, Ex. 7 **33.** -1.6; Sec. 2.2, Ex. 2 **35.** 8; Sec. 2.2, Ex. 4 **37.** 140; Sec. 2.2, Ex. 7 **39.** 2; Sec. 2.3, Ex. 1 **41.** 10; Sec. 2.4, Ex. 2

43. $\dfrac{V}{wh} = l$; Sec. 2.5, Ex. 5 **45.** $(-\infty, -10]$ ⟵———→ (-10) ; Sec. 2.8, Ex. 2

CHAPTER 3 GRAPHING

Section 3.1
Practice Exercises

1. a. Africa/Middle East region, 145 million Internet users   **b.** 640 million more Internet users   **2. a.** 70 beats per minute   **b.** 60 beats per minute
c. 5 minutes after lighting   **3.**   **4. a.** (2004, 65), (2005, 67), (2006, 96), (2007, 86), (2008, 79), (2009, 79), (2010, 72)

b.

5. a. yes   **b.** yes   **c.** no   **6. a.** $(0, -8)$ **b.** $(6, 4)$ **c.** $(-3, -14)$

7.

	x	y
a.	-2	8
b.	3	-12
c.	0	0

8.

	x	y
a.	-10	-4
b.	0	-2
c.	10	0

9.

x	0	1	2	3	4
y	12,000	10,200	8400	6600	4800

Vocabulary, Readiness & Video Check 3.1

1. x-axis; y-axis   **3.** quadrants; four   **5.** one   **7.** horizontal: top tourist countries; vertical: number of arrivals (in millions) to these countries
9. Data occurring in pairs of numbers can be written as ordered pairs, called paired data, and then graphed on a coordinate system.   **11.** a linear equation in one variable

Exercise Set 3.1

1. France   **3.** France, U.S., Spain, Italy, and China   **5.** 43 million   **7.** 71,000   **9.** 2011; 103,000   **11.** 15.9   **13.** from 1998 to 2000

15. 2014   **17.**   (1, 5) and (3.7, 2.2) are in quadrant I, $\left(-1, 4\frac{1}{2}\right)$ is in quadrant II, $(-5, -2)$ is in quadrant III, $(2, -4)$ and $\left(\frac{1}{2}, -3\right)$

are in quadrant IV, $(-3, 0)$ lies on the x-axis, $(0, -1)$ lies on the y-axis   **19.** $(0, 0)$ **21.** $(3, 2)$
23. $(-2, -2)$ **25.** $(2, -1)$ **27.** $(0, -3)$ **29.** $(1, 3)$ **31.** $(-3, -1)$

33. a. (2006, 25.5), (2007, 26.3), (2008, 27.7), (2009, 29.4), (2010, 31.8)   **b.** In the year 2010, the worldwide box office was $31.8 billion.
c.   **d.** The worldwide box office increased every year.   **35. a.** (0.50, 10), (0.75, 12), (1.00, 15), (1.25, 16), (1.50, 18),
(1.50, 19), (1.75, 19), (2.00, 20)   **b.** When Minh studied 1.25 hours, her quiz score was 16.   **c.**

d. answers may very

37. a. (2313, 2), (2085, 1), (2711, 21), (2869, 39), (2920, 42), (4038, 99), (1783, 0), (2493, 9)   **b.**   **c.** The farther from the equator,
the more snowfall.   **39.** yes; no; yes   **41.** yes; yes   **43.** no; yes; yes

45. $(-4, -2)$, $(4, 0)$ **47.** $(-8, -5)$, $(16, 1)$ **49.** $0; 7; -\frac{2}{7}$ **51.** $2; 2; 5$

53. $0; -3; 2$ **55.** $2; 6; 3$ **57.** $-12; 5; -6$ **59.** $\frac{5}{7}; \frac{5}{2}; -1$ **61.** $0; -5; -2$

63. $2; 1; -6$

65. a. 13,000; 21,000; 29,000   **b.** 45 desks   **67. a.** 5.52; 6.00; 6.48   **b.** year 9; 2009   **c.** 2016
d. In 2005, the average cinema admission price was $6.48.   **69.** In 2010, there were 3755 Walmart stores in the U.S.
71. year 8: 100 stores; year 9: 105 stores; year 10: 100 stores   **73.** The y-values are all 0.   **75.** $y = 5 - x$
77. $y = -\frac{1}{2}x + \frac{5}{4}$ **79.** $y = -2x$ **81.** $y = \frac{1}{3}x - 2$ **83.** false   **85.** true   **87.** negative; negative

89. positive; negative   **91.** 0; 0   **93.** y **95.** no; answers may vary   **97.** answers may vary   **99.** $(4, -7)$ **101.** 26 units   **103. a.** $(-2, 6)$
b. 28 units   **c.** 45 sq units

Section 3.2
Practice Exercises

1. a. yes   **b.** no   **c.** yes   **d.** yes   **2.**   **3.**   **4.**   **5.**

6.   **7.**   The graph of $y = -2x + 3$ is the same as the graph of $y = -2x$ except that the graph of $y = -2x + 3$ is moved 3 units upward.

8. a.   **b.** We predict 725 thousand computer software application engineers in the year 2020.

Graphing Calculator Explorations 3.2

1.   **3.**   **5.**

Vocabulary, Readiness & Video Check 3.2

1. In the definition, x and y both have an understood power of 1. Example 3 shows an equation where y has a power of 2, so it is not a linear equation in two variables.   **3.** An infinite number of points make up the line and each point corresponds to an ordered pair that is a solution of the linear equation in two variables.

Exercise Set 3.2

1. yes   **3.** yes   **5.** no   **7.** yes   **9.**

x	y
6	0
4	-2
5	-1

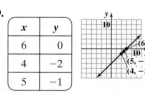

11.

x	y
1	-4
0	0
-1	4

13.

x	y
0	0
6	2
-3	-1

15.

x	y
0	3
1	-1
2	-5

17.   **19.**   **21.**   **23.**

25.   **27.**   **29.**   **31.**   **33.**   **35.**

37.
39.
41.
43.
45.

47. c   **49.** d   **51. a.** $(8, 31)$ **b.** In 2008, there were 31 million joggers.   **c.** 40 million joggers   **53. a.** $(8, 207.6)$ **b.** In 2008, there were 207.6 million people with driver's licenses.   **c.** 225.2 million   **55.** $(4, -1)$ **57.** $3; -3$ **59.** $0; 0$ **61.** $y = x + 5$

63. $2x + 3y = 6$ **65.** $x + y = 12; y = 9$ cm   **67.** answers may vary   **69.** $0; 1; 1; 4; 4$

Section 3.3
Practice Exercises
1. x-intercept: $(-4, 0)$ **2.** x-intercepts: $(-2, 0), (2, 0)$ **3.** x-intercept: $(0, 0)$ **4.** x-intercept: none   **5.** x-intercepts: $(-1, 0), (5, 0)$
  y-intercept: $(0, -6)$ y-intercept: $(0, -3)$ y-intercept: $(0, 0)$ y-intercept: $(0, 3)$ y-intercepts: $(0, 2), (0, -2)$

6.
7.
8.
9.
10.

Graphing Calculator Explorations 3.3
1.   **3.**   **5.** $-2.2x + 6.8y = 15.5$

Vocabulary, Readiness & Video Check 3.3
1. linear   **3.** horizontal   **5.** y-intercept   **7.** $y; x$ **9.** Because x-intercepts lie on the x-axis; because y-intercepts lie on the y-axis.
11. For a horizontal line, the coefficient of x will be 0 and the coefficient of y will be 1; for a vertical line, the coefficient of y will be 0 and the coefficient of x will be 1.

Exercise Set 3.3
1. $(-1, 0); (0, 1)$ **3.** $(-2, 0); (2, 0); (0, -2)$ **5.** $(-2, 0); (1, 0); (3, 0); (0, 3)$ **7.** $(-1, 0); (1, 0); (0, 1); (0, -2)$ **9.** infinite   **11.** 0
13.
15.
17.
19.
21.
23.

25.
27.
29.
31.
33.
35.

37.
39.
41.
43.
45.
47.

49. C   **51.** E   **53.** B   **55.** $\frac{3}{2}$ **57.** 6   **59.** $-\frac{6}{5}$ **61.** false   **63.** true   **65.** $(0, 200)$; no chairs and 200 desks are manufactured,
67. 300 chairs   **69. a.** $(62, 0)$ **b.** 62 years after 2002, 0 people will attend the movies at the theater.   **c.** answers may very   **71.** $x = 1$
73. answers may vary   **75.** answers may vary

Section 3.4
Practice Exercises

1. -1 **2.** $\frac{1}{3}$ **3.** $m = \frac{2}{3}$; y-intercept: $(0, -2)$ **4.** $m = 6$; y-intercept: $(0, -5)$ **5.** $m = -\frac{5}{2}$; y-intercept: $(0, 4)$ **6.** $m = 0$

7. slope is undefined   **8. a.** perpendicular   **b.** neither   **c.** parallel   **9.** 25%   **10.** $m = \frac{0.75 \text{ dollar}}{1 \text{ pound}}$; The Wash-n-Fold charges $0.75 per pound of laundry.

Graphing Calculator Explorations 3.4

1.   **3.**

Vocabulary, Readiness & Video Check 3.4

1. slope   **3.** 0   **5.** positive   **7.** $y; x$ **9.** solve the equation for y; the slope is the coefficient of x.   **11.** slope-intercept form; this form makes the slope easy to see, and you need to compare slopes to determine if two lines are parallel or perpendicular.

Exercise Set 3.4

1. -1 **3.** undefined   **5.** $-\frac{2}{3}$ **7.** 0   **9.** $m = -\frac{4}{3}$ **11.** undefined slope   **13.** $m = \frac{5}{2}$ **15.** negative   **17.** undefined   **19.** upward
21. horizontal   **23.** line 1   **25.** line 2   **27.** D   **29.** B   **31.** E   **33.** undefined slope   **35.** $m = 0$ **37.** undefined slope

39. $m = 0$ **41.** $m = 5$ **43.** $m = -0.3$ **45.** $m = -2$ **47.** $m = \frac{2}{3}$ **49.** undefined slope   **51.** $m = \frac{1}{2}$ **53.** $m = 0$ **55.** $m = -\frac{3}{4}$

57. $m = 4$ **59. a.** 1   **b.** -1 **61. a.** $\frac{9}{11}$ **b.** $-\frac{11}{9}$ **63.** neither   **65.** neither   **67.** parallel   **69.** perpendicular   **71.** $\frac{3}{5}$ **73.** 12.5%

75. 40%   **77.** 37%; 35%   **79.** $m = \frac{1}{1}$ or 1; Every 1 year, there are 1 million more U.S. households with televisions.   **81.** $m = 0.47$; It costs $0.47 per 1 mile to own and operate a compact car.   **83.** $y = 2x - 14$ **85.** $y = -6x - 11$ **87.** $m = \frac{1}{2}$ **89.** answers may vary   **91.** 2005 to 2006
93. 2000; 28.5 mi per gallon   **95.** from 2008 to 2009   **97.** $x = 6$ **99. a.** $(2007, 2207)$; $(2010, 2333)$ **b.** 42   **c.** For the years 2007 through 2010, the number of heart transplants increased at a rate of 42 per year.   **101.** The slope through $(-3, 0)$ and $(1, 1)$ is $\frac{1}{4}$. The slope through $(-3, 0)$ and $(-4, 4)$ is -4. The product of the slopes is -1, so the sides are perpendicular.   **103.** -0.25 **105.** 0.875   **107.** The line becomes steeper.

Integrated Review

1. $m = 2$ **2.** $m = 0$ **3.** $m = -\frac{2}{3}$ **4.** undefined slope   **5.**   **6.** $x + y = 3$ **7.**

13. parallel   **14.** neither   **15. a.** $(0, 587)$ **b.** In 2000, there were 587 thousand bridges on public roads.   **c.** 1.7   **d.** For the years 2000 through 2009, the number of bridges on public roads increased at a rate of 1.7 thousand per year.   **16. a.** $(9, 26.6)$ **b.** In 2009, the revenue for online advertising was $26.6 billion.

Section 3.5
Practice Exercises

1. **2.** **3.** $y = \frac{1}{2}x + 7$ **4.** $4x - y = 5$ **5.** $5x + 4y = 19$ **6.** $x = 3$ **7.** $y = 3$
8. a. $y = -1500x + 195{,}000$ **b.** $\$105{,}000$

Graphing Calculator Explorations 3.5

1. **3.**   **5.**

Vocabulary, Readiness & Video Check 3.5

1. slope-intercept; m; b **3.** y-intercept; fraction   **5.** Write the equation with x- and y- terms on one side of the equal sign and a constant on the other side.   **7.** Example 6: $y = -3$; Example 7: $x = -2$

Exercise Set 3.5

1. **3.** **5.** **7.** **9.** **11.**

13. $y = 5x + 3$ **15.** $y = -4x - \frac{1}{6}$ **17.** $y = \frac{2}{3}x$ **19.** $y = -8$ **21.** $y = -\frac{1}{5}x + \frac{1}{9}$ **23.** $-6x + y = -10$ **25.** $8x + y = -13$
27. $3x - 2y = 27$ **29.** $x + 2y = -3$ **31.** $2x - y = 4$ **33.** $8x - y = -11$ **35.** $4x - 3y = -1$ **37.** $8x + 13y = 0$ **39.** $x = 0$
41. $y = 3$ **43.** $x = -\frac{7}{3}$ **45.** $y = 2$ **47.** $y = 5$ **49.** $x = 6$ **51.** $y = -\frac{1}{2}x + \frac{5}{3}$ **53.** $y = -x + 17$ **55.** $x = -\frac{3}{4}$
57. $y = x + 16$ **59.** $y = -5x + 7$ **61.** $y = 7$ **63.** $y = \frac{3}{2}x$ **65.** $y = -3$ **67.** $y = -\frac{4}{7}x - \frac{18}{7}$ **69. a.** $s = 32t$ **b.** 128 ft/sec
71. a. $y = -33x + 356$ **b.** 92 thousand gasoline-electric hybrids   **73. a.** $y = 0.6x + 85$ **b.** 93.4 persons per sq mi   **75. a.** $y = -1.75x + 60$
b. 32 million   **77. a.** $S = -1000p + 13{,}000$ **b.** 9500 Fun Noodles   **79.** -1 **81.** 5   **83.** no   **85.** yes   **87.** point-slope
89. slope-intercept   **91.** horizontal   **93.** answers may vary   **95. a.** $3x - y = -5$ **b.** $x + 3y = 5$ **97. a.** $3x + 2y = -1$
b. $2x - 3y = 21$

Section 3.6
Practice Exercises

1. Domain: $\{0, 1, 5\}$: Range: $\{-2, 0, 3, 4\}$ **2. a.** function   **b.** not a function   **3. a.** not a function   **b.** function   **4. a.** function
b. function   **c.** function   **d.** not a function   **5. a.** function   **b.** function   **c.** function   **d.** not a function   **6. a.** 69°F   **b.** February
c. yes   **7. a.** $h(2) = 9$; $(2, 9)$ **b.** $h(-5) = 30$; $(-5, 30)$ **c.** $h(0) = 5$; $(0, 5)$ **8. a.** domain: $(-\infty, \infty)$ **b.** domain: $(-\infty, 0) \cup (0, \infty)$
9. a. domain: $[-4, 6]$; range: $[-2, 3]$ **b.** domain: $(-\infty, \infty)$; range: $(-\infty, 3]$

Vocabulary, Readiness & Video Check 3.6

1. relation   **3.** range   **5.** vertical   **7.** A relation is a set of ordered pairs and an equation in two variables defines a set of ordered pairs. Therefore, an equation in two variables can also define a relation.   **9.** A vertical line represents one x-value paired with many y-values. A function only allows an x-value paired with exactly one y-value, so if a vertical line intersects a graph more than once, there's an x-value paired with more than one y-value, and we don't have a function.

Exercise Set 3.6

1. $\{-7, 0, 2, 10\}$; $\{-7, 0, 4, 10\}$ **3.** $\{0, 1, 5\}$; $\{-2\}$ **5.** yes   **7.** no   **9.** no   **11.** yes   **13.** yes   **15.** no   **17.** yes   **19.** yes
21. yes   **23.** no   **25.** no   **27.** 9:30 p.m.   **29.** January 1 and December 1   **31.** yes; it passes the vertical line test   **33.** $\$4.25$ per hour
35. 2009   **37.** yes; answers may vary   **39.** $\$1.50$ **41.** more than 1 ounce and less than or equal to 2 ounces   **43.** yes; answers may vary
45. $-9, -5, 1$ **47.** $6, 2, 11$ **49.** $-6, 0, 9$ **51.** $2, 0, 3$ **53.** $5, 0, -20$ **55.** $5, 3, 35$ **57.** $(3, 6)$ **59.** $\left(0, -\frac{1}{2}\right)$ **61.** $(-2, 9)$
63. $(-\infty, \infty)$ **65.** all real number except -5 or $(-\infty, -5) \cup (-5, \infty)$ **67.** $(-\infty, \infty)$ **69.** domain: $(-\infty, \infty)$; range: $[-4, \infty)$ **71.** domain:
$(-\infty, \infty)$; range: $(-\infty, \infty)$ **73.** domain: $(-\infty, \infty)$; range: $\{2\}$ **75.** -1 **77.** -1 **79.** $-1, 5$ **81.** $(-2, 1)$ **83.** $(-3, -1)$
85. $f(-5) = 12$ **87.** $(3, -4)$ **89.** $f(5) = 0$ **91. a.** 166.38 cm   **b.** 148.25 cm   **93.** answers may vary   **95.** $f(x) = x + 7$
97. a. 11   **b.** $2a + 7$ **99. a.** 16   **b.** $a^2 + 7$

Chapter 3 Vocabulary Check

1. solution **2.** *y*-axis **3.** linear **4.** *x*-intercept **5.** standard **6.** *y*-intercept **7.** slope-intercept **8.** point-slope **9.** *y*
10. *x*-axis **11.** *x* **12.** slope **13.** function **14.** domain **15.** range **16.** relation

Chapter 3 Review

1.   **3.**   **5.**   **7. a.** $(5.00, 50), (8.50, 100), (20.00, 250), (27.00, 500)$ **b.**

9. no; yes **11.** yes; yes **13.** $(7, 44)$ **15.** $(-3, 0); (1, 3); (9, 9)$ **17.** 2005; 2500; 7000 **19.**

21.   **23.**   **25.**   **27.** $(4, 0), (0, -2)$ **29.** $(-2, 0), (2, 0), (0, 2), (0, -2)$

31.   **33.**   **35.**   **37.**   **39.** $m = -\dfrac{3}{4}$ **41.** d **43.** c **45.** $\dfrac{3}{4}$ **47.** 4

49. 3 **51.** 0 **53.** perpendicular **55.** neither **57.** $m = 44$; Every 1 year, 44 thousand (44,000) more students graduate with an associate's
degree. **59.** $m = -3; (0, 7)$ **61.** $m = 0; (0, 2)$ **63.**   **65.**   **67.** $y = -5x + \dfrac{1}{2}$ **69.** c

71. b **73.** $(0, 1859)$ **75.** $3x + y = -5$ **77.** $y = -3$ **79.** $6x + y = 11$ **81.** $x + y = 6$ **83.** $x = 5$ **85.** $x = 6$ **87.** no
89. yes **91.** no **93.** no **95. a.** 6 **b.** 10 **c.** 5 **97. a.** 45 **b.** -35 **c.** 0 **99.** $(-\infty, \infty)$ **101.** domain:$[-3, 5]$ range: $[-4, 2]$
103. domain:$\{3\}$; range: $(-\infty, \infty)$ **105.** 7; -1; -3 **107.** $(3, 0); (0, -2)$ **109.**   **111.**   **113.**
115. $m = -1$ **117.** $m = 2$ **119.** $m = \dfrac{2}{3}; (0, -5)$ **121.** $5x + y = 8$
123. $4x + y = -3$ **125.** $y = 238x + 2134$

Chapter 3 Test

1.   **2.**   **3.**   **4.**   **5.**

6. $\dfrac{2}{5}$ **7.** 0 **8.** -1 **9.** 3 **10.** undefined **11.** $m = \dfrac{7}{3}; \left(0, -\dfrac{2}{3}\right)$ **12.** neither **13.** $x + 4y = 10$ **14.** $7x + 6y = 0$
15. $8x + y = 11$ **16.** $x = -5$ **17.** $x - 8y = -96$ **18.** yes **19.** no **20. a.** 0 **b.** 0 **c.** 60 **21.** all real numbers except -1 or
$(-\infty, -1) \cup (-1, \infty)$ **22. a.** *x*-intercepts: $(0, 0), (4, 0)$; *y*-intercept: $(0, 0)$ **b.** domain: $(-\infty, \infty)$; range: $(-\infty, 4]$ **23. a.** *x*-intercept: $(2, 0)$;
y-intercept; $(0, -2)$ **b.** domain: $(-\infty, \infty)$; range: $(-\infty, \infty)$ **24.** $(7, 20)$ **25.** 210 liters **26.** 490 liters **27.** July **28.** $63°F$ **29.** January,
February, March, November, December **30. a.** $(2003, 66.0); (2004, 65.4); (2005, 65.4); (2006, 65.6); (2007, 64.9); (2008, 63.7); (2009, 62.1)$
31. a. $m = -8$; Every 1 year, 8 million fewer movie tickets are sold. **b.** $(0, 1380), (5, 1340)$ **c.** $y = -8x + 1380$
d. In 2015, we predict that 1300 million movie tickets will be sold in the U.S. and Canada.
b.

Chapter 3 Cumulative Review

1. a. $<$ **b.** $>$ **c.** $>$; Sec. 1.2, Ex. 1   **3.** $\frac{2}{39}$; Sec. 1.3, Ex. 3   **5.** $\frac{8}{3}$; Sec. 1.4, Ex. 3   **7. a.** -19 **b.** 30   **c.** -0.5 **d.** $-\frac{4}{5}$ **e.** 6.7

f. $\frac{1}{40}$; Sec. 1.5, Ex. 6   **9. a.** -6;   **b.** 6.3; Sec. 1.6, Ex. 4   **11. a.** -6 **b.** 0   **c.** $\frac{3}{4}$; Sec. 1.7, Ex. 10   **13. a.** $22 + x$ **b.** $-21x$; Sec. 1.8, Ex. 3

15. a. -3 **b.** 22   **c.** 1   **d.** -1 **e.** $\frac{1}{7}$; Sec. 2.1, Ex. 1   **17.** 17; Sec. 2.2, Ex. 1   **19.** 6; Sec. 2.2, Ex. 5   **21.** $3x + 3$; Sec. 2.2, Ex. 10

23. 0; Sec. 2.3, Ex. 4   **25.** 242 Republicans, 193 Democrats; Sec. 2.4, Ex. 4   **27.** 40 ft; Sec. 2.5, Ex. 2   **29.** $\frac{y-b}{m} = x$; Sec. 2.5, Ex. 6

31. 40% solution: 8 liters; 70% solution: 4 liters; Sec. 2.6, Ex. 7   **33.** $[-1, \infty)$; Sec. 2.8, Ex. 1   **35.** $[1, 4)$; Sec. 2.8, Ex. 10

37. a. solution   **b.** not a solution   **c.** solution; Sec. 3.1, Ex. 5   **39. a.** yes   **b.** yes   **c.** no   **d.** yes; Sec. 3.2, Ex. 1   **41.** 0; Sec. 3.4, Ex. 6

43. $y = \frac{1}{4}x - 3$; Sec. 3.5, Ex. 3

CHAPTER 4 SOLVING SYSTEMS OF LINEAR EQUATIONS

Section 4.1
Practice Exercises

1. no   **2.** yes   **3.** $(8, 5)$ **4.** $(-3, -5)$ **5.** no solution; inconsistent system; { } or $\varnothing$

6. infinite number of solutions; consistent system, $\{(x, y)\,|\,3x + 4y = 12\}$ or $\{(x, y)\,|\,9x + 12y = 36\}$ **7.** one solution   **8.** no solution

Graphing Calculator Explorations 4.1
1. $(0.37, 0.23)$ **3.** $(0.03, -1.89)$

Vocabulary, Readiness & Video Check 4.1
1. dependent   **3.** consistent   **5.** inconsistent   **7.** The ordered pair must satisfy all equations of the system in order to be a solution of the system, so we must check that the ordered pair is a solution of both equations.   **9.** Writing the equations of a system in slope-intercept form lets you see their slope and y-intercept. Different slopes mean one solution; same slope with different y-intercepts means no solution; same slope with same y-intercept means infinite number of solutions.

Exercise Set 4.1
1. one solution, $(-1, 3)$ **3.** infinite number of solutions   **5. a.** no   **b.** yes   **7. a.** yes   **b.** no   **9. a.** yes   **b.** yes   **11. a.** no   **b.** no
13. **15.** **17.** **19.** **21.** **23.**

25. no solution   **27.**   **29.**   **31.** no solution; { } or $\varnothing$ **33.** infinite number of solutions;

$\{(x, y)\,|\,y - 3x = -2\}$ or $\{(x, y)\,|\,6x - 2y = 4\}$

35.   **37.**   **39.**   **41.** infinite number of solutions;   **43.** intersecting, one solution

$\{(x, y)\,|\,6x - y = 4\}$
or $\left\{(x, y)\,\middle|\,\frac{1}{2}y = -2 + 3x\right\}$

45. parallel; no solution   **47.** identical lines; infinite number of solutions   **49.** intersecting; one solution   **51.** intersecting; one solution

53. identical lines; infinite number of solutions   **55.** parallel; no solution   **57.** 2   **59.** $-\frac{2}{5}$ **61.** 2

63. answers may vary; possible answer   **65.** answers may vary; possible answer   **67.** answers may vary   **69.** 1988–1989; 2001–2002

71. 2003, 2004, 2005, 2006, 2007   **73.** answers may vary   **75. a.** $(4, 9)$ **b.**   **c.** yes   **77.** answers may vary

Section 4.2
Practice Exercises

1. $(8, 7)$ **2.** $(-3, -6)$ **3.** $\left(4, \dfrac{2}{3}\right)$ **4.** $(-3, 2)$ **5.** infinite number of solutions; $\left\{(x, y)\left|\dfrac{1}{4}x - y = 2\right.\right\}$ or $\{(x, y)\,|\,x = 4y + 8\}$

6. no solution; $\{\ \}$ or $\varnothing$

Vocabulary, Readiness & Video Check 4.2

1. $(1, 4)$ **3.** infinite number of solutions   **5.** $(0, 0)$ **7.** You solved one equation for a variable. Now be sure to substitute this expression for the variable into the *other* equation.

Exercise Set 4.2

1. $(2, 1)$ **3.** $(-3, 9)$ **5.** $(2, 7)$ **7.** $\left(-\dfrac{1}{5}, \dfrac{43}{5}\right)$ **9.** $(2, -1)$ **11.** $(-2, 4)$ **13.** $(4, 2)$ **15.** $(-2, -1)$ **17.** no solution; $\{\ \}$ or $\varnothing$

19. $(3, -1)$ **21.** $(3, 5)$ **23.** $\left(\dfrac{2}{3}, -\dfrac{1}{3}\right)$ **25.** $(-1, -4)$ **27.** $(-6, 2)$ **29.** $(2, 1)$ **31.** no solution; $\{\ \}$ or $\varnothing$ **33.** infinite number of

solutions; $\left\{(x, y)\left|\dfrac{1}{3}x - y = 2\right.\right\}$ or $\{(x, y)\,|\,x - 3y = 6\}$ **35.** $\left(\dfrac{1}{2}, 2\right)$ **37.** $(1, -3)$ **39.** $-6x - 4y = -12$ **41.** $-12x + 3y = 9$ **43.** $5n$

45. $-15b$ **47.** answers may vary   **49.** no; answers may vary   **51. c;** answers may vary   **53. a.** $(13, 492)$ **b.** In $1970 + 13 = 1983$, the number of men and women receiving bachelor's degrees was the same.   **c.** answers may vary   **55.** $(-2.6, 1.3)$ **57.** $(3.28, 2.11)$

Section 4.3
Practice Exercises

1. $(5, 3)$ **2.** $(3, -4)$ **3.** no solution; $\{\ \}$ or $\varnothing$ **4.** infinite number of solutions; $\{(x, y)\,|\,4x - 3y = 5\}$ or $\{(x, y)\,|\,-8x + 6y = -10\}$

5. $(2, 2)$ **6.** $\left(-\dfrac{8}{5}, \dfrac{6}{5}\right)$

Vocabulary, Readiness & Video Check 4.3

1. false   **3.** true   **5.** The multiplication property of equality; be sure to multiply *both* sides of the equation by the number chosen.

Exercise Set 4.3

1. $(1, 2)$ **3.** $(2, -3)$ **5.** $(-2, -5)$ **7.** $(5, -2)$ **9.** $(-7, 5)$ **11.** $(6, 0)$ **13.** no solution; $\{\ \}$ or $\varnothing$ **15.** infinite number of solutions;

$\{(x, y)\,|\,-x + 5y = -1\}$ or $\{(x, y)\,|\,3x - 15y = 3\}$ **17.** $\left(2, -\dfrac{1}{2}\right)$ **19.** $(-2, 0)$ **21.** $(1, -1)$ **23.** no solution; $\{\ \}$ or $\varnothing$ **25.** $\left(\dfrac{12}{11}, -\dfrac{4}{11}\right)$

27. $\left(\dfrac{3}{2}, 3\right)$ **29.** infinite number of solutions; $\left\{(x, y)\left|\dfrac{10}{3}x + 4y = -4\right.\right\}$ or $\{(x, y)\,|\,5x + 6y = -6\}$ **31.** $(1, 6)$ **33.** $\left(-\dfrac{1}{2}, -2\right)$ **35.** infinite

number of solutions; $\left\{(x, y)\left|\dfrac{x}{3} - y = 2\right.\right\}$ or $\left\{(x, y)\left|-\dfrac{x}{2} + \dfrac{3y}{2} = -3\right.\right\}$ **37.** $\left(-\dfrac{2}{3}, \dfrac{2}{5}\right)$ **39.** $(2, 4)$ **41.** $(-0.5, 2.5)$ **43.** $(2, 5)$

45. $(-3, 2)$ **47.** $(0, 3)$ **49.** $(5, 7)$ **51.** $\left(\dfrac{1}{3}, 1\right)$ **53.** infinite number of solutions; $\left\{(x, y)\left|\dfrac{x + 2}{2} = \dfrac{y + 11}{3}\right.\right\}$ or $\left\{(x, y)\left|\dfrac{x}{2} = \left(\dfrac{2y + 16}{6}\right)\right.\right\}$

55. $(-8.9, 10.6)$ **57.** $2x + 6 = x - 3$ **59.** $20 - 3x = 2$ **61.** $4(n + 6) = 2n$ **63.** $2; 6x - 2y = -24$ **65. b;** answers may vary

67. answers may vary   **69. a.** $b = 15$ **b.** any real number except 15   **71.** $(-4.2, 9.6)$ **73. a.** $(7, 22)$ **b.** In 2015 $(2008 + 7)$, the percent of workers age 25–34 and the percent of workers age 55 and older will be the same.   **c.** 22% of the workforce for each of these age groups.

Integrated Review

1. $(2, 5)$ **2.** $(4, 2)$ **3.** $(5, -2)$ **4.** $(6, -14)$ **5.** $(-3, 2)$ **6.** $(-4, 3)$ **7.** $(0, 3)$ **8.** $(-2, 4)$ **9.** $(5, 7)$ **10.** $(-3, -23)$

11. $\left(\dfrac{1}{3}, 1\right)$ **12.** $\left(-\dfrac{1}{4}, 2\right)$ **13.** no solution; $\{\ \}$ or $\varnothing$ **14.** infinite number of solutions; $\{(x, y)\,|\,-x + 2y = 3\}$ or $\{(x, y)\,|\,3x - 6y = -9\}$

15. $(0.5, 3.5)$ **16.** $(-0.75, 1.25)$ **17.** infinite number of solutions; $\{(x, y)\,|\,x = 3y - 7\}$ or $\{(x, y)\,|\,2x - 6y = -14\}$ **18.** no solution; $\{\ \}$ or $\varnothing$

19. $(7, -3)$ **20.** $(-1, -3)$ **21.** answers may vary   **22.** answers may vary

Section 4.4
Practice Exercises
1. $(-1, 2, 1)$ **2.** { } or $\varnothing$ **3.** $\left(\frac{2}{3}, -\frac{1}{2}, 0\right)$ **4.** $\{(x, y, z)\mid 2x + y - 3z = 6\}$ **5.** $(6, 15, -5)$

Vocabulary, Readiness & Video Check 4.4
1. a, b, d **3.** yes; answers may vary **5.** Once we have one equation in two variables, we need to get another equation in the *same* two variables, giving us a system of two equations in two variables. We solve this new system to find the value of two variables. We then substitute these values into an original equation to find the value of the third.

Exercise Set 4.4
1. $(-1, 5, 2)$ **3.** $(-2, 5, 1)$ **5.** $(-2, 3, -1)$ **7.** $\{(x, y, z)\mid x - 2y + z = -5\}$ **9.** $\varnothing$ **11.** $(0, 0, 0)$ **13.** $(-3, -35, -7)$
15. $(6, 22, -20)$ **17.** $\varnothing$ **19.** $(3, 2, 2)$ **21.** $\{(x, y, z)\mid x + 2y - 3z = 4\}$ **23.** $(-3, -4, -5)$ **25.** $\left(0, \frac{1}{2}, -4\right)$ **27.** $(12, 6, 4)$
29. 15 and 30 **31.** 5 **33.** $-\frac{5}{3}$ **35.** answers may vary **37.** answers may vary **39.** $(1, 1, -1)$ **41.** $(1, 1, 0, 2)$ **43.** $(1, -1, 2, 3)$
45. answers may vary

Section 4.5
Practice Exercises
1. a. 2208 **b.** yes; answers may vary **2.** 18, 12 **3.** 17 and 12 **4. a.** Adult: $19 **b.** Child: $6 **c.** No, the regular rates are less than the group rate **5.** Atlantique: 500 kph; V150: 575 kph **6.** 0.95 liter of water; 0.05 liter of 99% HCL **7.** 1500 packages **8.** 40°, 60°, 80°

Vocabulary, Readiness & Video Check 4.5
1. Up to now we've been choosing one variable/unknown and translating to one equation. To solve by a system of equations, we'll choose two variables to represent two unknowns and translate to two equations. **3.** The ordered triple still needs to be interpreted in the context of the application. Each value actually represents the angle measure of a triangle, in degrees.

Exercise Set 4.5
1. c **3.** b **5.** a **7.** $\begin{cases} x + y = 15 \\ x - y = 7 \end{cases}$ **9.** $\begin{cases} x + y = 6500 \\ x = y + 800 \end{cases}$ **11.** 33 and 50 **13.** 10 and 8 **15.** 14 and -3 **17.** Cabrera: 126; Rodriguez: 125
19. child's ticket: $18; adult's ticket: $29 **21.** quarters: 53; nickels: 27 **23.** McDonald's: $73.50; The Ohio Art Company: $3.50 **25.** daily fee: $32;
mileage charge: $0.25 per mi **27.** distance downstream = distance upstream = 18 mi; time downstream: 2 hr; time upstream: $4\frac{1}{2}$ hr; still water: 6.5 mph;
current: 2.5 mph **29.** still air: 455 mph; wind: 65 mph **31.** $4\frac{1}{2}$ hr **33.** 12% solution: $7\frac{1}{2}$ liters; 4% solution: $4\frac{1}{2}$ liters **35.** $4.95 beans: 113 lb;
$2.65 beans: 87 lb **37.** 60°, 30° **39.** 20°, 70° **41.** number sold at $9.50: 23; number sold at $7.50: 67 **43.** $2\frac{1}{4}$ mph and $2\frac{3}{4}$ mph
45. 30%: 50 gal; 60%: 100 gal **47.** length: 42 in.; width: 30 in. **49. a.** 2010 **b.** answers may vary **51. a.** answers may vary **b.** 2003
53. $x = 75; y = 105$ **55.** 625 units **57.** 3000 units **59.** 1280 units **61. a.** $R(x) = 450x$ **b.** $C(x) = 200x + 6000$ **c.** 24 desks
63. 2 units of Mix A; 3 units of Mix B; 1 unit of Mix C **65.** 5 in.; 7 in.; 7 in.; 10 in. **67.** 18, 13, and 9 **69.** free throws: 594; 2-pt field goals: 566;
3-pt fields goals: 145 **71.** $x = 60; y = 55; z = 65$ **73.** $(3, \infty)$ **75.** $\left[\frac{1}{2}, \infty\right)$ **77.** a **79.** width: 9 ft; length: 15 ft **81.** $a = 3, b = 4, c = -1$
83. $a = 0.5, b = 24.5, c = 849$; 2015: 1774 thousand students **85.** $(7, 215)$

Chapter 4 Vocabulary Check
1. dependent **2.** system of linear equations **3.** consistent **4.** solution **5.** addition; substitution **6.** inconsistent **7.** independent

Chapter 4 Review
1. a. no **b.** yes **c.** no **3. a.** no **b.** no **c.** yes **5.** **7.** **9.**

11. no solution; { } or $\varnothing$ **13.** $(-1, 4)$ **15.** $(3, -2)$ **17.** infinite number of solutions; $\{(x, y)\mid 4y = 2x + 6\}$ or $\{(x, y)\mid x - 2y = -3\}$
19. no solution; { } or $\varnothing$ **21.** $(-6, 2)$ **23.** $(3, 7)$

25. infinite number of solutions; $\{(x, y)\mid 2x - 6y = -1\}$ or $\left\{(x, y)\mid -x + 3y = \frac{1}{2}\right\}$ **27.** $(8, -6)$ **29.** $(2, 0, 2)$ **31.** $\left(-\frac{1}{2}, \frac{3}{4}, 1\right)$ **33.** $\varnothing$
35. $(1, 1, -2)$ **37.** -6 and 22 **39.** current of river: 3.2 mph; speed in still water: 21.1 mph **41.** egg: $0.40; strip of bacon: $0.65
43. 17 pennies; 20 nickels; 16 dimes **45.** two sides: 22 cm each; third side: 29 cm

47.

49. $(3, 2)$ **51.** $\left(1\frac{1}{2}, -3\right)$ **53.** infinite number of solutions; $\{(x, y)\,|\,3x - y = 4\}$ or $\{(x, y)\,|\,4y = 12x - 16\}$ **55.** $(-5, 2)$ **57.** $(-1, 3, 5)$ **59.** 4 and 8   **61.** 24 nickels and 41 dimes   **63.** 28 units, 42 units, 56 units

Chapter 4 Test

1. false   **2.** false   **3.** true   **4.** false   **5.** no   **6.** yes

7. $(-4, 2)$

8. $(-4, 1)$ **9.** $\left(\frac{1}{2}, -2\right)$ **10.** $(4, -2)$ **11.** no solution; $\{\ \}$ or $\varnothing$ **12.** $(4, -5)$ **13.** $(7, 2)$ **14.** $(5, -2)$ **15.** 78, 46   **16.** 120 cc   **17.** Texas: 248 thousand; Missouri: 108 thousand   **18.** 3 mph; 6 mph   **19.** $(-1, -2, 4)$ **20.** $\varnothing$ **21.** $23°, 45°, 112°$

Chapter 4 Cumulative Review

1. a. $<$ **b.** $=$ **c.** $>$; Sec. 1.2, Ex. 6   **3. a.** commutative property of multiplication   **b.** associative property of addition   **c.** identity element for addition   **d.** commutative property of multiplication   **e.** multiplicative inverse property   **f.** additive inverse property   **g.** commutative and associative properties of multiplication; Sec. 1.8, Ex. 6   **5.** $-2x - 1$; Sec. 2.1, Ex. 7   **7.** 8; Sec. 2.2, Ex. 4   **9.** 6; Sec. 2.2, Ex. 5   **11.** 12; Sec. 2.3, Ex. 3   **13.** 10; Sec. 2.4, Ex. 2   **15.** $x = \dfrac{y - b}{m}$; Sec. 2.5, Ex. 6   **17.** $[2, \infty)$; Sec. 2.8, Ex. 3

19.
; Sec. 3.3, Ex. 7   **21.** $-\dfrac{8}{3}$; Sec. 3.4, Ex. 1   **23.** slope: $\dfrac{3}{4}$; y-intercept: $(0, 6)$; Sec. 3.4, Ex. 3   **25.** slope: $\dfrac{3}{4}$; y-intercept: $(0, -1)$; Sec. 3.4, Ex. 5   **27.** $y = -2x + 3$; $2x + y = 3$; Sec. 3.5, Ex. 4   **29.** $x = -1$; Sec. 3.5, Ex. 6   **31.** domain: $\{-1, 0, 3\}$; range: $\{-2, 0, 2, 3\}$; Sec. 3.6, Ex. 1   **33. a.** function   **b.** not a function; Sec. 3.6, Ex. 2   **35.** one solution; Sec. 4.1, Ex. 8   **37.** $\left(6, \dfrac{1}{2}\right)$; Sec. 4.2, Ex. 3   **39.** $(6, 1)$; Sec. 4.3, Ex. 1   **41.** $(-4, 2, -1)$; Sec. 4.4, Ex. 1   **43.** 7 and 11; Sec. 4.5, Ex. 3

CHAPTER 5   EXPONENTS AND POLYNOMIALS

Section 5.1
Practice Exercises

1. a. 27   **b.** 4   **c.** 64   **d.** -64 **e.** $\dfrac{27}{64}$ **f.** 0.0081   **g.** 75   **2. a.** 243   **b.** $\dfrac{3}{8}$ **3. a.** 3^{10} **b.** y^5 **c.** z^5 **d.** x^{11} **e.** $(-2)^8$ **f.** $b^3 \cdot t^5$ **4.** $15y^7$ **5. a.** $y^{12}z^4$ **b.** $-7m^5n^{14}$ **6. a.** z^{21} **b.** 4^{18} **c.** $(-2)^{15}$ **7. a.** p^5r^5 **b.** $36b^2$ **c.** $\dfrac{1}{64}x^6y^3$ **d.** $81a^{12}b^{16}c^4$ **8. a.** $\dfrac{x^5}{y^{10}}$ **b.** $\dfrac{32a^{20}}{b^{15}}$ **9. a.** z^4 **b.** 25   **c.** 64   **d.** $\dfrac{q^5}{t^2}$ **e.** $6x^2y^2$ **10. a.** -1 **b.** 1   **c.** 1   **d.** 1   **e.** 1   **f.** 7   **11. a.** $\dfrac{z^2}{144}$ **b.** $64x^{18}$ **c.** y^{13} **12. a.** 63   **b.** 2   **c.** $\dfrac{x^6}{9y^8}$ **d.** $-z^{30}$

Vocabulary, Readiness & Video Check 5.1

1. exponent   **3.** add   **5.** 1   **7.** Example 4 can be written as $-4^2 = -1 \cdot 4^2$, which is similar to Example 7, $4 \cdot 3^2$, and shows why the negative sign should not be considered part of the base when there are no parentheses.   **9.** Be careful not to confuse the power rule with the product rule. The power rule involves a power raised to a power (exponents are multiplied), and the product rule involves a product (exponents are added).   **11.** the quotient rule

Exercise Set 5.1

1. exponent: 2; base: 3   **3.** exponent: 2; base: 4   **5.** exponent: 2; base: x **7.** 49   **9.** -5 **11.** -16 **13.** 16   **15.** 0.00001   **17.** $\dfrac{1}{81}$ **19.** 224   **21.** -250 **23.** 4   **25.** 135   **27.** 150   **29.** $\dfrac{32}{5}$ **31.** x^7 **33.** $(-3)^{12}$ **35.** $15y^5$ **37.** $x^{19}y^6$ **39.** $-72m^3n^8$ **41.** $-24z^{20}$ **43.** $20x^5$ sq ft   **45.** x^{36} **47.** p^8q^8 **49.** $8a^{15}$ **51.** $x^{10}y^{15}$ **53.** $49a^4b^{10}c^2$ **55.** $\dfrac{r^9}{s^9}$ **57.** $\dfrac{m^5p^5}{n^5}$ **59.** $\dfrac{4x^2z^2}{y^{10}}$ **61.** $64z^{10}$ sq dm   **63.** $27y^{12}$ cu ft   **65.** x^2 **67.** -64 **69.** p^6q^5 **71.** $\dfrac{y^3}{2}$ **73.** 1   **75.** 1   **77.** -7 **79.** 2   **81.** -81 **83.** $\dfrac{1}{64}$ **85.** b^6 **87.** a^9 **89.** $-16x^7$ **91.** $a^{11}b^{20}$ **93.** $26m^9n^7$ **95.** z^{40} **97.** $64a^3b^3$ **99.** $36x^2y^2z^6$ **101.** $3x$ **103.** $81x^2y^2$ **105.** 9   **107.** $\dfrac{y^{15}}{8x^{12}}$ **109.** $2x^2y$ **111.** 2   **113.** $\dfrac{x^{18}}{4y^{22}}$ **115.** $-b^5$ **117.** $2y - 10$ **119.** $-x - 4$ **121.** $-x + 5$ **123.** c   **125.** e   **127.** answers may vary   **129.** answers may vary   **131.** 343 cu m   **133.** volume   **135.** answers may vary   **137.** answers may vary   **139.** x^{9a} **141.** a^{5b} **143.** x^{5a} **145.** \$1045.85

Section 5.2
Practice Exercises

1. a. degree 3　**b.** degree 2　**c.** degree 1　**d.** degree 8　**e.** degree 0
these, degree 3　**3.**

Term	Numerical Coefficient	Degree of Term
$-3x^3y^2$	-3	5
$4xy^2$	4	3
$-y^2$	-1	2
$3x$	3	1
-2	-2	0

2. a. trinomial, degree 2　**b.** binomial, degree 1　**c.** none of
4. a. 4　**b.** -21　**5.** 114 ft; 66 ft　**6. a.** $-2y$　**b.** $z + 5z^3$
c. $14x^3$　**d.** $4a^2 - 12$　**e.** $\frac{1}{3}x^4 + \frac{11}{24}x^3 - x^2$
7. $-3x^2 + 5xy + 5y^2$　**8.** $x^2 + 2x + 4 + 5x + 3x^2$; $4x^2 + 7x + 4$
9. a. $5y^2 - 3y + 2x - 9$　**b.** $-8a^2b - 3ab^2$
10. $7x^3 - 6x + 7$　**11.** $2x^3 - 4x^2 + 4x - 6$
12. $7x - 11$　**13. a.** $-5a^2 - ab + 6b^2$
b. $3x^2y^2 - 10xy - 4xy^2 + 5 - 6y^2$

Graphing Calculator Explorations 5.2
1. $x^3 - 4x^2 + 7x - 8$　**3.** $-2.1x^2 - 3.2x - 1.7$　**5.** $7.69x^2 - 1.26x + 5.3$

Vocabulary, Readiness & Video Check 5.2
1. binomial　**3.** trinomial　**5.** constant　**7.** The degree of the polynomial is the greatest degree of any of its terms, so we need to find the degree of each term first.　**9.** simplifying it

Exercise Set 5.2

1. 1; binomial　**3.** 3; none of these　**5.** 6; trinomial　**7.** 8; binomial　**9.** 3　**11.** 2　**13.** 57　**15.** 499　**17.** 1　**19.** $-\frac{11}{16}$　**21.** 1134 ft

23. 1006 ft　**25.** 164 thousand　**27.** $23x^2$　**29.** $12x^2 - y$　**31.** $7s$　**33.** $-1.1y^2 + 4.8$　**35.** $-\frac{7}{12}x^3 + \frac{7}{5}x^2 + 6$　**37.** $5a^2 - 9ab + 16b^2$

39. $-3x^2 + 10$　**41.** $-x^2 + 14$　**43.** $-2x + 9$　**45.** $2x^2 + 7x - 16$　**47.** $8t^2 - 4$　**49.** $-2z^2 - 16z + 6$　**51.** $2x^3 - 2x^2 + 7x + 2$
53. $-y^2 - 3y - 1$　**55.** $2x^2 + 11x$　**57.** $-16x^4 + 8x + 9$　**59.** $7x^2 + 14x + 18$　**61.** $3x - 3$　**63.** $7x^2 - 4x + 2$　**65.** $62x^2 + 5$
67. $7x^2 - 2x + 2$　**69.** $12x + 2$　**71.** $4y^2 + 12y + 19$　**73.** $4x^2 + 7x + x^2 + 5x$; $5x^2 + 12x$　**75.** $-2a - b + 1$　**77.** $3x^2 + 5$
79. $6x^2 - 2xy + 19y^2$　**81.** $8r^2s + 16rs - 8 + 7r^2s^2$　**83.** $-5.42x^2 + 7.75x - 19.61$　**85.** $3.7y^4 - 0.7y^3 + 2.2y - 4$　**87.** $6x^2$
89. $-12x^8$　**91.** $200x^3y^2$　**93.** $18x + 44$　**95.** $(x^2 + 7x + 4)$ ft　**97.** $(3y^2 + 4y + 11)$ m　**99.** 7.33 million　**101.** answers may vary
103. answers may vary　**105.** b　**107.** e　**109. a.** $4z$　**b.** $3z^2$　**c.** $-4z$　**d.** $3z^2$; answers may vary　**111. a.** m^3　**b.** $3m$　**c.** $-m^3$
d. $-3m$; answers may vary　**113.** $3x^{2a} + 2x^a + 0.7$　**115.** $4x^{2y} + 2x^y - 11$　**117.** $4x^2 - 3x + 6$　**119.** $-x^2 - 6x + 10$　**121.** $3x^2 - 12x + 13$
123. a. $2a - 3$　**b.** $-2x - 3$　**c.** $2x + 2h - 3$　**125. a.** $4a$　**b.** $-4x$　**c.** $4x + 4h$　**127.** 2; 2　**129.** 4; 3; 3; 4　**131.** $2x^2 + 4xy$

Section 5.3
Practice Exercises
1. $10y^2$　**2.** $-2z^8$　**3.** $\frac{7}{72}b^9$　**4. a.** $27x^6 + 33x$　**b.** $-12x^5 + 54x^4 - 12x^3$　**5.** $10x^2 + 11x - 6$　**6.** $25x^2 - 30xy + 9y^2$
7. $2y^3 + 5y^2 - 7y + 20$　**8.** $s^3 + 6s^2t + 12st^2 + 8t^3$　**9.** $5x^3 - 23x^2 + 17x - 20$　**10.** $x^5 - 2x^4 + 2x^3 - 3x^2 + 2$
11. $5x^4 - 3x^3 + 11x^2 + 8x - 6$

Vocabulary, Readiness & Video Check 5.3
1. distributive　**3.** $(5y - 1)(5y - 1)$　**5.** No. The monomials are unlike terms.　**7.** Yes. The parentheses have been removed for the vertical format, but every term in the first polynomial is still distributed to every term in the second polynomial.

Exercise Set 5.3
1. $-28n^{10}$　**3.** $-12.4x^{12}$　**5.** $-\frac{2}{15}y^3$　**7.** $-24x^8$　**9.** $6x^2 + 15x$　**11.** $-2a^2 - 8a$　**13.** $6x^3 - 9x^2 + 12x$　**15.** $-6a^4 + 4a^3 - 6a^2$

17. $-4x^3y + 7x^2y^2 - xy^3 - 3y^4$　**19.** $4x^4 - 3x^3 + \frac{1}{2}x^2$　**21.** $x^2 + 7x + 12$　**23.** $a^2 + 5a - 14$　**25.** $x^2 + \frac{1}{3}x - \frac{2}{9}$　**27.** $12x^4 + 25x^2 + 7$

29. $4y^2 - 16y + 16$　**31.** $12x^2 - 29x + 15$　**33.** $9x^4 + 6x^2 + 1$　**35. a.** $-4y^4$　**b.** $3y^2$　**c.** answers may vary　**37.** $x^3 - 5x^2 + 13x - 14$
39. $x^4 + 5x^3 - 3x^2 - 11x + 20$　**41.** $10a^3 - 27a^2 + 26a - 12$　**43.** $x^3 + 6x^2 + 12x + 8$　**45.** $8y^3 - 36y^2 + 54y - 27$
47. $12x^2 - 64x - 11$　**49.** $10x^3 + 22x^2 - x - 1$　**51.** $2x^4 + 3x^3 - 58x^2 + 4x + 63$　**53.** $8.4y^7$　**55.** $-3x^3 - 6x^2 + 24x$
57. $2x^2 + 39x + 19$　**59.** $x^2 - \frac{2}{7}x - \frac{3}{49}$　**61.** $9y^2 + 30y + 25$　**63.** $a^3 - 2a^2 - 18a + 24$　**65.** $8x^3 - 60x^2 + 150x - 125$
67. $32x^3 + 48x^2 - 6x - 20$　**69.** $6x^4 - 8x^3 - 7x^2 + 22x - 12$　**71.** $(4x^2 - 25)$ sq yd　**73.** $(6x^2 - 4x)$ sq in.
75. $5a + 15a = 20a$; $5a - 15a = -10a$; $5a \cdot 15a = 75a^2$; $\frac{5a}{15a} = \frac{1}{3}$　**77.** $-3y^5 + 9y^4$, cannot be simplified; $-3y^5 - 9y^4$, cannot be simplified;
$-3y^5 \cdot 9y^4 = -27y^9$; $\frac{-3y^5}{9y^4} = -\frac{y}{3}$　**79. a.** $6x + 12$　**b.** $9x^2 + 36x + 35$; answers may vary　**81.** $13x - 7$　**83.** $30x^2 - 28x + 6$
85. $-7x + 5$　**87.** $x^2 + 3x$　**89.** $x^2 + 5x + 6$　**91.** $11a$　**93.** $25x^2 + 4y^2$　**95. a.** $a^2 - b^2$　**b.** $4x^2 - 9y^2$　**c.** $16x^2 - 49$
d. answers may vary　**97.** $(x^2 + 6x + 5)$ sq units

Section 5.4
Practice Exercises

1. $x^2 - 3x - 10$ **2.** $4x^2 - 13x + 9$ **3.** $9x^2 + 42x - 15$ **4.** $16x^2 - 8x + 1$ **5. a.** $b^2 + 6b + 9$ **b.** $x^2 - 2xy + y^2$
c. $9y^2 + 12y + 4$ **d.** $a^4 - 10a^2b + 25b^2$ **6. a.** $3x^2 - 75$ **b.** $16b^2 - 9$ **c.** $x^2 - \frac{4}{9}$ **d.** $25s^2 - t^2$ **e.** $4y^2 - 9z^4$
7. a. $4x^2 - 21x - 18$ **b.** $49b^2 - 28b + 4$ **c.** $x^2 - 0.16$ **d.** $3x^6 - \frac{9}{7}x^4 + \frac{2}{7}x^2 - \frac{6}{49}$ **e.** $x^3 + 6x^2 + 3x - 2$

Vocabulary, Readiness & Video Check 5.4
1. false **3.** false **5.** a binomial times a binomial **7.** Multiplying gives you four terms, and the two like terms will always subtract out.

Exercise Set 5.4

1. $x^2 + 7x + 12$ **3.** $x^2 + 5x - 50$ **5.** $5x^2 + 4x - 12$ **7.** $20y^2 - 125y + 30$ **9.** $6x^2 + 13x - 5$ **11.** $x^2 + \frac{1}{3}x - \frac{2}{9}$ **13.** $x^2 + 4x + 4$
15. $4x^2 - 4x + 1$ **17.** $9a^2 - 30a + 25$ **19.** $25x^2 + 90x + 81$ **21.** $a^2 - 49$ **23.** $9x^2 - 1$ **25.** $9x^2 - \frac{1}{4}$ **27.** $81x^2 - y^2$
29. $4x^2 - 0.01$ **31.** $a^2 + 9a + 20$ **33.** $a^2 + 14a + 49$ **35.** $12a^2 - a - 1$ **37.** $x^2 - 4$ **39.** $9a^2 + 6a + 1$ **41.** $4x^3 - x^2y^4 + 4xy - y^5$
43. $x^3 - 3x^2 - 17x + 3$ **45.** $4a^2 - 12a + 9$ **47.** $25x^2 - 36z^2$ **49.** $x^{10} - 8x^5 + 15$ **51.** $x^2 - 0.64$ **53.** $a^7 - 3a^3 + 11a^4 - 33$
55. $3x^2 - 12x + 12$ **57.** $6b^2 - b - 35$ **59.** $49p^2 - 64$ **61.** $\frac{1}{9}a^4 - 49$ **63.** $15x^4 - 5x^3 + 10x^2$ **65.** $4r^2 - 9s^2$
67. $9x^2 - 42xy + 49y^2$ **69.** $16x^2 - 25$ **71.** $64x^2 + 64x + 16$ **73.** $a^2 - \frac{1}{4}y^2$ **75.** $\frac{1}{25}x^2 - y^2$ **77.** $3a^3 + 2a^2 + 1$
79. $(2x + 1)(2x + 1)$ sq ft or $(4x^2 + 4x + 1)$ sq ft **81.** $\frac{5b^5}{7}$ **83.** $-2a^{10}b^5$ **85.** $\frac{2y^8}{3}$ **87.** $\frac{1}{3}$ **89.** 1 **91.** c **93.** d **95.** 2; 2
97. $(x^4 - 3x^2 + 1)$ sq m **99.** $(24x^2 - 32x + 8)$ sq m **101.** $(x^2 + 10x + 25)$ sq units **103.** answers may vary **105.** answers may vary
107. answers may vary **109.** $x^2 + 2xy + y^2 - 9$ **111.** $a^2 - 6a + 9 - b^2$

Integrated Review

1. $35x^5$ **2.** $32y^9$ **3.** -16 **4.** 16 **5.** $2x^2 - 9x - 5$ **6.** $3x^2 + 13x - 10$ **7.** $3x - 4$ **8.** $4x + 3$ **9.** $7x^6y^2$ **10.** $\frac{10b^6}{7}$
11. $144m^{14}n^{12}$ **12.** $64y^{27}z^{30}$ **13.** $48y^2 - 27$ **14.** $98x^2 - 2$ **15.** $x^{63}y^{45}$ **16.** $27x^{27}$ **17.** $2x^2 - 2x - 6$ **18.** $6x^2 + 13x - 11$
19. $2.5y^2 - 6y - 0.2$ **20.** $8.4x^2 - 6.8x - 5.7$ **21.** $x^2 + 8xy + 16y^2$ **22.** $y^2 - 18yz + 81z^2$ **23.** $2x + 8y$ **24.** $2y - 18z$
25. $7x^2 - 10xy + 4y^2$ **26.** $-a^2 - 3ab + 6b^2$ **27.** $x^3 + 2x^2 - 16x + 3$ **28.** $x^3 - 2x^2 - 5x - 2$ **29.** $6x^5 + 20x^3 - 21x^2 - 70$
30. $20x^7 + 25x^3 - 4x^4 - 5$ **31.** $2x^3 - 19x^2 + 44x - 7$ **32.** $5x^3 + 9x^2 - 17x + 3$ **33.** cannot simplify **34.** $25x^3y^3$ **35.** $125x^9$
36. $\frac{x^3}{y^3}$ **37.** $2x$ **38.** x^2

Section 5.5
Practice Exercises

1. a. $\frac{1}{125}$ **b.** $\frac{3}{y^4}$ **c.** $\frac{5}{6}$ **d.** $\frac{1}{25}$ **e.** $\frac{1}{x^5}$ **2. a.** s^5 **b.** 8 **c.** $\frac{y^5}{x^7}$ **d.** $\frac{9}{64}$ **3. a.** $\frac{1}{x^5}$ **b.** $5y^7$ **c.** z^5 **d.** $\frac{81}{25}$ **4. a.** $\frac{b^{15}}{a^{20}}$
b. x^{10} **c.** $\frac{q^2}{25p^{16}}$ **d.** $\frac{6y^2}{x^7}$ **e.** $-27x^6y^9$ **5. a.** 7×10^{-6} **b.** 2.07×10^7 **c.** 4.3×10^{-3} **d.** 8.12×10^8 **6. a.** 0.000367
b. 8,954,000 **c.** 0.00002009 **d.** 4054 **7. a.** 4000 **b.** 20,000,000,000

Graphing Calculator Explorations 5.5
1. 5.31 EE 3 **3.** 6.6 EE −9 **5.** 1.5×10^{13} **7.** 8.15×10^{19}

Vocabulary, Readiness & Video Check 5.5

1. $\frac{1}{x^3}$ **3.** scientific notation **5.** A negative exponent has nothing to do with the sign of the simplified result. **7.** When you move the decimal point to the left, the sign of the exponent will be positive; when you move the decimal point to the right, the sign of the exponent will be negative.
9. the quotient rule

Exercise Set 5.5

1. $\frac{1}{64}$ **3.** $\frac{1}{81}$ **5.** $\frac{7}{x^3}$ **7.** 32 **9.** −64 **11.** $\frac{8}{15}$ **13.** p^3 **15.** $\frac{q^4}{p^5}$ **17.** $\frac{1}{x^3}$ **19.** z^3 **21.** $\frac{4}{9}$ **23.** $-p^4$ **25.** −2 **27.** x^4
29. p^4 **31.** m^{11} **33.** r^6 **35.** $\frac{1}{x^{15}y^9}$ **37.** $\frac{1}{x^4}$ **39.** $\frac{1}{a^2}$ **41.** $4k^3$ **43.** $3m$ **45.** $-\frac{4a^5}{b}$ **47.** $-\frac{6x^2}{y^3}$ **49.** $\frac{a^{30}}{b^{12}}$ **51.** $\frac{1}{x^{10}y^6}$
53. $\frac{z^2}{4}$ **55.** $\frac{1}{32x^5}$ **57.** $\frac{49a^4}{b^6}$ **59.** $a^{24}b^8$ **61.** x^9y^{19} **63.** $-\frac{y^8}{8x^2}$ **65.** $\frac{6x}{7y^2}$ **67.** $\frac{25b^{33}}{a^{16}}$ **69.** 7.8×10^4 **71.** 1.67×10^{-6}
73. 6.35×10^{-3} **75.** 1.16×10^6 **77.** 2×10^9 **79.** 2.4×10^3 **81.** 0.0000000008673 **83.** 0.033 **85.** 20,320 **87.** 700,000,000
89. 9,460,000,000,000 **91.** 1.84×10^{11} **93.** 155,000,000,000 **95.** 35,000 **97.** 0.000036 **99.** 0.0000000000000000028 **101.** 0.0000005
103. 200,000 **105.** $\frac{5x^3}{3}$ **107.** $\frac{5z^3y^2}{7}$ **109.** $5y - 6 + \frac{5}{y}$ **111.** $\frac{27}{x^6z^3}$ cu in. **113.** $9a^{13}$ **115.** −5 **117.** answers may vary
119. a. 1.3×10^1 **b.** 4.4×10^7 **c.** 6.1×10^{-2} **121.** answers may vary **123.** a^m **125.** $27y^{6z}$ **127.** −394.5 **129.** 1.3 sec

Section 5.6
Practice Exercises

1. $2t + 1$ **2.** $4x^4 + 5x - \dfrac{3}{x}$ **3.** $3x^3y^3 - 2 + \dfrac{1}{5x}$ **4.** $x + 3$ **5.** $2x + 3 + \dfrac{-10}{2x + 1}$ or $2x + 3 - \dfrac{10}{2x + 1}$ **6.** $3x^2 - 2x + 5 + \dfrac{-13}{3x + 2}$ or

$3x^2 - 2x + 5 - \dfrac{13}{3x - 2}$ **7.** $3x^2 - 2x - 9 + \dfrac{5x + 22}{x^2 + 2}$ **8.** $x^2 - 3x + 9$

Vocabulary, Readiness & Video Check 5.6

1. dividend, quotient, divisor **3.** a^2 **5.** y **7.** the common denominator

Exercise Set 5.6

1. $12x^3 + 3x$ **3.** $4x^3 - 6x^2 + x + 1$ **5.** $5p^2 + 6p$ **7.** $-\dfrac{3}{2x} + 3$ **9.** $-3x^2 + x - \dfrac{4}{x^3}$ **11.** $-1 + \dfrac{3}{2x} - \dfrac{7}{4x^4}$ **13.** $x + 1$ **15.** $2x + 3$

17. $2x + 1 + \dfrac{7}{x - 4}$ **19.** $3a^2 - 3a + 1 + \dfrac{2}{3a + 2}$ **21.** $4x + 3 - \dfrac{2}{2x + 1}$ **23.** $2x^2 + 6x - 5 - \dfrac{2}{x - 2}$ **25.** $x + 6$ **27.** $x^2 + 3x + 9$

29. $-3x + 6 - \dfrac{11}{x + 2}$ **31.** $2b - 1 - \dfrac{6}{2b - 1}$ **33.** $ab - b^2$ **35.** $4x + 9$ **37.** $x + 4xy - \dfrac{y}{2}$ **39.** $2b^2 + b + 2 - \dfrac{12}{b + 4}$

41. $5x - 2 + \dfrac{2}{x + 6}$ **43.** $x^2 - \dfrac{12x}{5} - 1$ **45.** $6x - 1 - \dfrac{1}{x + 3}$ **47.** $6x - 1$ **49.** $-x^3 + 3x^2 - \dfrac{4}{x}$ **51.** $x^2 + 3x + 9$

53. $y^2 + 5y + 10 + \dfrac{24}{y - 2}$ **55.** $-6x - 12 - \dfrac{19}{x - 2}$ **57.** $x^3 - x^2 + x$ **59.** $2a^3 + 2a$ **61.** $2x^3 + 14x^2 - 10x$ **63.** $-3x^2y^3 - 21x^3y^2 - 24xy$

65. $9a^2b^3c + 36ab^2c - 72ab$ **67.** $(3x^3 + x - 4)$ ft **69.** c **71.** answers may vary **73.** $(2x + 5)$ m **75.** $9x^{7a} - 6x^{5a} + 7x^{2a} - 1$

Section 5.7
Practice Exercises

1. $4x^2 + x + 7 + \dfrac{12}{x - 1}$ **2.** $x^3 - 5x + 21 - \dfrac{51}{x + 3}$ **3. a.** -4 **b.** -4 **4.** 15

Vocabulary, Readiness & Video Check 5.7

1. The last number n is the remainder and the other numbers are the coefficients of the variables in the quotient; the degree of the quotient is one less than the degree of the dividend

Exercise Set 5.7

1. $x + 8$ **3.** $x - 1$ **5.** $x^2 - 5x - 23 - \dfrac{41}{x - 2}$ **7.** $4x + 8 + \dfrac{7}{x - 2}$ **9.** 3 **11.** 73 **13.** -8 **15.** $x^2 + \dfrac{2}{x - 3}$ **17.** $6x + 7 + \dfrac{1}{x + 1}$

19. $2x^3 - 3x^2 + x - 4$ **21.** $3x - 9 + \dfrac{12}{x + 3}$ **23.** $3x^2 - \dfrac{9}{2}x + \dfrac{7}{4} + \dfrac{47}{8(x - \frac{1}{2})}$ **25.** $3x^2 + 3x - 3$ **27.** $3x^2 + 4x - 8 + \dfrac{20}{x + 1}$

29. $x^2 + x + 1$ **31.** $x - 6$ **33.** 1 **35.** -133 **37.** 3 **39.** $-\dfrac{187}{81}$ **41.** $\dfrac{95}{32}$ **43.** answers may vary **45.** $-\dfrac{5}{6}$ **47.** 54 **49.** 8

51. -32 **53.** 48 **55.** 25 **57.** -2 **59.** yes **61.** no **63.** $(x^3 - 5x^2 + 2x - 1)$ cm **65.** $x^3 + \dfrac{5}{3}x^2 + \dfrac{5}{3}x + \dfrac{8}{3} + \dfrac{8}{3(x - 1)}$

67. $(x + 3)(x^2 + 4) = x^3 + 3x^2 + 4x + 12$ **69.** 0 **71.** $x^3 + 2x^2 + 7x + 28$

Chapter 5 Vocabulary Check

1. term **2.** FOIL **3.** trinomial **4.** degree of a polynomial **5.** binomial **6.** coefficient **7.** degree of a term **8.** monomial
9. polynomials **10.** distributive

Chapter 5 Review

1. base: 7; exponent: 9 **3.** base: 5; exponent: 4 **5.** 512 **7.** -36 **9.** 1 **11.** y^9 **13.** $-6x^{11}$ **15.** x^8 **17.** $81y^{24}$ **19.** x^5

21. a^4b^3 **23.** $\dfrac{x^3y^4}{4}$ **25.** $40a^{19}$ **27.** 3 **29.** b **31.** 7 **33.** 8 **35.** 5 **37.** 5 **39.** 4000 ft; 3984 ft; 3856 ft; 3600 ft **41.** $15a^2 + 4a$

43. $-6a^2b - 3b^2 - q^2$ **45.** $8x^2 + 3x + 6$ **47.** $-7y^2 - 1$ **49.** $4x - 13y$ **51.** 290 **53.** $(6x^2y - 12x + 12)$ cm **55.** $8a + 28$

57. $-7x^3 - 35x$ **59.** $-6a^4 + 8a^2 - 2a$ **61.** $2x^2 - 12x - 14$ **63.** $x^2 - 18x + 81$ **65.** $4a^2 + 27a - 7$ **67.** $25x^2 + 20x + 4$

69. $x^4 + 7x^3 + 4x^2 + 23x - 35$ **71.** $x^4 + 4x^3 + 4x^2 - 16$ **73.** $x^3 + 21x^2 + 147x + 343$ **75.** $x^2 + 14x + 49$ **77.** $9x^2 - 42x + 49$

79. $25x^2 - 90x + 81$ **81.** $49x^2 - 16$ **83.** $4x^2 - 36$ **85.** $(9x^2 - 6x + 1)$ sq m **87.** $\dfrac{1}{49}$ **89.** $\dfrac{2}{x^4}$ **91.** 125 **93.** $\dfrac{17}{16}$ **95.** x^8

97. r **99.** c^4 **101.** $\dfrac{1}{x^6y^{13}}$ **103.** a^{11m} **105.** $27x^3y^{6z}$ **107.** 2.7×10^{-4} **109.** 8.08×10^7 **111.** 9.1×10^7 **113.** 867,000

115. 0.00086 **117.** 1,431,280,000,000,000 **119.** 0.016 **121.** $\dfrac{1}{7} + \dfrac{3}{x} + \dfrac{7}{x^2}$ **123.** $a + 1 + \dfrac{6}{a - 2}$ **125.** $a^2 + 3a + 8 + \dfrac{22}{a - 2}$

127. $2x^3 - x^2 + 2 - \dfrac{1}{2x - 1}$ **129.** $\left(5x - 1 + \dfrac{20}{x^2}\right)$ ft **131.** $3x^2 + 6x + 24 + \dfrac{44}{x - 2}$ **133.** $x^4 - x^3 + x^2 - x + 1 - \dfrac{2}{x + 1}$

135. $3x^3 + 13x^2 + 51x + 204 + \dfrac{814}{x - 4}$ **137.** 3043 **139.** $-\dfrac{1}{8}$ **141.** $\dfrac{2x^6}{3}$ **143.** $\dfrac{x^{16}}{16y^{12}}$ **145.** $11x - 5$ **147.** $5y^2 - 3y - 1$

149. $28x^3 + 12x$ **151.** $x^3 + x^2 - 18x + 18$ **153.** $25x^2 + 40x + 16$ **155.** $4a - 1 + \dfrac{2}{a^2} - \dfrac{5}{2a^3}$ **157.** $2x^2 + 7x + 5 + \dfrac{19}{2x - 3}$

Chapter 5 Test

1. 32 **2.** 81 **3.** -81 **4.** $\dfrac{1}{64}$ **5.** $-15x^{11}$ **6.** y^5 **7.** $\dfrac{1}{r^5}$ **8.** $\dfrac{y^{14}}{x^2}$ **9.** $\dfrac{1}{6xy^8}$ **10.** 5.63×10^5 **11.** 8.63×10^{-5} **12.** 0.0015

13. 62,300 **14.** 0.036 **15. a.** $4,3;7,3;1,4;-2,0$ **b.** 4 **16.** $-2x^2 + 12xy + 11$ **17.** $16x^3 + 7x^2 - 3x - 13$ **18.** $-3x^3 + 5x^2 + 4x + 5$

19. $x^3 + 8x^2 + 3x - 5$ **20.** $3x^3 + 22x^2 + 41x + 14$ **21.** $6x^4 - 9x^3 + 21x^2$ **22.** $3x^2 + 16x - 35$ **23.** $9x^2 - \dfrac{1}{25}$ **24.** $16x^2 - 16x + 4$

25. $64x^2 + 48x + 9$ **26.** $x^4 - 81b^2$ **27.** 1001 ft; 985 ft; 857 ft; 601 ft **28.** $(4x^2 - 9)$ sq in. **29.** $\dfrac{x}{2y} + 3 - \dfrac{7}{8y}$ **30.** $x + 2$

31. $9x^2 - 6x + 4 - \dfrac{16}{3x + 2}$ **32. a.** 960 ft **b.** 953.44 ft **33.** $4x^3 - 15x^2 + 45x - 136 + \dfrac{407}{x + 3}$ **34.** 91

Chapter 5 Cumulative Review

1. a. true **b.** true **c.** false **d.** true; Sec. 1.2, Ex. 2 **3. a.** $\dfrac{64}{25}$ **b.** $\dfrac{1}{20}$ **c.** $\dfrac{5}{4}$; Sec. 1.3, Ex. 4 **5. a.** 9 **b.** 125 **c.** 16 **d.** 7

e. $\dfrac{9}{49}$; Sec. 1.4, Ex. 1 **7. a.** -10 **b.** -21 **c.** -12; Sec. 1.5, Ex. 3 **9.** -12; Sec. 1.6, Ex. 3 **11. a.** $\dfrac{1}{22}$ **b.** $\dfrac{16}{3}$ **c.** $-\dfrac{1}{10}$ **d.** $-\dfrac{13}{9}$; Sec. 1.7, Ex. 5

13. a. $(5 + 4) + 6$ **b.** $-1 \cdot (2 \cdot 5)$; Sec. 1.8, Ex. 2 **15. a.** $22 + x$ **b.** $-21x$; Sec. 1.8, Ex. 3 **17. a.** $15x + 10$ **b.** $-2y - 0.6z + 2$

c. $-9x - y + 2z - 6$; Sec. 2.1, Ex. 5 **19.** 17; Sec. 2.2, Ex. 1 **21.** 6; Sec. 2.2, Ex. 5 **23.** -10; Sec. 2.4, Ex. 1 **25.** 10; Sec. 2.4, Ex. 2

27. width: 4 ft; length: 10 ft; Sec. 2.5, Ex. 4 **29.** $\dfrac{5F - 160}{9} = C$; Sec. 2.5, Ex. 8 **31.** ←———(———)———→; Sec. 2.8, Ex. 9 **33. a.** $(0, 12)$ **b.** $(2, 6)$

c. $(-1, 15)$; Sec. 3.1, Ex. 6 **35.** ; Sec. 3.2, Ex. 2 **37.** ; Sec. 3.3, Ex. 9 **39.** undefined slope; Sec. 3.4, Ex. 7

41. $9x^2 - 6x - 1$ (Sec. 5.2, Ex. 11) **43.** $-6x^7$; Sec. 5.1, Ex. 4 **45.** $12x^3 - 12x^2 - 9x + 2$; Sec. 5.2, Ex. 10 **47.** $4x^2 - 4xy + y^2$; Sec. 5.3, Ex. 6
49. $3m + 1$; Sec. 5.6, Ex. 1

CHAPTER 6 FACTORING POLYNOMIALS

Section 6.1
Practice Exercises

1. a. 6 **b.** 1 **c.** 4 **2. a.** y^4 **b.** x **3. a.** $5y^2$ **b.** x^2 **c.** a^2b^2 **4. a.** $4(t + 3)$ **b.** $y^4(y^4 + 1)$ **5.** $8b^2(-b^4 + 2b^2 - 1)$ or
$-8b^2(b^4 - 2b^2 + 1)$ **6.** $5x(x^3 - 4)$ **7.** $\dfrac{1}{9}z^3(5z^2 + z - 2)$ **8.** $4ab^3(2ab - 5a^2 + 3)$ **9.** $(y - 2)(8 + x)$ **10.** $(p + q)(7xy^3 - 1)$
11. $(x + 3)(y + 4)$ **12.** $(5x - 3)(8x^2 + 3)$ **13.** $(2x + 3y)(y - 1)$ **14.** $(7a + 5)(a^2 + 1)$ **15.** $(y - 3)(4x - 5)$ **16.** cannot be
factored by grouping **17.** $3(x - a)(y - 2a)$

Vocabulary, Readiness & Video Check 6.1
1. factors **3.** least **5.** false **7.** The GCF of a list of numbers is the largest number that is a factor of all numbers in the list. **9.** When factoring
out a GCF, the number of terms in the other factor should have the same number of terms as your original polynomial.

Exercise Set 6.1
1. 4 **3.** 6 **5.** 1 **7.** y^2 **9.** z^7 **11.** xy^2 **13.** 7 **15.** $4y^3$ **17.** $5x^2$ **19.** $3x^3$ **21.** $9x^2y$ **23.** $10a^6b$ **25.** $3(a + 2)$
27. $15(2x - 1)$ **29.** $x^2(x + 5)$ **31.** $2y^3(3y + 1)$ **33.** $4(x - 2y + 1)$ **35.** $3x(2x^2 - 3x + 4)$ **37.** $a^2b^2(a^5b^4 - a + b^3 - 1)$
39. $4(2x^5 + 4x^4 - 5x^3 + 3)$ **41.** $\dfrac{1}{3}x(x^3 + 2x^2 - 4x^4 + 1)$ **43.** $(x^2 + 2)(y + 3)$ **45.** $(y + 4)(z - 3)$ **47.** $(z^2 - 6)(r + 1)$
49. $-2(x + 7)$ **51.** $-x^5(2 - x^2)$ **53.** $-3a^2(2a^2 - 3a + 1)$ **55.** $(x + 2)(x^2 + 5)$ **57.** $(x + 3)(5 + y)$ **59.** $(3x - 2)(2x^2 + 5)$
61. $(5m^2 + 6n)(m + 1)$ **63.** $(y - 4)(2 + x)$ **65.** $(2x - 1)(x^2 + 4)$ **67.** not factorable by grouping **69.** $(x - 2y)(4x - 3)$
71. $(5q - 4p)(q - 1)$ **73.** $x(x^2 + 1)(2x + 5)$ **75.** $2(2y - 7)(3x^2 - 1)$ **77.** $2x(16y - 9x)$ **79.** $(x + 2)(y - 3)$ **81.** $7xy(2x^2 + x - 1)$
83. $(4x - 1)(7x^2 + 3)$ **85.** $-8x^8y^5(5y + 2x)$ **87.** $3(2a + 3b^2)(a + b)$ **89.** $x^2 + 7x + 10$ **91.** $b^2 - 3b - 4$ **93.** 2, 6 **95.** $-1, -8$
97. $-2, 5$ **99.** b **101.** factored **103.** not factored **105.** answers may vary **107.** answers may vary **109. a.** 1200 million
b. 1120 million **c.** $-20(x^2 - 15x - 6)$ **111.** $12x^3 - 2x; 2x(6x^2 - 1)$ **113.** $(n^3 - 6)$ units **115.** $(x^n + 2)(x^n + 3)$
117. $(3x^n - 5)(x^n + 7)$

Section 6.2
Practice Exercises

1. $(x + 2)(x + 3)$ **2.** $(x - 10)(x - 7)$ **3.** $(x + 7)(x - 2)$ **4.** $(p - 9)(p + 7)$ **5.** prime polynomial **6.** $(x + 3y)(x + 4y)$
7. $(x^2 + 12)(x^2 + 1)$ **8.** $(x - 6)(x - 8)$ **9.** $4(x - 3)(x - 3)$ **10.** $3y^2(y - 7)(y + 1)$

Vocabulary, Readiness & Video Check 6.2

1. true　　**3.** false　　**5.** $+5$　　**7.** -3　　**9.** $+2$　　**11.** 15 is positive, so its factors would have to either be both positive or both negative. Since the factors need to sum to -8, both factors must be negative.

Exercise Set 6.2

1. $(x+6)(x+1)$　　**3.** $(y-9)(y-1)$　　**5.** $(x-3)(x-3)$ or $(x-3)^2$　　**7.** $(x-6)(x+3)$　　**9.** $(x+10)(x-7)$　　**11.** prime
13. $(x+5y)(x+3y)$　　**15.** $(a^2-5)(a^2+3)$　　**17.** $(m+13)(m+1)$　　**19.** $(t-2)(t+12)$　　**21.** $(a-2b)(a-8b)$　　**23.** $2(z+8)(z+2)$
25. $2x(x-5)(x-4)$　　**27.** $(x-4y)(x+y)$　　**29.** $(x+12)(x+3)$　　**31.** $(x-2)(x+1)$　　**33.** $(r-12)(r-4)$　　**35.** $(x+2y)(x-y)$
37. $3(x+5)(x-2)$　　**39.** $3(x-18)(x-2)$　　**41.** $(x-24)(x+6)$　　**43.** prime　　**45.** $(x-5)(x-3)$　　**47.** $6x(x+4)(x+5)$
49. $4y(x^2+x-3)$　　**51.** $(x-7)(x+3)$　　**53.** $(x+5y)(x+2y)$　　**55.** $2(t+8)(t+4)$　　**57.** $x(x-6)(x+4)$　　**59.** $2t^3(t-4)(t-3)$
61. $5xy(x-8y)(x+3y)$　　**63.** $3(m-9)(m-6)$　　**65.** $-1(x-11)(x-1)$　　**67.** $\frac{1}{2}(y-11)(y+2)$　　**69.** $x(xy-4)(xy+5)$
71. $2x^2+11x+5$　　**73.** $15y^2-17y+4$　　**75.** $9a^2+23ab-12b^2$　　**77.** $x^2+5x-24$　　**79.** answers may vary
81. $2x^2+28x+66; 2(x+3)(x+11)$　　**83.** $-16(t-5)(t+1)$　　**85.** $\left(x+\frac{1}{4}\right)\left(x+\frac{1}{4}\right)$ or $\left(x+\frac{1}{4}\right)^2$　　**87.** $(x+1)(z-10)(z+7)$
89. $(x^n+10)(x^n-2)$　　**91.** $5;8;9$　　**93.** $3;4$　　**95.** $8;16$　　**97.** $6;26$

Section 6.3
Practice Exercises

1. $(2x+5)(x+3)$　　**2.** $(5x-4)(3x-2)$　　**3.** $(4x-1)(x+3)$　　**4.** $(7x-y)(3x+2y)$　　**5.** $(2x^2-7)(x^2+1)$　　**6.** $x(3x+2)(x+5)$
7. $-1(4x-3)(2x+1)$　　**8.** $(x+7)^2$　　**9.** $(2x+9y)(2x+y)$　　**10.** $(6n^2-1)^2$　　**11.** $3x(2x-7)^2$

Vocabulary, Readiness & Video Check 6.3

1. perfect square trinomial　　**3.** perfect square trinomial　　**5.** d　　**7.** Consider the factors of the first and last terms and the signs of the trinomial. Continue to check by multiplying until you get the middle term of the trinomial.　　**9.** The first and last terms are squares, a^2 and b^2, and the middle term is $2 \cdot a \cdot b$ or $-2 \cdot a \cdot b$.

Exercise Set 6.3

1. $x+4$　　**3.** $10x-1$　　**5.** $5x-2$　　**7.** $(2x+3)(x+5)$　　**9.** $(y-1)(8y-9)$　　**11.** $(2x+1)(x-5)$　　**13.** $(4r-1)(5r+8)$
15. $(10x+1)(x+3)$　　**17.** prime　　**19.** $(3x-5y)(2x-y)$　　**21.** $(3m-5)(5m+3)$　　**23.** $x(3x+2)(4x+1)$　　**25.** $3(7b+5)(b-3)$
27. $(3z+4)(4z-3)$　　**29.** $2y^2(3x-10)(x+3)$　　**31.** $(2x-7)(2x+3)$　　**33.** $-1(x-6)(x+4)$　　**35.** $x(4x+3)(x-3)$
37. $(4x-9)(6x-1)$　　**39.** $(x+11)^2$　　**41.** $(x-8)^2$　　**43.** $(4a-3)^2$　　**45.** $(x^2+2)^2$　　**47.** $2(n-7)^2$　　**49.** $(4y+5)^2$
51. $(2x+11)(x-9)$　　**53.** $(8x+3)(3x+4)$　　**55.** $(3a+b)(a+3b)$　　**57.** $(x-4)(x-5)$　　**59.** $(p+6q)^2$　　**61.** $(xy-5)^2$
63. $b(8a-3)(5a+3)$　　**65.** $2x(3x+2)(5x+3)$　　**67.** $2y(3y+5)(y-3)$　　**69.** $5x^2(2x-y)(x+3y)$　　**71.** $-1(2x-5)(7x-2)$
73. $p^2(4p-5)^2$　　**75.** $(3x-2)(x+1)$　　**77.** $(4x+9y)(2x-3y)$　　**79.** prime　　**81.** $(3x-4y)^2$　　**83.** $(6x-7)(3x+2)$
85. $(7t+1)(t-4)$　　**87.** $(7p+1)(7p-2)$　　**89.** $m(m+9)^2$　　**91.** prime　　**93.** $a(6a^2+b^2)(a^2+6b^2)$　　**95.** x^2-4　　**97.** a^3+27
99. $25-34$　　**101.** answers may vary　　**103.** no　　**105.** answers may vary　　**107.** $4x^2+21x+5; (4x+1)(x+5)$　　**109.** $\left(2x+\frac{1}{2}\right)^2$
111. $(y-1)^2(4x^2+10x+25)$　　**113.** 8　　**115.** $a^2+2ab+b^2$　　**117.** $2;14$　　**119.** 2　　**121.** $-3xy^2(4x-5)(x+1)$
123. $(y-1)^2(2x+5)^2$　　**125.** $(3x^n+2)(x^n+5)$　　**127.** answers may vary

Section 6.4
Practice Exercises

1. $(5x+1)(x+12)$　　**2.** $(4x-5)(3x-1)$　　**3.** $2(5x+1)(3x-2)$　　**4.** $5m^2(8m-7)(m+1)$　　**5.** $(4x+3)^2$

Vocabulary, Readiness & Video Check 6.4

1. a　　**3.** b　　**5.** This gives us a four-term polynomial, which may be factored by grouping.

Exercise Set 6.4

1. $(x+3)(x+2)$　　**3.** $(y+8)(y-2)$　　**5.** $(8x-5)(x-3)$　　**7.** $(5x^2-3)(x^2+5)$　　**9. a.** $9,2$　　**b.** $9x+2x$　　**c.** $(3x+1)(2x+3)$
11. a. $-20,-3$　　**b.** $-20x-3x$　　**c.** $(3x-4)(5x-1)$　　**13.** $(3y+2)(7y+1)$　　**15.** $(7x-11)(x+1)$　　**17.** $(5x-2)(2x-1)$
19. $(2x-5)(x-1)$　　**21.** $(2x+3)^2$　　**23.** $(2x+3)(2x-7)$　　**25.** $(5x-4)(2x-3)$　　**27.** $x(2x+3)(x+5)$
29. $2(8y-9)(y-1)$　　**31.** $(2x-3)(3x-2)$　　**33.** $3(3a+2)(6a-5)$　　**35.** $a(4a+1)(5a+8)$　　**37.** $3x(4x+3)(x-3)$
39. $y(3x+y)(x+y)$　　**41.** prime　　**43.** $5(x+5y)^2$　　**45.** $6(a+b)(4a-5b)$　　**47.** $p^2(15p+q)(p+2q)$　　**49.** $2(9a^2-2)^2$
51. $(7+x)(5+x)$ or $(x+7)(x+5)$　　**53.** $(6-5x)(1-x)$ or $(5x-6)(x-1)$　　**55.** x^2-4　　**57.** $y^2+8y+16$　　**59.** $81z^2-25$
61. x^3-27　　**63.** $10x^2+45x+45; 5(2x+3)(x+3)$　　**65.** $(x^n+2)(x^n+3)$　　**67.** $(3x^n-5)(x^n+7)$　　**69.** answers may vary

Section 6.5
Practice Exercises

1. $(x+9)(x-9)$　　**2. a.** $(3x-1)(3x+1)$　　**b.** $(6a-7b)(6a+7b)$　　**c.** $\left(p+\frac{5}{6}\right)\left(p-\frac{5}{6}\right)$　　**3.** $(p^2-q^5)(p^2+q^5)$
4. a. $(z^2+9)(z+3)(z-3)$　　**b.** prime polynomial　　**5.** $y(6y+5)(6y-5)$　　**6.** $5(4y^2+1)(2y+1)(2y-1)$
7. $-1(3x+10)(3x-10)$ or $(10+3x)(10-3x)$　　**8.** $(x+4)(x^2-4x+16)$　　**9.** $(x-5)(x^2+5x+25)$　　**10.** $(3y+1)(9y^2-3y+1)$
11. $4(2x-5y)(4x^2+10xy+25y^2)$

Graphing Calculator Explorations 6.5

	$x^2 - 2x + 1$	$x^2 - 2x - 1$	$(x - 1)^2$
$x = 5$	16	14	16
$x = -3$	16	14	16
$x = 2.7$	2.89	0.89	2.89
$x = -12.1$	171.61	169.61	171.61
$x = 0$	1	-1	1

Vocabulary, Readiness & Video Check 6.5

1. difference of two cubes   **3.** sum of two cubes   **5.** $(7x)^2$ **7.** $(2y)^3$ **9.** In order to recognize the binomial as a difference of squares and also to identify the terms to use in the special factoring formula.   **11.** First rewrite the original binomial with terms writtten as cubes. Answers will then vary depending on your interpretation.

Exercise Set 6.5

1. $(x + 2)(x - 2)$ **3.** $(9p + 1)(9p - 1)$ **5.** $(5y - 3)(5y + 3)$ **7.** $(11m + 10n)(11m - 10n)$ **9.** $(xy - 1)(xy + 1)$
11. $\left(x - \dfrac{1}{2}\right)\left(x + \dfrac{1}{2}\right)$ **13.** $-1(2r + 1)(2r - 1)$ **15.** prime   **17.** $(-6 + x)(6 + x)$ or $-1(6 + x)(6 - x)$ **19.** $(m^2 + 1)(m + 1)(m - 1)$
21. $(m^2 + n^9)(m^2 - n^9)$ **23.** $(x + 5)(x^2 - 5x + 25)$ **25.** $(2a - 1)(4a^2 + 2a + 1)$ **27.** $(m + 3n)(m^2 - 3mn + 9n^2)$
29. $5(k + 2)(k^2 - 2k + 4)$ **31.** $(xy - 4)(x^2y^2 + 4xy + 16)$ **33.** $2(5r - 4t)(25r^2 + 20rt + 16t^2)$ **35.** $(r + 8)(r - 8)$
37. $(x + 13y)(x - 13y)$ **39.** $(3 - t)(9 + 3t + t^2)$ **41.** $2(3r + 2)(3r - 2)$ **43.** $x(3y + 2)(3y - 2)$ **45.** $8(m + 2)(m^2 - 2m + 4)$
47. $xy(y - 3z)(y + 3z)$ **49.** $4(3x - 4y)(3x + 4y)$ **51.** $9(4 - 3x)(4 + 3x)$ **53.** $(xy - z^2)(x^2y^2 + xyz^2 + z^4)$ **55.** $\left(7 - \dfrac{3}{5}m\right)\left(7 + \dfrac{3}{5}m\right)$
57. $(t + 7)(t^2 - 7t + 49)$ **59.** $n(n^2 + 49)$ **61.** $x^2(x^2 + 9)(x + 3)(x - 3)$ **63.** $pq(8p + 9q)(8p - 9q)$ **65.** $xy^2(27xy + 1)$
67. $a(5a - 4b)(25a^2 + 20ab + 16b^2)$ **69.** $16x^2(x + 2)(x - 2)$ **71.** 6   **73.** -2 **75.** $\dfrac{1}{5}$ **77.** $(x + 2 + y)(x + 2 - y)$
79. $(a + 4)(a - 4)(b - 4)$ **81.** $(x + 3 + 2y)(x + 3 - 2y)$ **83.** $(x^n + 10)(x^n - 10)$ **85.** $(x + 6)$ **87.** answers may vary
89. a. 2560 ft   **b.** 1920 ft   **c.** 13 sec   **d.** $16(13 - t)(13 + t)$ **91. a.** 1456 ft   **b.** 816 ft   **c.** 10 sec   **d.** $16(10 + t)(10 - t)$

Integrated Review
Practice Exercises

1. $(3x - 1)(2x - 3)$ **2.** $(3x + 1)(x - 2)(x + 2)$ **3.** $3(3x - y)(3x + y)$ **4.** $(2a + b)(4a^2 - 2ab + b^2)$ **5.** $6xy^2(5x + 2)(2x - 3)$

Exercise Set

1. $(x + y)^2$ **2.** $(x - y)^2$ **3.** $(a + 12)(a - 1)$ **4.** $(a - 10)(a - 1)$ **5.** $(a + 2)(a - 3)$ **6.** $(a - 1)^2$ **7.** $(x + 1)^2$
8. $(x + 2)(x - 1)$ **9.** $(x + 1)(x + 3)$ **10.** $(x + 3)(x - 2)$ **11.** $(x + 3)(x + 4)$ **12.** $(x + 4)(x - 3)$ **13.** $(x + 4)(x - 1)$
14. $(x - 5)(x - 2)$ **15.** $(x + 5)(x - 3)$ **16.** $(x + 6)(x + 5)$ **17.** $(x - 6)(x + 5)$ **18.** $(x + 8)(x + 3)$ **19.** $2(x + 7)(x - 7)$
20. $3(x + 5)(x - 5)$ **21.** $(x + 3)(x + y)$ **22.** $(y - 7)(3 + x)$ **23.** $(x + 8)(x - 2)$ **24.** $(x - 7)(x + 4)$ **25.** $4x(x + 7)(x - 2)$
26. $6x(x - 5)(x + 4)$ **27.** $2(3x + 4)(2x + 3)$ **28.** $(2a - b)(4a + 5b)$ **29.** $(2a + b)(2a - b)$ **30.** $(4 - 3x)(7 + 2x)$
31. $(5 - 2x)(4 + x)$ **32.** prime   **33.** prime   **34.** $(3y + 5)(2y - 3)$ **35.** $(4x - 5)(x + 1)$ **36.** $y(x + y)(x - y)$ **37.** $4(t^2 + 9)$
38. $(x + 1)(x + y)$ **39.** $(x + 1)(a + 2)$ **40.** $9x(2x^2 - 7x + 1)$ **41.** $4a(3a^2 - 6a + 1)$ **42.** $(x + 16)(x - 2)$ **43.** prime
44. $(4a - 7b)^2$ **45.** $(5p - 7q)^2$ **46.** $(7x + 3y)(x + 3y)$ **47.** $(5 - 2y)(25 + 10y + 4y^2)$ **48.** $(4x + 3)(16x^2 - 12x + 9)$
49. $-(x - 5)(x + 6)$ **50.** $-(x - 2)(x - 4)$ **51.** $(7 - x)(2 + x)$ **52.** $(3 + x)(1 - x)$ **53.** $3x^2y(x + 6)(x - 4)$ **54.** $2xy(x + 5y)(x - y)$
55. $5xy^2(x - 7y)(x - y)$ **56.** $4x^2y(x - 5)(x + 3)$ **57.** $3xy(4x^2 + 81)$ **58.** $2xy^2(3x^2 + 4)$ **59.** $(2 + x)(2 - x)$ **60.** $(3 + y)(3 - y)$
61. $(s + 4)(3r - 1)$ **62.** $(x - 2)(x^2 + 3)$ **63.** $(4x - 3)(x - 2y)$ **64.** $(2x - y)(2x + 7z)$ **65.** $6(x + 2y)(x + y)$
66. $2(x + 4y)(6x - y)$ **67.** $(x + 3)(y + 2)(y - 2)$ **68.** $(y + 3)(y - 3)(x^2 + 3)$ **69.** $(5 + x)(x + y)$ **70.** $(x - y)(7 + y)$
71. $(7t - 1)(2t - 1)$ **72.** prime   **73.** $(3x + 5)(x - 1)$ **74.** $(7x - 2)(x + 3)$ **75.** $(x + 12y)(x - 3y)$ **76.** $(3x - 2y)(x + 4y)$
77. $(1 - 10ab)(1 + 2ab)$ **78.** $(1 + 5ab)(1 - 12ab)$ **79.** $(3 + x)(3 - x)(1 + x)(1 - x)$ **80.** $(3 + x)(3 - x)(2 + x)(2 - x)$
81. $(x + 4)(x - 4)(x^2 + 2)$ **82.** $(x + 5)(x - 5)(x^2 + 3)$ **83.** $(x - 15)(x - 8)$ **84.** $(y + 16)(y + 6)$ **85.** $2x(3x - 2)(x - 4)$
86. $2y(3y + 5)(y - 3)$ **87.** $(3x - 5y)(9x^2 + 15xy + 25y^2)$ **88.** $(6y - z)(36y^2 + 6yz + z^2)$ **89.** $(xy + 2z)(x^2y^2 - 2xyz + 4z^2)$
90. $(3ab + 2)(9a^2b^2 - 6ab + 4)$ **91.** $2xy(1 + 6x)(1 - 6x)$ **92.** $2x(x + 3)(x - 3)$ **93.** $(x + 2)(x - 2)(x + 6)$
94. $(x - 2)(x + 6)(x - 6)$ **95.** $2a^2(3a + 5)$ **96.** $2n(2n - 3)$ **97.** $(a^2 + 2)(a + 2)$ **98.** $(a - b)(1 + x)$ **99.** $(x + 2)(x - 2)(x + 7)$
100. $(a + 3)(a - 3)(a + 5)$ **101.** $(x - y + z)(x - y - z)$ **102.** $(x + 2y + 3)(x + 2y - 3)$ **103.** $(9 + 5x + 1)(9 - 5x - 1)$
104. $(b + 4a + c)(b - 4a - c)$ **105.** answers may vary   **106.** yes; $9(x^2 + 9y^2)$ **107.** a, c   **108.** b, c

Section 6.6
Practice Exercises

1. $-4, 5$ **2.** $-\dfrac{3}{4}, 12$ **3.** $0, \dfrac{6}{7}$ **4.** $-4, 12$ **5.** $\dfrac{4}{3}$ **6.** $-3, \dfrac{2}{3}$ **7.** $-6, 4$ **8.** $-3, 0, 3$ **9.** $\dfrac{2}{3}, \dfrac{3}{2}, 5$ **10.** $-3, 0, 2$
11. The x-intercepts are $(2, 0)$ and $(4, 0)$.

Graphing Calculator Explorations 6.6

1. $-0.9, 2.2$ **3.** no real solution   **5.** $-1.8, 2.8$

Vocabulary, Readiness & Video Check 6.6

1. quadratic **3.** $3, -5$ **5.** One side of the equation must be a factored polynomial and the other side must be zero. **7.** To find the x-intercepts of any graph in two variables, we let $y = 0$. Doing this with our quadratic equation gives us an equation $= 0$, which we can solve by factoring.

Exercise Set 6.6

1. $6, 7$ **3.** $2, -1$ **5.** $-9, -17$ **7.** $0, -6$ **9.** $0, 8$ **11.** $-\frac{3}{2}, \frac{5}{4}$ **13.** $\frac{7}{2}, -\frac{2}{7}$ **15.** $\frac{1}{2}, -\frac{1}{3}$ **17.** $-0.2, -1.5$ **19.** $9, 4$ **21.** $-4, 2$

23. $0, 7$ **25.** $8, -4$ **27.** $4, -4$ **29.** $-3, 12$ **31.** $\frac{7}{3}, -2$ **33.** $-5, 5$ **35.** $-2, \frac{1}{6}$ **37.** $0, 4, 8$ **39.** $\frac{3}{4}$ **41.** $-\frac{1}{2}, 0, \frac{1}{2}$ **43.** $-\frac{3}{8}, 0, \frac{1}{2}$

45. $-3, 2$ **47.** $-20, 0$ **49.** $\frac{17}{2}$ **51.** $-\frac{1}{2}, \frac{1}{2}$ **53.** $-\frac{3}{2}, -\frac{1}{2}, 3$ **55.** $-5, 3$ **57.** $-\frac{5}{6}, \frac{6}{5}$ **59.** $2, -\frac{4}{5}$ **61.** $-\frac{4}{3}, 5$ **63.** $-4, 3$

65. $\frac{8}{3}, -9, 0$ **67.** -7 **69.** $0, \frac{3}{2}$ **71.** $0, 1, -1$ **73.** $-6, \frac{4}{3}$ **75.** $\frac{6}{7}, 1$ **77.** $\left(-\frac{4}{3}, 0\right), (1, 0)$ **79.** $(-2, 0), (5, 0)$ **81.** $(-6, 0), \left(\frac{1}{2}, 0\right)$

83. e **85.** b **87.** c **89.** $\frac{47}{45}$ **91.** $\frac{17}{60}$ **93.** $\frac{15}{8}$ **95.** $\frac{7}{10}$ **97.** didn't write equation in standard form; should be $x = 4$ or $x = -2$

99. answers may vary; for example $(x - 6)(x + 1) = 0$ **101.** answers may vary; for example, $x^2 - 12x + 35 = 0$ **103. a.** $300; 304; 276; 216;$

$124; 0; -156$ **b.** 5 sec **c.** 304 ft **d.**

$y = -16x^2 + 20x + 300$

105. $0, \frac{1}{2}$ **107.** $0, -15$

Section 6.7
Practice Exercises

1. 2 sec **2.** There are two numbers. They are -4 and 12. **3.** base: 35 ft; height: 12 ft **4.** 7 and 8 or -6 and -5 **5.** leg: 8 units; leg: 15 units; hypotenuse: 17 units

Vocabulary, Readiness & Video Check 6.7

1. In applications, the context of the problem needs to be considered. Each exercise resulted in both a positive and a negative solution, and a negative solution is not appropriate for any of the problems.

Exercise Set 6.7

1. width $= x$; length $= x + 4$ **3.** x and $x + 2$ if x is an odd integer **5.** base $= x$; height $= 4x + 1$ **7.** 11 units **9.** 15 cm, 13 cm, 70 cm, 22 cm
11. base $= 16$ mi; height $= 6$ mi **13.** 5 sec **15.** width $= 5$ cm; length $= 6$ cm **17.** 54 diagonals **19.** 10 sides **21.** -12 or 11 **23.** 14, 15
25. 13 feet **27.** 5 in. **29.** 12 mm, 16 mm, 20 mm **31.** 10 km **33.** 36 ft **35.** 9.5 sec **37.** 20% **39.** length: 15 mi; width: 8 mi

41. 105 units **43.** 2 million **45.** 1.9 million **47.** 2003 **49.** answers may vary **51.** $\frac{4}{7}$ **53.** $\frac{3}{2}$ **55.** $\frac{1}{3}$

57. slow boat: 8 mph; fast boat: 15 mph **59.** 13 and 7 **61.** width: 29 m; length: 35 m **63.** answers may vary

Chapter 6 Vocabulary Check

1. quadratic equation **2.** factoring **3.** greatest common factor **4.** perfect square trinomial **5.** difference of two squares **6.** difference of two cubes **7.** sum of two cubes **8.** 0 **9.** hypotenuse **10.** leg **11.** hypotenuse

Chapter 6 Review

1. $2x - 5$ **3.** $4x(5x + 3)$ **5.** $(2x + 3)(3x - 5)$ **7.** $(x - 1)(3x + 2)$ **9.** $(2a + b)(5a + 7b)$ **11.** $(x + 4)(x + 2)$ **13.** prime
15. $(x + 6y)(x - 2y)$ **17.** $2(3 - x)(12 + x)$ **19.** $10a(a - 1)(a - 10)$ **21.** $-48, 2$ **23.** $(2x + 1)(x + 6)$ **25.** $(3x + 4y)(2x - y)$
27. $5y(2y - 3)(y + 4)$ **29.** $2(3x - 5)^2$ **31.** $(2x + 3)(2x - 3)$ **33.** prime **35.** $(2x + 3)(4x^2 - 6x + 9)$ **37.** $2(3 - xy)(9 + 3xy + x^2y^2)$
39. $(4x^2 + 1)(2x + 1)(2x - 1)$ **41.** $-6, 2$ **43.** $-\frac{1}{5}, -3$ **45.** $-4, 6$ **47.** $2, 8$ **49.** $-\frac{2}{7}, \frac{3}{8}$ **51.** $-\frac{2}{5}$ **53.** 3 **55.** $0, -\frac{7}{4}, 3$

57. c **59.** 9 units **61.** width: 20 in.; length: 25 in. **63.** 19 and 20 **65. a.** 17.5 sec and 10 sec; The rocket reaches a height of 2800 ft on its way up and on its way back down. **b.** 27.5 sec **67.** $7(x - 9)$ **69.** $\left(m + \frac{2}{5}\right)\left(m - \frac{2}{5}\right)$ **71.** $(y + 2)(x - 1)$ **73.** $3x(x - 9)(x - 1)$

75. $2(x + 3)(x - 3)$ **77.** $5(x + 2)^2$ **79.** $2xy(2x - 3y)$ **81.** $3(8x^2 - x - 6)$ **83.** $(x + 3)(x + 2)(x - 2)$

85. $5x^2 - 9x - 2; (5x + 1)(x - 2)$ **87.** $-\frac{7}{2}, 4$ **89.** $0, -7, -4$ **91.** $0, 16$ **93.** length: 6 in.; width: 2 in. **95.** $28x^2 - \pi x^2; x^2(28 - \pi)$

Chapter 6 Test

1. $(x + 7)(x + 4)$ **2.** $(7 - m)(7 + m)$ **3.** $(y + 11)^2$ **4.** $(a + 3)(4 - y)$ **5.** prime **6.** $(y - 12)(y + 4)$ **7.** prime
8. $3x(3x + 1)(x + 4)$ **9.** $(3a - 7)(a + b)$ **10.** $(3x - 2)(x - 1)$ **11.** $(x + 12y)(x + 2y)$ **12.** $5(6 + x)(6 - x)$
13. $(6t + 5)(t - 1)$ **14.** $(y + 2)(y - 2)(x - 7)$ **15.** $x(1 + x^2)(1 + x)(1 - x)$ **16.** $-xy(y^2 + x^2)$ **17.** $(4x - 1)(16x^2 + 4x + 1)$

18. $8(y-2)(y^2+2y+4)$ **19.** $-9, 3$ **20.** $-7, 2$ **21.** $-7, 1$ **22.** $0, \frac{3}{2}, -\frac{4}{3}$ **23.** $0, 3, -3$ **24.** $-3, 5$ **25.** $0, \frac{5}{2}$ **26.** 17 ft
27. 8 and 9   **28.** 7 sec   **29.** hypotenuse: 25 cm; legs: 15 cm, 20 cm

Chapter 6 Cumulative Review

1. a. $9 \le 11$ **b.** $8 > 1$ **c.** $3 \ne 4$; Sec. 1.2, Ex. 3   **3. a.** $\frac{6}{7}$ **b.** $\frac{11}{27}$ **c.** $\frac{22}{5}$; Sec. 1.3, Ex. 2   **5.** $\frac{14}{3}$; Sec. 1.4, Ex. 5   **7. a.** -12
b. -1; Sec. 1.5, Ex. 7   **9. a.** -32 **b.** -14 **c.** 90; Sec. 1.7, Ex. 1   **11. a.** $4x$ **b.** $11y^2$ **c.** $8x^2 - x$ **d.** $5n^2$; Sec. 2.1, Ex. 3
13. 140; Sec. 2.2, Ex. 7   **15.** -11; Sec. 2.2, Ex. 6   **17.** $\frac{16}{3}$; Sec. 2.3, Ex. 2   **19.** shorter: 12 in.; longer: 36 in.; Sec. 2.4, Ex. 3

21.   ; Sec. 3.2, Ex. 5   **23.** $m = \frac{3}{4}$; y-intercept: $(0, -1)$; Sec. 3.4, Ex. 5   **25. a.** 250   **b.** 1; Sec. 5.1, Ex. 2   **27. a.** 2   **b.** 5

c. 1   **d.** 6   **e.** 0; Sec. 5.2, Ex. 1   **29.** $9x^2 - 6x - 1$; Sec. 5.2, Ex. 11   **31.** $6x^2 - 11x - 10$; Sec. 5.3, Ex. 5

33. $9y^2 + 6y + 1$; Sec. 5.4, Ex. 4   **35. a.** $\frac{1}{9}$ **b.** $\frac{2}{x^3}$ **c.** $\frac{3}{4}$ **d.** $\frac{1}{16}$ **e.** $\frac{1}{y^4}$ (Sec. 5.5, Ex. 1)

37. a. 3.67×10^8 **b.** 3.0×10^{-6} **c.** 2.052×10^{10} **d.** 8.5×10^{-4}; Sec. 5.5, Ex. 5   **39.** $x + 4$; Sec. 5.6, Ex. 4

41. a. x^3 **b.** y; Sec. 6.1, Ex. 2   **43.** $(x+3)(x+4)$; Sec. 6.2, Ex. 1   **45.** $(4x-1)(2x-5)$; Sec. 6.3, Ex. 2   **47.** $(5a+3b)(5a-3b)$;
Sec. 6.5, Ex. 2b   **49.** $3, -1$; Sec. 6.6, Ex. 1

APPENDIX A   OPERATIONS ON DECIMALS/PERCENT, DECIMAL, AND FRACTION TABLE

1. 17.08   **3.** 12.804   **5.** 110.96   **7.** 2.4   **9.** 28.43   **11.** 227.5   **13.** 2.7   **15.** 49.2339   **17.** 80   **19.** 0.07612   **21.** 4.56   **23.** 648.46
25. 767.83   **27.** 12.062   **29.** 61.48   **31.** 7.7   **33.** 863.37   **35.** 22.579   **37.** 363.15   **39.** 7.007

APPENDIX B   REVIEW OF ALGEBRA TOPICS

B.1 Practice Exercises

1. -4 **2.** $\frac{5}{6}$ **3.** $-\frac{3}{4}$ **4.** $\frac{5}{4}$ **5.** $-\frac{1}{8}, 2$

Exercise Set B.1

1. $-3, -8$ **3.** -2 **5.** $\frac{1}{4}, -\frac{2}{3}$ **7.** $1, 9$ **9.** 0   **11.** 5   **13.** $\frac{3}{5}, -1$ **15.** no solution   **17.** $\frac{1}{8}$ **19.** 0   **21.** $6, -3$ **23.** all real numbers

25. $\frac{2}{5}, -\frac{1}{2}$ **27.** $\frac{3}{4}, -\frac{1}{2}$ **29.** 29   **31.** -8 **33.** $-\frac{1}{3}, 0$ **35.** $-\frac{7}{8}$ **37.** $\frac{31}{4}$ **39.** 1   **41.** $-7, 4$ **43.** $4, 6$ **45.** $-\frac{1}{2}$
47. a. incorrect   **b.** correct   **c.** correct   **d.** incorrect   **49.** $K = -11$ **51.** $K = 24$ **53.** -4.86 **55.** 1.53

B.2 Practice Exercises

1. a. $3x + 6$ **b.** $6x - 1$ **2.** $3x + 18.1$ **3.** $14, 34, 70$ **4.** $450

Vocabulary & Readiness Check B.2

1. $>$ **3.** $=$ **5.** $31, 32, 33, 34$ **7.** $18, 20, 22$ **9.** $y, y+1, y+2$ **11.** $p, p+1, p+2, p+3$

Exercise Set B.2

1. $4y$ **3.** $3z + 3$ **5.** $(65x + 30)$ cents   **7.** $10x + 3$ **9.** $2x + 14$ **11.** -5 **13.** $45, 225, 145$ **15.** approximately 1612.41 million acres
17. 7747 earthquakes   **19.** 1275 shoppers   **21.** 23%   **23.** 417 employees   **25.** $29°, 35°, 116°$ **27.** 28 m, 36 m, 38 m
29. 18 in., 18 in., 27 in., 36 in.   **31.** $75, 76, 77$ **33.** Fallon's ZIP code is 89406; Fernley's ZIP code is 89408; Gardnerville Ranchos' ZIP code is 89410
35. 55 million; 97 million; 138 million   **37.** biomedical engineer: 12 thousand; skin care specialist: 15 thousand; physician assistant: 29 thousand
39. B767-300ER: 207 seats; B737-200: 119 seats; F-100: 87 seats   **41.** $430.00   **43.** $446,028   **45.** 1,800,000 people   **47.** $40°, 140°$
49. $64°, 32°, 84°$ **51.** square: 18 cm; triangle: 24 cm   **53.** $76, 78, 80$ **55.** Darlington: 61,000; Daytona: 159,000   **57.** Tokyo: 36.67 million; New
York: 19.43 million; Mexico City: 19.46 million   **59.** 40.5 ft; 202.5 ft; 240 ft   **61.** incandescent: 1500 bulb hours; fluorescent: 100,000 bulb hours;
halogen: 4000 bulb hours   **63.** Milwaukee Brewers: 77 wins; Houston Astros: 76 wins; Chicago Cubs: 75 wins   **65.** Guy's Tower: 469 ft; Queen Ma[...]
Hospital: 449 ft; Galter Pavilion: 402 ft

B.3 Practice Exercises

1.   **a.** Quadrant IV   **b.** y-axis   **c.** Quadrant II   **d.** x-axis   **e.** Quadrant III   **f.** Quadrant I

2. $y = -3x - 2$ **3.**

Exercise Set B.3

1. $(5, 2)$ **3.** $(3, 0)$ **5.** $(-5, -2)$ **7.** $(-1, 0)$ **9.** Quadrant I   **11.** Quadrant II   **13.** Quadrant III
15. y-axis   **17.** Quadrant III   **19.** x-axis   **21.** Quadrant IV   **23.** x-axis   **25.** Quadrant III
27.   **29.**   **31.**   **33.**   **35.** 1   **37.** -4 **39.** $1, 3$ **41.** $g(-1) = -2$

B.4 Practice Exercises

1. a. $3xy(4x - 1)$ **b.** $(7x + 2)(7x - 2)$ **c.** $(5x - 3)(x + 1)$ **d.** $(x^2 + 2)(3 + x)$ **e.** $(2x + 5)^2$ **f.** cannot be factored
2. a. $(4x + y)(16x^2 - 4xy + y^2)$ **b.** $7y^2(x + 3y)(x - 3y)$ **c.** $3(x + 2 + b)(x + 2 - b)$ **d.** $x^2y(xy + 3)(x^2y^2 - 3xy + 9)$
e. $(x + 7 + 9y)(x + 7 - 9y)$

Exercise Set B.4

1. $2y^2 + 2y - 11$ **3.** $x^2 - 7x + 7$ **5.** $25x^2 - 30x + 9$ **7.** $2x^3 - 4x^2 + 5x - 5 + \dfrac{8}{x + 2}$ **9.** $(x - 4 + y)(x - 4 - y)$
11. $x(x - 1)(x^2 + x + 1)$ **13.** $2xy(7x - 1)$ **15.** $4(x + 2)(x - 2)$ **17.** $(3x - 11)(x + 1)$ **19.** $4(x + 3)(x - 1)$ **21.** $(2x + 9)^2$
23. $(2x + 5y)(4x^2 - 10xy + 25y^2)$ **25.** $8x^2(2y - 1)(4y^2 + 2y + 1)$ **27.** $(x + 5 + y)(x^2 + 10x + 25 - xy - 5y + y^2)$ **29.** $(5a - 6)^2$
31. $7x(x - 9)$ **33.** $(b - 6)(a + 7)$ **35.** $(x^2 + 1)(x + 1)(x - 1)$ **37.** $(5x - 11)(2x + 3)$ **39.** $5a^3b(b^2 - 10)$ **41.** prime
43. $10x(x - 10)(x - 11)$ **45.** $a^3b(4b - 3)(16b^2 + 12b + 9)$ **47.** $2(x - 3)(x^2 + 3x + 9)$ **49.** $(3y - 5)(y^4 + 2)$
51. $100(z + 1)(z^2 - z + 1)$ **53.** $(2b - 9)^2$ **55.** $(y - 4)(y - 5)$ **57.** $A = 9 - 4x^2 = (3 + 2x)(3 - 2x)$

B.5 Practice Exercises

1. a. $\dfrac{2n + 1}{n(n - 1)}$ **b.** $-x^2$ **2. a.** $-\dfrac{y^3}{21(y + 3)}$ **b.** $\dfrac{7x + 2}{x + 2}$ **3. a.** $\dfrac{20p + 3}{5p^4q}$ **b.** $\dfrac{5y^2 + 19y - 12}{(y + 3)(y - 3)}$ **c.** 3   **4.** 1

Exercise Set B.5

1. $\dfrac{1}{2}$ **3.** $\dfrac{1 + 2x}{8}$ **5.** $\dfrac{2(x - 4)}{(x + 2)(x - 1)}$ **7.** 4   **9.** -5 **11.** $\dfrac{2x + 5}{x(x - 3)}$ **13.** -2 **15.** $\dfrac{(a + 3)(a + 1)}{a + 2}$ **17.** $-\dfrac{1}{5}$
19. $\dfrac{4a + 1}{(3a + 1)(3a - 1)}$ **21.** $-1, \dfrac{3}{2}$ **23.** $\dfrac{3}{x + 1}$ **25.** -1 **27. a.** $\dfrac{x}{5} - \dfrac{x}{4} + \dfrac{1}{10}$ **b.** Write each rational expression term so that the denominator
is the LCD, 20.   **c.** $\dfrac{-x + 2}{20}$ **29.** b   **31.** d   **33.** d

APPENDIX C   AN INTRODUCTION TO USING A GRAPHING UTILITY

The Viewing Window and Interpreting Window Settings Exercise Set

1. yes   **3.** no   **5.** answers may vary   **7.** answers may vary   **9.** answers may vary
13. Xmin $= -9$ Ymin $= -12$ **15.** Xmin $= -10$ Ymin $= -25$ **17.** Xmin $= -10$ Ymin $= -30$
9   Ymax $= 12$ Xmax $= 10$ Ymax $= 25$ Xmax $= 10$ Ymax $= 30$
Yscl $= 2$ Xscl $= 2$ Yscl $= 5$ Xscl $= 1$ Yscl $= 3$

g Window Exercise Set

   11.   **13.**

15.   **17.**   **19.**   **21.**

APPENDIX D   SOLVING SYSTEMS OF EQUATIONS BY MATRICES

Practice Exercises

1. $(2, -1)$ **2.** $\{\ \}$ or $\varnothing$ **3.** $(-1, 1, 2)$

Exercise Set

1. $(2, -1)$ **3.** $(-4, 2)$ **5.** $\{\ \}$ or $\varnothing$ **7.** $\{(x, y) \mid 3x - 3y = 9\}$ **9.** $(-2, 5, -2)$ **11.** $(1, -2, 3)$ **13.** $(4, -3)$ **15.** $(2, 1, -1)$
17. $(9, 9)$ **19.** $\{\ \}$ or $\varnothing$ **21.** $\{\ \}$ or $\varnothing$ **23.** $(1, -4, 3)$ **25.** c

APPENDIX E   SOLVING SYSTEMS OF EQUATIONS BY DETERMINANTS

1. 26 **3.** -19 **5.** 0 **7.** $(1, 2)$ **9.** $\{(x, y) \mid 3x + y = 1\}$ **11.** $(9, 9)$ **13.** 8 **15.** 0 **17.** 54 **19.** $(-2, 0, 5)$ **21.** $(6, -2, 4)$
23. 16 **25.** 15 **27.** $\dfrac{13}{6}$ **29.** 0 **31.** 56 **33.** $(-3, -2)$ **35.** $\{\ \}$ or $\varnothing$ **37.** $(-2, 3, -1)$ **39.** $(3, 4)$ **41.** $(-2, 1)$

43. $\{(x, y, z) \mid x - 2y + z = -3\}$ **45.** $(0, 2, -1)$ **47.** 5 **49.** 0; answers may vary   **51.** $\begin{matrix} + & - & + & - \\ - & + & - & + \\ + & - & + & - \\ - & + & - & + \end{matrix}$ **53.** -125 **55.** 24

APPENDIX F   MEAN, MEDIAN, AND MODE

1. mean: 29, median: 28, no mode   **3.** mean: 8.1, median: 8.2, mode: 8.2   **5.** mean: 0.6, median: 0.6, mode: 0.2 and 0.6
7. mean: 370.9, median: 313.5, no mode   **9.** 1214.8 ft   **11.** 1117 ft   **13.** 6.8   **15.** 6.9   **17.** 85.5   **19.** 73   **21.** 70 and 71
23. 9   **25.** 21, 21, 24

APPENDIX G   REVIEW OF ANGLES, LINES, AND SPECIAL TRIANGLES

1. $71°$ **3.** $19.2°$ **5.** $78\frac{3}{4}°$ **7.** $30°$ **9.** $149.8°$ **11.** $100\frac{1}{2}°$ **13.** $m\angle 1 = m\angle 5 = m\angle 7 = 110°; m\angle 2 = m\angle 3 = m\angle 4 = m\angle 6 = 70°$

15. $90°$ **17.** $90°$ **19.** $90°$ **21.** $45°, 90°$ **23.** $73°, 90°$ **25.** $50\frac{1}{4}°, 90°$ **27.** $x = 6$ **29.** $x = 4.5$ **31.** 10 **33.** 12

PRACTICE FINAL EXAM

1. -48 **2.** -81 **3.** $\dfrac{1}{64}$ **4.** $-\dfrac{1}{3}$ **5.** $-3x^3 + 5x^2 + 4x + 5$ **6.** $16x^2 - 16x + 4$ **7.** $3x^3 + 22x^2 + 41x + 14$ **8.** $(y - 12)(y + 4)$

9. $3x(3x + 1)(x + 4)$ **10.** $5(6 + x)(6 - x)$ **11.** $(a + b)(3a - 7)$ **12.** $8(y - 2)(y^2 + 2y + 4)$ **13.** $\dfrac{y^{14}}{x^2}$ **14.** $\dfrac{25}{7}$ **15.** $(-\infty, -2]$

16. $-7, 1$ **17.**   **18.**   **19.** $m = -1$ **20.** $m = 3$ **21.** $8x + y = 11$ **22.** $x = -5$ **23.** $\left(\dfrac{1}{2}, -2\right)$

24. no solution; $\{\ \}$ or $\varnothing$ **25.** $9x^2 - 6x + 4 - \dfrac{16}{3x + 2}$ **26. a.** 0 **b.** 0 **c.** 60 **27.** x-intercepts: $(0, 0), (4, 0)$; y-intercept: $(0, 0)$;

domain: $(-\infty, \infty)$; range: $(-\infty, 4]$ **28.** $401, 802$ **29.** $2\frac{1}{2}$ hr   **30.** 120 cc   **31.** $\{x \mid x \text{ is a real number}, x \neq -1, x \neq -3\}$ **32.** $\dfrac{19x - 6}{2x + 5}$

33. $\dfrac{2(x + 5)}{x(y + 5)}$ **34.** $\dfrac{3a - 4}{(a - 3)(a + 2)}$ **35.** $\dfrac{5y^2 - 1}{y + 2}$ **36.** $\dfrac{30}{11}$ **37.** -6 **38.** no solution   **39.** 5 or 1   **40.** $6\sqrt{6}$ **41.** 5

42. $\dfrac{8a^{1/3}c^{2/3}}{b^{5/12}}$ **43.** $-x\sqrt{5x}$ **44.** -20 **45.** $1, \dfrac{2}{3}$ **46.** $\left(\dfrac{3}{2}, 5\right]$ **47.** $(-\infty, -2) \cup \left(\dfrac{4}{3}, \infty\right)$ **48.** $\dfrac{3 \pm \sqrt{29}}{2}$ or $\dfrac{3}{2} \pm \dfrac{\sqrt{29}}{2}$ **49.** 2, 3

50. $\left(-\infty, -\dfrac{3}{2}\right) \cup (5, \infty)$ **51.**   **52.** domain: $(-\infty, \infty)$; range: $(-\infty, -1]$ **53.**

54. domain: $(-\infty, \infty)$; range: $(-3, \infty)$ **55.** $f(x) = -\dfrac{1}{2}x$ **56.** $f(x) = -\dfrac{1}{3}x + \dfrac{5}{3}$ **57.** $2\sqrt{26}$ units **58.** $\left(-4, \dfrac{7}{2}\right)$ **59.** $\dfrac{3\sqrt{y}}{y}$

60. $\dfrac{8 - 6\sqrt{x} + x}{8 - 2x}$ **61.** 16 **62.** 7 ft **63. a.** 272 ft **b.** 5.12 sec **64.** $0 - 2i\sqrt{2}$ **65.** $0 - 3i$ **66.** $7 + 24i$ **67.** $-\dfrac{3}{2} + \dfrac{5}{2}i$

68. $(g \circ h)(x) = x^2 - 6x - 2$ **69.** one-to-one; $f^{-1}(x) = \dfrac{-x + 6}{2}$ **70.** $\log_5 \dfrac{x^4}{x + 1}$ **71.** -1 **72.** $\dfrac{1}{2}\left(\dfrac{\log 4}{\log 3} - 5\right)$; -1.8691 **73.** 22

74. $\dfrac{43}{21}$ **75.** $\dfrac{1}{2}$ **76.**   **77.** 64,805 prairie dogs **78.**   **79.**   **80.**

81. $(-5, -1), (-5, 1), (5, -1), (5, 1)$ **82.** $-\dfrac{1}{5}, \dfrac{1}{6}, -\dfrac{1}{7}, \dfrac{1}{8}, -\dfrac{1}{9}$ **83.** 155 **84.** 1 **85.** 10 **86.** $32x^5 + 80x^4y + 80x^3y^2 + 40x^2y^3 + 10xy^4 + y^5$

Index

Photo Credits